Higher GCSE for Edexcel

Course Editors

Peter McGuire   Ken Smith

Spirals grow according to a simple numerical sequence.

You can find out more about sequences in section 5.

OXFORD
UNIVERSITY PRESS

OXFORD
UNIVERSITY PRESS
Great Clarendon Street, Oxford OX2 6DP

Oxford University Press is a department of the University of Oxford.
It furthers the University's objective of excellence in research, scholarship,
and education by publishing worldwide in

Oxford   New York
Auckland   Bangkok   Buenos Aires   Cape Town   Chennai
Dar es Salaam   Delhi   Hong Kong   Istanbul   Karachi   Kolkata
Kuala Lumpur   Madrid   Melbourne   Mexico City   Mumbai   Nairobi
São Paulo   Shanghai   Taipei   Tokyo   Toronto

Oxford is a registered trade mark of Oxford University Press
in the UK and in certain other countries

Many thanks to the original authors of this series for the use of their material:
Sue Briggs   Peter McGuire   Derek Philpott   Susan Shilton   Ken Smith

The authors would like to thank Paul Metcalf for his authoritative coursework guidance; and Keith Gordon and Trevor Senior for
their invaluable contribution to the revised content of this book.

Database right Oxford University Press (maker)

First published 2001

British Cataloguing in Publication Data

Data available

ISBN 0 19 914809 0

The publishers would like to thank Edexcel for their kind permission to reproduce past paper questions. Edexcel
accept no responsibility for the answers to the past paper questions which are the sole responsibility of the
publishers.

The publishers and authors are grateful to the following:

Illustrators	Gecko, Oxford Illustrators, Nick Hawken, Pat Moffett, Ian Dicks, Philip Reeve
Photographers	Mike Dudley, Martin Sookias, Andrew Ward
Photographic Libraries	Mary Evans Picture Library
Suppliers	Eurostar
Cover artwork	Pictor Photo Library

Typeset in Great Britain by Mathematical Composition Setters Ltd, Hilltop Business Park, Devizes Road, Salisbury, Wiltshire.
Printed and bound in Spain by Edelvives, Zaragoza

About this book

This book is designed to help you achieve your best possible grade in the **Edexcel Specification A** Higher GCSE examination. It can also be used for the **Modular Specification B** examination. The book is divided into two parts: a full-colour part containing the GCSE content that you need to learn, and a black-and-white part containing plenty of exam practice and answers.

This is more than just a book of questions: it is a learning package that will help you to make the most of your mathematical talents and expertise. You can be confident that you will be well prepared for your Edexcel GCSE examination.

Wordfinder

As well as a detailed **Contents** list and an **index**, the book contains a **Wordfinder** on pages 10 and 11. This provides an alphabetical list of the mathematical terms used in the book, and tells you where to find them.

Starting points

The content of the book is divided into sections, each covering a particular topic. Each section begins with **Starting points**, which lists the facts and techniques that you should already know. There are some questions for you to try out before starting the section.

Sections

Colour is used in the sections in the following ways:

◆ Yellow panels contain explanations and worked examples.
◆ The more difficult questions in an exercise are numbered in blue – for example, on page 17:
  4 Copy and complete: a) $\frac{\square}{x} - \frac{5}{3x} = \frac{19}{3x}$
◆ Blue text is used at times to stress important points – for example, on page 97, (factor of ax + factor of c)(factor of ax + factor of c) highlights the key terms in factorising quadratics.
◆ Words in the margin that link with the main text are coloured red. For example, on page 235: supplementary is defined in the margin and referred to in the main text.
  There are also plenty of exercises to consolidate your learning.
  A **non-calculator icon** is used to identify exercises where you should not use a calculator.

End points

Each section finishes with **Endpoints**, where the main work of the section is summarized. These are excellent for revision purposes.

Skills break

At certain points throughout the book there are **Skills breaks**. Each one provides a variety of questions all linked to the same data, and allows you to draw on the skills and techniques that you have learned.

In focus

Towards the end of the book are **In focus** pages which relate to a particular section, and you can use these for in-depth revision.

Coursework

There is a separate **Coursework Guidance** section, which details what you need to do for your investigative task and your statistical task. It contains sample tasks, with **Moderator comments** to help you get better marks.

Exam questions

The **Exam questions** section contains hundreds of past paper questions from AQA to help you prepare for your exam. There are also two **practice exam papers**, one calculator and one non-calculator, so that you can gain familiarity and confidence with the new Edexcel examination style.

Answers

Numerical **answers** are given at the end of the book.

Good luck in your exams!

CONTENTS

Note for students taking the modular GCSE course:

If you are following **Edexcel Specification B (1388) modular**, these symbols will tell you which module the topic is assessed in:

■ ■   Stage 1 (comprising module 1)
■ ■   Stage 2 (comprising module 2)
■ ■ ■ Stage 3 (comprising the terminal examination)

The coursework component (contained within the terminal assessment) is covered in the Coursework Guidance section.

■   Means that the Topic goes slightly beyond the Higher level.

Section 1   Fractions   12

■ Prime products, multiples and factors
■ Fractions
■ Using algebraic fractions

Section 2   Properties of Shapes   20

■ Angles in triangles
■ Parallel lines
■ Properties of polygons
■ Angles in polygons

Section 3   Algebraic Manipulation   29

■ Using brackets
■ Multiplying terms and simplifying
■ Common factors
■ Multiplying two brackets
■ Algebraic proof
■ Factorising
■ Using factorisation

Section 4   Comparing Data   44

■ Calculating the interquartile range
■ Drawing and using a stem and leaf plot
■ Calculating the standard deviation
■ Calculating the standard deviation of a frequency distribution
■ Comparing sets of data
■ Using cumulative frequencies to find the median
■ Drawing box-and-whisker plots
■ Comparing frequency distributions
■ Misleading diagrams

A note on accuracy

Make sure your answer is given to any degree of accuracy stated in the question, for example 2 dp or 1 sf. Where it is not stated, choose a sensible degree of accuracy for your answer, and make sure you work to a greater degree of accuracy through the problem. For example, if you choose to give an answer to 3 sf, work to at least 4 sf through the problem, then round your final answer to 3 sf.

Examination groups differ in their approach to accuracy. Some say that you should not give your final answer to a greater degree of accuracy than that used for the data in the question, but others state answers should be given to 3 sf.

If you are in any doubt, check with your examination group.

Metric and imperial units

	Metric	Imperial	Some approximate conversions
Length	millimetres (mm) centimetres (cm) metres (m) kilometres (km) 1 cm = 10 mm 1 m = 100 cm 1 km = 1000 m	inches (in) feet (ft) yards (yd) miles 1 ft = 12 in 1 yd = 3 ft 1 mile = 1760 yd	1 inch = 2.54 cm 1 foot ≈ 30.5cm 1 metre ≈ 39.4 in 1 mile ≈ 1.61 km
Mass	grams (g) kilograms (kg) tonnes 1 kg = 1000 g 1 tonne = 1000 kg	ounces (oz) pounds (lb) stones 1 lb = 16 oz 1 stone = 14 lb	1 pound ≈ 454 g 1 kilogram ≈ 2.2 lb
Capacity	millilitres (ml) centilitres (cl) litres 1 cl = 10 ml 1 litre = 100 cl = 1000 ml	pints (pt) gallons 1 gallon = 8 pints	1 gallon ≈ 4.55 litres 1 litre ≈ 1.76 pints ≈ 0.22 gallons

Starting points

You need to know about ...   ... so try these questions

A Multiples, factors and prime numbers

- ◆ The **common multiples** of two numbers are those that are multiples of both.

  Example   Multiples of 4 are: 4, 8, 12, 16, 20, 24, ...
  Multiples of 6 are: 6, 12, 18, 24, 30, 36, ...

  Common multiples of 4 and 6 are: 12, 24, 36, ...
  The **least common multiple** of 6 and 4 is 12.

- ◆ The **common factors** of two numbers are those that are factors of both.

  Example   Factors of 4 are: 1, 2 and 4.
  Factors of 6 are: 1, 2, 3 and 6.

  Common factors of 4 and 6 are: 1 and 2.
  The **highest common factor** of 4 and 6 is 2.

- ◆ A number is **prime** if it has exactly two different factors.

  Example   5 is a prime number: its factors are 1 and 5.

B Writing a number as a product of primes

- ◆ The factors of a number that are prime are called **prime factors**.

- ◆ A multiplication of prime factors is called a **product of primes**.

- ◆ One way to write a number as its product of primes is to break it down into factor pairs until a product of primes is reached.

  Example   Write 63 as a product of primes.

  As a product of primes:
  $63 = 3 \times 3 \times 7$
  $\quad = 3^2 \times 7$ in index notation.

C Equivalent fractions

- ◆ Two fractions equal in value are called **equivalent** fractions, e.g. $\frac{1}{2}$ and $\frac{5}{10}$ are equivalent fractions.

- ◆ To find equivalent fractions, multiply or divide the numerator ('top') and denominator ('bottom') by the same number.

  Examples

- ◆ A fraction in its lowest terms is an equivalent fraction where the numerator and denominator have no common factors except 1.

  Example   In its lowest terms, $\frac{6}{9}$ is written as $\frac{2}{3}$.

A1 Give three common multiples of:
  a 5 and 8   b 9 and 12

A2 Find the least common multiple of:
  a 2 and 7   b 3 and 5
  c 6 and 8   d 2 and 4

A3 List the common factors of:
  a 24 and 30   b 25 and 30

A4 What is the highest common factor of:
  a 2 and 7   b 6 and 8
  c 4 and 8   d 36 and 54?

A5 Explain why 1 is not prime.

A6 List all the prime numbers between 30 and 40.

A7 Explain why 2 is the only even prime number.

B1 Write each of these as a product of primes in index notation.
  a 20   b 36
  c 385   d 504

B2 Evaluate each product of primes:
  a $2^5 \times 3^2 \times 7$
  b $3^3 \times 5 \times 11^2$

C1 Which of these fractions is equivalent to $\frac{4}{10}$?

$$\frac{8}{20}, \frac{7}{13}, \frac{12}{30}, \frac{6}{15}, \frac{2}{5}$$

C2 Write three equivalent fractions for:
  a $\frac{6}{8}$ b $\frac{2}{9}$

C3 Write each fraction in its lowest terms.
  a $\frac{15}{25}$ b $\frac{6}{36}$

D Mixed numbers and improper fractions

♦ An improper fraction is one where the numerator is larger than the denominator ('top-heavy'), e.g $\frac{11}{4}$

♦ An improper fraction is greater than 1, so it can be written as a **mixed number**, a mixture of whole numbers and fractions.

Example $\frac{11}{4} = \frac{8}{4} + \frac{3}{4} = 2\frac{3}{4}$

♦ Any whole number can be written as an improper fraction.

Example $5 = \frac{5}{1}$

E Calculating with fractions

♦ To **add** or **subtract** fractions:

❖ find a common multiple of the denominators.

❖ find equivalent fractions with a common multiple as the new denominator

❖ add or subtract the fractions.

Example $\frac{3}{4} - \frac{1}{6} = \frac{9}{12} - \frac{2}{12} = \frac{7}{12}$

♦ To **multiply** fractions:

❖ multiply the numerators

❖ multiply the denominators.

Example $\frac{2}{3} \times \frac{1}{5} = \frac{2}{15}$

♦ Two numbers that multiply together to give 1 are **reciprocals** of each other:

Example The reciprocal of $\frac{3}{4}$ is $\frac{4}{3}$.

The reciprocal of 1.5 is $\frac{2}{3}$.

Note The reciprocal of zero is undefined.

♦ Dividing by a fraction has the same effect as multiplying by its reciprocal so, to **divide** fractions:

❖ write the division as a multiplication

❖ multiply the fractions.

Example $\frac{1}{4} \div \frac{2}{3} = \frac{1}{4} \times \frac{3}{2} = \frac{3}{8}$

D1 Write as a mixed number:

a $\frac{5}{4}$ b $\frac{8}{3}$

c $\frac{40}{12}$ d $\frac{20}{4}$

D2 Write as an improper fraction:

a $2\frac{4}{7}$ b $1\frac{1}{2}$

c $4\frac{5}{8}$ d 3

E1 Find the reciprocal of:

a $\frac{5}{4}$ b 3

c $2\frac{1}{2}$ d $1\frac{2}{3}$

e $1\frac{3}{4}$ f $\frac{5}{8}$

g 1.4   h 2.6

i 3.2   j 0

E2 Give each answer in its lowest terms.

a $\frac{5}{7} - \frac{3}{7}$ b $\frac{1}{3} + \frac{2}{5}$

c $\frac{2}{3} \times \frac{3}{7}$ d $\frac{3}{8} \times \frac{4}{3}$

e $\frac{3}{4} \div \frac{4}{5}$ f $\frac{5}{6} \div 10$

g $1 \div \frac{4}{5}$ h $3 \div \frac{5}{3}$

E3 What is the value of a, in fractional form, when $\frac{1}{a} = \frac{7}{4}$?

Prime products, multiples and factors

Prime products can be used to find highest common factors and least common multiples.

Example 1 Find **a** the highest common factor of 72 and 60
b least common multiple of 72 and 60

As prime products, $72 = 2 \times 2 \times 2 \times 3 \times 3$
$60 = 2 \times 2 \times 3 \times 5$.

a 2 appears at least twice
3 appears at least once in each prime product:
$2 \times 2 \times 2 \times 3 \times 3$ and $2 \times 2 \times 3 \times 5$.

So the **highest common factor** is $2 \times 2 \times 3 = 12$.

b 2 appears at most three times in a prime product $(2 \times 2 \times 2 \times 3 \times 3)$
3 appears at most twice in a prime product $(2 \times 2 \times 2 \times 3 \times 3)$
5 appears at most once in a prime product $(2 \times 2 \times 3 \times 5)$.

So the **least common multiple** is $2 \times 2 \times 2 \times 3 \times 3 \times 5 = \mathbf{360}$.

Exercise 1.1
Multiples, factors and primes

1 **a** Find the highest common factor of **i** 240 and 168 **ii** 260 and 180.
b Find the least common multiple of **i** 45 and 60 **ii** 450 and 360.

2 **a** Choose two prime numbers from this list 7, 13, 19, 23, 29.
b Find their highest common factor and least common multiple.
c Investigate for all different pairs of prime numbers from the list.

A product is the result of a multiplication.

For example, the product of 3 and 6 is 18.

HCF is shorthand for highest common factor.

LCM is shorthand for least common multiple.

3 For any pair of numbers, Sue thinks there could be a rule that links the product, the highest common factor and the least common multiple.

She makes a table.

Numbers	Product	HCF	LCM
12, 70	840	2	420
7, 24			
4, 36			
70, 110			

a Copy and complete the table.
b For any pair of numbers, find a rule that links the product, the highest common factor and the least common multiple.
c Use your rule to find the least common multiple of 24 and 36.

4 Two numbers have a highest common factor of 8 and a least common multiple of 160. Find a pair of numbers that fit this description.

5 Four flatmates wash their hair regularly: Di every 2 days, Pete every 3 days, Alison every 4 days, and Jake every 5 days.
All four people wash their hair on 1 June.
What is the next date when they will all wash their hair?

6 Each edge of a cuboid-shaped box measures a whole number of centimetres. The areas of the three different faces are 120 cm², 96 cm² and 80 cm².
Find the volume of the box.

It may help to find a rule that gives the number of factors a number has from its prime product.

7 **a** Write 84 as a product of primes.
b List the factors of 84 as products of primes.
c How many factors has 84?
d For whole numbers less than 1000, find the number with the most factors.

Fractions

♦ One way to add or subtract fractions with different denominators is to use the **least common multiple** of the denominators as the new denominator.

Example $\frac{5}{6} - \frac{1}{4} = \frac{10}{12} - \frac{3}{12} = \frac{7}{12}$

♦ One way to deal with mixed numbers is to convert to **improper fractions** before doing any calculation.

Example $1\frac{1}{4} \times \frac{1}{5} = \frac{5}{4} \times \frac{1}{5} = \frac{5}{20} = \frac{1}{4}$

Exercise 1.2
Fractions

1 Give each answer as a fraction in its lowest terms.

 a $\frac{3}{4} + \frac{1}{10}$ **b** $1\frac{2}{3} \times 2\frac{1}{4}$ **c** $3\frac{1}{8} - 1\frac{3}{16}$ **d** $1\frac{1}{5} \div \frac{3}{10}$

2 Give each answer in its lowest terms.

 a $2\frac{3}{5} - 1\frac{1}{3}$ **b** $1\frac{1}{4} - 1\frac{5}{8}$ **c** $\frac{3}{5} \times 1\frac{1}{4}$ **d** $2\frac{1}{2} \div \frac{3}{5}$

3 Give each answer in its lowest terms.

 a $2\frac{2}{3} \div 1\frac{1}{2}$ **b** $\frac{3}{4} \times 1\frac{3}{5}$ **c** $2\frac{1}{2} - 1\frac{5}{9}$ **d** $1\frac{1}{4} + 2\frac{1}{2} + 1\frac{3}{5}$

4 If $\frac{1}{a} = \frac{1}{b} - \frac{1}{c}$

 what is the value of a, in fractional form, when $b = 2$ and $c = 5$?

5 What is the value of k if $1 - \frac{k}{12} = \frac{k}{24}$?

> A fraction with a numerator of 1 is called a unit fraction.
>
> $\frac{1}{2}$, $\frac{1}{13}$ and $\frac{1}{21}$ are examples of unit fractions.
>
> Do not include $\frac{1}{1}$ as a unit fraction.

6 Explain why it is not possible to find two unit fractions that add to give a number greater than 1.

7 Joe claims that, when n is a positive integer, the value of the expression $\frac{n^5}{5} + \frac{n^3}{3} + \frac{7n}{15}$ is a positive integer.

 Show that Joe's claim is true for values of n from 1 to 5.

> Joe's claim is true for **all** positive integers.

8 These are the first three lines in a sequence of sums:

 a What is the sum of the fractions on:
   i the 3rd line
   ii the 8th line
 b Why can the sum of the fractions on any line never be greater than 1?

 $\frac{1}{2} + \frac{1}{4} = \frac{3}{4}$

 $\frac{1}{2} + \frac{1}{4} + \frac{1}{8} = \frac{7}{8}$

 $\frac{1}{2} + \frac{1}{4} + \frac{1}{8} + \frac{1}{16} =$

9 Find two different unit fractions that add to give $\frac{2}{7}$.

10 Find three different unit fractions that add to give 1.

> Questions **9 – 12** may take some time using trial and improvement.
>
> Try to find a simpler strategy to solve each problem.

11 **a** Show that the sum and product of 3 and $1\frac{1}{2}$ are equal.
 b Find another pair of fractions whose sum and product are equal.

12 We can use each digit from 1 to 9 once to make a fraction equivalent to $\frac{1}{4}$:

 $$\frac{3942}{15768} = \frac{1}{4}$$

 Use each digit from 1 to 9 once to find a fraction equivalent to $\frac{1}{2}$.

We can use these rules for fractions when we work with algebraic fractions.

- ◆ To find equivalent algebraic fractions, multiply or divide the numerator and denominator by the same number or expression.

  Example
  $$\frac{n}{n^2} = \frac{1}{n}$$
  $\div n$ (top), $\div n$ (bottom)

- ◆ To add or subtract algebraic fractions with the same denominator, add or subtract the numerators.

  Example $\dfrac{5}{x+1} - \dfrac{2}{x+1} = \dfrac{3}{x+1}$

- ◆ To multiply algebraic fractions, multiply the numerators and multiply the denominators.

  Example $\dfrac{3}{x} \times \dfrac{2}{y} = \dfrac{6}{xy}$

- ◆ To divide algebraic fractions, use the rule that dividing by a fraction has the same effect as multiplying by its reciprocal.

  Example $\dfrac{5}{x+1} \div \dfrac{1}{x-1} = \dfrac{5}{x+1} \times \dfrac{x-1}{1} = \dfrac{5(x-1)}{x+1}$

Exercise 1.3
Fractions and algebra

1 Which of these is equivalent to $\dfrac{x+y}{8}$?

   (K) $\dfrac{x}{4} \times \dfrac{y}{2}$ (L) $\dfrac{x}{8} + \dfrac{y}{8}$ (M) $\dfrac{x}{4} + \dfrac{y}{4}$ (N) $\dfrac{x}{8} \div \dfrac{1}{y}$

2 Sort these into four pairs of equivalent expressions.

   (P) $\dfrac{2}{3}$ (Q) $\dfrac{2}{x} \div \dfrac{x}{3}$ (R) $\dfrac{4}{x} + \dfrac{2}{x}$ (S) $\dfrac{2x}{3x}$

   (T) $\dfrac{8}{x}$ (U) $\dfrac{6}{x^2}$ (V) $\dfrac{4x}{3} \times \dfrac{6}{x^2}$ (W) $\dfrac{6}{x}$

Example
As a single fraction,
$\dfrac{3x}{4} \times \dfrac{2}{y}$ is $\dfrac{6x}{4y}$.

In its simplest form,
$\dfrac{6x}{4y}$ is $\dfrac{3x}{2y}$.

3 Write each of these as a single fraction. Give each answer in its simplest form.

  a $\dfrac{n}{3} \times \dfrac{1}{n^2}$ **b** $\dfrac{3}{x} + \dfrac{5}{x}$ **c** $\dfrac{a}{10} - \dfrac{b}{10}$ **d** $\dfrac{p}{8} + \dfrac{3p}{8}$

  e $\dfrac{m}{4} \div \dfrac{n}{3}$ **f** $\dfrac{7v}{8} - \dfrac{3v}{4}$ **g** $\dfrac{z}{5y} \times \dfrac{y}{3}$ **h** $\dfrac{c}{6} \div \dfrac{c}{12}$

4 Copy and complete:

  a $\dfrac{x}{5} - \dfrac{2}{5} = \dfrac{x-2}{\square}$ **b** $\dfrac{2}{m} \times \dfrac{\square}{\square} = \dfrac{n}{3m}$ **c** $\dfrac{y}{x} + \dfrac{z}{\square} = \dfrac{y+z}{x}$

  d $\dfrac{6}{\square} \div \dfrac{1}{n^2} = 6n$ **e** $\dfrac{3t}{10} + \dfrac{\square}{10} = \dfrac{t}{2}$ **f** $\dfrac{2}{b+3} \div \dfrac{1}{\square} = \dfrac{2(b-2)}{b+3}$

5 Sort these into four pairs of equivalent expressions.

   (A) $\dfrac{x}{3}$ (B) $\dfrac{1}{x+1}$ (C) $\dfrac{3}{3(x+1)}$ (D) $\dfrac{x}{x(x-1)}$

   (E) $\dfrac{3}{x+1}$ (F) $\dfrac{1}{x-1}$ (G) $\dfrac{3x}{9}$ (H) $\dfrac{3(x-1)}{(x+1)(x-1)}$

To add or subtract algebraic fractions with **different** denominators, find equivalent fractions with the same denominator.

Examples

- $\dfrac{y}{3} + \dfrac{y}{4}$

$$\overset{\times 4}{\dfrac{y}{3} = \dfrac{4y}{12}} \quad \text{and} \quad \overset{\times 3}{\dfrac{y}{4} = \dfrac{3y}{12}}$$
$$\underset{\times 4}{\phantom{\dfrac{y}{3}}} \qquad\qquad \underset{\times 3}{\phantom{\dfrac{y}{4}}}$$

So $\dfrac{y}{3} + \dfrac{y}{4} = \dfrac{4y}{12} + \dfrac{3y}{12}$

$\qquad\quad = \dfrac{4y + 3y}{12} = \dfrac{7y}{12}$

- $\dfrac{2}{a} - \dfrac{3}{b}$

$$\overset{\times b}{\dfrac{2}{a} = \dfrac{2b}{ab}} \quad \text{and} \quad \overset{\times a}{\dfrac{3}{b} = \dfrac{3a}{ab}}$$
$$\underset{\times b}{\phantom{\dfrac{2}{a}}} \qquad\qquad \underset{\times a}{\phantom{\dfrac{3}{b}}}$$

So $\dfrac{2}{a} - \dfrac{3}{b} = \dfrac{2b}{ab} - \dfrac{3a}{ab} = \dfrac{2b - 3a}{ab}$

- $\dfrac{1}{p + 1} + \dfrac{1}{p - 2}$

$$\overset{\times (p-2)}{\dfrac{1}{p + 1} = \dfrac{(p - 2)}{(p + 1)(p - 2)}} \quad \text{and} \quad \overset{\times (p+1)}{\dfrac{1}{p - 2} = \dfrac{(p + 1)}{(p + 1)(p - 2)}}$$
$$\underset{\times (p-2)}{} \qquad\qquad\qquad \underset{\times (p+1)}{}$$

So $\dfrac{1}{p + 1} + \dfrac{1}{p - 2} = \dfrac{(p - 2)}{(p + 1)(p - 2)} + \dfrac{(p + 1)}{(p + 1)(p - 2)}$

$\qquad\qquad\qquad\qquad = \dfrac{(p - 2) + (p + 1)}{(p + 1)(p - 2)} = \dfrac{2p - 1}{(p + 1)(p - 2)}$

Exercise 1.4
Adding and subtracting algebraic fractions

1 **a** Which of these is not equivalent to $\dfrac{5}{c}$?

A $\quad \dfrac{15}{3c}$ B $\quad \dfrac{5(c + 1)}{c(c + 1)}$ C $\quad \dfrac{5c^3}{c^2}$ D $\quad \dfrac{5a}{ac}$

b Write as a single fraction $\dfrac{5}{c} + \dfrac{7}{3c}$.

2 Sort these into four pairs of equivalent expressions.

E $\quad \dfrac{10x}{21}$ F $\quad \dfrac{x}{6} + \dfrac{x}{30}$ G $\quad \dfrac{x}{5}$ H $\quad \dfrac{x}{10}$

I $\quad \dfrac{3x}{8} - \dfrac{x}{3}$ J $\quad \dfrac{3x}{10} - \dfrac{x}{5}$ K $\quad \dfrac{x}{24}$ L $\quad \dfrac{x}{3} + \dfrac{x}{7}$

3 Write each of these as a single fraction in its simplest form.

a $\dfrac{2m}{3} + \dfrac{m}{12}$ **b** $\dfrac{3p}{4} - \dfrac{p}{8}$ **c** $\dfrac{q}{2} + \dfrac{r}{5}$ **d** $\dfrac{s}{t} - \dfrac{s}{2}$

e $\dfrac{4}{x} - \dfrac{5}{y}$ **f** $\dfrac{6}{f} + \dfrac{5}{2f}$ **g** $\dfrac{1}{p + 3} + \dfrac{1}{p - 1}$ **h** $\dfrac{2}{z} - \dfrac{1}{z + 6}$

4 Copy and complete:

a $\dfrac{\square}{x} - \dfrac{5}{3x} = \dfrac{19}{3x}$ **b** $\dfrac{\square}{x} + \dfrac{2}{x + 5} = \dfrac{5(x + 3)}{x(x + 5)}$

c $\dfrac{\square}{x + 1} + \dfrac{3}{x} = \dfrac{3}{x(x + 1)}$ **d** $\dfrac{1}{x + 1} + \dfrac{\square}{x - 2} = \dfrac{3x}{(x + 1)(x - 2)}$

Thinking ahead to ...
using algebraic fractions

A This is a sequence of pairs of calculations.

$$\frac{2}{3} - \frac{2}{5} = \frac{4}{15} \qquad \frac{2}{3} \times \frac{2}{5} =$$

$$\frac{2}{4} - \frac{2}{6} = \qquad \frac{2}{4} \times \frac{2}{6} =$$

$$\frac{2}{5} - \frac{2}{7} = \qquad \frac{2}{5} \times \frac{2}{7} =$$

...   ...

a Copy and complete these calculations.
b Write down some more pairs of calculations in this sequence.
c Comment on the results of these calculations.

Using algebraic fractions

> This explanation is a type of proof.
>
> You can see that it will be true for any value of n.

- For the above calculations, the numerator of each fraction is 2 and the denominator of the second fraction is always 2 more than the first.

- So if the first fraction is $\frac{2}{n}$, then the second fraction is $\frac{2}{n+2}$.

- Subtract: $\dfrac{2}{n} - \dfrac{2}{n+2} = \dfrac{2(n+2)}{n(n+2)} - \dfrac{2n}{n(n+2)} = \dfrac{2n+4}{n(n+2)} - \dfrac{2n}{n(n+2)}$

$$= \dfrac{2n+4-2n}{n(n+2)} = \dfrac{4}{n(n+2)}$$

- Multiply: $\dfrac{2}{n} \times \dfrac{2}{n+2} = \dfrac{4}{n(n+2)}$

- Both calculations give the result $\dfrac{4}{n(n+2)}$.

So we have shown that for any pair of fractions of the form $\frac{2}{n}$ and $\frac{2}{n+2}$ the results of subtracting them and multiplying them are equal.

Exercise 1.5
Using algebraic fractions

1 This is a sequence of pairs of calculations.

$$\frac{3}{4} - \frac{3}{7} = \frac{9}{28} \qquad \frac{3}{4} \times \frac{3}{7} =$$

$$\frac{3}{5} - \frac{3}{8} = \qquad \frac{3}{5} \times \frac{3}{8} =$$

$$\frac{3}{6} - \frac{3}{9} = \qquad \frac{3}{6} \times \frac{3}{9} =$$

...   ...

a Complete the calculations above to show that the results are equal for each of these three pairs.
b Explain why we can write any pair of fractions in this sequence in the form $\dfrac{3}{n}$ and $\dfrac{3}{n+3}$.
c Use algebra to show that, for **any** pair of calculations in this sequence the results will be equal.

2 **a** Find some pairs of **unit** fractions that subtract and multiply to give equal results.
b Describe a rule that you think is true for these pairs of unit fractions.
c Use algebra to show that your rule is true.

End points

You should be able to ...   ... so try these questions

A Use multiples and factors to solve problems

A1 Find the highest common factor and least common multiple for each pair of numbers.

a	45 and 60	**b**	75 and 325
c	120 and 275	**d**	54 and 144
e	108 and 56	**f**	81 and 350
g	125 and 320	**h**	65 and 196

A2 **a** Find the highest common factor of 105 and 126.
b Find the least common multiple of 105 and 126.

A3 Two numbers less than 30 have 3 as their highest common factor and 216 as their least common multiple.
What are the two numbers?

B Calculate with fractions

B1 When $x = \frac{1}{3}$, $y = \frac{5}{6}$ and $z = 1\frac{2}{3}$, calculate, in fractional form, the value of:

a $2xy$ **b** $y - xz$ **c** $\dfrac{x + y}{z}$

B2 **a** $1\frac{3}{5} + 2\frac{3}{4}$ **b** $2\frac{5}{8} \div 1\frac{1}{2}$ **c** $3\frac{1}{4} - 1\frac{3}{8}$ **d** $2\frac{2}{3} \times 1\frac{5}{8}$

B3 What fraction of ABCD is shaded?

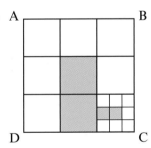

C Use algebraic fractions

C1 Write each of these as a single fraction in its simplest form.

a $\dfrac{2x}{3} - \dfrac{x}{6}$ **b** $\dfrac{y}{4} \times \dfrac{3}{y}$ **c** $\dfrac{z}{3} \div \dfrac{1}{9}$

d $\dfrac{3}{a} - \dfrac{7}{b}$ **e** $\dfrac{5}{c} - \dfrac{4}{c+1}$ **f** $\dfrac{1}{d+6} + \dfrac{1}{d-5}$

Some points to remember

- ◆ Least common multiple = Product ÷ Highest common factor.
- ◆ To add and subtract fractions (including algebraic), first find equivalent fractions with the same denominator.
- ◆ Dividing by a fraction has the same effect as multiplying by its reciprocal.

Starting points

You need to know about ...

... so try these questions

A Naming angles and triangles

- Any angle less than 90° is an **acute angle**.
- Any angle equal to 90° is a **right angle**.
- Any angle between 90° and 180° is an **obtuse angle**.
- Any angle between 180° and 360° is a **reflex angle**.

- Any triangle which has:
  - three sides of equal length
  - three equal angles (60°)

  is an **equilateral triangle**.

- Any triangle which has:
  - two sides of equal length
  - two equal angles

  is an **isosceles triangle**.

- Any triangle which has no sides of equal length and no equal angles is a **scalene triangle**.
- Any triangle which has one right angle is a **right-angled triangle**.

B Angle sums

- Angles at a point on a straight line add up to 180°.

$$a + b = 180°$$

- Angles round a point add up to 360°.

$$c + d + e = 360°$$

- Vertically opposite angles are equal.

- Angles in a triangle add up to 180°.

$$x + y + z = 180°$$

C Parallel lines

At each point where a straight line crosses a set of parallel lines there are two pairs of vertically opposite angles.

Parallel lines are marked with arrows.

Equal angles are marked with the same colour.

A1

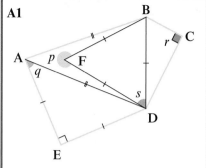

a What type of angle is:
  i p **ii** q **iii** r?
b What type of triangle is:
  i BFD   **ii** BCD?
c Which triangles are isosceles?

B1 In the diagram above calculate:
a the size of angle s
b angle p
c angle $A\hat{D}E$.

B2 On this diagram, angles marked with the same letter are equal in size.

a Work out angles a and b.
b Explain why a triangle can only have one obtuse angle.

C1

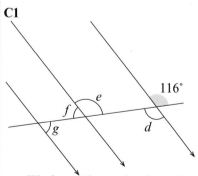

Work out the angles d to g in this diagram.

D Quadrilaterals

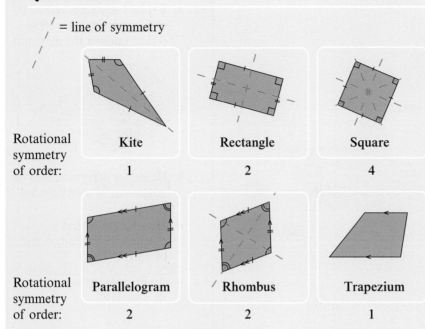

/ = line of symmetry

	Kite	Rectangle	Square
Rotational symmetry of order:	1	2	4

	Parallelogram	Rhombus	Trapezium
Rotational symmetry of order:	2	2	1

E Polygons

♦ In ABCDE:
  ❖ the **interior angles** are marked in red
  ❖ the angles marked in blue are not interior angles.

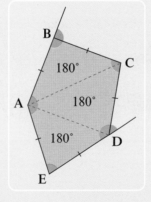

♦ The **sum of the interior angles** of a polygon with *n* sides is: $(n - 2) \times 180°$
So for ABCDE the sum of interior angles is: $(5 - 2) \times 180°$
  $= 3 \times 180°$
  $= 540°$

♦ In a **regular polygon** all the sides are equal and the interior angles are equal.

♦ ABCDE is an **irregular polygon** The sides are all equal but the interior angles are not.

Name of polygon	Number of sides	Sum of interior angles	Interior angle of a regular polygon
Triangle	3	180° ——÷3——▶	60°
Quadrilateral	4	360° ——÷4——▶	90°
Pentagon	5	540° ——÷5——▶	108°
Hexagon	6	720° ——÷6——▶	120°
Heptagon	7		
Octagon	8		
Nonagon	9		
Decagon	10		

Another expression for the **sum of the interior angles** of a polygon with *n* sides is: $(180° \times n) - 360°$

D1 Name all the quadrilaterals that fit each of these labels.

① There is only one pair of parallel lines.

② All angles are equal.

③ All sides are of equal length.

④ Opposite angles are equal.

D2 Draw a trapezium with one line of symmetry.

E1 What is the sum of the interior angles of an octagon?

E2 Calculate the angle *a* in this pentagon.

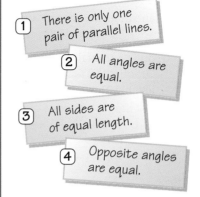

E3 Calculate the interior angle of a regular heptagon to the nearest degree.

E4 A dodecagon has 12 sides.
  a What is the sum of the interior angles of a dodecagon?
  b Calculate the interior angle of a regular dodecagon.

F Triangles and proof

The angle sum of a triangle is 180°.

How can you prove this for any triangle?

♦ You could
  – draw a triangle
  – cut off the 3 vertical angles
  – arrange them on a straight line .

Angles of a straight line = 180°.

So $a + b + c = 180°$

ie the angle sum of a triangle is 180°.

♦ You could
  – Draw a triangle
  – Provide an exact copy of the triangle drawn
  – Arrange the two triangles to make a quadrilateral

The angle sum of a quadrilateral is 360°.

So $a + b + c + a + b + c = 360°$

ie $\quad\quad\quad 2a + 2b + 2c = 360°$

ie $\quad\quad\quad\quad a + b + c = 180°$

ie the angle sum of a triangle is 180°.

The external angle of a triangle is equal to the sum of the two opposite interior angles.

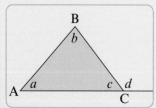

d is the external angle at c

now

$c + d = 180°$ [angles on a straight line]

ie $c = 180° - d$

and $a + b + c = 180°$ [angles sum of a triangle]

making c the subject $\quad c = 180° - (a + b)$

So $\quad\quad\quad 180° - d = 180° - (a + b)$

ie $\quad\quad\quad\quad\quad d = a + b$

F1 a Explain why the angle sum of a quadrilateral is 360°. (Hint: Look at the diagram).

b Hence, or otherwise, find the angle sum of a seven-sided polygon.

c How may sides has a polygon with an angle sum of 1800°?

F2 a $\triangle ABC$ is isosceles. $B\hat{C}D = 110°$

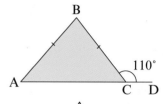

Find $A\hat{B}C$.

b $\triangle ABC$ is isosceles. $B\hat{C}D = x°$

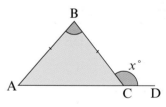

Use the fact that the external angle of a triangle is equal to the sum of the two opposite interior angles to prove that $A\hat{B}C = 2x - 180$.

Angles in triangles

To calculate an angle you may need to work out some other angles first.

Example

Calculate the angle EĜF.

♦ You should sketch a diagram and label each angle that you calculate.

Sketch

△ stands for triangle

An angle can be written in different ways.

For example:

DĈE is the same angle as DĈG and EĈD

DÊC is the same angle as DÊA and CÊD.

You may not need to calculate all the intermediate angles.

To calculate EĜF

Calculation …	*… Reason*
AĈB = CÂB…	…ABC is an isosceles △
= (180° − 44°) ÷ 2	
= 68°	
DĈE = 68°…	…Vertically opposite ACB
DÊC = 180° − (68° + 53°)…	…Angle sum of △
= 59°	
FÊG = 59°…	…Vertically opposite DEC
GÊF = EF̂G…	…EFG is an isosceles △
EĜF = 180° − (59° × 2)…	…Angle sum of △

So the angle EĜF = 62°

Exercise 2.1
Angles in triangles

You will need to work out some other angles first.

1

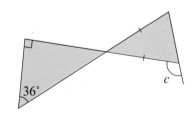

Calculate the angles *a*, *b* and *c* in these diagrams.
Give a reason for each calculation.

2 **a** Which is the easiest angle to calculate in this diagram?

b Calculate the angles *a* to *f* in this diagram.

c In what order did you calculate the angles? Explain why.

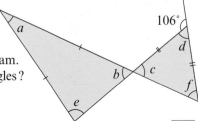

Parallel lines

In each of these diagrams a straight line crosses two parallel lines.

- In each diagram a pair of **corresponding angles** is labelled. Corresponding angles are equal.

- In each diagram a pair of **alternate angles** is labelled. Alternate angles are equal.

Exercise 2.2
Angles in parallel lines

1 **a** List five pairs of corresponding angles in this diagram.
   b List three pairs of alternate angles.

To find corresponding angles in a diagram you could look for an F shape which may be upside down and/or back to front.

To find alternate angles in a diagram you could look for a Z shape which may be back to front.

2 Sketch these diagrams. Work out the angles *a*, *b* and *c*. You may need to calculate some other angles first.

3 In this diagram AS, BR and NQ intersect to make the triangle DPO. CE, FI, JM and NQ are parallel.

   a List three pairs of corresponding angles along the line:

   i AS   **ii** BR

   b Explain why DĜH and DĤI are not corresponding angles.
   c List three pairs of alternate angles in this diagram.
   d Calculate each of these angles.

i HD̂G	**ii** AD̂C
iii GK̂L	**iv** HL̂K
v QP̂L	**vi** NÔR

Give a reason for each calculation that you do.

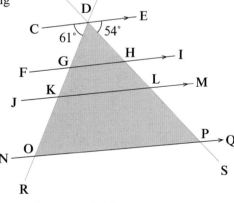

4 In each of these diagrams there is one pair of parallel lines.

  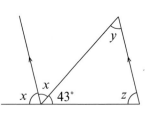

Sketch these diagrams and calculate each of the angles marked with a letter.

5 a Work out each of these angles in ABCD.

   i AB̂D   **ii** AD̂B
   iii BD̂C   **iv** BĈD

   b Which two lines are parallel?
   c What is the mathematical name
      for ABCD?
   d Explain why ABCD is not a rhombus.

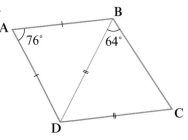

Properties of polygons

Exercise 2.3
Properties of quadrilaterals

1 AB and CD are plastic strips joined by red and yellow elastic bands.
ABCD is a parallelogram; its diagonals intersect at M.
You can stretch the parallelogram if you fix AB and pull CD sideways.

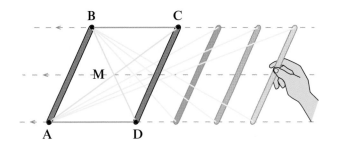

Below are some diagrams of the parallelogram as it is stretched.
ABC′D′ is a rhombus.

  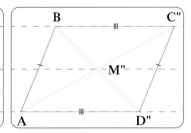

   a Trace the angles AB̂C, AB̂D and CB̂D.
   b Use your tracings to find out what happens to each of
      these angles as the parallelogram is stretched.

      i AB̂C   **ii** AB̂D   **iii** CB̂D

   c What happens to AM̂B as the parallelogram is stretched?
   d What type of angle is each of these?

      i AM̂B   **ii** AM̂′B   **iii** AM̂″B

The interior angles of ABCD
are marked in green.

If you bisect a line or
angle, you cut it into
2 equal parts.

If two lines bisect each
other, they are both cut
into two equal lengths.

2

Which of these statements do you think is always true:

a for a parallelogram   **b** for a rhombus?

25

Angles in polygons

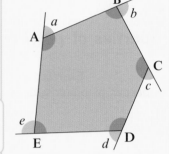

♦ At each vertex of a polygon the angle between an extended side and the adjacent side is called **an exterior angle**.

In ABCDE:

❖ the exterior angles are marked in orange
❖ the interior angles are marked in green.

♦ The sum of the exterior angles of any polygon is 360°.

In ABCDE:
$a + b + c + d + e = 360°$

You can show this by tracing the angles and fitting them together round a point.

♦ At each vertex the sum of the interior angle and exterior angle is 180°.

Exercise 2.4
Exterior angles
of polygons

1   For this polygon:

   a   calculate each exterior angle
   b   check that the total of the exterior angles is 360°.

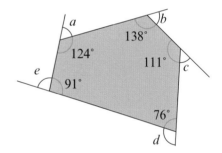

2   A dodecagon has 12 sides.
In this regular dodecagon one side is extended to form the angle p.

   a   Explain why the exterior angles of a regular dodecagon are all equal to 360° ÷ 12.
   b   Calculate the angle p.
   c   Calculate the interior angle of a regular dodecagon.

3   This is part of regular nonagon drawn inside a circle with centre C. One side of the nonagon is extended to form the angle e. Calculate the angles e to h.

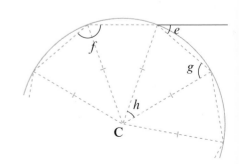

Exercise 2.5
Triangles investigation

You can mark eight points that are equally spaced on the circumference of a circle if you:
- draw a circle on square grid paper
- mark in lines that are vertical, horizontal and at 45° to the horizontal.

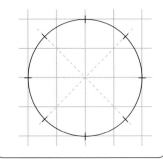

1 This eight-point circle has the points A to H equally spaced on the circumference.
Δ ABD is drawn by joining three of the points.

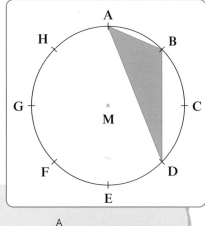

This is how a student calculated the exterior angle at A for Δ ABD.

To find the exterior angle at A

AM̂D = 135°
MÂD = (180° − 135°) ÷ 2   Δ AMD isosceles
    = 22.5°

AM̂B = 45°
MÂB = (180° − 45°) ÷ 2   Δ AMB isosceles
    = 67.5°

DÂB = MÂB − MÂD
    = 67.5° − 22.5°
    = 45°

So the exterior angle at A is **135°**.

a Explain why AM̂D is 135°.
b For triangle ABD:
  i calculate the exterior angles at B and D
  ii check that the total of the exterior angles is 360°.

2 Triangle ACF is also drawn on an eight-point circle.

a For triangle ACF:
  i calculate each interior angle
  ii calculate each exterior angle.
b How many different triangles is it possible to draw in an eight-point circle?
c What different exterior angles are possible for triangles drawn on an eight-point circle?

Do not count any that are reflections or rotations of another polygon.

End points

You should be able to ...   ... so try these questions

A Calculate angles in parallel lines

A1 Calculate the angles a, b and c in this diagram.

B Use the properties of polygons

B1 Polygons A to E are drawn on an equilateral grid.

    a Which of these polygons:
      i is a regular polygon
      ii has only one obtuse angle?
    b Give a mathematical name for each of the polygons A to E.

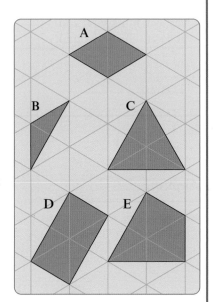

C Calculate angles in polygons

C1 For each of the polygons B and E:
    a calculate the interior angles
    b calculate the exterior angles.

C2 What is the exterior angle of a regular octagon?

Some points to remember

- For a polygon with n sides:

  - the sum of the interior angles is $(n - 2) \times 180°$
  - the sum of the exterior angles is $360°$
  - each exterior angle of a regular polygon is $360° \div n$.

- Examples of quadrilaterals

	Square	Rectangle	Kite	Rhombus	Parallelogram
The diagonals: • bisect the interior angles • bisect each other • intersect at 90°.	✓ ✓ ✓	✗ ✓ ✗	✗ ✗ ✓	✓ ✓ ✓	✗ ✓ ✗
Number of lines of symmetry	4	2	1	2	0
Order of rotational symmetry	4	2	1	2	2

Starting points
You need to know about ...

... so try these questions

A Multiplying out brackets

◆ To multiply out brackets, multiply every term inside the bracket by the term outside.

Example 1

$2(3a^2 + 4a - 6) = (2 \times 3a^2) + (2 \times 4a) - (2 \times 6)$
$= 6a^2 + 8a - 12$

We say that $2(3a^2 + 4a - 6)$ and $6a^2 + 8a - 12$ are **equivalent expressions** because:

$2(3a^2 + 4a - 6) = 6a^2 + 8a - 12$ for any value of a.

Example 2

$2(3a - 4b - 2) + 4(2a - 6) = 6a - 8b - 4 + 8a - 24$
$= 14a - 8b - 28$

So $14a - 8b - 28$ is equivalent to $2(3a - 4b - 2) + 4(2a - 6)$

B Algebraic fractions

◆ To find equivalent algebraic fractions, multiply or divide the numerator and denominator by the same number or expression.

Example

$$\frac{n^2}{3n} = \frac{n}{3} \quad \begin{array}{c} \div n \\ \div n \end{array}$$

◆ To add or subtract algebraic fractions with different denominators:
  ❖ find equivalent fractions with the same denominator
  ❖ add or subtract the numerators.

Example 1 $\quad \dfrac{2}{p + 3} + \dfrac{3}{p}$

$= \dfrac{2p}{(p + 3)p} + \dfrac{3(p + 3)}{(p + 3)p}$

$= \dfrac{2p + 3(p + 3)}{(p + 3)p}$

$= \dfrac{5p + 9}{(p + 3)p}$

Example 2 $\quad \dfrac{2}{a} - \dfrac{5}{3a}$

$= \dfrac{6}{3a} - \dfrac{5}{3a}$

$= \dfrac{1}{3a}$

◆ To multiply algebraic fractions, multiply the numerators and multiply the denominators.

Example

$$\frac{x}{2} \times \frac{5}{x - 1} = \frac{5x}{2(x - 1)}$$

◆ To divide algebraic fractions, use the rule that dividing by a fraction has the same effect as multiplying by its reciprocal.

Example

$$\frac{3}{x + 1} \div \frac{2}{y} = \frac{3}{x + 1} \times \frac{y}{2} = \frac{3y}{2(x + 1)}$$

A1 Which of these expressions is equivalent to $5a + 7$?

A $\quad 2(3a + 5)$

B $\quad 3(a + 2) + 2(a + 2)$

C $\quad 4(2a + 1) + 3(1 - a)$

D $\quad 5(2a + 1) + 2(1 - a)$

A2 Simplify the expression
  a $3(a - 5) + 5(2a - 3)$
  b $4(x - 2) + 3(4 - 3x)$
  c $2(x - 1) + 3(2x - 5) + 4(x - 3)$
  d $3(x - 5) - 4(2x - 1)$
  e $3(4a - 2b) + 2(3b - 6a + 2)$

B1 Write each of these as a single fraction, in its simplest form.

  a $\dfrac{2}{p + 2} + \dfrac{4}{p}$ **b** $\dfrac{8p}{9} \times \dfrac{3}{2p}$

  c $\dfrac{1}{p} - \dfrac{1}{(p + 5)}$ **d** $\dfrac{5p}{8} \div \dfrac{3p}{16}$

  e $\dfrac{3}{(p + 1)} + \dfrac{2}{p - 1}$

  f $\dfrac{4}{3p + 2} + \dfrac{1}{p - 1}$

  g $\dfrac{p + 3}{4} + \dfrac{p + 2}{5}$

  h $\dfrac{p + 3}{4} \times \dfrac{5}{p - 2}$

  i $\dfrac{2p - 3}{3} \times \dfrac{4}{p + 5}$

  j $\dfrac{4p + 5}{3} \div \dfrac{2p - 1}{4}$

Using brackets

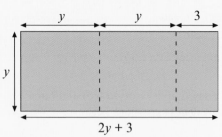

◆ You can use brackets to write an expression for the shaded area in each of these rectangles.

Shaded area = $p(p-2)$
$= p^2 - 2p$

Shaded area = $y(2y+3)$
$= 2y^2 + 3y$

Exercise 3.1
Using brackets

1 For each of these rectangles write an expression for the shaded area:
  a with brackets   **b** without brackets.

For some of the shaded rectangles you will need to find an expression for a missing dimension first.

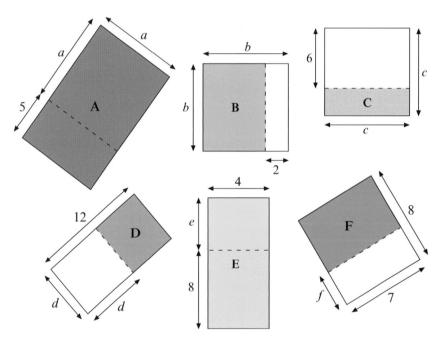

2 For each of P, Q and R write an expression for the shaded area:
  a with brackets   **b** without brackets.

3 Write an expression for the width of rectangles A to E.

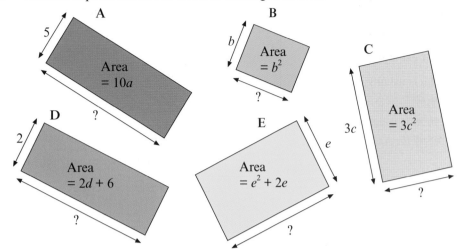

4 Copy and complete these.

a $4x + 12 = 4(\square + \square)$ b $6p - 4 = 2(\square - \square)$

c $2a + 8 = \square(a + \square)$ d $10 - 5q = \square(2 - \square)$

e $3t^2 - 4t = \square(\square - \square)$ f $6s^2 + 7s = \square(\square + 7)$

Multiplying terms and simplifying

◆ When you subtract a bracket each term must have the correct sign.

Example 1	Example 2	Example 3
$30 - (5 + 2)$	$30 - (5 - 2)$	$30 - 2(3 + 5)$
$= 30 - 5 - 2$	$= 30 - 5 + 2$	$= 30 - (6 + 10)$
$= 23$	$= 27$	$= 30 - 6 - 10$
		$= 14$

Example 4	Example 5	Example 6
$5x - (x + 3)$	$5x - (4 - x)$	$5x - 3(y - 4)$
$= 5x - x - 3$	$= 5x - 4 + x$	$= 5x - (3y - 12)$
$= 4x - 3$	$= 6x - 4$	$= 5x - 3y + 12$

Exercise 3.2
Subtracting brackets

1 Multiply out and simplify:

a $3b - 5(2 - b)$ b $12 - 3(2x - 4)$ c $6c - 3(c + 4)$

d $6y - 5(3 - y)$ e $6 - 2(a + 3)$ f $5a - 2(7 - b)$

2 Which of these expressions is equivalent to $2 - x$?

A $\boxed{2(x + 4) - 3(x + 2)}$ B $\boxed{2(x + 3) - (3x - 4)}$

C $\boxed{3(x - 2) - 2(x - 4)}$ D $\boxed{5(x - 2) - 3(2x - 4)}$

3 Simplify each of these expressions.

a $2(3a + 3) - (a + 1)$ b $3(x + 4) - (2x - 3)$

c $2(2a + 3) - 3(4 - a)$ d $2(x + 4) - 3(2x - 1)$

e $5(x - 3) - 2(4 + x)$ f $5(3x + 2) - 2(4x + 3)$

g $2(x - 3) - (x + 3)$ h $3(3x + 2y) - 2(y - 4x)$

In any term the letters are usually written in alphabetical order.

For example:

$2ba$ is usually written as $2ab$

$4n^2m$ is usually written as $4mn^2$.

♦ You can **multiply terms** by grouping numbers, and each of the letters.

Example 1

$2m \times 3n$
$= 2 \times m \times 3 \times n$
$= 2 \times 3 \times m \times n$
$= 6mn$

Example 2

$2ab \times a$
$= 2 \times a \times b \times a$
$= 2 \times a \times a \times b$
$= 2a^2b$

Example 3

$2p \times 3p^2$
$= 2 \times p \times 3 \times p \times p$
$= 2 \times 3 \times p \times p \times p$
$= 6p^3$

The letters in each term are usually written in alphabetical order.

♦ **Like terms** must have exactly the same letters in them.

Example 1

$2p^2r = 2 \times p \times p \times r$
$8p^2r = 8 \times p \times p \times r$
So $2p^2r$ and $8p^2r$ are like terms.

Example 2

$3pr^2 = 3 \times p \times r \times r$
$2p^2r = 2 \times p \times p \times r$
So $2p^2r$ and $3pr^2$ are **not** like terms.

♦ To **simplify an expression** collect together any **like terms**.

These **can be simplified** by collecting like terms.
$2a^2b + 3ab^2 + 4a^2b = 6a^2b + 3ab^2$
$2x^2 + 2x + 3x^2 - x + 4 = 5x^2 + x + 4$

These **will not simplify** as there are no like terms.
$2a^2b + 3ab^2$
$2x^2 + 4x + 3$

Exercise 3.3
Multiplying terms and simplifying

1 Multiply these terms.

   a $3a \times 2b$ **b** $p \times 3q$ **c** $4y \times 5x$ **d** $5q \times 6p$
   e $x \times 2x$ **f** $ab \times a$ **g** $2xy \times y$ **h** $2ab \times 3a$
   i $2p^2 \times 3q$ **j** $a^3 \times a^2$ **k** $2b^2 \times 3b$ **l** $5c^3 \times 2b$

2 Find four pairs of equivalent terms.

   A $(2b^2)^3$ **B** $6b^5$ **C** $3b^2 \times 2b^4$ **D** $5b^5$ **E** $8b^6$

   F $3b^2 \times 2b^3$ **G** $6(b^4)^2$ **H** $6b^6$ **I** $6b^8$

3 Multiply out these brackets.

   a $a(b + 4)$ **b** $m(2n + 3p)$ **c** $2x(3y + 2z)$
   d $c(a + c)$ **e** $p(p - q)$ **f** $4a(a - b)$
   g $a(2b - 4c)$ **h** $2a(3a + 4b)$ **i** $4p(2q - 3p)$
   j $2pq(3p + 2q)$ **k** $4xy(x - 2y)$ **l** $3xy(x^2 - y^2)$

4 Simplify these where possible.

   a $4x^2 + x - 2x^2$ **b** $5a + 2ab - a + 3ab$
   c $x^2 + x^3 - 2x$ **d** $4a - 3b + 7a + 5b$
   e $4p^2 - pq + 6q + pq$ **f** $ab + 2a - ab + 4a$

5 Which of these expressions is equivalent to $2a^2b - 3ab - 5ab^2$?

   A $2a(ab + b) + 5b(ab - a)$ **B** $ab(2a - 2) - a(b - 5b^2)$

   C $a(b + 2ab) - ab(4 + 5b)$

6 Multiply out and simplify:

   a $2(2a + 3b) + 5(a + 4b)$ **b** $2(2x + 4y) + 3(2x - y)$
   c $x(x - 3) - x(x + 4)$ **d** $2x(3x + 2y) + x(4x - y)$
   e $ab(a + b) + ab(a - b)$ **f** $3a(ab + b) - 2b(ab - b)$

7 Simplify these expressions.

   a $2a(3a - b) + 4b(2a + 3b)$ **b** $5xy(2x + 4y) + 3x(2xy - 2y)$

   c $pq(2p - 3q) - 2p(3pq - 2q^2)$ **d** $2mn(3m - 4n) - 4m^2(2n - 3m)$

8 Write each of these as a single fraction in its simplest form.

   a $\dfrac{3}{x + 1} + \dfrac{2}{2x + 1}$ **b** $\dfrac{4}{x + 2} - \dfrac{3}{x + 1}$

   c $\dfrac{5}{x - 3} - \dfrac{2}{x + 4}$ **d** $\dfrac{3x}{x + 2} - \dfrac{2}{x + 4}$

Thinking ahead to ...
common factors

A   In this triangle puzzle:

   ◆   the numbers in squares on each side are multiplied to give the numbers in circles

   ◆   the numbers in the circles are added to give the total.

   Copy and complete triangles 1 and 2.

B

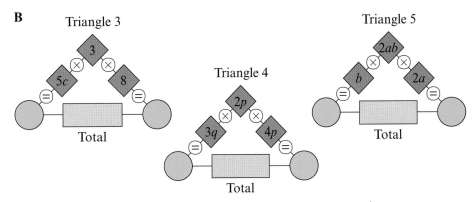

For each of the triangles 3, 4 and 5, write an expression for the total.

C   Copy and complete these triangle puzzles.

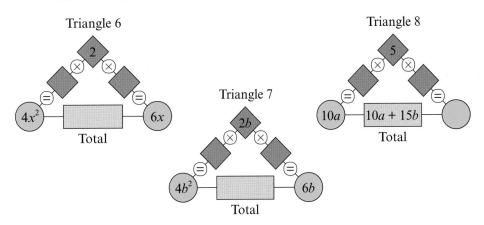

Common factors

The factors of a number are all **whole numbers**.

♦ A whole number can be written as a product of factors.

Examples

$48 = 12 \times 4$	$72 = 12 \times 6$
$48 = 2 \times 24$	$72 = 2 \times 36$
…	…

12 and 2 are common factors of 48 and 72.

♦ A term can be written as a product of factors.

Examples

$3a^2 = 3 \times a^2$	$6ab = 3 \times 2ab$
$3a^2 = a \times 3a$	$6ab = a \times 6b$
…	…

3 and a are common factors of $3a^2$ and $6ab$.

♦ To **factorise an expression** look for a common factor of the terms and write the expression using brackets.

Example

$$3a^2 + 6ab = 3(a^2 + 2ab) = 3a(a + 2b)$$

$3 \times a^2$ $3 \times 2ab$ $a \times a$ $a \times 2b$

So 3 is a common factor of $3a^2$ and $6ab$

So a is a common factor of a^2 and $2ab$

So $3a^2 + 6ab = 3a(a + 2b)$

This is **factorised fully** as there are no other common factors.

Exercise 3.4
Common factors

When you factorise an expression, check that the two expressions are equivalent by multiplying out the bracket.

Example

Factorise $3ab^2 + 6a^2$
$3ab^2 + 6a^2 = 3a(b^2 + 2a)$

Check

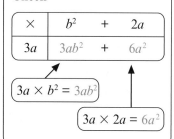

$\times$	b^2	$+$	$2a$
$3a$	$3ab^2$	$+$	$6a^2$

$3a \times b^2 = 3ab^2$

$3a \times 2a = 6a^2$

1 Factorise these fully.

a $2x + 14$	**b** $8x - 10y$	**c** $5x + xy$	**d** $pq + 7p$
e $6d + 4de$	**f** $6ab + 9a$	**g** $2a - 8ab$	**h** $3a^2 + 12a$
i $15xy + 20yz$	**j** $a^2b + ab^2$	**k** $12c^2d - 15cd$	**l** $25x^2y + 15yz$

2 Draw a complete solution for triangles L and M.

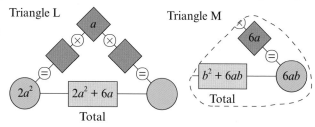

Triangle L

Triangle M

$2a^2$ $2a^2 + 6a$

Total

$b^2 + 6ab$ $6ab$

Total

3 **a** In triangle N what term, other than 1, can be in the top square?
b Draw a complete solution for triangle N.

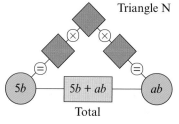

Triangle N

$5b$ $5b + ab$ ab

Total

4 Draw a complete solution for triangles O and P.

Triangle O

c^2 $c^2 + 8c$

Total

Triangle P

$4d + 6b$ $6b$

Total

In these puzzles do not use the number 1 in the top square.

5 **a** Draw two different solutions for triangle Q.

b How many different solutions are there for triangle Q?

Triangle Q

6 Draw a complete solution for triangle R.

Triangle R

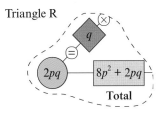

7 Factorise these fully.

a $5x + 10y + 20$
b $6a - 9b + 12c$
c $2x^2 + 3x + xy$
d $14x - 28y + 21z$
e $2x^2 + 8xy + 6x$
f $6ab^2 + 2a^2b + 5ab$

Thinking ahead to ...
multiplying two brackets

The total area of this shape is $43 \times 28 \text{ cm}^2$.

One way to find the area is:

◆ split the shape into 4 rectangles

◆ find the area of each rectangle in cm^2
   $20 \times 40 = 800$
   $20 \times 3 = 60$
   $8 \times 40 = 320$
   $8 \times 3 = 24$

◆ add the areas.
   The total area is 1204 cm^2.

There is more than one correct expression.

A Using brackets the area of this shape can be written as $(x + 3)(x + 2)$.

This shape is split into four rectangles.

Find an expression for:

a the area of each rectangle
b the total area of the shape.

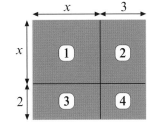

B Shapes P and Q are split into rectangles.

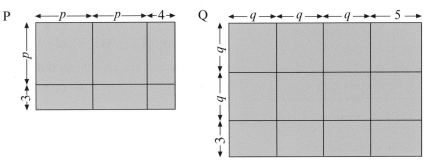

For each of the shapes P and Q write an expression for the total area:

a with brackets   **b** without brackets in its simplest form.

C Shape R is split into four rectangles.

a Which of these is an expression for the shaded area?

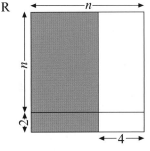

R

A $n(n + 2) - 4n$	**B** $(n + 2)(n - 4)$
C $n(n + 2) - 4(n + 2)$	**D** $(n - 2)(n - 4)$
E $n(n - 4) + 2(n - 4)$	**F** $n(n + 2) - 8$

b Write and simplify an expression for the shaded area without brackets.

Multiplying two brackets

♦ You can multiply out brackets from $(2n + 3)(3n + 4)$ like this:

❖ $(2n + 3)(3n + 4) = (2n + 3) \times (3n + 4)$

❖ Work in a table:

×	$2n$	$+3$
$3n$	$6n^2$	$9n$
$+4$	$8n$	12

❖ The total is: $6n^2 + 9n + 8n + 12$
which simplifies to: $6n^2 + 17n + 12$

❖ So, $(2n + 3)(3n + 4) = 6n^2 + 17n + 12$ for any value of n.

❖ $(2n + 3)(3n + 4)$ and $6n^2 + 17n + 12$ are equivalent expressions.

Exercise 3.5
Multiplying out brackets

1 Which of these expressions is equivalent to $(n + 1)(n + 8)$?

   A $n^2 + 8n + 8$ B $2n + 9$ C $n^2 + 9n + 8$ D $2n + 8$

2 **a** Which of these expressions gives the area of this rectangle?

   A $n^2 + 10n + 7$ B $n^2 + 10n + 10$

   C $n^2 + 7n + 7$ D $n^2 + 7n + 10$

  b Explain your answer.

3 For each of these, multiply out the brackets and simplify.

  a $(a + 1)(a + 3)$ **b** $(d + 5)(d + 9)$ **c** $(3e + 1)(e + 7)$
  d $(2a + 1)(5a + 4)$ **e** $(2b + 3)(3b + 5)$ **f** $(2c + 7)(3c + 2)$

4 For each of these, multiply out the brackets and simplify.

$(x + 1)^2 = (x + 1)(x + 1)$

  a $(x + 1)^2$ **b** $(x + 2)^2$ **c** $(x + 3)^2$

Comment on any pattern you see in your results.

5 Copy and complete:

×	x	-4
x	☐	☐
-2	☐	☐

So $(x - 4)(x - 2) =$ ☐

6 **a** This shaded square is surrounded by four rectangles,
each x cm by 3 cm, where $x > 3$.
Write an expression for the area
of the shaded square:
  i with brackets
  ii without brackets.
  b Write an expression for the shaded
square if the rectangles are:
    i x cm by 4 cm, where $x > 4$
    ii x cm by 5 cm, where $x > 5$
    iii x cm by y cm, where $x > y$.
Write each answer without brackets
and simplify.

7 Copy and complete:

×	2x	−5
3x	☐	−15x
+1	☐	☐

So $(2x - 5)(3x + 1) =$ ☐

8 For each of these, multiply out the brackets and simplify.

a $(z + t)(2z + t)$ **b** $(3k + m)(2k + 5m)$ **c** $(2c + 3d)(c + 7d)$
d $(3p - q)(2p + 5q)$ **e** $(f - g)(5f - 3g)$ **f** $(3w - v)(7w + v)$

9 Find four pairs of equivalent expressions.

A $(2a + 3)(a - 2)$ **B** $(2a - 3)(a + 2)$ **C** $(2a - 1)(a + 6)$

D $(2a - 1)(a - 6)$ **E** $2a^2 - 13a - 6$ **F** $2a^2 + a - 6$

G $2a^2 - 13a + 6$ **H** $2a^2 + 11a - 6$ **I** $2a^2 - a - 6$

10 For each of these, multiply out the brackets and simplify.

a $(z + t)(z - t)$ **b** $(2k + m)(2k - m)$ **c** $(2c - 3d)(2c + 3d)$
d $(3p - q)(3p + q)$ **e** $(5f + 3g)(5f - 3g)$ **f** $(7w - v)(7w + v)$

Comment on any pattern you see in your results.

11 Which of these expressions J to N gives the area shaded in this square?

> There is more than one correct expression.

J $(a - 3b)^2$ **K** $a^2 - 6ab + 9b^2$

L $6ab + a^2$ **M** $a^2 - 9b^2$

N $(a - 3b)(a + 3b)$

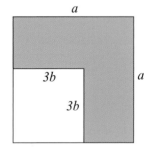

12 a Multiply out and simplify:
  i $(x + 1)^2$ **ii** $(x + 1)^3$ **iii** $(x + 1)^4$
b Look at the pattern in the coefficients.
  Use it to write down $(x + 1)^6$ without brackets (in its simplest from).

13 Write each of these without brackets and simplify.

a $a(a - 2)(a + 5)$ **b** $(p - 3)(p - 4)(p + 2)$
c $2q(2q + 3)(q - 7)$ **d** $(x + 5)(2x - 1)(x + 2)$

Thinking ahead to ...
algebraic proofs

A a Copy and complete these questions which follow a pattern.

$(3 \times 4) - (1 \times 6) =$ ☐
$(4 \times 5) - (2 \times 7) =$ ☐
$(5 \times 6) - (3 \times 8) =$ ☐
. . .
. . .
. . .
(☐ × ☐) − (100 × ☐) = ☐

b Describe what happens to the answers in the pattern.
c Write an expression for the nth question in this pattern.

Algebraic proof

♦ Algebra can be used to prove that some statements are true.

Example Prove that the answer to every line in this pattern is 6.

❖ For any value of n, the nth line in this pattern can be written as:
$(n + 2)(n + 3) - n(n + 5)$

$$3 \times 4 - 1 \times 6$$
$$4 \times 5 - 2 \times 7$$
$$5 \times 6 - 3 \times 8$$
$$\ldots$$

❖ This can be simplified:
$$(n + 2)(n + 3) - n(n + 5) = (n^2 + 5n + 6) - (n^2 + 5n)$$
$$= n^2 + 5n + 6 - n^2 - 5n$$
$$= 6$$

This proves that for any value of n the answer will be 6.

Exercise 3.6
Algebraic proof

1 For each of these patterns:

a copy and complete the examples

A
$2 \times 3 - 1 \times 4 =$
$3 \times 4 - 2 \times 5 =$
$4 \times 5 - 3 \times 6 =$
⋮   ⋮

B
$2 \times 2 - 1 \times 3 =$
$3 \times 3 - 2 \times 4 =$
$4 \times 4 - 3 \times 5 =$
⋮   ⋮

C
$4 \times 5 - 1 \times 8 =$
$5 \times 6 - 2 \times 9 =$
$6 \times 7 - 3 \times 10 =$
⋮   ⋮

b write an expression for the nth line
c prove that every line of the pattern gives the same answer and state the answer.

2 Each of these is an expression for the nth line of a pattern.

D $(n + 1)(n + 6) - n(n + \square) =$

E $(n + 2)(n + \square) - n(n + 5) =$

F $(n + \square)(n + 4) - n(n + 9) =$

a For each of the expressions D, E and F:
  i find the missing number
  ii calculate the answer for the pattern.
b In expression G below, a, b and c are constants.

G $(n + a)(n + b) - n(n + c) =$

  i Write a relationship that connects a, b and c.
  ii What is the answer for this pattern?

3 For each of these patterns:

a copy and complete the examples

A
$3 \times 4 - 1 \times 8 =$
$4 \times 5 - 2 \times 9 =$
$5 \times 6 - 3 \times 10 =$
⋮   ⋮

B
$3 \times 5 - 1 \times 8 =$
$4 \times 6 - 2 \times 9 =$
$5 \times 7 - 3 \times 10 =$
⋮   ⋮

C
$1 \times 6 - 3 \times 3 =$
$2 \times 7 - 4 \times 4 =$
$3 \times 8 - 5 \times 5 =$
⋮   ⋮

b write an expression for the nth line
c describe what happens to the answers in each pattern.

4 Write some lines in a pattern for which the answer to the nth line is:

a $n + 4$ b $n - 2$ c $10 - n$

Factorising

> To factorise an expression is to write it as a **multiplication** of its factors. For example:
> $x^2 + 5x + 4$ factorises to give
> $(x + 4)(x + 1)$
> or $(x + 1)(x + 4)$

Example The expression $n^2 + 2n - 8$ has no common factor but it can be factorised. This is one way to factorise $n^2 + 2n - 8$.

❖ Think about a table that gives a total of $n^2 + 2n - 8$ and fill in the parts you are sure about.

×	n	
n	n^2	
		− 8

❖ Try values that give − 8 in the correct position.

❖ So $n^2 + 2n - 8 = (n + 4)(n - 2)$ or $(n - 2)(n + 4)$

❖ The total for this table is $n^2 - 2n - 8$ which **is not** what you want.

×	n	− 4
n	n^2	− 4n
+ 2	2n	− 8

❖ The total for this table is $n^2 + 2n - 8$ which **is** what you want.

×	n	+ 4
n	n^2	4n
− 2	− 2n	− 8

Exercise 3.7
Factorising

1 Factorise these expressions.

  a $x^2 + 8x + 7$ **b** $p^2 + 9p + 8$ **c** $t^2 + 10t + 9$
  d $m^2 + 8m + 12$ **e** $n^2 + 6n + 9$ **f** $a^2 + 13a + 36$

2 Copy and complete these statements.

  a $x^2 + 6x + \square = (x + 4)(x + 2)$ **b** $q^2 + 6q + \square = (q + 5)(q + 1)$
  c $r^2 + \square r + 10 = (r + 5)(r + 2)$ **d** $y^2 - \square y + 10 = (y - 1)(y - 10)$
  e $t^2 + 7t + 12 = (t + 4)(\square \square \square)$ **f** $p^2 - 7p - 8 = (p + 1)(\square \square \square)$

3 Which pair of expressions multiply to give $x^2 + 3x - 4$?

  $\boxed{x + 1}$ $\boxed{x - 1}$ $\boxed{x + 2}$ $\boxed{x - 2}$ $\boxed{x + 4}$ $\boxed{x - 4}$

4 Which pair of expressions multiply to give $x^2 - 6x + 8$?

  $\boxed{x + 4}$ $\boxed{x - 1}$ $\boxed{x + 2}$ $\boxed{x - 2}$ $\boxed{x - 8}$ $\boxed{x - 4}$

5 Factorise these expressions.

  a $p^2 + 2p - 3$ **b** $m^2 + 3m - 10$ **c** $t^2 - 4t - 5$
  d $r^2 - 3r - 28$ **e** $x^2 - 8x + 15$ **f** $n^2 - 7n + 6$
  g $t^2 - t - 12$ **h** $b^2 - 4b - 12$ **i** $x^2 + 4x - 12$

6 Which pair of expressions multiply to give $x^2 - 16$?

  $\boxed{x - 16}$ $\boxed{x - 8}$ $\boxed{x - 4}$ $\boxed{x + 1}$ $\boxed{x + 4}$ $\boxed{x + 2}$

7 Factorise these expressions.

  a $t^2 - 9$ **b** $r^2 - 25$ **c** $16p^2 - 1$
  d $9x^2 - 4$ **e** $x^2 - y^2$ **f** $x^2 - 9p^2$

8 Which of these cannot be factorised as in the Example above?

  A $x^2 + x + 15$ B $x^2 + 9x + 20$ C $x^2 - 6x + 12$

- You can use a table to factorise expressions like $2n^2 - 7n + 3$, where the **coefficient** of n^2 is not equal to 1.

×	n
$2n$	$2n^2$
	+3

- Think about a table that gives a total of $2n^2 - 7n + 3$ and fill in the parts you are sure about.

- Try values that give +3 in the correct position, and give a negative coefficient of n.

×	n	−1
$2n$	$2n^2$	$-2n$
-3	$-3n$	+3

- The total for this table is $2n^2 - 5n + 3$ which **is not** what you want.

×	n	−3
$2n$	$2n^2$	$-6n$
-1	$-n$	+3

- The total for this table is $2n^2 - 7n + 3$ which **is** what you want.

- So $2n^2 - 7n + 3 = (n - 3)(2n - 1)$ or $(2n - 1)(n - 3)$

Exercise 3.8
Factorising

1 Which pair of expressions multiply to give $2x^2 + 7x + 6$?

$\boxed{2x + 6}$ $\boxed{2x + 3}$ $\boxed{2x + 2}$ $\boxed{2x + 1}$ $\boxed{x + 1}$ $\boxed{x + 2}$ $\boxed{x + 3}$ $\boxed{x + 6}$

2 Factorise these expressions.

a $3x^2 - 10x + 3$ b $4y^2 + y - 3$ c $4p^2 - 11p - 3$
d $4x^2 - x - 3$ e $3x^2 + 8x - 3$ f $3a^2 + 10a + 3$
g $5n^2 - 11n + 2$ h $3x^2 - x - 4$ i $3x^2 - 4x + 1$

3 This puzzle has been completed but most clues are missing.

Algebra Puzzle

	1		**2**		**3**	
	$+ 9x^2$		+ 1	+ 4x	$+ 4x^2$	
4						
$+ x^2$	- 1		$+ x^2$		- 1	
		5		**6**		
- 4x		$+ 3x^2$	- 2x	- 5		
7				**8**		**9**
+ 3	$+ 4x^2$	+ 8x		- 4x	- 1	$+ 5x^2$
		10	**11**			
		+ 4	- 5x	$+ x^2$		+ x
	12				**13**	
	- 9		$+ x^2$		$+ x^2$	- 4
	14					
	$+ 4x^2$	- x	- 14		- 49	

Clues

Across
2 $(2x + 1)(2x + 1)$
4 $(x - 1)(x$
5 $(x + 1)($
7 $(2x + 1)$
8 $(x - 1)$
10
13
14

Down
1 $(3x - 1)(3x + 1)$
2
3
4
5
6
9
11
12
13

For every clue find a pair of brackets that multiply to give the correct expression.

a Write a full set of clues for this puzzle.
b Make up your own puzzle like this.

4 For each of these find the numerical value of a and b
such that for all values of x:

    a $x^2 - 12x + a = (x - b)^2$ **b** $x^2 - ax + 9 = (x - b)^2$

    c $9x^2 - ax + 1 = (3x - b)^2$ **d** $x^2 - ax + a = (x - b)^2$

> If there is a common factor in all the terms, take that out first then factorise.
>
> **Example**
>
> $2x^2 + 10x + 8$
> $= 2(x^2 + 5x + 4)$
> $= 2(x + 1)(x + 4)$
> This is factorised fully.

5 Find a common factor and factorise each of these expressions fully.

    a $3x^2 - 9x + 6$ **b** $6x^2 + 21x + 15$ **c** $6x^2 + 16x - 6$

    d $14x^2 - 21x - 14$ **e** $3x^2 - 6x + 3$ **f** $4x^2 - 4$

6   **a**   Factorise fully $n^3 - n$.

    b   Show that $n^3 - n$ is even for all integer values of n.

7 Factorise these fully.

    a $x^2 + 2xy + y^2$ **b** $4x^2 + 8xy + 4y^2$ **c** $9x^2 - 16y^2$

Using factorisation

Exercise 3.9
Using factorisation

1 Three consecutive numbers are added together.

    a   If the smallest number is p, write each other number in terms of p.

    b   **i**   Write an expression for the sum of the three numbers.

        ii   Simplify the expression.

      iii   Explain why this shows that the sum of three
consecutive numbers is always a multiple of 3.

2   **a**   Evaluate the expression $n^2 + n - 6$ for:

        i $n = 1$ **ii** $n = 2$ **iii** $n = 3$ **iv** $n = 4$

    b   Factorise $n^2 + n - 6$.

    c   Explain why this shows that the value of $n^2 + n - 6$
is even for any value of n.

3 Show that $n^2 - 6n + 9 \geqslant 0$ for all values of n.

4 Kim puts this cross anywhere on
this size 8 grid. She multiplies
the corner numbers in pairs and
finds the difference.

Example

$20 \times 27 - 11 \times 18 = 342$
$39 \times 46 - 30 \times 37 = 684$

1	2	3	4	5	6	7	8
9	⊗	11		13	14	15	16
17	18	19	20	21	22	23	24
25		27	⊗	⊗	30		32
33	34	35	36	37	38	39	40
41	42	43	44			46	⊗	48
49	50	51	52	53	54	55	56

    a   **i**   If the number in the centre
of the cross is y, write each
of the corner numbers in
terms of y.

        ii   Write an expression for the
difference of the products.

      iii   Show that the difference will be $18y$ for all possible values of y.

    b   Kim uses the same cross on a size n grid.

        i   Write the corner numbers in terms of n and y.

        ii   Write an expression for the difference of the products.

      iii   What would be the difference for a cross with $y = 16$ on a size 9 grid?

> Because the cross cannot be placed on the edge of the grid some values of y are not possible.
>
> **Example**
>
> On the 8 grid these values of y are not possible:
> 1, 2, 3, 4, 5, 6, 7, 8, 9, 16, 17, 24, 25, … .

5 Show that the product of three consecutive numbers must be a multiple of 6.

SECTION 3 ALGEBRAIC MANIPULATION

Exercise 3.10
Using the difference of two squares

1 The expression $a^2 - b^2$ is called the difference of two squares.

   a Factorise $a^2 - b^2$.

   b Use this to find the value of:

     i $98^2 - 2^2$ **ii** $47^2 - 3^2$

2 **a** Copy and complete this sequence of lines.

   b Describe any patterns that you notice.

   c Write an expression for the nth line in this sequence and simplify it.

   d Write down the exact value of:

     i $1234^2 - 1233^2$

     ii $123123123123^2 - 123123123122^2$

$$2^2 - 1^2 =$$
$$3^2 - 2^2 =$$
$$4^2 - 3^2 =$$
$$5^2 - 4^2 =$$
$$6^2 - 5^2 =$$
$$\vdots \quad \vdots$$

3 **a** Use algebra to explain the pattern in these answers.

   b Use the pattern to write down the value of:

     i $128^2 - 123^2$

     ii $307^2 - 302^2$

$$6^2 - 1^2 = 35$$
$$7^2 - 2^2 = 45$$
$$8^2 - 3^2 = 55$$
$$9^2 - 4^2 = 65$$
$$\vdots \quad \vdots \quad \vdots$$

♦ Some algebraic fractions can be simplified by factorising.

Example

$$\frac{x^2 + 5x + 6}{x^2 + 2x - 3} = \frac{(x+3)(x+2)}{(x+3)(x-1)} = \frac{(x+2)}{(x-1)}$$

$$\div (x+3)$$
$$\div (x+3)$$

Exercise 3.11
Factors in algebraic fractions

1 **a** Find the value, in fractional form, of:

$$\frac{n-6}{n^2 - 5n - 6}$$

   when:

     i $n = 1$ **ii** $n = 2$ **iii** $n = 3$

   b Describe any patterns that you notice.

   c **i** Factorise and simplify the fraction.

     ii Use this to explain any patterns you found.

2 **a** Simplify each of these fractions as far as possible.

     i $\dfrac{2n+6}{2n^2 + 4n - 6}$ **ii** $\dfrac{n^2 - n - 6}{n^2 - 3n}$

     iii $\dfrac{n^2 + 5n}{2n + 10}$ **iv** $\dfrac{2n^2 - 4n}{n^2 - 5n + 6}$

   b Give the value of each fraction when $n = 50$.

3 **a** Express $\dfrac{x^2 + 3}{3} + \dfrac{x(x+9)}{6}$ as a single fraction and simplify.

   b Show that the value of this is an integer for all integer values of x.

End points

You should be able to ...

... so try these questions

A Multiply out brackets

A1 Simplify these expressions.
  a $2(2b - 4) + 6(4 + 3b)$ **b** $4(2b - 4) + 6(5 + 3b)$
  c $3ab(b - a) + 7ab(b + a)$ **d** $3xy(x - 3) - 7xy(y + 4)$

A2 Which of these expressions is equivalent to $(t + 5)(t - 3)$?

  A $t^2 + 8t + 15$ **B** $t^2 + 8t - 15$ **C** $t^2 + 2t - 15$

A3 For each of these, multiply out the brackets and simplify.
  a $(a + 1)(a + 8)$ **b** $(b + 4)^2$ **c** $(5c + 2)(c + 3)$
  d $(d + 2)(d - 1)$ **e** $(2e + 5)(3e - 10)$ **f** $(f - 7)(3f - 2)$

A4 These questions follow a pattern.
  a Write the next three lines of this pattern.
  b What is the answer to the 20th line
      of this pattern?
  c Write an expression for the nth line
      of this pattern.
  d Prove that the answer to any line of
      this pattern will be a multiple of 3.

$(2 \times 7) - (1 \times 5)$
$(3 \times 8) - (2 \times 6)$
$(4 \times 9) - (3 \times 7)$
...

B Factorise expressions

B1 Factorise these fully.
  a $8p + 4q$ **b** $6a - 12b$ **c** $a^2 + ab$
  d $7m + 3mn$ **e** $8xy + 10y$ **f** $4ab + 6a^2$
  g $3xy^2 - 5x^2y$ **h** $4pq - 6p^2q$ **i** $2g^2h - 5h^2$

B2 **A** $k + 2$ **B** $k - 7$ **C** $k - 2$ **D** $k + 14$ **E** $k + 7$ **F** $k - 1$

  Which pair of expressions multiply to give:
  a $k^2 + 5k - 14$ **b** $k^2 - 9k + 14$ **c** $k^2 + 13k - 14$?

B3 Factorise these expressions.
  a $x^2 + 12x + 11$ **b** $x^2 + 9x + 14$ **c** $x^2 + 4x - 5$
  d $x^2 + x - 6$ **e** $x^2 - x - 20$ **f** $x^2 - 5x + 6$
  g $x^2 - 100$ **h** $2x^2 - 11x + 15$ **i** $9x^2 - 16$
  j $5x^2 + 4x - 1$ **k** $x^2 - 4y^2$ **l** $4x^2 - 4xy + y^2$

B4 Find two pairs of equivalent expressions.

  A $\dfrac{1}{a + 1} + \dfrac{2}{a}$ **B** $\dfrac{3a + 6}{a^2 + 2a}$ **C** $\dfrac{3}{a - 1} - \dfrac{3}{a + 1}$

  D $\dfrac{2a^2}{5a^3} \times \dfrac{15a}{2a}$ **E** $\dfrac{15a}{a^2 - 1} \times \dfrac{2}{5a}$ **F** $\dfrac{2}{a - 1} \div \dfrac{a - 1}{3}$

B5 **a** Simplify $\dfrac{x^2 - 8x + 16}{3x - 12}$ as far as possible.

  b For what values of x is $\dfrac{x^2 - 8x + 16}{3x - 12}$ positive?

Starting points
You need to know about ...

... so try these questions

A Types of data

Data may be described as discrete or continuous.

♦ Discrete data is data which can only be of certain definite value. Data on shoe sizes would be discrete data.

♦ Continuous data is data which can have any value within a range. Data on the width of hand-spans would be continuous.

A1 State whether the following data is continuous or discrete:
  a the number of fish in an aquarium
  b the weight of apples in an orchard
  c the quoted age of each person in a cinema
  d the number of chairs in each classroom of a school.

B Finding averages and the range

♦ For data in categories like colour, you can only find one average:
  ❖ the **mode** (the **modal** category is the most common).

> Red Blue Yellow Blue Green Black Red Blue
> The modal colour is **Blue**.

♦ For numerical data, you can find several averages and the range:
  ❖ the **mode** is the most common value (or values)
  ❖ the **range** is the difference between the highest and lowest values

> 87 43 101 56 87 67   Mode = **87**
> Range = **58** (101 – 43)

  ❖ the **median** is the middle value when the data is in order (for an **even** number of values, take the median as halfway between the middle pair of values)

> 43 56 67 ¦ 87 87 101
> Median = **77**

  ❖ the **mean** is the total of all the values divided by the number of values.

> $$\frac{87 + 43 + 101 + 56 + 87 + 67}{6}$$ Mean = **73.5**

B1

X	15	42	33	37	84	42	50
	81	29	26	67	15	19	55

Y	38	25	106	78	44	62
	13	90	25	31	25	

For each set of data, find:
  a the mode
  b the median
  c the mean
  d the range.

B2

> Mode 3 and 7
> Median 6
> Mean 6

These are averages for a set of data with 8 values.
List what the values might be.

C Deciding which average to use

♦ The **mean** is the most widely used average.
It is not a sensible average to use for data with **extreme values**, values which are much smaller or much greater than the others.

G.T. Small & Son – Monthly Salaries (£)					
870	870	870	870	1050	1050
1050	1210	1210	1210	2080	2330

Mean = £1222.50
Median = £1050
Mode = £870

10 of the 12 salaries are smaller than the mean, so the **median** is the more sensible average to use.

♦ The **mode** can also be a poor choice of average.
For this data, it is a poor choice because it is the lowest salary.

C1

S. Fry & Partners
Weekly Wages (£)
112   285   285   340   340
340   372   372   388

Find:
  a the modal wage
  b the median wage
  c the mean wage
  d For each average wage:
    i decide whether it is sensible to use it or not
    ii if you think it is not sensible, explain why.

D Finding averages from a frequency table

- For data in categories:
  - the **mode** is the category with the highest frequency.

Make of car	Ford	Rover	Vaux.	Others
Frequency	9	6	2	7

The modal make of car is **Ford**.

- For numerical data:
  - the **mode** is the value (or values) with the highest frequency
  - the **range** is the difference between the highest and lowest values

No. of people in car	1	2	3	4	5
Frequency	3	10	6	3	2

Mode = **2** people
Range = **4** people
(5 − 1)

  - the **median** is the middle value when the data is in order

1 1 1 2 2 2 2 2 2 2 2 2 2 3 3 3 3 3 3 4 4 4 5 5
Median = **2** people

  - the **mean** is the total of all the values divided by the total frequency.

Number of people in car	Frequency		Total number of people
1	3	1 × 3	3
2	10	2 × 10	20
3	6	3 × 6	18
4	3	4 × 3	12
5	2	5 × 2	10
	24		63

Mean = $\frac{63}{24}$ = **2.6** people (to 1 dp)

E Constructing pie charts

Make of car	Ford	Rover	Vaux.	Others	Total
Frequency	9	6	2	7	24

- For a percentage pie chart, calculate the percentage in each category:
  - there are 2 Vauxhall cars out of 24, so
    100 ÷ 24 × 2 = 8.3% (to 1 dp)

- For an angle pie chart, calculate the angle for each category:
  - there are 9 Ford cars out of 24, so
    360 ÷ 24 × 9 = 135°.

	Freq	Sector	Size
Ford	9	37.5%	135°
Rover	6	25%	90°
Vauxhall	2	8.3%	30°
Others	7	29.2%	105°
Totals	24	100%	360°

Ford
Rover
Vauxhall
Others

NUMBER OF CHILDREN IN CAR

1	0	1	2	1	1	0	0
4	1	0	1	0	0	2	0
2	0	3	0	0	2	0	1

COLOUR OF CAR

Red	Blue	Green	White
Silver	Red	White	Black
Black	Green	Red	Blue
Black	Blue	Blue	Silver
Red	White	Blue	Brown
Blue	Black	Brown	Red

D1 Present the colour-of-car data in a frequency table.

D2 Find the modal colour of car.

D3 Present the number-of-children-in-car data in a frequency table.

D4 Find:
  a the modal number of children in a car
  b the range of the number of children in a car.

D5 Find:
  a the median number of children in a car
  b the mean number of children in a car.

E1 Use your frequency table from Question **D1** to calculate:
  a the percentage for each colour
  b the angle for each colour.

E2 Draw a pie chart to show the colour of car data.

F Diagrams that present data

Pictogram

Ford	🚗🚗🚗🚗🚗
Rover	🚗🚗🚗
Vauxhall	🚗
Others	🚗🚗🚗🚗

🚗 stands for 2 cars

Bar chart

Ford	
Rover	
Vauxhall	
Others	

Number of cars
0 2 4 6 8 10

Bar-line graph

Number of cars

Ford Rover Vaux. Others
Make of car

Frequency diagram

Frequency

Number of people in car
1 2 3 4

Passenger Destinations 1994/95

Percentage

Gatwick Heathrow
Airport

- UK
- Europe
- North Atlantic
- Others

**Split bar chart
or
Component
bar chart**

**Line
graph**

Passenger changes 1989 - 1995

—— Gatwick   —— Heathrow

Percentage change
+12
+8
+4
0
-4
-8
-12

1989 1990 1991 1992 1993 1994 1995
Year

**Main Passenger Destinations
Scottish Airports 1994/95**

■ Glasgow ■ Edinburgh □ Aberdeen

UK

Europe

0 10 20 30 40 50 60 70 80
Number of flights (000's)

**Comparative
bar chart**

Use your frequency tables from Questions **D1** and **D3** to answer Questions **F1** to **F4**.

F1 Draw a bar-line graph to show the colour-of-car data.

F2 Draw a frequency diagram to show the number-of-children-in-car data.

F3 Draw a pictogram to show the colour-of-car data.

F4 Draw a bar chart to show the colour-of-car data.

F5

Southampton to Channel Islands 1994/95		
	Number of passengers (000's)	Number of flights (000's)
Jersey	156	4.0
Guernsey	100	3.4
Alderney	31	2.9
Totals	287	10.3

Calculate the percentage of passengers going to:
a Jersey   **b** Guernsey
c Alderney

F6 Calculate the percentage of flights going to each of the three islands.

F7 Draw a split bar chart to show the two sets of data.

F8

% change in no. of passengers					
	1990	1991	1992	1993	1994
Glasgow	11.0	⁻3.1	12.4	7.4	8.8
Edinburgh	5.3	⁻6.1	8.4	7.2	10.3

Draw a line graph to show this data for Glasgow and Edinburgh.

F9

NUMBER OF FLIGHTS 1994/95 (000's)		
	Heathrow	Gatwick
UK	75	33
Europe	252	111
North Atlantic	40	19
Others	47	21

Draw a comparative bar chart to show this data.

Thinking ahead to ...
calculating the
interquartile range

10-ring target

A   These are Viv's scores in 12 arrows at a 10-ring target.

Ring score	1	2	3	4	5	6	7	8	9	Total
Frequency	1	0	0	2	1	3	4	0	1	12

a   Calculate the range of the scores.
b   Explain why the range is not a sensible measure of spread for Viv's scores.

Calculating the interquartile range

Because the spread of the
middle 50% of the data is
measured, the interquartile
range is not affected by any
extreme values in the data.

♦   The **interquartile range** of a set of data measures how spread out the
middle 50% of the data is.

♦   To calculate the interquartile range:

Ring score	1	2	3	4	5	6	7	8	9	Total
Frequency	1	0	0	2	1	3	4	0	1	12

You can divide the data
into four quarters by first
dividing it into two halves.

The end values are the
medians of the two halves.

❖   list the data in order

1   4   4   5   6   6   6   7   7   7   7   9

❖   divide the data into four quarters

1   4   4 ┊ 5   6   6 ┊ 6   7   7 ┊ 7   7   9

❖   find the end values of the middle 50% of the data

1   4   4 ┊ 5   6   6 ┊ 6   7   7 ┊ 7   7   9
          4.5   **7**
       Lower quartile   **Upper quartile**

❖   calculate the difference between the upper and lower quartiles.

Interquartile range = 7 − 4.5
= 2.5

Exercise 4.1
Interquartile range

1   These are the scores for three archers.

Ring score	2	3	4	5	6	7	8	Total
Frequency	1	0	3	2	5	3	2	16

William

Bryony

Ring score	4	5	6	7	8	9	Total
Frequency	2	4	3	3	0	2	14

Ring score	2	3	4	5	6	7	8	9	10	Total
Frequency	1	1	2	3	5	3	0	3	2	20

Daniel

A set of data presented in
a frequency table is called a
frequency distribution.

a   **i**   For each archer list the data.
       ii   Calculate the interquartile range of their scores.

b   Which archer is the most consistent?
Explain your answer.

Drawing and using a stem and leaf plot

* The stem and leaf plot is a frequency diagram.
* The actual data is displayed together with its frequency.
* Part of the value of each piece of data is used to fix the data class ie the **stem**.

Part of the value is listed in the diagram ie the **leaves**

Example

Show this set of data with a stem and leaf plot

6, 13, 23, 42, 30, 32, 36, 27, 24, 32, 40, 45, 8

> As the data is listed and shown in order on a stem and leaf plot the median value can be easily found. Here the median value is 6.

```
    4 | 0  2  5
    3 | 0  2  2  6
stem 2 | 3  4  7        leaves
    1 | 3
    0 | 6  8
```

Key 1|3 = 13

Exercise 4.2
Stem and leaf plots

1 Draw a stem and leaf plot for each data set.

a 23, 12, 14, 26, 38, 46, 33, 32, 19, 7, 24, 12, 40, 20
b 15, 22, 24, 20, 10, 12, 31, 30, 24, 26, 26, 24, 32, 40
c 42, 16, 9, 7, 6, 18, 25, 6, 24, 30, 36, 25, 30, 41, 16, 44
d 38, 14, 22, 56, 18, 24, 28, 37, 40, 30, 32, 28, 46, 40, 28

2 The data gives the number of minutes waited by people to fly on the 'London Eye'.

44, 56, 50, 52, 42, 40, 38, 44, 52, 54, 53, 38, 30
41, 40, 51, 59, 62, 34, 40, 47, 50, 54, 50, 57

a Draw a stem and leaf plot to show this data.
b Find the median value for the data set.

You can use a stem and leaf plot to help you to compare distributions.

Example

This data shows the points scored by members of two teams over the past six weeks.

Team A
12, 23, 34, 18, 7, 0, 9, 8, 12, 0, 7, 0, 6, 0, 22, 15, 0, 9

Team B
8, 14, 6, 22, 31, 14, 0, 0, 9, 12, 0, 17, 0, 18, 6, 0, 4, 16

Use a stem and leaf plot and compare the data sets.

The median for each data set is between the 9th and the 10th values. You can easily find this from the stem and leaf plot.

Median
Both teams have the same median points start value of 8.5.

You may choose to use the interquartile range as part of your comparison.

Range
Team A has a range of 34 [34 – 0]

Team B of has a range of 31 [31 – 0]

Overall the performance of the teams is similar, but team B is slightly more consistent.

Exercise 4.3
Comparing data using
stem and leaf plots

1 These data sets show the length of time (to the nearest minute) spent by customers in two different supermarkets on the same day.

Supermarket A

31, 14, 12, 27, 8, 38, 15, 42, 46, 32, 28

9, 28, 30, 34, 42, 21, 20, 12, 8, 4, 6

24, 33, 52, 46, 38, 35, 30, 18, 22, 34

Supermarket B

26, 15, 19, 34, 36, 28, 24, 14, 22, 37

40, 29, 22, 20, 28, 33, 30, 16, 41, 22

17, 26, 30, 41, 44, 43, 30, 32, 7, 12, 26, 44

a Draw a stem and leaf plot to show both data sets.
b Give the median value for the data in each set.
c Give the range for each data set.
d Compare the two sets of data.
   What general statements do you feel able to make?

2 This system and leaf plot shows the distribution of marks in the same test by two groups of students.

```
        Group A                    Group B

           5 5 5 5 | 5 | 1 3 4         Key  |1| 6 = 16
           2 1 1 0 | 4 | 0 3 5 8 8
   7 6 6 5 5 5 4 0 | 3 | 2 5 6 6 8 9 9       4 |3| = 34
   8 7 4 4 4 4 3 1 | 2 | 0 3 4 4 6 6 6 9
         8 6 6 4 0 | 1 | 6 8 9 9 9
               7 5 | 0 | 4
```

a Give the median test score for each group
b What can you say about the range for each data set?
c Which group do you think performed better in the test?
   Give reasons for your answer.

3 This data gives the length of time (seconds) taken for telephone calls by two different call centres.

Call Centre A

24, 38, 46, 30, 27, 46, 54, 18, 20, 37, 35, 62

58, 64, 70, 32, 27, 20, 18, 26, 35, 44, 56, 68

75, 60, 36, 45, 19, 27, 35, 50, 63, 74, 55, 40

Call Centre B

53, 42, 47, 16, 22, 12, 20, 30, 35, 38, 47, 76

66, 54, 46, 19, 30, 32, 38, 45, 52, 64, 72, 75

11, 20, 36, 42, 53, 38, 24, 19, 23, 28, 24, 20

a Draw a stem and leaf plot to show both data sets.
b Which call centre is more efficient ?
   Give reasons for your choice.
c Calculate the mean time for a call from each centre.

Thinking ahead to ...
calculating the
standard deviation

A   In a competition, archers fire ten arrows in each round.
Kate and Bob each have a mean round score of 61 in eight rounds.

35 50 74 41 56
79 73 80   **Kate**

36 54 35 65 63
82 83 70   **Bob**

Whose round scores do you think are the more consistent?
Explain your answer.

Calculating the standard deviation

◆ The most widely used measure of dispersion is the **standard deviation**.

To calculate the standard deviation:
❖ calculate the mean of the values
❖ calculate the **squared deviation** for each value
      i.e. the square of the difference between the value and the mean
❖ calculate the square root of the mean squared deviation.

Example   Calculate the standard deviation of Kate's scores.

x		Squared Deviation $(x - \bar{x})^2$
35	$(35 - 61)^2$	676
41	$(41 - 61)^2$	400
50	$(50 - 61)^2$	121
56	$(56 - 61)^2$	25
73	$(73 - 61)^2$	144
74	$(74 - 61)^2$	169
79	$(79 - 61)^2$	324
80	$(80 - 61)^2$	361
488		2220

$\frac{488}{8} = 61$

Mean score $(\bar{x})$

$\sqrt{\frac{2220}{8}} = $ **16.7** (to 3 sf)

Standard deviation

The standard deviation, σ,
can be written as a formula:

$$\sigma = \sqrt{\frac{\Sigma f(x - \bar{x})^2}{n}}$$

where σ is the Greek
letter 'sigma'
$\Sigma(x - \bar{x})^2$ is the
total of the
squared deviations
and n is the number
of values

Exercise 4.4
Standard deviation

1   Use the data given above to calculate the standard deviation of Bob's scores.

2   **a**   Calculate the mean of Paula's round scores.
     b   **i** Calculate their standard deviation.
            ii Check your answer using the
                  alternative formula.

35 45 50
60 75   **Paula**

Standard deviation will not
be tested in a written exam
but may be useful for the
Ma4 coursework task.

An alternative formula for
the standard deviation is:

$$\sigma = \sqrt{\frac{\Sigma x^2}{n} - \bar{x}^2}$$

where Σx^2 is the total of
the squares
of each value

Thinking ahead to ...
calculating the
standard deviation of a
frequency distribution

A   These are Bob's scores from his two best rounds in the competition.

Ring score	5	6	7	8	9	10
Frequency	1	0	1	3	4	1

Round 6

Ring score	6	7	8	9	10
Frequency	2	2	0	3	3

Round 7

For each round:
a   list Bob's scores
b   calculate the standard deviation of the scores.

Calculating the standard deviation of a frequency distribution

♦ To calculate the standard deviation of a frequency distribution:

❖ calculate the mean of all the values
❖ calculate the squared deviation for each different value
❖ multiply each squared deviation by its frequency
❖ calculate the square root of the mean squared deviation.

Example   Calculate the standard deviation of Bob's Round 6 scores.

The standard deviation, σ, can be written as a formula:

$$\sigma = \sqrt{\frac{\Sigma f(x - \bar{x})^2}{\Sigma f}}$$

where $\Sigma f(x - \bar{x})^2$ is the total of the squared deviations
and Σf is the total frequency.

Score x	Frequency f	Total score fx	Squared deviations $(x - \bar{x})^2$	$f(x - \bar{x})^2$
5	1	5	10.24	10.24
6	0	0	4.84	0
7	1	7	1.44	1.44
8	3	24	0.04	0.12
9	4	36	0.64	2.56
10	1	10	3.24	3.24
	10	82		17.60

$$\frac{82}{10} = 8.2$$

Mean score ($\bar{x}$)

$$\sqrt{\frac{17.60}{10}} = \mathbf{1.33} \text{ (to 3 sf)}$$

Standard deviation

Exercise 4.5
Standard deviation of a
frequency distribution

1   **a**   Use this method to calculate the standard deviation of Bob's Round 7 scores from Question **A** above.
b   In which round do Bob's scores show less variation? Explain.

2

Ring score	2	3	4	5	6	7	8	9	Total
Frequency	11	8	5	3	3	4	6	10	50

Paula

Ring score	2	3	4	5	6	7	8	9	10	Total
Frequency	4	5	7	11	13	10	6	3	1	60

Zoe

Ring score	2	3	4	5	6	7	8	9	10	Total
Frequency	6	10	12	9	6	9	11	10	7	80

Matt

a   Draw a frequency diagram to show:
  i Paula's scores   **ii** Zoe's scores   **iii** Matt's scores.
b   Calculate the standard deviation of each archer's scores.
c   Comment on the shape of your frequency diagrams and your answers for the standard deviations.

Comparing sets of data

♦ One way to compare sets of data is to compare two types of statistic:

a an average

b a measure of dispersion.

Example Compare Zoe's and Matt's round scores using the mean and the standard deviation.

	Zoe	Matt
Mean	56.5	60.25
Standard deviation	6.60	10.0

(to 3 sf)

a Matt's round scores are higher on average.

b Zoe is more consistent because her scores show less variation than Matt's scores.

> Use the statistical function on your calculator to check these values for the mean and the standard deviation.

Exercise 4.6
Comparing sets of data

1

a Calculate the mean round score for each archer.

b Calculate the standard deviation of each set of scores.

c Use the mean and the standard deviation to compare the sets of data.

2

Ring score	4	5	6	7	8	Total
Frequency	5	5	7	6	2	25

Dean

Leah

Ring score	3	4	5	6	7	8	Total
Frequency	1	3	7	6	2	1	20

Ring score	3	4	5	6	7	Total
Frequency	7	9	4	3	7	30

Jack

Compare these distributions using the mean and the standard deviation.

3

Ring score	3	4	5	6	7	8	9	10	Total
Frequency	3	7	4	1	1	0	0	2	18

Eliza

Ring score	2	3	4	5	6	7	8	Total
Frequency	1	4	3	4	2	1	1	16

Sam

> When you compare data which has extreme values, using the median and the interquartile range can give a better comparison.

a **i** For each archer list the scores.

ii Find the median score

iii Calculate the interquartile range of the scores.

b Use the median and interquartile range to compare the two distributions.

Thinking ahead to ...
using cumulative frequencies
to find the median

A

Ring score	5	6	7	8	9	10	Total
Frequency	3	2	4	0	3	3	15	Salim

Ring score	5	6	7	8	9	Total
Frequency	7	8	13	18	14	60

Emily

a   i   List all Salim's scores.
    ii Find Salim's median score.
b   i   List all Emily's scores.
    ii Find Emily's median score.

Using cumulative frequencies to find the median

♦ The median can be found without listing all the data.

♦ To find the median using cumulative frequencies:
   ❖ calculate the cumulative frequencies
   ❖ use the total frequency to decide where the median is
   ❖ find the middle value.

The cumulative frequencies
are the running totals of
the frequencies.
For example: 7 + 8 = 15.

Example   Find the median of Emily's scores.

Ring score	Frequency	Cumulative Frequency
5	7	7
6	8	15
7	13	28
8	18	46
9	14	60

The total frequency is 60, so the median score is halfway between the 30th largest and the 31st largest.

The 28th largest score is 7.

All the scores between the 29th and 46th largest are 8.

The final cumulative
frequency here is 60:
check it is equal to the
total frequency.

The 30th and 31st largest scores are both 8, so
Median score = **8**

Exercise 4.7
Finding the median using
cumulative frequencies

1

Ring score	3	4	5	6	7	8	Total
Frequency	7	10	5	1	6	11	40

Lee

Faith

Ring score	4	5	6	7	8	Total
Frequency	11	7	8	9	10	45

Ring score	1	2	3	4	5	6	7	8	9	Total
Frequency	2	4	2	3	1	4	7	9	7	39

Aqib

Ring score	1	2	3	4	5	6	7	8	9	10	Total
Frequency	6	9	5	4	2	5	6	4	3	4	48

Find each archer's median score.

Tegan

2

Ring score	4	5	6	7	8	9	10
Cumulative Frequency	7	18	31	40	48	62	80

Jake

a   Explain why Jake's median score is 7.5.
b   Explain why the interquartile range of this distribution is 3.

Thinking ahead to ...
box-and-whisker plots

A   A survey of three fast food restaurants recorded the number of chips in a serving. A sample of 80 servings was taken from each restaurant.

Restaurant	32	33	34	35	36	37	38	39	40	41	42	43	44	Total
						Number of chips								
X	1	2	3	5	9	13	14	12	8	5	4	3	1	80
Y	4	6	11	14	13	11	8	6	4	3	0	0	0	80
Z	1	1	2	6	9	13	15	13	10	6	2	1	1	80

a   **i**   Which restaurant do you think gives more chips in a serving?
　　ii   Explain your answer.

b   **i**   Find the median number of chips for each restaurant.
　　ii   Calculate the interquartile range for each distribution.

Drawing box-and-whisker plots

◆ A **box-and-whisker plot** shows a frequency distribution by using:

❖ the lowest and highest values
❖ the median
❖ the lower and upper quartiles.

Example

Draw a box-and-whisker plot for these chips from restaurant W.

Number of chips	34	35	36	37	38	39	40	41	42	43
Frequency	1	2	4	7	12	14	16	15	7	2
Cumulative frequency	1	3	7	14	26	40	56	71	78	80

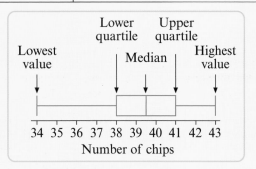

Exercise 4.8
Drawing box-and-whisker plots

1   Copy this box-and-whisker diagram on squared paper. Use the data from Question **A** to draw a box-and-whisker plot for each restaurant.

2   Write a short report that compares the number of chips per serving from the four fast food restaurants.

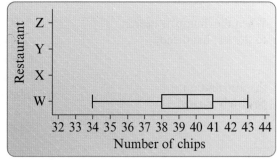

Comparing frequency distributions

◆ You can compare frequency distributions by considering their shape:
  ❖ this distribution can be described as **skewed**
    (the larger frequencies are nearer to one end than the other)

> A **frequency polygon** is a line graph which shows the frequencies that make up a distribution.
>
> You can compare two or more distributions on the same diagram by plotting the frequency polygons.

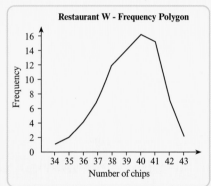

  ❖ this distribution can be described as **bell-shaped**
    (the frequencies are larger in the middle, and tail off towards each end).

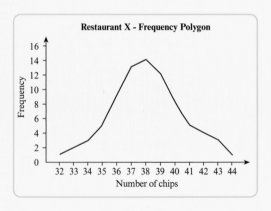

Exercise 4.9
Comparing distributions

1 a Draw the frequency polygon for restaurant X on squared paper.
   b Draw a frequency polygon for restaurant Z on the same diagram.
   c Compare the two distributions.

> A skewed distribution that has the 'hump' nearer to
>
> the right-hand end is **negatively skewed**.
>
> When the 'hump' is nearer to the left-hand end,
>
> the distribution is **positively skewed**.

2 a Draw the skewed frequency polygon for restaurant W, starting the scale on the horizontal axis at 32 chips.
   b Draw a frequency polygon for restaurant Y on the same diagram.
   c Compare the two distributions.

3 For this distribution, the mean number of chips is less than the median number, which is less than the modal number.

   a For each of the other 3 restaurants:
      i calculate the mean number of chips
      ii draw a similar diagram.
   b Describe the link between the shape of a distribution and the mean, the median, and the mode.

Misleading diagrams

◆ Statistical diagrams can be misleading in several ways, including:

❖ when the vertical axis does not start at 0

The vertical axis starts at £200.

This gives the impression that the amount given in 1996 was 10 times the amount given in 1995, not 2 times.

❖ when enlargements of a shape are used.

The 1996 note is 2 times the height *and* 2 times the width of the 1995 note.

This gives the impression that the amount given in 1996 was 4 times the amount given in 1995.

Exercise 4.10
Misleading diagrams

1   Draw a misleading diagram to show this revenue data by using:

a   a vertical scale which does not start at 0
b   enlargements of a shape.

WD   *Wilton Dale Films*

	1994	**1996**
Revenue (£m)	6.1	18.3

2   Draw a misleading diagram to show this data for number of visitors.

WD   *Wilton Dale Theme Parks*

	1994	**1995**	**1996**
Number of visitors (000's)	24	36	72

3

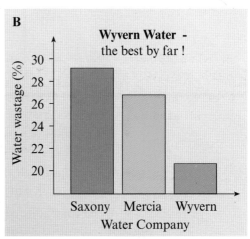

Explain why each of these diagrams is misleading.

End points
You should be able to ...   ... so try these questions

A Calculate the mean and the standard deviation

A1 For Mel's round scores, calculate:
a the mean
b the standard deviation.

43 64 67 58 62
69 83 78 **Mel**

B Understand the effect of adjusting a set of data on the mean and standard deviation

B1 Jason scores 5 less than Mel in each round.
Give the mean and standard deviation of Jason's round scores.

C Calculate the standard deviation of a frequency distribution

C1

Ring score	5	6	7	8	9	10	Total	
Frequency	6	9	13	14	11	7	60	**Robin**

Calculate the mean and standard deviation of Robin's scores.

D Compare sets of data

D1 a Copy and complete this table using your answers to Question **C1**.
b Use the statistics in your table to compare Robin and Tina.

	Robin	Tina
Mean		7.42
Standard deviation		1.30

E Find the median and the interquartile range of a frequency distribution

E1 For Robin's scores, find:
a the median
b the interquartile range.

F Draw a box-and-whisker plot

F1 Draw a box-and-whisker plot for Robin's scores.

G Recognise when diagrams used to present data are misleading

G1 X

Y

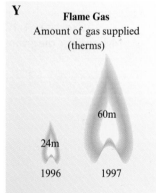

Explain why each of these diagrams is misleading.

Some points to remember

◆ If you adjust each value in a set of data by a **certain percentage**, the mean and the standard deviation of the data are both adjusted by the same percentage.

◆ If you adjust each value in a set of data by a **fixed amount**, the mean of the data is adjusted by the same amount but the standard deviation is left unchanged.

◆ When comparing data which has extreme values, using the median and interquartile range can give a better comparison than using the mean and standard deviation.

Starting points

You need to know about ...

... so try these questions

A Continuing a sequence

- A **sequence** of numbers usually follows a pattern or rule.

- Each number in a sequence is called a **term**.

  For example, in the sequence: 3, 5, 7, 9, 11, ... , the 3rd term is 7.

- A sequence can often be continued by finding a pattern in the **differences**.

- In Sequence P, the **first difference** is 6 each time.

- In Sequence Q, the **second difference** is 2 each time.
  So continue the sequence by adding 9, then 11, and so on.

B A rule for a sequence

These are the first three matchstick patterns in a sequence.

Pattern 1   Pattern 2   Pattern 3

- The number of matches in each pattern can be shown in a table.

Pattern number (n)	Number of matches (m)
1	9
2	16
3	23
4	30

- The pattern number goes up by 1 each time.   (+1 between each pattern number)

- The number of matches goes up by 7 each time.   (+7 between each number of matches)

- So a rule that links the number of matches (m) with the pattern number (n) begins $m = 7n$ ...

- A rule that fits all the results in the table is $m = 7n + 2$

- This rule can be used to calculate the number of matches in **any** pattern, for example: in Pattern 10 there are $(7 \times 10) + 2 = 72$ matches.

A1 Find the 6th and 7th term in:
  a sequence P
  b sequence Q.

A2 What is the 10th term in this sequence?

  4, 7, 10, 13, 16, ...

A3 For each sequence, find the next three terms.
  a 2, 8, 14, 20, 26, ...
  b 2, 5, 11, 20, 32, ...
  c 2, 3, 9, 20, 36, ...

A4 **a** What are the second differences in this sequence?

  7, 16, 31, 52, ...

  b What is the 5th term?

B1 These are the first three patterns in a sequence.

Pattern 1

Pattern 2

Pattern 3

  a Draw pattern 5.

  b How many matches are in pattern 9?

  c Make a table for the first five patterns in this sequence.

  d Which of these rules fits the results in your table?

  $m = 4n + 2$ $m = 5n + 1$

  $m = 6n - 1$

Sequences and mappings

These equilateral triangles are the first three in a sequence of shapes.

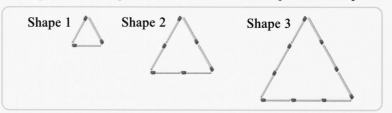

Shape 1   Shape 2   Shape 3

- Data for this sequence can be shown in a table.

Shape number	1	2	3	4
Number of matches	3	6	9	12

- The data can also be shown in a **mapping diagram** like this.

Shape number		Number of matches
1	→	3
2	→	6
3	→	9
4	→	12 ...

- The number of matches is 3 times the shape number.
  For example, the 50th shape in the sequence uses 150 matches.

  Using n to stand for the shape number,
  the rule for the mapping diagram can be written: $n \longrightarrow 3n$

Exercise 5.1
Sequences and mappings

1 These are the first three patterns in a sequence.

Copy and complete the mapping diagram for the sequence.

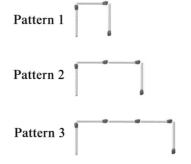

Pattern 1

Pattern 2

Pattern 3

Pattern number		Number of matches
1	→	3
2	→	☐
3	→	☐
4	→	☐
⋮		⋮
20	→	☐
⋮		⋮
n	→	☐

2 These patterns of touching squares are the first four in a sequence.

Pattern 1   Pattern 2   Pattern 3   Pattern 4

a Draw a mapping diagram for the first six patterns of touching squares.
b Find a rule for the sequence in the form $n \longrightarrow ....$, where n is the pattern number.
c Use your rule to calculate the number of matches in the 100th pattern.
d Which pattern would use 620 matches?
e Each touching square now has one extra match added as a diagonal.
   Which pattern will now use 620 matches?

Thinking ahead to ...
finding rules

A   These are the first three patterns in sequence A.

Sequence A

Pattern 1   Pattern 2   Pattern 3

How many matchsticks are in the 100th pattern?
Explain how you worked it out.

Finding rules

Example **Find a rule for the number of matches (*m*) in the *n*th pattern in**
sequence A above.

♦ **Method 1** Look at how the patterns are made.

Pattern 1   Pattern 2   Pattern 3

$1 + (3 \times 1)$ $1 + (3 \times 2)$ $1 + (3 \times 3)$

❖ So a rule for the number of matches (*m*) in the *n*th pattern is **m = 1 + 3n**

♦ **Method 2** Look at differences.

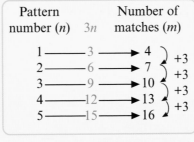

Pattern number (*n*)	3*n*	Number of matches (*m*)	
1	3	4	+3
2	6	7	+3
3	9	10	+3
4	12	13	+3
5	15	16	+3

❖ The pattern number goes up by 1 each time.

❖ The number of matches goes up by 3 each time so there is a linear rule that begins $m = 3n$ ... .

Examples of linear rules are:

$$m = 4n + 3$$
$$y = 2 - 5x$$
$$a = 3b - 1$$

Rules such as $m = n^2 + 1$ and
$y = \dfrac{5}{x} - 6$ are non-linear.

❖ Compare 3*n* with the number of matches.

❖ The number of matches is 1 more than 3*n* each time.

❖ So a rule for the number of matches (*m*) in the *n*th pattern is **m = 3n + 1**.

Exercise 5.2
Finding rules

1   These triangle patterns are the first three in sequence B.

Sequence B

Pattern 1   Pattern 2   Pattern 3

a Find a rule for the number of matches (*m*) in the *n*th triangle pattern.
Explain your method.
b Use your rule to find the number of matches in the 8th pattern.
c Check your answer by drawing the 8th pattern and counting the matches.

2 Sequence C

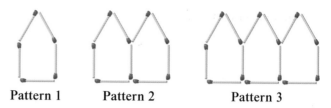

Pattern 1   Pattern 2   Pattern 3

   a For sequence C, find a rule for the number of matches (m) in the nth pattern.
Explain your method.

   b Calculate the number of matches in the 40th pattern.

   c Which pattern uses exactly 129 matches?

3 Sequence D

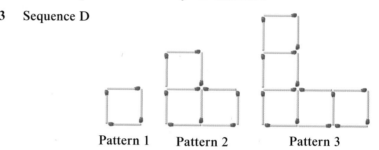

Pattern 1   Pattern 2   Pattern 3

   a For sequence D, find a rule for the number of matches (m) in the nth pattern.
Explain your method.

   b How many matches are in the 100th pattern?

4 This mapping diagram fits a sequence of matchstick patterns.

Pattern number (n)	Number of matches (m)
1	6
2	10
3	14
4	18
5	22

   a Draw a sequence of matchstick patterns that fits this mapping diagram.

   b Find a rule for the number of matches (m) in the nth pattern.

> Any letter can stand for the shape number.
>
> For example, the rule
> $n \longrightarrow 3n + 2$
>
> can also be written as:
> $p \longrightarrow 3p + 2$
>
> or
> $s \longrightarrow 3s + 2$
>
> and so on.

5 Copy and complete each mapping diagram.

   a

   b

   c

Thinking ahead to ...
finding the *n*th term

A 7, 9, 11, 13, 15, 17, ...

    a Write the next two terms in this sequence.
    b Find the 12th term.
    c What is the 50th term?

The *n*th term of a sequence

Example Find an expression for the *n*th term in the sequence
7, 9, 11, 13, 15, ...

♦ The sequence can be displayed in a table like this:

Term number (*n*)	1	2	3	4	5
Term	7	9	11	13	15

♦ The difference for the terms is 2 each time.
So there is a linear expression for the *n*th term that begins **2*n*** ... .

> The difference between terms in a sequence is often called the **list difference**.

♦ Comparing the sequence with the sequence $n \longrightarrow 2n$

Term number (*n*)	1	2	3	4	5
2*n*	2	4	6	8	10

shows that each term is 5 more than 2*n*.
So an expression for the *n*th term of the sequence
7, 9, 11, 13, 15, ... is **2*n* + 5**.

Exercise 5.3
Finding the *n*th term

1 A 6, 9, 12, 15, 18, ...   B 1, 6, 11, 16, 21, ...
   C 13, 23, 33, 43, 53, ...   D 2, 10, 18, 26, 34, ...

For each of the sequences A to D:

    a find an expression for the *n*th term
    b use your expression to calculate the 50th term.

2 A student has tried to find the *n*th term of this sequence.

> 5, 8, 11, 14, 17, ...
>
> *n*th term is *n* + 3 **X**

    a Explain the mistake you think has been made.
    b Find a correct expression for the *n*th term of this sequence.

3 The 2nd term of a sequence is 7.
Which of these could not be an expression for the *n*th term?

   3*n* + 1   11 − 2*n*   *n* + 5   *n* + 7   5*n* − 3

4 List the first 5 terms of the sequence whose *n*th term is 4 − 3*n*.

5 Find an expression for the *n*th term of each of these sequences.
    a 20, 18, 16, 14, 12, ...
    b 22, 12, 2, ¯8, ¯18, ...
    c ¯1, ¯3, ¯5, ¯7, ¯9, ...
    d 10, 5, 0, ¯5, ¯10, ...

Extending number patterns

Exercise 5.4
Extending patterns

1 Morag finds an expression for the *n*th number in this sequence.

> 4, 10, 18, 28, 40, ...

This is her working:

> | 1st number | 4 | $= 1 \times 4$ |
> |---|---|---|
> | 2nd number | 10 | $= 2 \times 5$ |
> | 3rd number | 18 | $= 3 \times 6$ |
> | 4th number | 28 | $= 4 \times 7 ...$ |
>
> So *n*th number $\qquad = n \times (n + 3)$

a Show Morag's line of working for the 5th number.
b Find the 10th number in this sequence.
c Explain how Morag's working helps to find an expression for the *n*th number in this sequence.

2 These are the first five triangle numbers:

> 1, 3, 6, 10, 15, ...

The triangle numbers follow this pattern:

> 1st triangle number $\qquad 1 = \dfrac{1 \times 2}{2}$
>
> 2nd triangle number $\qquad 3 = \dfrac{2 \times 3}{2}$
>
> 3rd triangle number $\qquad 6 = \dfrac{3 \times 4}{2}$
>
> 4th triangle number $\qquad 10 = \dfrac{4 \times 5}{2}$

a What is the next line in this pattern?
b Use the pattern to find the 12th triangle number.
c Find an expression for the *n*th triangle number.

3 These are the first five powers of 2:

> 2, 4, 8, 16, 32, ...

Powers of 2 follow this pattern:

> | 1st power | 2 | | $= 2^1$ |
> |---|---|---|---|
> | 2nd power | 4 | $= 2 \times 2$ | $= 2^2$ |
> | 3rd power | 8 | $= 2 \times 2 \times 2$ | $= 2^3$ |
> | 4th power | 16 | $= 2 \times 2 \times 2 \times 2 = 2^4$ |

a What is the next line in this pattern?
b Use the pattern to find the 8th power of 2.
c Write an expression for the *n*th power of 2.

Writing rules in different ways

Exercise 5.5
Different ways
to write rules

1   These hollow square tile designs are the first three in a sequence.

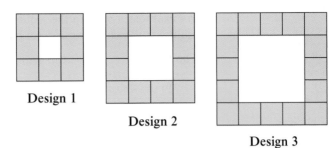

Design 1

Design 2

Design 3

Three students find a rule for the number of tiles in the nth design.
All three students are correct.

Andrew	Aisha	Fiona
Number of tiles	Number of tiles	Number of tiles
$= 4(n + 1)$	$= 4n + 4$	$= 2(n + 2) + 2n$

The way each student wrote their rule shows how they found it.

Andrew drew this diagram to show how he found his rule.

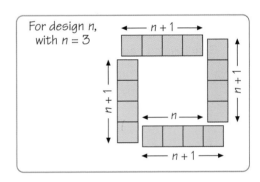

For design n, with $n = 3$

Fiona's rule is not as easy to use as the other two rules.

Using Fiona's rule to find the number of tiles in the 10th design gives:

Number of tiles

$= 2 \times (10 + 2) + (2 \times 10)$
$= 24 + 20$
$= 44$

a   Draw a diagram for Aisha's rule.
b   Draw a diagram for Fiona's rule.
c   Show how you can calculate the number of tiles in the 50th design using:
    i Andrew's rule   ii Aisha's rule   iii Fiona's rule
d   Which design has 324 tiles?
    Explain how you found your result.

2   These designs are the first three in a sequence.

Design 1   Design 2   Design 3

a   Find two different ways of writing a rule for the number of tiles in the nth design.
b   Explain how you found your results.

Generalising other sequences

♦ Some sequences are generated by multiplying by one number each time. For example, a term in the sequence 3, 9, 27, 81, ... is obtained by multiplying each previous term by 3.

The general term u_n for this sequence is 3^n.

Term number (n)	1	2	3	4	5 ...	n
Term	3^1	3^2	3^3	3^4	3^5	3^n

Sequences like this where subsequent terms are multiplied by the same value are known as **geometric sequences**.

♦ Other sequences can be based on the one above. For instance, the sequence 1, 3, 9, 27, ... has the general term u_n as 3^{n-1}. In this case the multiplier between terms is still 3.

♦ Where a sequence is given only in fractions treat it as two separate sequences, one for the numerator and another for the denominator.

For example, the sequence $\frac{2}{5}, \frac{3}{11}, \frac{4}{29}, \frac{5}{83}, \frac{6}{245}, \ldots$

has the general term $\frac{n+1}{3^n+2}$.

> The general terms of a sequence is the nth value. It is often written u_n.
> u_1 is the first value
> u_2 is the second value...

> Any number to the power of 0 is 1, so $3^0 = 1$

Exercise 5.6
Generalising sequencies

1   Find the general term for each of these geometric sequences.

   a   2, 4, 8, 16, 32, ...   b   1, 3, 7, 15, 31, ...

   c   1, 2, 4, 8, 16, ...   d $\frac{1}{4}, \frac{1}{2}, 1, 2, 4, \ldots$

   e   1, $\frac{1}{3}, \frac{1}{9}, \frac{1}{27}, \frac{1}{81}, \ldots$ f $\frac{1}{4}, \frac{1}{16}, \frac{1}{64}, \frac{1}{256}, \ldots$

2   Find the general term for these fractional sequences:

   a $\frac{1}{99}, \frac{2}{98}, \frac{3}{97}, \frac{4}{96}$ b $\frac{1}{4}, \frac{4}{8}, \frac{9}{16}, \frac{16}{32}, \ldots$

   c $\frac{3}{1}, \frac{6}{8}, \frac{9}{27}, \frac{12}{64}$ d $\frac{2}{3}, \frac{5}{5}, \frac{10}{9}, \frac{17}{17}, \ldots$

3   The general term for the sequence 4, 16, 64, 256, ... is 4^n. Use this to find the general term for the sequences:

   a   196, 184, 136, ⁻56, ...   b   256, 64, 16, 4, 1, ...

4   Morag is finding the general term for the sequence 4, 10, 18, 28, 40, ... This is her working. (see Exercise 5.4 question 1)

The general term for the sequence can be found in a similar way.

> ⁻1, 0, 3, 8, 15, ...

   a   Show how the first five terms can be built up by Morag's method.

1st number	4	$= 1 \times 4$
2nd number	10	$= 2 \times 5$
3rd number	18	$= 3 \times 6$
4th number	28	$= 4 \times 7$
So		$u_n = n \times (n + 3)$
		$= n^2 + 3n$

   b   Write the general term for the sequence in the form $u_n = \ldots$.

End points

You should be able to ...   ... so try these questions

A   Find a rule that fits a sequence of patterns

A1   These are the first three matchstick patterns in a sequence.

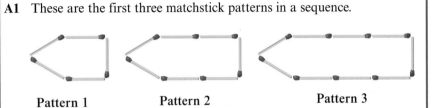

Pattern 1   Pattern 2   Pattern 3

  a Find a rule for the number of matches (m) in the nth pattern. Explain your method.
  b Use your rule to find the number of matches in the pattern 246.

B   Find a general rule for a sequence of numbers or fractions

B1   A 5, 9, 13, 17, ...   B 6, 7, 8, 9, 10, ...
        C 9, 12, 15, 18, 21, ...   D 5, 20, 45, 80, 125, ...
        E ⁻3, ⁻8, ⁻13, ⁻18, ...   F ⁻49, ⁻41, ⁻33, ⁻25, ⁻17, ...
        G ⁻1, 11, 23, 35, 47, ...   H 4, 13, 22, 31, 40, ...

For each of the sequences A to F:
  a   find a general term, u_n
  b   calculate u_{20}.

B2   Find the general term for each of these geometric sequences.

  a 27, 81, 243, 729, ...   **b** 8, 16, 32, 64, ...
  c 4, 6, 10, 18, ...   **d** 1, 13, 61, 253, ...

B3   Find the general term for each of these fractional sequences.

  a $\frac{2}{2}$ $\frac{4}{5}$ $\frac{8}{10}$ $\frac{16}{17}$ $\frac{32}{26}$ **b** $\frac{3}{3}$ $\frac{5}{12}$ $\frac{7}{27}$ $\frac{9}{48}$ $\frac{11}{75}$

Some points to remember

- ◆ It is often possible to find a rule for the nth pattern in a sequence of patterns by looking at how each pattern can be made.

- ◆ In a sequence: ◆ if the first differences are k each time, there is a simple linear expression for the nth term that begins kn ... .

    ◆ if the terms are fractions treat the numerators and denominators as separate sequences.

Decorum Design

DDC is the favourite shop for trade and private buyers who want a new look for bathrooms, kitchens and bedrooms. Here are some of our items but come to the shop to see our full range.

WALLPAPER – rolls

width 53 cm, length 10 metres.

FLORAL DESIGN £5.49 per roll.

£4.97 each for 12 rolls or more

ANTIQUE EMBOSSED £7.99 per roll

WALLPAPER PASTE £4.99 – covers 10 sq metres

TRY OUR ANTIQUE EMBOSSED PAPERS TO COVER THAT TATTY WALL

ALL PAINT PRICES REDUCED BY 20% FOR NEXT THREE WEEKS

EMULSION PAINTS – Top quality own brand

BRILLIANT WHITE	1 litre	£3.42
	2 ($\frac{1}{2}$) litre	£8.45
	5 litre	£16.99
PASTEL SHADES	2 ($\frac{1}{2}$) litre	£11.99
	5 litre	£19.49

A litre tin will cover about 8 m² with a single coat.
Two coats needed over very dark surfaces.

When calculating how much paint to order, do not subtract the area of doors and windows.

WALL TILES – imported Italian and French

JARDIN RANGE – Box of 10 tiles £1.79

ASSISI RANGE – Box of 10 tiles £1.99

JARDIN

ASSISI

For those who have not caught up with metric units yet.
  1 foot = 0.3048 metres   1 inch = 25.4 millimetres

All prices include VAT at 17.5%

TILE-FIX CEMENT – £7.99 a tub, covers 4 sq. metres

FORRET – Box of 10 wall tiles £2.14

BENETIA – Box of 10 tiles £2.14

FORRET

BENETIA

FLOOR TILES

QUARRY TILES – terracotta, 120mm x 120 mm, 31p each

CERAMIC REGULAR SHAPED TILES – choice of patterns

PRICES PER TILE:

A	£1.55
B	£1.75
C	£3.79
D	£3.49

TYPE B TILE CLEARANCE
WE ARE SELLING THESE TILES AT ONLY 16% OF THEIR USUAL PRICE

We also sell small square tiles to fit with our type C tile. Pack of ten £5.75

TILE CEMENT – 12 kg bag – £17.89 – enough for 10 square metres of floor.

COLOURED GROUT £7.69 per tub – enough for 15 square metres of floor.

When calculating what to order, allow one complete tile for every part of a tile you need.

DESIGN SERVICE

We offer a free design service for bathrooms and kitchens. Just give us your plans to a scale of 1:50 and we will calculate how much paint, wallpaper or tiling you need.

1 Spencer decides to tile the wall above a bath with Jardin style tiles.
He wants to cover an area 2.5 m by 65 cm.
a How many tiles will he need to buy?
b What will this cost him (including Tile-Fix)?
c What is the total cost ex-VAT?

2 a Describe the shape of a type B floor tile and give the size of one interior angle.
b What is the reduced price of one type B tile?

3 Mike uses Decorum's design service to calculate the number of quarry tiles he should buy for a floor which is 3.82 metres by 4.15 metres.
a Make a scale drawing of the floor to the correct scale.
b Calculate the number of tiles he needs.
c Decorum allow for 5 % of the tiles breaking. How many should Mike buy?

4 For type D tiles:
a What is the mathematical name of the shape?
b What is the size of an internal angle?
c What is the length of a side?

5 Steve's floor is 3.95 metres by 2.37 metres, and he wants to tile it with type A tiles. He works out that the area of the floor is 9.36 m² and that the area of one tile is 0.0529 m².
He says the number of tiles he needs is: 9.36 ÷ 0.0529 = 177 tiles
a What is wrong with Steve's method?
b How many tiles does he really need?
c What is the cost including grout and cement?

6 Which size tin of brilliant white paint is the best value for money? Explain your answer.

7 The dimensions of a floor are given as 13 ft 6 inches by 11 ft 10 inches.
Calculate the ex-VAT cost of tile cement and grout for this floor.

8 Decorum are thinking of selling smaller bags of tile cement. They have chosen a 5 kg size as most useful. If they price it at the same unit cost as the 12 kg bag, at what price should they sell it? Give your answer to the nearest penny.

9 a What is the mathematical name of the shape of the type C floor tile?
b Calculate the size of an internal angle of this shape.
c Calculate the discounted price of 50 type B tiles.

10 The 2½ litre size can of paint is 18 cm high.
Show that the diameter of this can, to the nearest millimetre is 133 mm.

11 The contents of a tub of Tile-Fix cement weigh 3.5 kg.
New regulations state that:
"Wall tile cement must be applied at a rate of **at least** 885 gm/m²".
a Does the information given by Decorum Design meet the new regulations? Explain your answer.
b The £7.99 tub of Tile-Fix is discontinued. Decorum Design sell a new tub to cover 5 m² at a price of £10.49.
i Is this an increase or decrease in price?
ii Give any change in price as a percentage of the £7.99 price, to the nearest whole number.

12 Type A floor tiles are 6 millimetres thick.
The contents of a box of 25 tiles weighs 17.8 kg.
Calculate the weight of 1 cm³ of tile to 1 dp.

13 Sally is asked to find the area of one type C floor tile. She measures a side to be 96 mm.
This is her working:

> Tile shape made up of 8 triangles.
> Area of one triangle is given by:
> 0.5 x 9.6 x 12.5 = 60
> Area of tile is given by:
> 60 x 8 = 480
> Area of tile is 480 cm².

a Explain why Sally's calculation must be wrong.
b Calculate the area of a type C tile. Give your answer correct to the nearest cm².

14 For a display, type D floor tiles are to be cut so that each tile gives two rhombus-shaped parts and two parts in the shape of an equilateral triangle.
a Sketch a type D tile and show how it can be cut to give the shapes for the display.
b Explain why each rhombus shape is more than 25% of the tile.
c Give the area of one equilateral triangle shape as a percentage of a tile (to 1 dp).

69

Starting points
You need to know about ...

... so try these questions

A Some mathematical terms

- Lines AB and CD are **perpendicular** to line XY because they would meet XY at right angles.

  XY is also **perpendicular** to AB and CD.

  AB and CD are **parallel**.

- These are some different types of triangle.

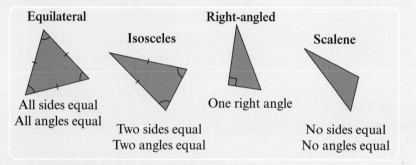

Equilateral — All sides equal, All angles equal

Isosceles — Two sides equal, Two angles equal

Right-angled — One right angle

Scalene — No sides equal, No angles equal

A1 a Draw a straight line PQ which is at an angle of 30° to the horizontal.
  b Now draw another straight line RS which you **estimate** to be perpendicular to PQ.
  c i At what angle is your RS to the horizontal?
    ii What angle do you think this should be?

A2 Can a triangle be both:
  a isosceles and scalene
  b right-angled and scalene
  c isosceles and right-angled
  d equilateral and right-angled?

B Congruent shapes

- Shapes are said to be congruent if they have the same shape or size or if they are reflections of each other.
  Example Triangles A and B are **congruent** to each other.

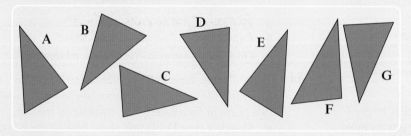

B1 Which of the triangles C to G is not congruent to triangle A?

B2 Draw another triangle which is congruent to triangle A.

B3 If two quadrilaterals both have sides of 12 cm, 13 cm, 14 cm and 15 cm are they necessarily congruent?
Explain your answer.

C Constructing a triangle, given all three sides

Example
Construct a triangle ABC where
AB = 4.4 cm, BC = 3.8 cm and CA = 3.2 cm.

- Make a rough sketch first.
- Draw a base line (say BC).
- Draw the locus of points 3.2 cm from C (purple arc).
- Draw the locus of points 4.4 cm from B (red arc).
- Where the arcs cross is point A
- Draw the triangle ABC.

C1 Draw a triangle PQR, where PR = 8 cm, PQ = 6 cm and RQ = 9 cm.

C2 Draw a triangle RST, where RS = 7.5 cm, ST = 7.5 cm and TR = 12.2 cm.
What type of triangle is this?

C3 A triangular field is 350 metres by 840 metres by 760 metres. Use a scale of 1 : 10 000 to construct a scale drawing of the field.

Constructing triangles from other data

◆ You can construct a triangle when you are not given the length of all three sides. You might be given **one side and two angles**.

△ABC means Triangle ABC.

∠B means angle B.

Example   Draw △ABC, where AB = 5 cm, ∠B = 55°, and ∠A = 43°.

Stage	**1**	Make a rough sketch.
	2	Make the side you know (AB) the base and draw it.
	3	At A, draw an angle of 43° with a protractor.
	4	At B, draw an angle of 55°.

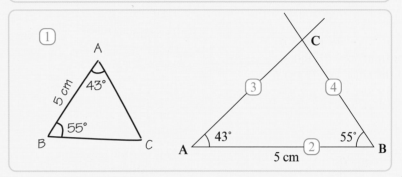

◆ You might be given **two sides and one angle**.

Example   Draw △RST, where RT = 6.5 cm, RS = 4.5 cm and ∠R = 46°.

Stage	**1**	Make a rough sketch.
	2	Make the long side (RT) the base, and draw it.
	3	At R, draw an angle of 46° and mark S, 4.5 cm from R.
	4	Draw the last side TS.

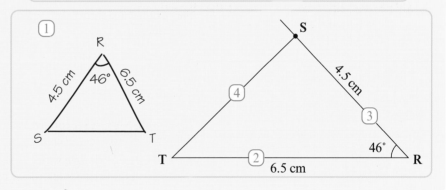

Exercise 6.1
Constructing triangles

1   Construct these triangles:

  a   △DEF, where DF = 6 cm, EF = 5 cm and ∠F = 69°
  b   △GHI, where GI = 7.2 cm, ∠G = 53° and ∠I = 42°
  c   △JKL, where JK = 8 cm, ∠J = 25° and ∠K = 125°
  d   △MNP, where NP = 6.3 cm, MP = 5.2 cm and ∠P = 131°.

2   Construct △QRS, where RQ = 8.3 cm, ∠R = 35° and ∠S = 68°. You will need to calculate another angle first.

Two of the triangles in Question **3** are almost identical but they cannot be referred to as congruent unless they **are** identical.

3   Construct these triangles to decide which two look identical:

  a   △IJK, where JK = 5.5 cm, IJ = 8 cm and ∠J = 50°
  b   △LMN, where LM = 8 cm, ∠L = 60° and ∠M = 50°
  c   △PQR, where PR = 6.5 cm, QR = 7.5 cm and ∠R = 70°.

Thinking ahead to ...
congruent triangles

A a Construct a triangle BCD where CD = 8.5 cm,
BD = 9.4 cm and ∠B = 54°.
b What is the length BC on your triangle?
c Construct a different triangle which still meets all the conditions in
Part **a** but has a different length for side BC.

Congruent triangles

SSS stands for the data
which is equal for both
triangles: Side, Side, Side

The order of the letters is
important, so SAS shows
that the angle is between
the two known sides
(i.e. the included angle):

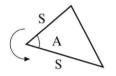

♦ There are four sets of conditions which can help you decide if two triangles
are congruent.

1 The **three sides** of one are equal
to the three sides of the other.
This can be referred to as SSS.

2 **Two angles and a side** of one are equal to two angles and
corresponding side of the other.

This is known as **ASA**
(or **AAS**).

3 **Two sides and the included angle** of one are equal to two sides and
the included angle of the other.

This is known as SAS.

4 They are both **right-angled** and have the **hypotenuse and one
other side** equal.

This is known as **RHS**.

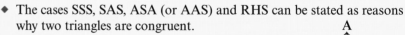

♦ The cases SSS, SAS, ASA (or AAS) and RHS can be stated as reasons
why two triangles are congruent.

Example Name a triangle which is congruent
to △BAD and state the case for
congruence.

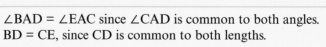

∠BAD = ∠EAC since ∠CAD is common to both angles.
BD = CE, since CD is common to both lengths.

Note that when you name
two shapes which are
congruent you must state
the letters in the
corresponding order.

i.e. △BAD is congruent to
△EAC, but △BAD is not
congruent to △AEC.

Therefore △BAD is congruent to △EAC. The case for congruence is AAS.

Exercise 6.2
Congruent triangles

1 In each of the following diagrams name a triangle which is congruent to △ABC and state the case for congruence.

a

b

c

d

e

f
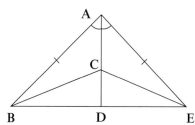

2 Simon said that the following two triangles were definitely congruent. He said there was a new case for congruence, **ASS**, which fitted them.

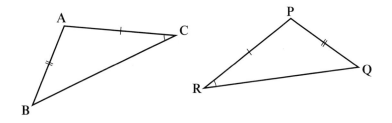

a Although the triangles might be congruent, explain why they need not necessarily be so.
b Construct a pair of triangles which match ASS but which are not congruent.

3 Sketch a pair triangles for each of these, state if the two are not necessarily congruent or certainly congruent and, if they are, the case for congruence.

a In △DEF and △GHI: DF = GI, DE = GH, EF = HI.
b In △ABC and △EFD: AB = DE, BC = EF, ∠ABC = ∠DEF.
c In △LMN and △RST: LN = RT, ∠LMN = ∠RTS, ∠LNM = ∠TSR.
d In △PQR and △STU: PR = ST, QR = TU, ∠QPR = ∠TSU = 90°.
e In △BCD and △EFG: BC = EG, BD = FG, ∠BCD = ∠FEG.
f In △RST and △UVW: ∠RTS = ∠VUW, VW = SR, ∠RST = ∠UVW.

Thinking ahead to ...
bisecting an angle

A pedestrian area is edged by two buildings which meet at an angle of 36°.
The plans say trees must be planted an equal distance from both buildings.

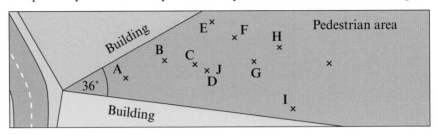

A   Which crosses on the diagram mark where trees could be planted?

> 'Equidistant from' means
> 'the same distance from'.

B   Draw two lines which meet at an angle of 36°.
Mark the locus of all points which are equidistant from both lines.

Bisecting an angle

> To bisect an angle means
> to draw a line which cuts it
> in two equal parts from its
> vertex.

It is useful to be able to bisect an angle without measuring it.
You can do this using a pair of compasses.

Stage 1
Draw an angle ABC.

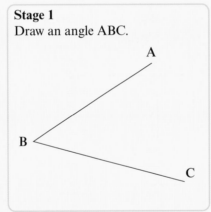

Stage 2
With centre B draw an arc so it
cuts AB and BC at D and E.

Stage 3
With centre D, draw an arc.
With centre E, draw an arc.

Stage 4
Draw the bisector BF.

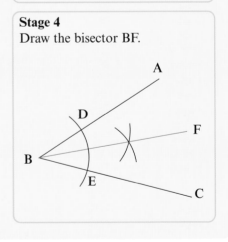

Exercise 6.3
Bisecting an angle

1   Use a protractor to draw each angle then bisect it using compasses.
   a 44°   **b** 100°   **c** 146°   **d** 90°

2   Use compasses to draw an equilateral triangle with sides of 8 cm.
   What size is each angle?
   Bisect one of the angles. What angle have you made?

Thinking ahead to ...
perpendicular bisectors

A Draw a straight line and
mark two points, A and B,
6 cm apart.

B Draw a circle at A and
another with the same
radius at B.

When two lines cross they
are said to intersect.

C Draw larger circles with
equal radii at A and B.
If they intersect, mark
the points of intersection.

D Continue by drawing
larger circles and marking
the points of intersection.

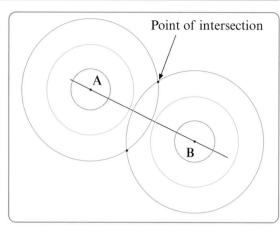

E **a** Draw the locus of all points of intersection of equal-sized circles.
b Describe the link between this locus and the line AB.

Perpendicular bisectors

A line which cuts a straight line exactly in half at right angles is called a
perpendicular bisector.

Example

To construct the perpendicular
bisector of the line EF.

♦ Draw the line EF.

♦ With centre E draw an arc
with a radius greater than
half of EF.

♦ With centre F draw another
arc with the same radius.

♦ Join the two points of
intersection.

N marks the midpoint of EF.

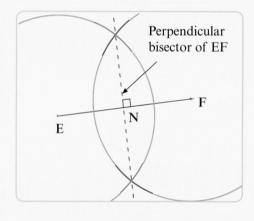

Exercise 6.4
Perpendicular bisectors

1 **a** Draw a line AB, 6 cm long. Construct the perpendicular bisector of AB.
b Mark any point on the bisector and measure its distance to A and to B.
c What can you say about the distance of any point on the
bisector from A and from B?

2 Draw the perpendicular bisectors of lines with these lengths:

a 10 cm   **b** 7.7 cm   **c** 4.6 cm

Check that both sides are equal in length and that you have right angles.

3 **a** Draw this triangle.
b Construct the perpendicular
bisector of each side.
c Where do all three bisectors intersect?
d Does this happen for other triangles?

4 a Draw a circle of radius 6 cm and mark its centre C.
b Draw a chord (AB).
c Construct the perpendicular bisector
of the chord.
d Draw two more chords and bisect them.
e What do you notice about where the
bisectors intersect?

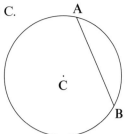

Meeting conditions

Rules that have to be met
such as 'the tap must be the
same distance from A and
B' are known as
conditions.

Constructions such as bisecting angles or lines can be used for making scale
drawings where conditions have to be met.

Example

A water tap is to be put in a large garden but it must meet these conditions:
1 It must be the same distance from the two greenhouses, A and B.
2 It must be the same distance from the grape vine wires as from the hedge.

Where must the tap be placed? How far is it from the tree?

To meet condition **1** you
draw the perpendicular
bisector of BA.
This line is the locus of
all points equidistant from
B and A.
To meet condition **2** you
bisect angle BAD.
This line is the locus of all
points equidistant from line
BA and line AD.

Where the two loci intersect
both conditions are met, so
the tap must be at this point.

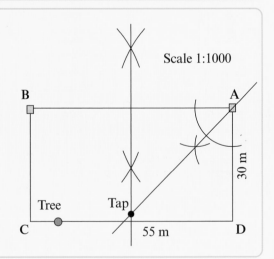

Exercise 6.5
Meeting conditions

1 a On the scale diagram above measure the distance in centimetres between
the tap and the tree.
b What is this actual distance in the garden?

2 Make a scale drawing to show where the tap will be if:
condition **1** stays the same
condition **2** says the tap must be equidistant from the wall and the hedge.

3 An Olympic javelin field has lines which make an angle of 29° to each other.
A thrower aims the javelin so that it flies equidistant from both lines.
The thrower hopes to reach the club record of 88 metres.

This diagram only
approximates to how a true
javelin field is marked out.
The throwing point actually
lies on an arc about 2 metres
wide which comes at the end
of a 36 metre run-up.

a Make a scale drawing of the field for throws up to 100 metres.
Use a scale of 1:1000.
b Mark the locus of all points 88 metres from the throwing point.
c Construct the locus of points equidistant from the sidelines.
d Mark where the thrower hopes the javelin will land.

4 Two lighthouses are 3.6 miles apart on a straight coastline.
A ferry sails into port by keeping the same distance from both lighthouses.
A fishing boat sails so that it is always 3 miles from the coast.

a Make a scale drawing of the coast to show the position
of the lighthouses. Use a scale of 1 cm to 0.5 miles.
b Show and label the course taken by the fishing boat.
c Construct and label the course taken by the ferry.
d Mark the point where there is the greatest risk of a collision.

To construct an angle of
60° without a protractor
you can construct an
equilateral triangle.

To construct an angle of
30°, first construct a 60°
angle, as above, then
bisect it.

5 Coastguard A is 14 km due west of coastguard B along a stretch
of straight coastline.
A ship S can be seen on a bearing of 030° from A and
on a bearing of 300° from B.

a Use a ruler and compasses
only to make a scale drawing
of the situation. Use a scale
of 1 cm to represent 2 km.
b From your drawing find the
distance of the ship from
coastguard B.

c The ship sails into shore so that its path bisects the angle ASB.
Construct this path and find its distance from A when it docks.

To draw a perpendicular
from a point X to a line
AB:
♦ draw an arc from X to
intersect AB in two
places
♦ from each intersection
draw equal arcs on the
other side of AB
♦ join the intersection of
these arcs to X.

6 a Construct a quadrilateral PQRS where RSP = 90°,
QR = 8.4 cm, RS = 9 cm, SP = 6 cm and PQ = 5.4 cm.
b Bisect angles RSP and SPQ, and let these bisectors meet at point T.
c Construct the perpendicular from T to meet PS at N.
d Draw a circle with radius TN and centre T.
Which sides of the quadrilateral does your circle touch ?

7 A buoy is moored 1000 metres from a long straight harbour wall.
A small boat sails so that it is always the same distance from the buoy as from
the wall. Investigate the path of the boat with the help of a scale drawing.

The locus of a right angle

Exercise 6.6
Right angles

'Adjacent' means 'next to'.

1 a Draw a line AB which is 8 centimetres long.
  b Identify the right angle on a set square.
    Place the set square so that the sides adjacent to the right angle
    touch both points A and B.
    Mark a point P at the right-angled vertex.
  c Rotate the set square to another position so adjacent sides
    touch A and B.
    Mark the new point P.

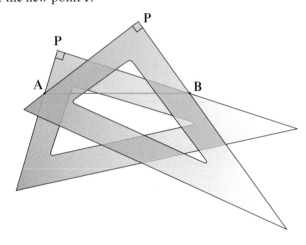

  d Mark the locus of all positions of P as you rotate the set square 360°.
    What shape is this locus?

2 a Draw a circle of any size.
  b Draw in a diameter and label it RS.
  c Join point R to any point, C, on the circumference of the circle.
  d Join C to S.
  e Measure angle RCS. What do you notice?
  f For any diameter RS and any point on the circumference C,
    what can you say about the triangle RCS?

3 In this circle point H is the centre and lines
  AG and GC are equal in length.
  Name six angles in the diagram which must
  be right angles.

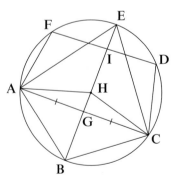

4 The cross-section of a roof is
  semicircular in shape.

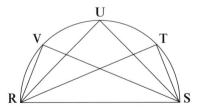

  Beam RV is 12 metres long and beam VS is 26 metres.
  Beam RU is equal in length to US.

  a Use what you know about the angles in a semicircle to
    calculate the diameter RS to 1 dp.
  b Calculate the length of RU to 1 dp.

End points

You should be able to ...   ... so try these questions

A Construct and draw triangles when you are given their sides or angles

A1 Construct △ABC where AB = 7 cm, AC = 6 cm and BC = 6 cm.

A2 Draw △DEF, where ∠EDF = 92°, ∠DFE = 47° and DF = 4.5 cm.

A3 Draw △PQR, where PQ = 7.4 cm, QR = 4.3 cm and ∠Q = 123°.

A4 Draw two different triangles STU which each have TU = 6 cm, ∠SUT = 40° and ST = 4.3 cm.

B Construct and use perpendicular bisectors

B1

B   6.5 cm   A

C   About 40°   D   5.7 cm

a Draw the parallelogram ABCD with BĈD about 40°.
b Construct perpendicular bisectors for the sides BC and AD.
c What can you say about the gradients of the two bisectors?

B2

C   18 m   E

18 m   24 m

D

Two dogs are tied at points D and E, 24 metres apart.
A cat at point C wishes to pass between the dogs so that it is always the same distance from each one.
Make a scale drawing and construct the path the cat must take.
Use a scale of 1 cm to 3 metres.

C Construct and use the bisectors of an angle

C1 Draw an angle of 110° with a protractor.
Construct the bisector of the angle.

C2 Construct △ABC where AB = 4.3 cm, BC = 6.8 cm and AC = 5.9 cm.
Bisect each of the angles.
What do you notice about where the bisectors intersect?

D Recognise and state the conditions for congruence

D1 For each pair of triangles, state if they are congruent or not necessarily congruent. For those that are congruent state their case for congruence.

a   b

c   d

e   f

E   **Draw loci from some conditions given**

E1   This garden is the shape of a trapezium with the dimensions given.

Trees are at the midpoints of sides AD and DC.

A new bush is to be planted:
- equidistant from each fence
- equidistant from each tree.

Make a scale drawing of the garden and show by construction the position of the bush. Use a scale of 1:100.

Some points to remember

- To construct an angle of 90°, draw a line and construct its perpendicular bisector.

- When asked to construct something do not rub out the construction lines when you finish.

- To construct an angle of 60°, construct an equilateral triangle.

- The perpendicular bisector of any chord will pass through the centre of the circle.

- All angles in a semicircle which are made by the diameter and a point on the circumference are right angles.

Starting points
You need to know about ...   ... so try these questions

A Fractions and decimals

♦ In recurring decimal notation, dots are placed over the first and last of the set of recurring digits.

For example: 0.236666666 ... = 0.23$\dot{6}$
              0.236363636 ... = 0.2$\dot{3}\dot{6}$
              0.236236236 ... = 0.$\dot{2}$36$\dot{6}$

♦ We can multiply recurring decimals by powers of 10.

For example: if n = 0.3232323232 ...
             then $10n$ = 3.2323232323 ...
                     $100n$ = 32.3232323232 ... and so on.

♦ Any fraction is equivalent to a terminating or recurring decimal.

For example: $\frac{3}{4}$ = 3 ÷ 4 = 0.75

$\frac{11}{30}$ = 11 ÷ 30 = 0.366666 ... = 0.36$\dot{6}$

B Index notation

♦ We say 5^4 is **5 to the power 4** or **5 raised to the power 4**.

$$5^4 = 5 \times 5 \times 5 \times 5 = 625 \text{ (4 is the index)}$$

♦ Numbers raised to a **negative power** are defined so that:

$$x^{-y} = \frac{1}{x^y} \quad \text{e.g. } 5^{-2} = \frac{1}{5^2} = \frac{1}{25} \, (= 0.04)$$

So, the division pattern in this table is continued:

5^3	5^2	5^1	5^0	5^{-1}	5^{-2}	5^{-3}	5^{-4}
125	25	5	1	$\frac{1}{5}$	$\frac{1}{25}$	$\frac{1}{125}$	$\frac{1}{625}$

÷5 ÷5 ÷5 ÷5 ÷5 ÷5 ÷5

C Square roots and cube roots

♦ The **square roots** of 9 are 3 and ⁻3 because,
3 squared is $3^2 = 3 \times 3 = 9$ and (⁻3) squared is $(^-3)^2 = ^-3 \times ^-3 = 9$

Where a square root can be positive or negative,
you should give the positive root unless stated otherwise.

'The square root of 9 is 3' can be written $\sqrt{9} = 3$ or $\sqrt[2]{9} = 3$.

Examples of square roots are: ♦ $\sqrt{1.44} = 1.2$

♦ $\sqrt{1\frac{7}{9}} = \sqrt{\frac{16}{9}} = \frac{4}{3}$

♦ The **cube root** of 64 is 4, because
4 cubed is $4^3 = 4 \times 4 \times 4 = 64$

This can be written $\sqrt[3]{64} = 4$.
Examples of cube roots are: ♦ $\sqrt[3]{729} = 9$
♦ $\sqrt[3]{(^-8)} = ^-2$

A1 Use recurring decimal notation to write these recurring decimals.
 a 0.777777 ...
 b 0.12323232323 ...
 c 4.56666666 ...

A2 If n = 0.565656 ... , what is:
 a $10n$ **b** $100n$ **c** $1000n$?

A3 Convert these fractions to decimals, using recurring decimal notation where necessary.
 a $\frac{1}{4}$ **b** $\frac{1}{3}$ **c** $\frac{6}{11}$
 d $\frac{17}{30}$ **e** $\frac{3}{8}$

B1 Write these in index notation.
 a 3 raised to the power 5
 b 4 to the power ⁻3

B2 Evaluate as an integer or in fractional form:
 a 3^4 **b** 3^{-2} **c** 4^0
 d 5^{-1} **e** 2^9 **f** $(^-6)^2$
 g $(\frac{2}{3})^2$ **h** $(\frac{-1}{4})^2$

C1 What is the value of:
 a the square root of 169
 b the cube root of 1000
 c the square root of 6.76
 d the cube root of 9.261 ?

C2 Evaluate correct to one decimal place:
 a $\sqrt{12}$ **b** $\sqrt{105}$ **c** $\sqrt{6.7}$

C3 Evaluate:
 a $\sqrt{49}$ **b** $\sqrt[3]{3.375}$
 c $\sqrt[3]{(^-1000)}$

C4 Evaluate in fractional form:
 a $\sqrt{\frac{1}{25}}$ **b** $\sqrt{\frac{49}{100}}$ **c** $\sqrt{1\frac{11}{25}}$

C5 Explain why any number has no more than one cube root.

Roots

It is also true that

$(^-1.2)^4 = 2.0736$ so a fourth root of 2.0736 is $^-1.2$.

If a root can be positive or negative, give the positive root as your answer (unless stated otherwise).

◆ As well as square and cube roots, there are fourth, fifth, sixth, … roots.

Examples

❖ $3^5 = 3 \times 3 \times 3 \times 3 \times 3 = 243$ so a fifth root of 243 is 3.
This can be written: $\sqrt[5]{243} = 3$.

❖ $1.2^4 = 1.2 \times 1.2 \times 1.2 \times 1.2 = 2.0736$ so a fourth root of 2.0736 is 1.2
This can be written: $\sqrt[4]{2.0736} = 1.2$

❖ $\left(\frac{1}{2}\right)^6 = \frac{1}{2} \times \frac{1}{2} \times \frac{1}{2} \times \frac{1}{2} \times \frac{1}{2} \times \frac{1}{2} = \frac{1}{64}$ so a sixth root of $\frac{1}{64}$ is $\frac{1}{2}$.
This can be written: $\sqrt[6]{\frac{1}{64}} = \frac{1}{2}$.

◆ Sometimes a root cannot be written exactly as a decimal or fraction.

Example   Find $\sqrt[5]{20}$ correct to 1 dp using trial and improvement.
$2^5 = 32$ (> 20 so 2 is too big)
$1.5^5 = 7.59375$ (< 20 so 1.5 is too small)
$1.9^5 = 24.76099$ (> 20 so 1.9 is too big)
$1.8^5 = 18.89568$ (< 20 so 1.8 is too small)
$1.85^5 \approx 21.66999$ (> 20 so 1.85 is too big)

The solution lies between 1.8 and 1.85 so $\sqrt[5]{20} = 1.8$ (to 1 dp).

Exercise 7.1
Roots

1 Calculate:
   a $\sqrt[4]{16}$ **b** $\sqrt[6]{11.390625}$ **c** $\sqrt[5]{1}$

2 Which of these are integers?
   a $\sqrt[3]{8}$ **b** $\sqrt[4]{12}$ **c** $\sqrt[6]{600}$ **d** $\sqrt[5]{^-32}$

3 Evaluate these, giving each answer as a fraction.
   a $\sqrt[3]{\frac{27}{64}}$ **b** $\sqrt[5]{\frac{32}{243}}$ **c** $\sqrt[7]{\frac{1}{78125}}$

4 Evaluate $\sqrt[4]{10}$ correct to 1 decimal place.

5 Find the value of x when:
   a $\sqrt[4]{x} = 3.5$ **b** $\sqrt[x]{1.728} = 1.2$ **c** $\sqrt[3]{x} = ^-4.5$

6 Copy and complete:
   a $\sqrt[2]{6^4} = 6^\square$ **b** $\sqrt[3]{2^6} = 2^\square$ **c** $\sqrt[4]{5^8} = 5^\square$

7 **a** Solve:
      i $\sqrt{x^x} = 16$ **ii** $\sqrt{x^x} = 216$
   b Make up two more problems like this that give integer values for x.

Using positive and negative indices

To multiply powers of the same number, **add** the indices.

Example 1

$3^2 \times 3^4$

$= 3^{2+4}$

$= 3^6$

$3^2 \times 3^4$

$= (3 \times 3) \times (3 \times 3 \times 3 \times 3)$

$= 3^6$

Example 2

$3^{-2} \times 3^4$

$= 3^{-2+4}$

$= 3^2$

$3^{-2} \times 3^4 = \frac{1}{3^2} \times 3^4$

$= \frac{3 \times 3 \times 3 \times 3}{3 \times 3}$

$= 3^2$

To divide powers of the same number, **subtract** the indices.

Example 1

$$\frac{4^5}{4^2}$$

$$= 4^{5-2}$$

$$= 4^3$$

$$\frac{4^5}{4^2}$$

$$= \frac{4 \times 4 \times 4 \times 4 \times 4}{4 \times 4}$$

$$= 4^3$$

Example 2

$$\frac{2^3}{2^7}$$

$$= 2^{3-7}$$

$$= 2^{-4}$$

$$\frac{2^3}{2^7}$$

$$= \frac{2 \times 2 \times 2}{2 \times 2 \times 2 \times 2 \times 2 \times 2 \times 2} = \frac{1}{2 \times 2 \times 2 \times 2} = \frac{1}{2^4}$$

$$= 2^{-4}$$

To raise a power of a number to another power, **multiply** the indices.

Example 3

$$(3^2)^3$$

$$= 3^{2 \times 3}$$

$$= 3^6$$

$$(3^2)^3$$

$$= (3 \times 3) \times (3 \times 3) \times (3 \times 3)$$

$$= 3^6$$

Exercise 7.2
Multiplying and dividing

1 Give the answer to each of these in index notation.

  a $6^2 \times 6^3$ **b** $5^5 \times 5^{-1}$ **c** $(7^2)^4$ **d** $\dfrac{3^5}{3^4}$ **e** $\dfrac{2^8}{2^{-3}}$ **f** $(5^3)^{-2}$

2 Copy and complete these calculations.

  a $7^3 \times 7^{\square} = 7^8$ **b** $4^{\square} \times 4^5 = 4^5$ **c** $3^{-4} \times 3^{\square} = 3^2$

  d $\dfrac{5^7}{5^{\square}} = 5^{-3}$ **e** $\dfrac{2^{\square}}{2^4} = 2$ **f** $(7^3)^{\square} = 7^{15}$

3 Simplify:

  a $x^5 \times x^3$ **b** $x^8 \div x^2$ **c** $(x^2)^5$ **d** $\dfrac{x^4}{x^2}$ **e** $\dfrac{x^5}{x}$ **f** $\dfrac{x^7}{x^9}$

Algebraic expressions involving indices can be simplified using the rules for indices.
For example:

$$x^2 \times x^3 = x^{3+2} = x^5$$

$$\frac{a^7}{a^2} = a^{7-2} = a^5$$

4 Copy and complete:

  a $(t^{\square})^4 = t^{12}$ **b** $(q^5)^{\square} = q^{-5}$ **c** $(p^2)^{\square} = \dfrac{1}{p^8}$

5 To what power must x^2 be raised to give:

  a x^{10} **b** x^{-4} **c** $\dfrac{1}{x^2}$?

6 A student has made mistakes in trying to simplify some expressions.

  a $a^2 \times a^4 = a^8$ ✗   **b** $a^{10} \div a^2 = a^5$ ✗

  c $a^3 \div a^{12} = a^9$ ✗   **d** $(a^4)^3 = a^7$ ✗

  Explain the mistakes, and simplify each expression correctly.

7 Solve these equations.

  a $2^x \times 2^x = 2^{16}$ **b** $(7^x)^x = 7^{36}$ **c** $\dfrac{3^x}{3^{4x}} = \dfrac{1}{27}$

8 Simplify these expressions as far as you can.

  a $\dfrac{4p^3 \times p^2}{2p^4}$ **b** $\dfrac{2q \times 3q^5}{5q^2}$ **c** $\dfrac{4r^5 \times 6r^2}{12r^3}$

Thinking ahead to ...
fractional indices

According to the rules for multiplying powers:

◆ $25^{\frac{1}{2}} \times 25^{\frac{1}{2}} = 25^{\frac{1}{2} + \frac{1}{2}} = 25^1 = 25$

◆ $27^{\frac{2}{3}} \times 27^{\frac{2}{3}} \times 27^{\frac{2}{3}} = 27^{\frac{2}{3} + \frac{2}{3} + \frac{2}{3}} = 27^2 = 729$

A What do you think could be the value of:

    a $25^{\frac{1}{2}}$ **b** $27^{\frac{2}{3}}$?

B What value does your calculator give for $16^{\frac{1}{4}}$?

Fractional indices

Fractional powers are defined so that rules for calculating with integer indices can also be used with fractional indices.

Example 1

◆ $9^{\frac{1}{2}} \times 9^{\frac{1}{2}} = 9^{\frac{1}{2} + \frac{1}{2}} = 9^1 = 9$, so $9^{\frac{1}{2}} = \sqrt[2]{9} = 3$

◆ $8^{\frac{1}{3}} \times 8^{\frac{1}{3}} \times 8^{\frac{1}{3}} = 8^{\frac{1}{3} + \frac{1}{3} + \frac{1}{3}} = 8^1 = 8$, so $8^{\frac{1}{3}} = \sqrt[3]{8} = 2$

In general, $x^{\frac{1}{n}} = \sqrt[n]{x}$

Example 2

◆ $8^{\frac{2}{3}} \times 8^{\frac{2}{3}} \times 8^{\frac{2}{3}} = 8^{\frac{2}{3} + \frac{2}{3} + \frac{2}{3}} = 8^2 = 64$

so, $8^{\frac{2}{3}} = \sqrt[3]{8^2} = \sqrt[3]{64} = 4$

◆ $16^{\frac{3}{4}} \times 16^{\frac{3}{4}} \times 16^{\frac{3}{4}} \times 16^{\frac{3}{4}} = 16^{\frac{3}{4} + \frac{3}{4} + \frac{3}{4} + \frac{3}{4}} = 16^3 = 4096$

so $16^{\frac{3}{4}} = \sqrt[4]{16^3} = \sqrt[4]{4096} = 8$

In general, $x^{\frac{m}{n}} = \sqrt[n]{x^m}$

Example 3

◆ $9^{-\frac{1}{2}} \times 9^{\frac{1}{2}} = 9^{-\frac{1}{2} + \frac{1}{2}} = 9^0 = 1$, so $9^{-\frac{1}{2}} = \frac{1}{9^{\frac{1}{2}}} = \frac{1}{\sqrt{9}} = \frac{1}{3}$

In general, $x^{-\frac{m}{n}} = \frac{1}{x^{\frac{m}{n}}} = \frac{1}{\sqrt[n]{x^m}}$

Exercise 7.3
Fractional indices

1 Find four matching pairs of equal value.

    a $16^{\frac{1}{2}}$ **b** $^-2$ **c** $\frac{1}{2}$ **d** $512^{\frac{1}{3}}$

    e $4^{-\frac{1}{2}}$ **f** 8 **g** 4 **h** $(^-32)^{\frac{1}{5}}$

2 Evaluate these as integers or in fractional form.

    a $36^{\frac{1}{2}}$ **b** $125^{\frac{1}{3}}$ **c** $81^{\frac{1}{4}}$

    d $49^{-\frac{1}{2}}$ **e** $8^{-\frac{1}{3}}$ **f** $1^{-\frac{1}{5}}$

3 From the list of fractions, $\frac{2}{9}, \frac{3}{2}, \frac{1}{3}, \frac{2}{3}, \frac{1}{9}$, which one is equivalent to:

    a $(\frac{4}{9})^{\frac{1}{2}}$ **b** $(\frac{1}{27})^{\frac{1}{3}}$?

4 Find four pairs of equivalent expressions.

    a $x^{-\frac{5}{3}}$ **b** $\dfrac{1}{\sqrt[5]{x^3}}$ **c** $x^{\frac{3}{5}}$ **d** $\sqrt[3]{x^5}$

    e $\dfrac{1}{\sqrt[3]{x^5}}$ **f** $\sqrt[5]{x^3}$ **g** $x^{-\frac{3}{5}}$ **h** $x^{\frac{5}{3}}$

5 Sort these into four pairs of equal value.

    a $64^{\frac{1}{2}}$ **b** 512 **c** 32 **d** $4^{\frac{5}{2}}$

    e $216^{\frac{2}{3}}$ **f** 8 **g** 36 **h** $16^{\frac{9}{4}}$

6 Which of these fractions is equivalent to $32^{-\frac{2}{5}}$?

    a $\frac{1}{4}$ **b** $-\frac{64}{5}$ **c** $\frac{5}{64}$ **d** $-\frac{1}{4}$

7 Evaluate these as integers or in fractional form.

    a $125^{\frac{2}{3}}$ **b** $81^{\frac{3}{4}}$ **c** $243^{\frac{2}{5}}$

    d $64^{\frac{7}{6}}$ **e** $4^{-\frac{3}{2}}$ **f** $27^{-\frac{4}{3}}$

8   A $x^{\frac{1}{3}}$ B 9^x C x^2 D $x^{\frac{1}{2}}$ E $x^{\frac{3}{4}}$ F $x^{\frac{2}{3}}$

    a Which of these expressions gives an integer value when:
        i $x = 9$ **ii** $x = 64$ **iii** $x = 16$?
    b Find a value for x that gives an integer value for all six expressions.

9 What is the value of p when $(p^{\frac{2}{3}})^{\frac{3}{2}} = 243$?

10 A number y is such that $y^{\frac{1}{2}} = \frac{1}{3}$. Find the value of:

    a $y^{\frac{3}{2}}$ **b** y^{-1}

Exercise 7.4
Solving equations

1 Solve:

    a $64^{\frac{1}{x}} = 4$ **b** $7^{2y} = \frac{1}{49}$ **c** $1024^{\frac{1}{5}} = 2^z$

    d $32^a = 2$ **e** $125^b = \frac{1}{5}$ **f** $2^{2c+1} = \frac{1}{128}$

    g $3 \times 4^p = 96$ **h** $\dfrac{8^q}{4} = 4$ **i** $8 \times 16^r = 1$

2 In this puzzle, the solution to each clue is the solution of an equation.
Copy and complete the puzzle.

Across

2 $3721^{-\frac{1}{2}} = \frac{1}{x}$

3 $y^{\frac{2}{5}} = 16$

6 $z^{\frac{2}{3}} = 121$

8 $v^{-\frac{1}{3}} = \frac{1}{3}$

Down

1 $w^{-2} = \frac{1}{100}$

2 $a^{\frac{1}{6}} = 2$

3 $\left(\frac{1}{b}\right)^{\frac{1}{2}} = \frac{1}{4}$

4 $c^{\frac{3}{5}} = 27$

5 $k^{-\frac{3}{4}} = \frac{1}{27}$

6 $m^{-1} = \frac{1}{17}$

7 $n^{-\frac{4}{5}} = \left(\frac{1}{2}\right)^4$

Thinking ahead to ...
square roots

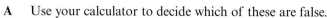

A   Use your calculator to decide which of these are false.

A $\sqrt{20} = \sqrt{10} \times \sqrt{2}$

B $\sqrt{20} = \sqrt{17} + \sqrt{3}$

C $\sqrt{20} = 2 \times \sqrt{5}$

D $\sqrt{20} = \dfrac{\sqrt{40}}{\sqrt{2}}$

E $\sqrt{20} = \sqrt{25} - \sqrt{5}$

Simplifying square roots

The rules for multiplying and dividing square roots also apply to other roots.

For example:
$a^{\frac{1}{3}} \times b^{\frac{1}{3}} = (a \times b)^{\frac{1}{3}}$

$a\sqrt{b} = a \times \sqrt{b}$

For example:
$2\sqrt{11} = 2 \times \sqrt{11}$

Expressions such as $5 + 2\sqrt{6}$ are said to be in **surd form**. They include roots that are not equivalent to integers or fractions.

Greek mathematicians thought of numbers such as $\sqrt{2}$ and $\sqrt{3}$ as absurd.

Rules for multiplying and dividing square roots are:

♦ $\sqrt{a} \times \sqrt{b} = \sqrt{ab}$

Example

$\sqrt{9} \times \sqrt{16} = 3 \times 4$
$\qquad\qquad = 12$

$\sqrt{9 \times 16} = \sqrt{3 \times 3 \times 4 \times 4}$
$\qquad\quad = \sqrt{(3 \times 4) \times (3 \times 4)}$
$\qquad\quad = 3 \times 4$
$\qquad\quad = 12$

So $\sqrt{9} \times \sqrt{16} = \sqrt{(9 \times 16)}$
$\qquad\qquad\qquad = \sqrt{144}$
$\qquad\qquad\qquad = 12$

♦ $\dfrac{\sqrt{a}}{\sqrt{b}} = \sqrt{\dfrac{a}{b}}$

Example

$\dfrac{\sqrt{100}}{\sqrt{4}} = \dfrac{10}{2} = 5$

$\sqrt{\dfrac{100}{4}} = \sqrt{\dfrac{10}{2} \times \dfrac{10}{2}}$
$\qquad = \dfrac{10}{2} = 5$

So $\dfrac{\sqrt{100}}{\sqrt{4}} = \sqrt{\dfrac{100}{4}} = \sqrt{25}$

So some expressions involving square roots can be simplified.

Example

♦ $(2\sqrt{11})^2 = (2 \times \sqrt{11}) \times (2 \times \sqrt{11})$
$\qquad\quad = 2 \times 2 \times \sqrt{11} \times \sqrt{11}$
$\qquad\quad = 4 \times 11$
$\qquad\quad = 44$

♦ $\sqrt{20} = \sqrt{4} \times \sqrt{5}$
$\qquad\; = 2\sqrt{5}$

♦ $(\sqrt{2} + \sqrt{3})^2 = 2 + \sqrt{6} + \sqrt{6} + 3$
$\qquad\qquad\quad = 5 + 2\sqrt{6}$

×	$\sqrt{2}$ +	$\sqrt{3}$
$\sqrt{2}$	2	$\sqrt{6}$
$+\sqrt{3}$	$\sqrt{6}$	3

Exercise 7.5
Simplifying square roots

In this exercise, do not use a calculator unless stated otherwise.

1 a   Which of these is not equivalent to $\sqrt{24}$?

A $2\sqrt{6}$

B $4\sqrt{6}$

C $\sqrt{8} \times \sqrt{3}$

D $\sqrt{4} \times \sqrt{6}$

E $\dfrac{\sqrt{72}}{\sqrt{3}}$

b   Check your results with a calculator.

2

A $(\sqrt{5} + \sqrt{2})^2$

B $(\sqrt{5} \times \sqrt{2})^2$

C $\dfrac{\sqrt{54}}{\sqrt{6}}$

D $\dfrac{\sqrt{100}}{\sqrt{5}}$

E $\sqrt{6} \times \sqrt{2}$

F $\sqrt{8} \times \sqrt{2}$

G $(\sqrt{12} - \sqrt{3})^2$

H $(4\sqrt{5})^2$

For each of these expressions:

a   decide if it gives an integer value
b   explain how you made your decision.

HIGHER GCSE

SECTION 7 POWERS AND SURDS

3 Sort these into five pairs of equal value.

(A) $\sqrt{3} \times \sqrt{5}$

(B) $\sqrt{8}$

(C) $\sqrt{2} \times \sqrt{2}$

(D) $2\sqrt{2}$

(E) $(\sqrt{2} + \sqrt{8})^2$

(F) 2

(G) $(\sqrt{3} - 1)^2$

(H) $\sqrt{15}$

(I) $4 - 2\sqrt{3}$

(J) 18

> When simplifying surds, write square roots in the form $a\sqrt{b}$ so that a and b are integers and b is as small as possible.

4 Simplify as far as you can, giving answers in surd form where necessary.

a $\sqrt{40}$

b $\sqrt{7} \times \sqrt{3}$

c $\dfrac{\sqrt{90}}{\sqrt{10}}$

d $\sqrt{2} \times \sqrt{32}$

e $\sqrt{3} \times \sqrt{15}$

f $(3\sqrt{5})^2$

g $(2 + \sqrt{7})^2$

h $(\sqrt{6} + \sqrt{12})^2$

i $(3 + \sqrt{5})(1 - \sqrt{2})$

j $(\sqrt{8} - \sqrt{2})^2$

k $(3\sqrt{2} + \sqrt{15})^2$

l $(2\sqrt{3})^4$

5 Give the area of each shape and leave your answer in simplified surd form.

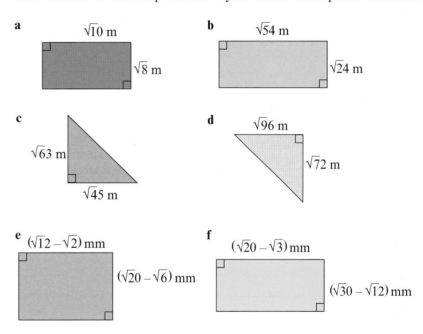

a $\sqrt{10}$ m, $\sqrt{8}$ m

b $\sqrt{54}$ m, $\sqrt{24}$ m

c $\sqrt{63}$ m, $\sqrt{45}$ m

d $\sqrt{96}$ m, $\sqrt{72}$ m

e $(\sqrt{12} - \sqrt{2})$ mm, $(\sqrt{20} - \sqrt{6})$ mm

f $(\sqrt{20} - \sqrt{3})$ mm, $(\sqrt{30} - \sqrt{12})$ mm

6 Explain why $\dfrac{\sqrt{54}}{\sqrt{216}}$ can be written as $\dfrac{1}{2}$.

Use surd form in your explanation.

7 A rectangle is $4\sqrt{5}$ cm wide.
The area of the rectangle is given as $48\sqrt{10}$
Find the length of the long side of the rectangle.
Give your answer in simplified surd form.

8 Find the value of:

a $(8 \times 10^{21})^{\frac{1}{3}}$

b $2^{\frac{1}{4}} \times 8^{\frac{1}{4}}$

c $\dfrac{54^{\frac{1}{3}}}{2^{\frac{1}{3}}}$

End points

You should be able to ...   ... so try these questions

A Evaluate roots

A1 Evaluate:

a $\sqrt[5]{243}$ b $\sqrt[3]{216}$ c the fourth root of 16

B Use rules for multiplying and dividing powers

B1 Copy and complete:

a $2^4 \times 2^{\square} = 2^{12}$ b $\dfrac{3^4}{3^{\square}} = \dfrac{1}{3^2}$ c $(7^2)^{\square} = 7^6$

B2 Simplify:

a $2x^3 \times x^4$ b $\dfrac{x^6}{x^2}$ c $(3x^3)^4$

C Work with indices

C1 Evaluate these as integers or in fractional form.

a $100^{\frac{1}{2}}$ b $64^{\frac{2}{3}}$ c $32^{-\frac{3}{5}}$

C2 Solve these equations.

a $27^x = 3$ b $6^x = \dfrac{1}{36}$ c $81^x = \dfrac{1}{3}$

D Simplify square roots

D1 Simplify these as far as you can.

a $\sqrt{2} \times \sqrt{5}$ b $\sqrt{32}$ c $(3\sqrt{7})^2$ d $(\sqrt{3} - \sqrt{2})^2$

E Work with surds

E1 The length and width of a rectangle are given as $3\sqrt{45}$ and $4\sqrt{30}$. Give the area of the rectangle in simplified surd form.

E2 This pattern consists of a set of six right-angled triangles as shown. Each triangle is labelled. In surd form, how long is the hypotenuse in:
a triangle 1
b triangle 2?

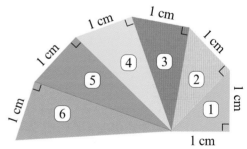

Some points to remember

Rules for indices:	$\bullet \quad a^m \times a^n = a^{m+n}$	$\bullet \quad a^{-m} = \dfrac{1}{a^m}$
	$\bullet \quad a^m \div a^n = a^{m-n}$	$\bullet \quad a^{\frac{m}{n}} = \sqrt[n]{a^m}$
	$\bullet \quad (a^m)^n = a^{mn}$	
Rules for square roots	$\bullet \quad \sqrt{a} \times \sqrt{b} = \sqrt{ab}$	$\bullet \quad \sqrt{\dfrac{a}{b}} = \dfrac{\sqrt{a}}{\sqrt{b}}$

Starting points

You need to know about ...   ... so try these questions

A Decimal places for rounding

♦ Numbers can be approximated to a set number of decimal places.

Examples

32.3743 to 2 decimal places (2 dp) is **32.37**.
32.3753 to 2 dp is **32.38** (5, or greater, in this position rounds the 7 up).

34.496 to 2 dp is **34.50** (the 6 makes 49 one larger, i.e. 50).

102.499 81 to 3 dp is **102.500** (3 places after the point must be shown).

A1 Round each number to 2 dp.
  a 23.4671   b 4.1627
  c 142.855   d 12.2962

A2 Round each number to 1 dp.
  a 56.48932   b 0.33928
  c 5.9642   d 599.999

B Significant figures for rounding

♦ Rounding to a set number of significant figures is another form of approximating. This is the most natural way to round.

Examples

32.3743 to 2 significant figures (2 sf) is **32**.
32.5743 to 2 sf is **33** (5, or greater, in this position rounds the 2 up).

34.496 to 3 sf is **34.5**.

0.000 2756 to 2 sf is **0.000 28**.

346 534.7945 to 3 sf is **347 000** and to 7 sf is **346 534.8**.

B1 Round each number to 2 sf.
  a 146   b 15.634
  c 3425.7   d 6.2521
  e 0.357 26   f 1097 423

B2 Round each number to 1 sf.
  a 32.87   b 167.2
  c 0.049 14   d 473 524
  e 96.65   f 0.000 086

C Calculating with indices

♦ When two index numbers are multiplied their powers are added.

Examples $6^5 \times 6^3 = 6^8$
$10^8 \times 10^{-3} = 10^5$
$4^{-6} \times 4^{-3} = 4^{-9}$

♦ When two index numbers are divided their powers are subtracted.

Examples $6^7 \div 6^2 = 6^5$
$10^{-5} \div 10^2 = 10^{-7}$

♦ When an index numbers is itself raised to a further power the powers are multiplied.

Example $(10^3)^4 = 10^{12}$
$(8^{-3})^2 = 8^{-6}$

C1 Calculate the following leaving your answers in index notation.
  a $8^7 \times 8^3$ b $6^6 \div 6^4$
  c $10^6 \div 10^8$ d $10^{-4} \times 10^2$
  e $4^{-4} \times 4^{-6}$ f $10^{-6} \div 10^{-8}$
  g $(5^2)^4$ h $(6^4)^{-3}$

D Standard form

♦ Very large numbers or very small ones are often expressed in standard form. The first part is a number between 1 and 10 and the second part is a power of ten.

Examples

Number	In standard form
15 000 000	1.5×10^7
0.000 000 002 54	2.54×10^{-9}
523 800	5.238×10^5
0.04	4×10^{-2}
146.356	1.46356×10^2

D1 Write each number in standard form.
  a 345 000   b 0.004 17
  c 42.97   d 4 million
  e 0.000 0023   f 6413.234

D2 Convert these standard form numbers to normal numbers.
  a 6.74×10^3
  b 1.5×10^{-4}
  c 6.5241×10^2
  d 2×10^{-7}

Limits of accuracy

The tolerance is the amount by which a value may vary.

The sign $\pm$ means **plus or minus**. So D is 74 miles, plus or minus 3 miles.

♦ Any measurement is only approximate because it is only as accurate as the instrument used to make it.

♦ Measurements are often given as having a certain tolerance.
You may measure the distance between Bristol and Oxford as 74 miles but mean it is 74 miles with a tolerance of 3 miles because your mileometer can have an error of 3 miles (i.e. the distance is between 71 and 77 miles).

This can be written as **$D = 74 \pm 3$** or as **$71 \leqslant D \leqslant 77$** where D is the distance in miles.

The numbers 71 and 77 are known as the **bounds** between which the distance can lie.

♦ Because of the problem of accuracy, measured values are rounded to a certain number of decimal places or significant figures.

   Example   A pencil measured as 12.6 cm to the nearest millimetre can have a true length anywhere between 12.55 cm and 12.65 cm.

   The value 12.55 is known as the **lower bound** and 12.65 as the **upper bound**.

Exercise 8.1
Limits of accuracy

1 Steve buys a piece of material of length 3 metres, correct to the nearest centimetre. What is the minimum length of the material?

2 Alison has a piece of wood of length 15.6 cm, correct to the nearest millimetre. What is:
   a the maximum length it could be
   b its minimum length?

3 Australia has a land area of 7 700 000 km^2 to the nearest 100 000 km^2.
   a What is the upper bound for the land area?
   b State the lower bound.
   c Write an inequality in L for the range of values for the land area.

4 The thickness t of a sheet of steel is given as 0.17 mm $\pm$ 0.01 mm.
   Write an inequality in t for the range of values the thickness can have.

Errors or approximations for measured values are often increased when these measurements are used in a calculation.

Example 1   A machine can cut card to the nearest millimetre.
             A card is to be cut 12.2 cm wide by 16.5 cm long.
             What are the maximum and minimum areas the card can have?

In Example 1 the length and width are both given correct to 3 sf but, surprisingly, the answer is only accurate to 2 sf.

A volume would be even more inaccurate as three lengths are multiplied – but it is interesting to consider how an answer can be less accurate than 1 sf!

The width can lie between 12.15 cm and 12.25 cm and the length between 16.45 and 16.55 cm.

So **the maximum area of card = 12.25 × 16.55 = 202.7375 cm²**
and **the minimum area of card = 12.15 × 16.45 = 199.8675 cm²**.

In this case, the maximum and minimum areas only appear similar when they are both given to 2 sf (i.e. area = 200 cm^2 to 2 sf).

Example 2

A cylinder has a volume of $640\,\text{cm}^3$ correct to 2 sf.
Ezra measures its height h to the nearest millimetre as $9.3\,\text{cm}$.
Between what bounds does the radius r of the cylinder lie?

The volume of the cylinder is given by $V = \pi r^2 h$

Rearranging gives $r^2 = \dfrac{V}{\pi h}$

For upper bound

$r^2 = \dfrac{645}{\pi \times 9.25}$

$r^2 = 22.195\,662\,33\ldots$

$r = 4.711\,227\,264\ldots\text{cm}$

For lower bound

$r^2 = \dfrac{635}{\pi \times 9.35}$

$r^2 = 21.617\,837\,19\ldots$

$r = 4.649\,498\,596\ldots$

> Note that for the upper bound, the greatest value of V is taken but the smallest value of h is used – because dividing by a smaller number gives a larger answer.

Here, the difference between the upper and lower bounds for r is about 6 hundredths of a centimetre.

Exercise 8.2
Accuracy in calculations

1 A box of cornflakes weighs 805 grams. The empty box weighs 55 grams.
Both weights are only accurate to the nearest 5 grams.
Calculate:
a the maximum weight of cornflakes in the box
b the minimum weight of cornflakes.

2 Twelve volumes of an encyclopedia are placed on a shelf.
Volumes 1 to 6 are each 3.5 cm wide and volumes 7 to 12 are each 4.3 cm wide, all measurements being to the nearest millimetre.
a What is the lower bound for the width of all twelve volumes?
b Calculate the difference between the upper and lower bounds.

3 A triangular field has the measurements shown.
Each side has been measured to the nearest metre.
a Calculate the range of possible values for the length L of the hedge to the nearest metre.
Express this as an inequality in L.
b Calculate the lower bound for the angle θ.

4 A rectangular badminton court measures 13.40 metres by 6.10 metres where measurements are taken correct to two decimal places.

Calculate the upper and lower bounds for:
a the area of the court
b the perimeter of the court.

5 The area of a trapezium is given by $A = \dfrac{h(a + b)}{2}$

where h is the perpendicular height and a and b are the lengths of the parallel sides.

Calculate the range of values for the area of this trapezium if all the measurements are given correct to 1 dp.

Using significant figures to estimate answers

One way to check if a calculation gives an answer of about the right size is to round each of the numbers to 1 sf.

Example

Here are some answers given by four students when they had to calculate the value of **43 183.5 × 184.23** without using a calculator.

a 795 569.6   **b** 79 556 962   **c** 7 955 696   **d** 79 557

Which answer is likely to be most accurate?

To 1 sf these numbers become   40 000 × 200
which is   40 000 × 2 × 100
                                                  = 80 000 × 100
                                                  = **8 000 000**

Answer **c** (7 955 696) is about the same order of magnitude as 8 000 000 so it is likely to be most accurate.

> A value which is of the correct order of magnitude is about the right size.

Exercise 8.3
Estimating answers

1   Work out estimates of the answers to each of these.
    Show all the stages you use.

    a   31.2 × 241.45   **b**   5677 × 3.764
    c   54 856 × 83.42   **d**   542 × 52
    e   56 234 ÷ 82.5   **f**   62 381.23 ÷ 578.23
    g   452 ÷ 2.34   **h**   28 536 ÷ 0.9623

2   A theatre sells 562 tickets at £28.50 each.

    a   Roughly what is their income from ticket sales?
    b   Why does rounding both numbers to 1 sf give too large an estimate?

3   France has a land area of 549 619 km².
    In 1990 the population was 56 304 000.
    Estimate the population density in people per km².

> Population density means the average (mean) number of people to each square kilometre.

4   When the numbers in 341.2 × 14.25 are rounded to 1 sf and then multiplied the estimate is much smaller than the true answer.
    For the problem 156 ÷ 34.7 the estimate is much larger.
    Explain why.

5   For each of these problems, say if rounding all numbers to 1 sf makes estimates too large, too small, or about the right size.

    a   56.5 × 1763.2   **b**   184 ÷ 19.6
    c   491.432 × 2061.4   **d**   445 × 84 632
    e   2265 ÷ 27.7   **f**   6834 ÷ 14.23
    g   453 782 + 242 565   **h**   7452.3 − 2837.324

6   For the problem 342 561 + 453, why is rounding to 1 sf not helpful?

7   In problems which only use addition and subtraction, when is rounding to 1 sf useful for finding an estimate?

Working with numbers less than 1

Example 1   Estimate the value of **342 × 0.052**.

> Approximating to 1 sf, this becomes 300 × 0.05.
> The answer to this estimate will be smaller than 300.
> One way to work out the value is to look for patterns.
>
> $$300 \times 5 = 1500$$
> $$300 \times 0.5 = 150$$
> $$300 \times 0.05 = 15 \quad \textbf{So the estimate is 15}.$$

Example 2   Estimate for the value of **26 ÷ 0.0056**.

> To 1 sf this is: 30 ÷ 0.006.
>
> $$30 \div 6 = 5$$
> $$30 \div 0.6 = 50$$
> $$30 \div 0.06 = 500$$
> $$30 \div 0.006 = 5000 \quad \textbf{So the estimate is 5000}.$$

Exercise 8.4
Calculating and
estimating answers

1   **a**   Calculate 342 × 52 without a calculator.
    b   Use the example above to help decide what 342 × 0.052 is.

2   Estimate the value of 45 × 0.0023. Show all the stages you use.
    Calculate the exact answer and check it with your estimate.

3   Estimate then calculate the values of these. Which are best and worst estimates?

   a   346.3 ÷ 0.04   **b**   26.23 × 0.67   **c**   876.2 × 0.000 23

   d   2.448 ÷ 0.0018   **e** $\dfrac{2567.245 \times 0.032}{54.23}$ **f** $\dfrac{78.4567 - 7.64}{0.0421}$

4   Estimate the volumes of these cuboids. Show the rounding you do.
    Do not use a calculator.

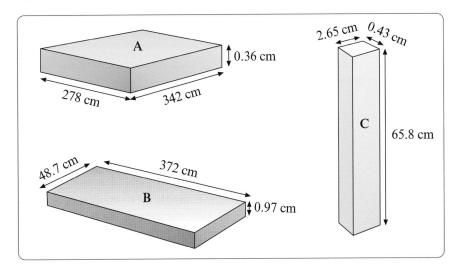

5   A cuboid is 113.6 cm long, 0.42 cm deep and has a volume of 18.42 cm³.
    Estimate its width.

Calculating with numbers in standard form

Calculations with very large numbers can be estimated by approximating each part to a number of significant figures and then using standard form.

Example 1   The land area of Australia is $7\,682\,300\,km^2$ and its population is $16\,260\,400$. Singapore has a land area of $580\,km^2$ and a population of $2\,645\,400$.
How do the population densities compare?

For Australia:
Rounding to 2 sf gives population as $16\,000\,000$ and area as $7\,700\,000\,km^2$.

$$\text{Population density} = \frac{\text{Population}}{\text{Land area}} = \frac{1.6 \times 10^7}{7.7 \times 10^6} = 0.21 \times 10 \text{ (to 2 sf)}$$

$$= 2.1 \text{ people per kilometre}^2.$$

For Singapore:
Rounding to 2 sf gives population as $2\,600\,000$ and area as $580\,km^2$.

$$\text{Population density} = \frac{2.6 \times 10^6}{5.8 \times 10^2} = 0.45 \times 10^4 \text{ (to 2 sf)}$$

$$= 4500 \text{ people per kilometre}^2.$$

Singapore therefore has a population density over 2000 times as great as that of Australia.

Example 2   The mass M of Jupiter is $1.25 \times 10^{27}\,kg$ and it has a radius of $71\,942\,km$. Use this formula to find its density.

$$\text{Density} = \frac{M}{\frac{4}{3}\pi r^3}$$

$$\text{Density} = \frac{1.25 \times 10^{27}}{\frac{4}{3} \times \pi \times (7.2 \times 10^4)^3} = \frac{3 \times 1.25 \times 10^{27}}{4 \times \pi \times (7.2)^3 \times 10^{12}}$$

$$= 0.000\,799\,51 \times 10^{15}.$$

$$= \mathbf{8 \times 10^{11} \; kg \; km^{-3} \; (2 \; sf).}$$

> When powers of ten are divided their indices are subtracted. For example:
>
> $10^7 \div 10^6 = 10^1$ or 10
>
> $10^6 \div 10^2 = 10^4$

> When powers of ten are raised to a further power the indices are multiplied. For example:
>
> $(10^4)^3 = 10^{12}$

Exercise 8.5
Standard form

1   Write each number in standard form.

   a   3647.5   **b**   102 072.62   **c**   576 174.87
   d   0.056   **e**   0.000 756 6   **f**   0.000 006 25

2   Give each value, not in standard form.

   a 3.746×10^5 **b** 5.808×10^3 **c** 3.42×10^7
   d 5.675×10^{-2} **e** 6.388×10^{-5} **f** 9.02×10^{-9}

3   A large rectangular of moorland is chosen as a part of a survey.
The rectangle is 36 040 m wide and 38 220 m long.
   a   Give the area of the rectangle in standard form.
   b   In standard form give the perimeter of the rectangle.

Exercise 8.6
Using standard form

1   When lightning strikes the Earth there is a lead stroke which travels down at about $1.6 \times 10^2\,km$ per second and a brighter return stroke which flashes up at about $1.4 \times 10^5\,km$ per second.
How many times faster is the return stroke than the lead stroke?

2   The Earth is approximately 1.5×10^8 km from the Sun.
Light travels at about 3×10^5 km per second.

How long does it take light from the Sun to reach the Earth?

3   The Earth can be considered to have a circular orbit around the Sun of
radius 149 600 000 km. Earth travels through space at 107 244 km per hour.

a   Approximate the speed and radius to 3 sf and write
each in standard form.

b   Use your figures to find roughly how long in hours the Earth
takes to make one orbit. What do we call this length of time?

4   A ream of paper is a stack of 500 sheets.
Each sheet of paper is 0.000 096 metres thick.

a   Write 500 and 0.000 096 in standard form.

b   Use your answers to part **a** to calculate the height of a ream of paper.

5   The mass of one atom of carbon is about 2×10^{-23} grams and the mass
of an oxygen atom is 2.66×10^{-23} grams.
A molecule of carbon dioxide gas (CO_2) has two atoms of oxygen and
one atom of carbon.

a   Calculate the mass of one carbon dioxide molecule.

b   Calculate the number of molecules in 1 gram of carbon dioxide gas.

6   The Amazon river discharges 1.05×10^{13} litres of water per minute
into the Atlantic.
There are estimated to be about 5.74×10^9 people alive today.

How long would it take the Amazon to fill a bath of 80 litres for every
person on Earth?

> The volume V of a cylinder
> is given by:
> $$V = \pi r^2 h$$
> where h is its height and r
> is its base radius.

7   The largest gasholder in the world is at Simmering near Vienna.
It is shaped like a cylinder, stands 84 metres tall, and holds 3×10^5 cubic
metres of gas.
Calculate the diameter of the gasholder in metres giving your
answer in standard form.

8   4×10^4 tonnes of cosmic dust are estimated to fall on the Earth each year.
The Earth has a diameter of about 1.3×10^7 metres.

a   Taking the Earth as a sphere, estimate its surface area giving your
answer in standard form to 2 sf.

b   How much cosmic dust falls on each square metre of the
Earth's surface each year?

> The surface area A of a
> sphere is given by:
> $$A = 4\pi r^2$$
> where r is its radius.

End points

You should be able to ...
... so try these questions

A   Understand upper and lower bounds

A1   A cylinder has a diameter of 6.7 cm and a height of 9.8 cm, both measurements given to the nearest millimetre.
   a   What is the upper bound of the diameter?
   b   What is the lower bound of the cylinders height?
   c   Calculate the range of values for the volume of the cylinder.
   d   Calculate the upper bound for the curved surface area of the cylinder. (Hint: the curved surface area of a cylinder of radius r and height h is $2\pi rh$).

B   Use significant figures to estimate answers

B1   By rounding numbers to 1 significant figure estimate the value of each of these:
   a 6453×48.734
   b $865.27 \div 0.000\,342$
   c $\dfrac{4.645 \times 0.000\,32}{34.82}$
   d $\dfrac{0.259 \times 0.422}{0.000\,772}$

C   Calculate with numbers in standard form

C1   Give each number in a standard form.
   a   360 000   **b**   100 700   **c**   0.000 007 57

C2   Calculate $346\,572.8 \times 0.000\,02$ giving the answer in standard form.

C3   The Strahov sports stadium in Prague can hold 2.4×10^5 spectators. If the average mass of a spectator is 5.4×10^{-2} tonnes calculate the total mass of the spectators when the stadium is full.

Some points to remember

♦ When a number is written as say 8.6 correct to 1 decimal place its true value can actually lie anywhere between 8.55 and 8.65.
8.55 is known as the **lower bound** and 8.65 as the **upper bound**.

♦ One method to calculate an estimate of the answer to a calculation is to round every number to 1 sf at the start. Beware: it is not sensible to give these answers to more than 1 sf.

Starting points
You need to know about ...

... so try these questions

A Expanding brackets

Expressions are often written including brackets.
By multiplying the terms you can remove, or expand, the brackets.

To remove the brackets from the expression $(y + 4)(y - 5)$ you can:

◆ Use a table

$\times$	y	$+4$
y	y^2	$+4y$
-5	$-5y$	-20

The table gives: $y^2 + 4y - 5y - 20$
Simplified gives: $\mathbf{y^2 - y - 20}$
So removing the brackets we have: $(y + 4)(y - 5) = y^2 - y - 20$

◆ Multiply each term in the second bracket by each term in the first bracket.
This gives:
$$(y + 4)(y - 5) = y(y - 5) + 4(y - 5)$$
$$= y^2 - 5y + 4y - 20$$
$$= \mathbf{y^2 - y - 20}$$

With a systematic approach you can deal with more than two brackets.
Remove the brackets from the expression $(n + 2)(n - 3)(2n + 1)$:
$$(n + 2)(n - 3)(2n + 1) = (n + 2)(2n^2 - 5n - 3)$$
$$= 2n^3 - 5n^2 - 3n + 4n^2 - 10n - 6$$
$$= 2n^3 - n^2 - 13n - 6$$

B Factorising quadratic expressions

To factorise an expression is to find two, or more, other expressions which when multiplied together produce the original expression.

◆ As $(y + 4)(y - 5) = y^2 - y - 20$
we say that $(y + 4)$ and $(y - 5)$ are factors of $y^2 - y - 20$
Factorising $y^2 - y - 20$ gives: $y^2 - y - 20 = (y + 4)(y - 5)$

◆ You can factorise expressions like $3n^2 + 2n - 8$ where the coefficient of n^2 is greater than 1.
Factorising $3n^2 + 2n - 8$ gives: $3n^2 + 2n - 8 = (3n - 4)(n + 2)$

◆ In general terms if you think of a quadratic expression as:
$$ax^2 + bx + c$$
Factorising gives:
(factor of ax + factor of c)(factor of ax + factor of c)

We must ensure that the factors of a and the factors of c are chosen so that they can be combined to give the value of b.

Factorising the expression $5x^2 - 8x - 4$ gives:
$$5x^2 - 8x - 4 = (5x + 2)(x - 2)$$
The factors of 5 are 5×1, the factors of 4 are 4×1, or 2×2
A total of $^-8$ cannot be made combining 5 and 1 with 4 and 1.
Combining 5 and 1 with 2 and 2 we have:
$$5 \times {}^-2 = {}^-10, 1 \times 2 = 2 \text{ and } {}^-10 + 2 = {}^-8$$

A1 Expand the brackets and simplify these expressions.
a $(y + 3)(y + 5)$
b $(k - 4)(k + 3)$
c $(n + 3)(n - 9)$
d $(w - 5)(w - 4)$
e $(v - 8)(v + 8)$

A2 Remove the brackets and simplify these expressions.
a $(2n + 3)(n - 4)$
b $(w - 8)(3w + 2)$
c $(3y - 4)(4y - 3)$
d $(2k - 3)^2$
e $(3v + 1)(v^2 - 3)$

A3 Remove the brackets and simplify these expressions.
a $2y(y - 3)(y + 2)$
b $3x(x + 1)^2$
c $(x + 1)(x - 3)(x + 5)$
d $(2n - 1)(2n - 3)(n + 1)$
e $(x + 2)^3$
f $(k - 3)(4 - 2k)(k + 2)$

B1 Factorise these expressions.
a $y^2 + 9y + 14$
b $k^2 - 3k - 40$
c $x^2 + 4x - 12$
d $w^2 + 5w - 36$
e $x^2 - 11x + 24$
f $y^2 - 9y + 8$
g $p^2 + 7p - 60$
h $b^2 + b - 72$
i $x^2 - 16x + 48$
j $n^2 - 25$
k $y^2 - 100$
l $a^2 - b^2$
m $4y^2 - 36$
n $16x^2 - 36y^2$
o $100a^2 - b^4$

C Solving linear equations

Linear equations can be solved by manipulating the terms of the equation so that the unknown is equated to a value.

Manipulation can be thought of as keeping the equation balanced. This can be seen when the equation $5x - 8 = 3x + 5$ is solved.

$$5x - 8 = 3x + 5$$
$$[+8] \qquad 5x = 3x + 13$$
$$[-3x] \qquad 2x = 13$$
$$[\div 2] \qquad \mathbf{x = 6.5}$$

Manipulation can also involve dealing with brackets or fractions. Dealing with brackets.

Solve the equation $\qquad 3(4x + 1) = 5(x - 3)$
[Remove the brackets] $\qquad 12x + 3 = 5x - 15$
$[-3] \qquad 12x = 5x - 18$
$[-5x] \qquad 7x = {}^-18$
$[\div 7] \qquad \mathbf{x = {}^-2.57}$ (2 dp) or $x = \frac{-18}{7}$

Dealing with fractions.

Solve the equation $\qquad \frac{3}{4}(x - 2) = \frac{1}{2}(3x - 4)$
[Multiply each side by 4] $\qquad 3(x - 2) = 2(3x - 4)$
[Remove the brackets] $\qquad 3x - 6 = 6x - 8$
$[+6] \qquad 3x = 6x - 2$
$[-6x] \qquad {}^-3x = {}^-2$
$[\div {}^-3] \qquad \mathbf{x = 0.67}$ (2 dp) or $x = \frac{2}{3}$

D Forming linear equations from problems

A problem given in words can often be solved by creating and solving a linear equation. This will be possible if one unknown is chosen and any other unknowns expressed in terms of the one unknown.

This can be seen when this problem is solved.

Lisa is 4 years younger than her sister Emma and 19 years older than her daughter Nicole. Together their ages total 96. How old is each of them?

Let Lisa be n years old.
Emma is 4 years older than Lisa i.e. $\qquad n + 4$
Nicole is 19 years younger than Lisa i.e. $\qquad n - 19$

Their ages total 96, so we have:

$$n + n + 4 + n - 19 = 96$$
$$3n - 15 = 96$$
$$[+15] \qquad 3n = 111$$
$$[\div 3] \qquad n = 37$$

This gives:

Lisa (n) is   **37 years old**
Emma ($n + 4$) is   **41 years old**
Nicole ($n - 19$) is   **18 years old**

You can check your answer to this sort of problem, as follows.

The total of the three ages is:

$$37 + 41 + 18 = 96$$

and 96 is the total for the ages given in the problem.

C1 Solve these linear equations.
  a $9y + 5 = 5y - 13$
  b $y - 8 = 11y - 42$
  c $3(4x - 5) = 9$
  d $28 = 7(3x - 5)$
  e $19 - 4x = 3(2x - 7)$

C2 Solve these linear equations.
  a $5(4x + 2) = 3(2x - 6)$
  b $8(2 - 3n) = 4(2n + 1)$
  c $7(w + 3) = 12(w - 7)$
  d $2(3k + 3) = 9(5k - 8)$
  e $6(9v - 2) = 5(6v + 8)$

C3 Solve these linear equations.
  a $\frac{2}{3}(3y + 1) = 18$
  b $\frac{3}{5}(3u - 4) = 12$
  c $\frac{5}{8}(2k + 4) = 15$
  d $\frac{1}{4}(8h - 12) = 21$
  e $\frac{7}{10}(4a - 5) = 2.1$

C4 Solve these linear equations.
  a $\frac{3}{5}(2w - 1) = \frac{1}{3}(3w - 6)$
  b $\frac{2}{3}(k + 1) = \frac{3}{4}(2k - 3)$
  c $\frac{1}{2}(8n - 4) = \frac{1}{3}(4n - 5)$

D1 A rectangle is 6 centimetres longer than it is wide.
  The rectangle has a perimeter of 48 cm.

  Write and solve an equation to find the length and width of the rectangle.

D2 In a game a player was asked to think of a number and add seven, then to multiply the answer by three.
  The player answered 81.

  Write and solve an equation to find the number the player first thought of.

D3 Three buses took fans to a match. Bus A carried 9 more fans than bus B. Bus C carried 3 fewer fans than bus A.

  The three buses carried a total of 147 fans.

  Write and solve an equation to find the number of fans on each bus.

Thinking ahead to ...
solving simultaneous
linear equations

A In a cafe, two teas and 4 coffees cost £4.60.
From this information:

    a Calculate the cost of one tea and two coffees. Explain your method.
    b Calculate the cost of three teas and six coffees. Explain your method.
    c Explain why the cost of six teas and eight coffees cannot easily be
    calculated.

B In a shop:
1 cola and 3 bags of crisps cost £1.52
2 colas and 4 bags of crisps cost £2.48.
Find the cost of:

    a 3 colas and 7 bags of crisps   **b** 1 cola and 1 bag of crisps
    c 1 bag of crisps   **d** 1 cola.

Solving simultaneous linear equations

When a linear relationship between two variables can be expressed by two or
more different equations, you can find the value of each variable by solving the
equations simultaneously.

One way to solve these equations is algebraically, the most common being a
combination of elimination and substitution.

Example

Find the values of a and b that satisfy the equations:

$$2a + b = 19$$
$$3a + 4b = 26$$

♦ Label the equations (1) and (2):

$$2a + b = 19 \ ... \ (1)$$
$$3a + 4b = 26 \ ... \ (2)$$

♦ Eliminate one variable by making the
coefficients of a or b the same in both
equations.
In this case multiply equation (1) by 4
(to eliminate b)

$$8a + 4b = 76 \ ... \ (3)$$
$$3a + 4b = 26 \ ... \ (2)$$

> The coefficients of b are
> now 4 in each of the
> equations (3) and (2).

♦ Subtract (2) from (3) to eliminate b

$$5a = 50$$

♦ Find the value of a:

$$\boldsymbol{a = 10}$$

♦ Substitute the value of a in one
equation

$$2a + b = 19$$
$$2(10) + b = 19$$
$$20 + b = 19$$
$$\boldsymbol{b = \ ^-1}$$

♦ Check your solution in one other equation
When $a = 10$ and $b = {}^-1$

$$3a + 4b = 26 \ ... \ (2)$$

$$\text{LHS gives } 3(10) + 4(^-1) = 26 \ = \text{RHS}$$

> LHS means left-hand side.
> RHS means right-hand
> side.

Exercise 9.1
Solving simultaneous
equations

1 Solve each pair of equations simultaneously to find values for x and y.

    a $x + 4y = 42$ **b** $11x + 3y = 91$ **c** $5x + 7y = 44$
       $2x + 5y = 57$ $3x + y = 25$ $x + 3y = 12$

    d $5x + 3y = 7$ **e** $12x + 5y = \ ^-9$ **f** $8x + y = 20$
       $4x + y = 7$ $5x + y = \ ^-7$ $11x + 4y = 17$

In these equations the only way to make the coefficients of one variable the same, is to multiply each equation by a different value.

This means that you create two new equations which you can label (3) and (4).

2 To find a value of m and n that satisfies these equations:

$$2m + 3n = 28 \dots (1)$$
$$3m + 4n = 37 \dots (2)$$

  a Multiply equation (1) by 3.
  b Multiply equation (2) by 2.
  c Subtract and find a value for n that satisfies both equations.
  d Substitute for n in one equation to find a value for m.
  e Check your solutions are correct.

3 Solve each pair of equations.

  a $2v + 3w = 40$ **b** $3v + 2w = 3$ **c** $4v + 2w = 8$
     $5v + 2w = 34$ $6v + 10w = 24$ $3v + 7w = {}^-5$

  d $3v + 5w = 19$ **e** $2v + 3w = 3$ **f** $8v + 4w = 16$
     $2v + 4w = 14$ $3v + 5w = 4$ $3v + 3w = 3$

  g $6v + 3w = 9$ **h** $11v + 2w = 17$ **i** $7v + 4w = 1$
     $4v + 5w = 3$ $2v + 3w = 11$ $2v + 3w = 4$

Sometimes to eliminate one variable when the coefficients are the same you have to add two equations.

Example

Find the values of x and y that satisfy the equations:

$$6x - 2y = 18 \dots (1)$$
$$5x + 3y = 1 \quad \dots (2)$$

♦ Make the coefficients of y the same by multiplying: (1) × 3 and (2) × 2

$$18x - 6y = 54 \dots (3)$$
$$10x + 6y = 2 \quad \dots (4)$$

♦ Eliminate y by adding: (3) + (4)

$$28x = 56$$

♦ Find x

$$x = 2$$

♦ Substitute $x = 2$ in (1)

$$6(2) - 2y = 18$$
$$12 - 2y = 18$$
$$-2y = 6$$
$$y = {}^-3$$

♦ Check $x = 2$ and $y = {}^-3$ in equation (2)

$$5x + 3y = 1 \quad \dots (2)$$
$$\text{LHS} = 5(2) + 3({}^-3) = 1 = \text{RHS}$$

Exercise 9.2
Solving simultaneous equations

1 Solve each pair of equations.

  a $a - b = 8$ **b** $5b + 2a = 29$ **c** $3a - b = 15$
     $4a + b = 42$ $b - 2a = 1$ $4a + 2b = 10$

  d $b + 3a = 2$ **e** $5a + 2b = 17$ **f** $7a + 5b = 22$
     $3b - a = 26$ $2a - 3b = 3$ $3a - 2b = 26$

  g $3a + 2b = 4$ **h** $5a - 2b = 24$ **i** $7a + 3b = 15$
     $2a - 3b = 7$ $2a - 7b = 22$ $5a - 4b = 23$

  j $4a + 5b = 13$ **k** $3a - 4b = 18$ **l** $5b + 3a = 17$
     $3a + 2b = 8$ $2a - 5b = 19$ $7b - 4a = 32$

2 Find values for k and n that satisfy $5k - n = 15$ and $3k - n = 5$.

> In some cases you will need to rearrange one or more of the equations before you can begin to solve them simultaneously.

3 Find values for m and n that satisfy the equation $5m - 2n = 28$, and also the equation $7m - 37 = 5n$.

4 Solve each pair of equations.

a $5x = 16 + 2y$
  $2x = 3y + 2$

b $4y = x + 17$
  $3y - 4x = 3$

c $5x = 7 + 3y$
  $2x = 4y$

d $5y = 7 - 3x$
  $7x = 3 - 5y$

e $3y = 17 - 4x$
  $5x = 7y + 32$

f $3x = 13 - 2y$
  $59 + 6y = 5x$

g $7y = 3x - 5$
  $5y - 2 = 4x$

h $y + 31 = 9x$
  $5x - 27 = 3y$

i $12x = 13 - 11y$
  $5x + 8y = 2$

j $x = y + 8$
  $29 + 4y = 3x$

k $4y = 5 - 3x$
  $12 = 5y - 2x$

l $7y = 7 - 7x$
  $11 - 2x = 5y$

Solving problems with simultaneous equations

From some problems you can create two equations with the variables. Solving the equations simultaneously will produce values that satisfy the problem.

Example

Two groups of friends met in a cafe. One group bought three teas and four coffees, this cost them a total of £5.35. The other group paid a total of £5.80 for five teas and three coffees.
Find the price charged in the cafe for coffee and tea.

> For ease of working you may prefer to work with integer values.
>
> Here the 535 is the total for the first group in pence.

♦ Decide on the variables: let the price of coffee be c (pence)
and the price of tea be t (pence)

♦ Create two different equations.

for the first group $3t + 4c = 535$
the second group $5t + 3c = 580$

♦ Solve the equations:

$3t + 4c = 535$ ... (1)
$5t + 3c = 580$ ... (4)

Multiply (1) by 3 and (2) by 4 to eliminate c:

$9t + 12c = 1605$ ... (3)
$20t + 12c = 2320$ ... (4)

Subtract: (4) – (3) $11t = 715$

Find t $t = 65$

Substitute $t = 65$ in (1)

$3t + 4c = 535$ ... (1)
$3(65) + 4c = 535$
$195 + 4c = 535$

Find c $4c = 340$
$c = 85$

♦ Check in equation (2) $5t + 3c = 580$
LHS = $5(65) + 3(85) = 325 + 255 = 580$ = RHS

The charge for coffee was 85 pence, and for tea was 65 pence.

Exercise 9.3
Solving problems

1 Two groups visited Waterworld. The first group of four adults and three children paid a total of £38 for their tickets. The second group of five adults and two children £40.50 for their tickets.
What are the charges for adult and child tickets at Waterworld?

When you check your answers it is always best to use the original word problem.

This is because you may have created an incorrect equation. This will not be shown up if you substitute your solutions in anything other than the original word problem.

2 Crispers is a snack food sold in bags of two sizes: regular and jumbo.
Three regular bags and four jumbo bags weigh a total of 264 g.
Five of each size weigh a total of 350 g.

Find the weight of each size of Crispers.

3 A bag contains 89 marbles. Some are large; some are small.
Each small marble weighs 2 g, and each large marble weighs 5 g.
The total weight of the marbles in the bag is 256 g.

a Write two different equations that describe this situation.
b Solve your equations to find the number of each marble type in the bag.

4 Mina pays her gas bill with a mixture of £5 and £10 notes.
Her gas bill is for £155, and she pays with a total of 22 notes.

How many of each type of note does she use to pay the bill?

5 A parking meter takes 10 p and 20 p coins. The meter was emptied and found to contain 380 coins with a total of £63.70.

How many of each type of coin were in the meter?

6 Two numbers are such that when you add three times one number to five times the other number a total of 46 is produced. The difference between the two numbers is 2.

What are the two numbers?

7 The line $y = mx + c$ passes through the points (3,10) and (5, 18).
Find the values of m and c.

8 A promoter sold 28 500 tickets for a pop concert. A standing ticket cost £8, and a ticket for a seat cost £12.50. All the tickets were sold and ticket sales produced a total of £283 350.

How many of each type of ticket were sold?

9 The line $mx + y = c$ passes through the points (2, 2) and (⁻1, 11).

a Find values of m and c.
b Give the equation of the line and one other point that lies on the line.

10 The curve $y = ax^2 + bx + c$ passes through the points (3, 13), (1, ⁻1) and (0, ⁻5).

a Find values for a, b, and c
b Give the equation of the curve.

11 The curve y= $ax^2 + bx + c$ passes through the points (1, 0), (0, 1) and (⁻1, 6).

a Find values for a, b, and c.
b Give the equation of the curve.

12 The curve $y - bx = ax^2 + c$ passes through the points (2, 6), (⁻1, 0),(⁻2, 10).

a Find values for a, b, and c.
b Give the equation of the curve.

13 Print Express print T-shirts. They have two printing machines: machine A prints 64 T-shirts an hour, and machine B prints 44 T-shirts an hour.
Print Express have an order for 1430 T-shirts and only a total of 25 hours to complete the printing.

For how many hours should they print T-shirts on each machine?

14 Two numbers are such that a half the smaller number added to two thirds of the larger number gives a total of sixteen.
What are the two numbers if they have a difference of ten?

Solving quadratic equations by inspection (factors)

Quadratic equations must have a term like x^2. Often they will have a term like $3x$ and a term which is a numerical value.
In general, quadratic equations have two different solutions or roots.

Example

◆ Solve the equation $\qquad\qquad\qquad\qquad x^2 + 5x - 14 = 0$

◆ Factorise $\qquad\qquad\qquad\qquad\qquad (x + 7)(x - 2) = 0$

Here we have a situation where two brackets are multiplied to give an answer of zero. This is only possible if either, or both, of the brackets is equal to zero.

In this case if $\quad(x + 7)(x - 2) = 0$
then: $\qquad\qquad$ either $(x + 7) = 0$ or $(x - 2) = 0$
which means $\qquad\qquad\qquad x = {}^-7$ or $x = 2$

◆ Solving the equation $\qquad\qquad\qquad x^2 + 5x - 14 = 0$

gives $\qquad\qquad\qquad\qquad\quad \mathbf{\textit{x} = {}^-7 \textbf{ or } \textit{x} = 2}$

Exercise 9.4
Solving quadratic equations by inspection

1 Solve these quadratic equations.

a $y^2 + 5y + 4 = 0$	**b** $y^2 + 9y + 18 = 0$	**c** $y^2 + 5y - 24 = 0$
d $x^2 + 6x - 7 = 0$	**e** $x^2 + 5x - 36 = 0$	**f** $x^2 + 2x - 63 = 0$
g $w^2 - 7w - 44 = 0$	**h** $w^2 - 8w - 105 = 0$	**i** $w^2 - 9w - 112 = 0$
j $a^2 - 8a + 15 = 0$	**k** $a^2 - 12a + 35 = 0$	**l** $a^2 - 11a + 30 = 0$
m $b^2 - 7b + 10 = 0$	**n** $b^2 + 31b + 84 = 0$	**o** $b^2 - 13b - 30 = 0$
p $c^2 + 7c - 60 = 0$	**q** $c^2 - 14c + 45 = 0$	**r** $c^2 + 12c - 45 = 0$
s $h^2 + h - 210 = 0$	**t** $h^2 - 2h - 399 = 0$	**u** $h^2 - 17h + 42 = 0$
v $n^2 + 3n - 180 = 0$	**w** $n^2 - 15n + 56 = 0$	**x** $n^2 - 9n - 136 = 0$

The basis of solving quadratics in this way is being able to factorise the quadratic equation that is given.
Remember that the equation might not be in the form: $ax^2 + bx + c = 0$

Example

Solve the equation $\qquad\qquad\qquad\qquad x^2 + 9x = 0$

◆ Factorise $\qquad\qquad\qquad\qquad\qquad x(x + 9) = 0$
which means $\qquad\qquad \mathbf{\textit{x} = 0 \textbf{ or } \textit{x} = {}^-9}$

Example

◆ Solve the equation $\qquad\qquad\qquad\qquad x^2 - 49 = 0$

◆ Factorise $\qquad\qquad x^2 - 49$ is known as a difference of two squares the squares being x^2 and 49 (i.e. 7^2)

$\qquad\qquad\qquad\qquad\qquad\qquad\qquad x^2 - 49 = 0$
gives $\qquad\qquad\qquad\qquad (x + 7)(x - 7) = 0$
which means $\qquad\qquad \mathbf{\textit{x} = {}^-7 \textbf{ or } \textit{x} = 7}$

Factorising a difference of two squares always produces a result in the same format.

Factorising $a^2 - b^2$ gives $(a + b)(a - b)$

Exercise 9.5
Solving quadratic equations

1 Solve these quadratic equations.

a $y^2 + 8y = 0$	**b** $y^2 - 5y = 0$	**c** $y^2 - 18y = 0$
d $h^2 - 100 = 0$	**e** $h^2 - 25 = 0$	**f** $h^2 - 81 = 0$

2 Solve these quadratic equations.

a $x^2 - 12x = 0$ **b** $x^2 + 79x = 0$ **c** $3x^2 + x = 0$
d $4x^2 - x = 0$ **e** $x^2 - 169 = 0$ **f** $x^2 - x = 0$
g $5x^2 - 2x = 0$ **h** $4x^2 + 5x = 0$ **i** $7x^2 + 2x = 0$

Quadratic equations, where the coefficient of (say) x^2 is greater than 1, can also be solved by factorising.

Example

Solve the equation $6x^2 - 17x + 12 = 0$

♦ Factorise $(3x - 4)(2x - 3) = 0$

which means $x = \frac{4}{3}$ or $x = \frac{3}{2}$

Exercise 9.6
Solving quadratic
equations

1 Solve these quadratic equations.

a $12x^2 - 5x - 2 = 0$ **b** $6x^2 - 13x - 5 = 0$ **c** $4x^2 - 4x - 3 = 0$
d $10y^2 - 3y - 1 = 0$ **e** $9y^2 + 9y - 4 = 0$ **f** $6y^2 - 7y + 2 = 0$
g $9h^2 + 3h - 2 = 0$ **h** $14a^2 - 12a - 2 = 0$ **i** $12a^2 + 2a - 4 = 0$
j $5c^2 - 11c + 2 = 0$ **k** $6c^2 + 16c - 6 = 0$ **l** $3c^2 - 16c + 16 = 0$
m $4w^2 - 4w - 24 = 0$ **n** $6w^2 - 16w + 8 = 0$ **o** $12w^2 - 22w - 4 = 0$

2 Solve these equations.

a $12x^2 - 6x = 0$ **b** $4x^2 - 12x = 0$ **c** $56x^2 + 14x = 0$
d $5y^2 = 8y$ **e** $16y^2 = 8y$ **f** $25y^2 - 1 = 0$
g $k^2 - \frac{1}{16} = 0$ **h** $3k^2 - 27k = 0$ **i** $5k = k^2$
j $w^2 = w$ **k** $w^2 - \frac{1}{9} = 0$ **l** $3w^2 - 4w = 0$
m $c^2 = 31c$ **n** $42c^2 - 18c = 0$ **o** $16c^2 - 9 = 0$

Solving quadratic equations using the formula

If a quadratic equation cannot be solved by factorising, a formula can be used to provide the solutions.

To solve the equation $ax^2 + bx + c = 0$ for x this formula is used:

$$x = \frac{-b \pm \sqrt{(b^2 - 4ac)}}{2a}$$

In the formula:
a is the coefficient of the term in x^2

b is the coefficient of the term in x

c is the numerical or (constant) value.

Example

Solve the equation $3x^2 + 4x - 1 = 0$

♦ Using the formula:
matching coefficients we have $a = 3, b = 4, c = {}^-1$

The formula gives $x = \frac{{}^-4 \pm \sqrt{16 - (4 \times 3 \times {}^-1)}}{(2 \times 3)}$

$x = \frac{{}^-4 \pm \sqrt{16 - ({}^-12)}}{6} = \frac{{}^-4 \pm \sqrt{28}}{6}$

$x = \frac{{}^-4 \pm 5.292}{6}$

When you use the formula you need to check that:
$b^2 - 4ac$
gives a positive result.

If $b^2 - 4ac$ gives a negative answer then $\sqrt{(\text{negative})}$ is not real. We say the equation has no real roots, so no solution is found.

So $x = \frac{{}^-4 + 5.292}{6} = \mathbf{0.22}$ **(2 dp)** or $x = \frac{{}^-4 - 5.292}{6} = {}^-\mathbf{1.55}$ **(2 dp)**

Exercise 9.7
Solving quadratic equations using the formula

1 Use the formula to solve these quadratic equations.
Give your answers correct to two decimal places (2 dp).

a $2x^2 + 3x - 4 = 0$	**b** $4x^2 + 3x - 5 = 0$	**c** $x^2 + 3x - 5 = 0$
d $y^2 + 5y + 3 = 0$	**e** $2y^2 + 7y + 1 = 0$	**f** $5y^2 + 8y + 1 = 0$
g $3p^2 - 5p + 1 = 0$	**h** $4p^2 - 8p + 2 = 0$	**i** $3p^2 - 3p - 3 = 0$
j $2w^2 + w - 5 = 0$	**k** $3w^2 - w - 8 = 0$	**l** $5w^2 - 5w + 1 = 0$

2 Solve these equations. Give your answers in surd form.

a $2a^2 + 2a - 3 = 0$	**b** $6a^2 + a - 6 = 0$	**c** $4a^2 - a - 4 = 0$
d $8c^2 + 8c - 1 = 0$	**e** $5c^2 + 8c + 1 = 0$	**f** $7c^2 + 9c + 1 = 0$
g $4 - 3n - 2n^2 = 0$	**h** $3 + 5n - n^2 = 0$	**i** $12 + 6n - 2n^2 = 0$

3 Solve these equations giving your answers correct to 2 dp.

a $x(2x + 3) = 7$ **b** $1 = x(7 - 3x)$ **c** $x(4x + 5) = 4$

Solving quadratic equations by completing the square

Another way to solve a quadratic equation that cannot be factorised is by **completing the square**. This might be quicker than using the formula.

Example

Solve the equation $x^2 + 6x - 1 = 0$

Check that $b^2 \geq 4ac$ for the equation.
If $b^2 < 4ac$ then:
$(b^2 - 4ac)$ is negative and the equation will have no solution.

◆ The equation cannot be factorised, but $b^2 \geq 4ac$ so it can be solved.

◆ If we look for a complete square which includes $x^2 + 6x$ we must start with $(x + 3)^2$.

The diagram shows that $(x + 3)^2$ gives:
$x^2 + 6x + 9$

We have:
$$x^2 + 6x + 9 = (x + 3)^2$$
$$x^2 + 6x = (x + 3)^2 - 9$$

When we replace $x^2 + 6x$ the original equation becomes:
$$(x + 3)^2 - 9 - 1 = 0$$
$$(x + 3)^2 - 10 = 0$$
$$(x + 3)^2 = 10$$

[√ each side]
$$x + 3 = \pm\sqrt{10}$$
$$x = \pm\sqrt{10} - 3$$
$$x = \pm 3.162 - 3$$
$$x = -\mathbf{6.16} \text{ (2dp) or } x = \mathbf{0.16} \text{ (2dp)}$$

Exercise 9.8
Solving quadratic equations by completing the square

1 **a** Show that $x^2 + 10x - 5$ can be solved using the square of $(x + 5)$.
   b Solve $x^2 + 10x - 5 = 0$ by completing the square.

2 Solve $x^2 + 8x - 3 = 0$ by completing the square.

3 Explain why $x^2 + 5x + 9 = 0$ cannot be solved.

4 By completing the square, where possible, solve these equations.

a $x^2 + 12x - 2 = 0$	**b** $x^2 + 6x - 8 = 0$	**c** $x^2 + 14x - 1 = 0$
d $x^2 + 4x + 5 = 0$	**e** $x^2 + 6x + 27 = 0$	**f** $x^2 + 8x + 6 = 0$

Accuracy
Give your answers correct to 2 dp, unless surd form is asked for.

5 Complete the square to solve these. Give your answer in surd form.

a $x^2 + 5x - 4 = 0$ **b** $x^2 + 7x - 2 = 0$ **c** $x^2 + 3x + 1 = 0$

Rearranging quadratic equations before solving them

A quadratic equation might be written in such a way that it does not look like your expectation of a quadratic equation.

Example

Solve the equation $(2x + 1)^2 = 3x(x - 1) + 9$

♦ Remove the brackets
$$(2x + 1)(2x + 1) = 3x(x - 1) + 9$$
$$4x^2 + 4x + 1 = 3x^2 - 3x + 9$$
$$x^2 + 7x - 8 = 0$$

♦ The quadratic equation $x^2 + 7x - 8 = 0$
can then solved by an appropriate method.

Example

Solve the equation $x + 6 = \dfrac{27}{x}$

♦ Remove the fraction by multiplying each term by x
$$x^2 + 6x = 27$$

♦ The quadratic equation $x^2 + 6x - 27 = 0$
can then be solved by an appropriate method.

Example

Solve the equation $\dfrac{x + 3}{4} = \dfrac{3}{x - 1}$

♦ Remove the fractions
$$(x + 3)(x - 1) = 12$$
♦ Remove the brackets
$$x^2 + 2x - 3 = 12$$
♦ The quadratic equation $x^2 + 2x - 15 = 0$
can then be solved by an appropriate method.

Example

Solve the equation $2x + 3 = \sqrt{(x^2 - 1)}$

♦ Remove the $\sqrt{}$ by squaring
$$(2x + 3)^2 = x^2 - 1$$
♦ Remove the bracket
$$(2x + 3)(2x + 3) = x^2 - 1$$
$$4x^2 + 12x + 9 = x^2 - 1$$
$$3x^2 + 12x + 10 = 0$$

♦ The quadratic equation $3x^2 + 12x + 10 = 0$
can then be solved by an appropriate method.

These are just some forms of manipulation you might use when faced with an equation you need to rearrange.

Exercise 9.9
Rearranging and solving quadratic equations

1 Rearrange and solve these equations. Give solutions correct to 2 dp.

a $x - 5 = \dfrac{36}{x}$ b $x(x - 7) = 60$ c $(x - 1)^2 = 64$

d $y = \dfrac{27}{(y + 6)}$ e $2y + 5 = \sqrt{(y^2 - 2)}$ f $y + 5 = \dfrac{6}{y}$

g $\dfrac{w - 2}{2} = \dfrac{7}{w - 3}$ h $\dfrac{w + 4}{2} = \dfrac{1}{2w - 1}$ i $36 = \dfrac{1}{w^2}$

j $\dfrac{4}{v^2} = 100$ k $3v^2 = 5v$ l $3v + 4 = \dfrac{5}{v} - 3$

m $\dfrac{3}{a} - 5 = 4a + 1$ n $\dfrac{2}{a - 1} + \dfrac{3}{a + 2} = 4$ o $100a = \dfrac{1}{a}$

Creating and solving quadratic equations from problems

Some problems enable you to create a quadratic equation which you can solve to find an answer. While a quadratic equation will have two solutions it is possible that only one of them will be appropriate as an answer.

Example

A rectangle is 5 metres longer than it is wide. The rectangle has an area of $456\,m^2$. Calculate the length of a diagonal of the rectangle.

♦ Show the situation on a diagram.

Let the width of the rectangle be w.
The length of the rectangle is $w + 5$
AB is a diagonal of the rectangle.

♦ Create and solve equation in w.

The area of the rectangle is $456\,m^2$
i.e.
$$w(w + 5) = 456$$
$$w^2 + 5w = 456$$
$$w^2 + 5w - 456 = 0$$
$$(w - 19)(w + 24) = 0$$
$$w = 19 \text{ or } w = {}^-24$$

The width of the rectangle is 19 m (the width cannot be ⁻24 m).
The length of the rectangle is 24 m (i.e. 19 + 5).

♦ To find the length of the diagonal AB.
By Pythagoras' rule:
$$AB^2 = 19^2 + 24^2$$
$$AB^2 = 937$$
$$AB = \sqrt{937} = 30.6 \text{ (1 dp)}$$

The length of a diagonal of the rectangle is 30.6 m (1 dp).

Exercise 9.10
Solving problems using quadratic equations

1   The width of a rectangle is 12 cm less than its length. The rectangle has an area of $448\,cm^2$.

a   Write and solve an equation to find the dimensions of the rectangle.
b   Calculate the length, to 2 dp, of a diagonal of the rectangle.

2   Two positive numbers multiplied together give 432.
One number is greater than the other number by six.
Find the two numbers.

3   A rectangle has a perimeter of 126 cm. The length of a diagonal of the rectangle is 45 cm.

Write and solve an equation to find:

a   the length of the rectangle
b   the area of the rectangle.

4   In triangle ABC the base is 4 cm longer than its height. ABC has an area of $117\,cm^2$.
Calculate the size of $A\hat{B}C$ to 2 dp.

5 Use the formula $p = vt + 0.5gt^2$ to find values for t to 2 dp when $p = 20$, $v = 6$ and $g = 1$.

6 The base of a right-angled triangle is 9 cm longer than the height of the triangle. The area of the triangle is 486 cm².

   a Calculate the length of the base and the height of the triangle.

   b Calculate the perimeter of the triangle.

7 The diagram shows a trapezium ABCD which has a height w. The lengths of AB and CD are given in terms of w. The area of ABCD is 93.5 cm².

   a Write and solve an equation to find a value for w.

   b The trapezium ABCD has the same area as triangle RST. Calculate the length of RT to 2 dp.

   c Calculate the size of RTS to 2 dp.

8 Two positive numbers differ by 4, and when multiplied give 2752.25 Write and solve an equation to find the two numbers.

9 In triangle TVM all the sides are given in terms of m.

   a Show that $m^2 = 12m$

   b Calculate the area of TVM.

   c Show that, to the nearest degree, $\angle$MTV = 37°.

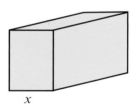

10 A concrete beam used to construct a bridge is in the shape of a cuboid. The beam is 2.8 metres longer than it is wide, and is 2.5 metres high. The volume of the beam is given as 52.7 m³.

   a Show that the beam is more than 6 metres long.

   b If the width of the beam is y metres show that the total surface area of the beam (S) is given by the equation:

$$S = 2y^2 + 15.6y + 14$$

11 This cuboid has a width of x cm. The height of the cuboid is 4 cm longer than its width. The depth of the cuboid is 6 cm longer than the width,

   a Write an expression in terms of x for the surface area of the cuboid.

   b Write your expression as a quadratic.

The surface area of the cuboid is 398 cm².

   c Write and show an equation to find a value for x.

   d Calculate the volume of the cuboid.

End points

You should be able to ...   ... so try these questions

A Solve simultaneous linear equations

A1 Solve these equations for x and y.
   a $5x - 3y = 21$
      $2x + 5y = {}^-4$
   b $2x - 3y = {}^-3$
      $7x - 2y = {}^-19$

B Solve problems with simultaneous equations

B1 Two groups of people bought tickets on the Cliff Railway. The first group of five adults and two children paid a total of £29.30. The second group of two adults and three children paid a total of £17.55.
Find the charges for adult and child tickets for the Cliff Railway.

C Solve quadratic equations by inspection

C1 Solve these quadratic equations.
   a $x^2 + 5x - 24 = 0$
   b $x^2 - 8x - 65 = 0$
   c $x^2 - 15x + 36 = 0$
   d $2x^2 - 2x - 12 = 0$

D Solve quadratic equations using the formula

D1 Solve these quadratic equations to 2 dp using the formula.
   a $x^2 + 6x - 2 = 0$ **b** $x^2 - 9x + 3 = 0$
   c $2x^2 + 9x + 3 = 0$ **d** $3x^2 - 5x + 6 = 0$

D2 Solve these equations leaving your answer in surd form.
   a $x^2 + 8x - 4 = 0$ **b** $x^2 - 6x - 8 = 0$

E Solve quadratic equations by completing the square

E1 By completing the square solve the equation $x^2 + 5x - 3 = 0$.

E2 Complete the square to solve the equation $x^2 + 8x - 5 = 0$.
Give your answer in surd form.

F Create and solve quadratic equations for problems

F1 A rectangle has an area of 570 cm². The rectangle is 23 cm longer than it is wide.
Write and solve an equation to find the dimensions of the rectangle.

Some points to remember

- When you are solving simultaneous equations you may have to rearrange one or both of them at the start.

- Check when starting to solve a quadratic equation that $b^2 \geqslant 4ac$.

- When creating equations to solve word problems do not introduce more unknowns than you need. Always try to express one unknown in terms of another unknown.

- You can always check a solution to an equation by substitution.

Starting points

You need to know about ...

... so try these questions

A The equation of a straight line

◆ You can use the coordinates of points on a line to find the equation of the line.

A1

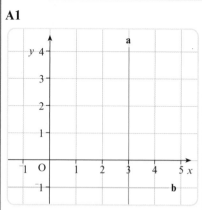

Write down the equation of the lines **a** and **b**.

B Reflections

◆ To describe a reflection you must give the mirror line. On a grid you can give the equation of the mirror line.

Example

B is the image of A after a reflection in $y = {}^-x$.

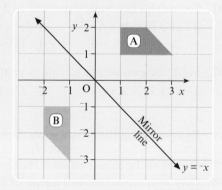

B1 a Copy this diagram.

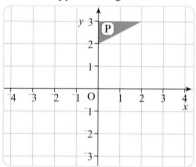

b Draw the image of P after a reflection in:
  i $y = x$ **ii** $x = {}^-1$

C Rotations

◆ To describe a rotation you must give:
  ❖ the angle and direction of rotation
  ❖ the centre of rotation.

◆ On a grid you can give the coordinates of the centre.

Example

  ❖ C is the image of A after a rotation of $^+90°$ (90° anticlockwise) about (4, 1).
  ❖ D is the image of A after a rotation of $^-90°$ (90° clockwise) about ($^-2$, 2).

C1

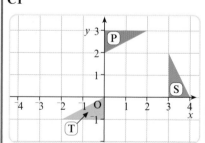

a Triangle S is the image of P after a rotation about (3, 3). What is the angle of rotation?

b Triangle T is the image of P after a rotation of 180°. Give the coordinates of the centre of rotation.

D Translations

* A translation only changes the position of a shape.

* On a grid you can use a vector to describe a translation.

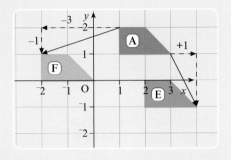

Example

❖ A is translated on to E by the vector $\begin{pmatrix} 1 \\ \bar{2} \end{pmatrix}$.

❖ A is translated on to F by the vector $\begin{pmatrix} \bar{3} \\ \bar{1} \end{pmatrix}$.

E Enlargements

* To describe an enlargement you must give:
  ❖ the centre of enlargement
  ❖ the scale factor (SF).

Example

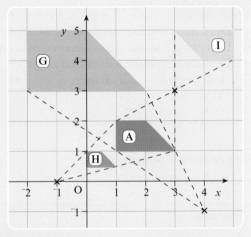

G is an enlargement of A with centre (4, ⁻1) and SF 2.

H is an enlargement of A with centre (⁻1, 0) and SF ½.

I is an enlargement of A with centre (3, 3) and SF ⁻1.

* If the SF is **greater than 1**, or **less than ⁻1**, the image is **larger** than the object.

* If the SF is **between 0 and 1**, or **between ⁻1 and 0**, the image is **smaller** than the object.
  (Although the image is smaller, it is still called an enlargement!)

* If the scale factor is **negative**, the image is on the opposite side of the centre of enlargement and upside down.

F Congruence and similarity

* Of the four main types of transformation, enlargement is the only one that changes the **size** of the object (unless the SF is ⁻1 or 1).

  ❖ Under either reflection, rotation, or translation:
  the object and image are always **congruent**,
  i.e. they have the same shape and size.

  ❖ Under enlargement:
  the object and image are only **similar**,
  i.e. they have the same shape but are different in size.

D1 These translations map P on to U and V.

Object	Translation	Image
P	$\begin{pmatrix} 2 \\ 0 \end{pmatrix}$	U
P	$\begin{pmatrix} \bar{1} \\ \bar{3} \end{pmatrix}$	V

On your diagram from Question **B1**, draw and label the image of P after each of these translations.

E1 Copy this diagram and enlarge triangle P with:
  a SF 2 and centre (⁻1, 4)
  b SF ½ and centre (0, 5)
  c SF ⁻2 and centre (2, 2.5).

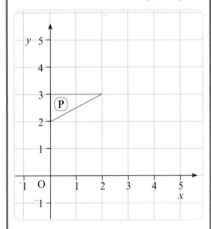

E2 On a pair of axes draw the shape with vertices A(1, 3) B(1, 5) C(2, 4) D(2, 3)
Enlarge the shape with:
  a SF ⁻1.5 centre (0, 2)
  b SF ⁻2 centre (2, 2)
  c SF ⁻3 centre (1, 2).

F1 a In this diagram which shapes are congruent to U?

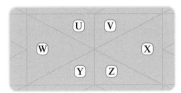

  b Explain why the triangle made by W, Y, and Z is similar to triangle U.

Thinking ahead to ...
combined transformations

A a Draw triangle A on axes with
$^-5 \leqslant x \leqslant 5$ and $^-5 \leqslant y \leqslant 5$.

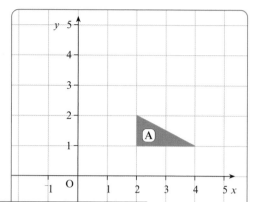

b These transformations map
triangle A on to B, C, D, E
and F.

Object	Transformation	Image
A	Reflection in the line y = x	B
A	Reflection in the line x = 1	C
A	Rotation of 180° about the origin	D
A	Rotation of $^-90°$ about the point (1, 0)	E
A	Translation $\begin{pmatrix} ^-4 \\ 2 \end{pmatrix}$	F

Draw and label the images B, C, D, E and F.
c Describe a transformation that maps B on to C.
d Describe a transformation that maps:
  i D on to E   **ii** E on to C   **iii** F on to E.

Combined transformations

♦ To describe a mapping you
can use a combination of
transformations.

Example

To map F on to G you can use:

a rotation of $^-90°$ about (1, 0)

followed by

a translation $\begin{pmatrix} ^-4 \\ 2 \end{pmatrix}$

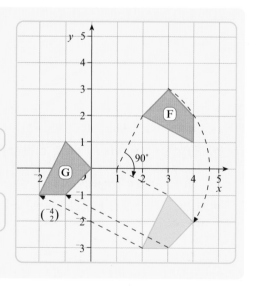

Exercise 10.1
Combined transformations

1 H is the image of F after:

a translation $\begin{pmatrix} ^-4 \\ 2 \end{pmatrix}$

followed by

a rotation of $^-90°$ about (1, 0)

Use axes with:
$^-5 \leqslant x \leqslant 6$ and
$^-5 \leqslant y \leqslant 5$

a Draw and label F and its image H.
b Compare G and H and comment on any differences.

2 These transformations map the quadrilateral F on to J and K.

Object	Transformations		Image
	First	Second	
F	Rotate 180° about (2, 1)	Rotate ⁺90° about (2, 1)	J
F	Rotate ⁺90° about (2, 1)	Rotate 180° about (2, 1)	K

> Use the same axes as you drew for Question **1**.

a Draw and label the images J and K.
b Compare J and K and comment on any differences.

3

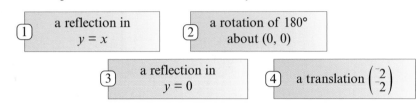

① a reflection in $y = x$

② a rotation of 180° about (0, 0)

③ a reflection in $y = 0$

④ a translation $\begin{pmatrix} ^-2 \\ 2 \end{pmatrix}$

Sort the transformations 1 to 4 into two pairs so that:

> in each pair the transformations are commutative.

> A pair of transformations are commutative if the image of an object is the same whichever transformation you use first.

Draw diagrams to explain your answers.

♦ Combined transformations can be equivalent to a single transformation.

Example

A rotation of ⁻90° about (0, 3) maps F on to G.
So

> a rotation of ⁻90° about (1, 0)

followed by

> a translation $\begin{pmatrix} ^-4 \\ 2 \end{pmatrix}$

is **equivalent to the single transformation**

> a rotation of ⁻90° about (0, 3)

Exercise 10.2
Equivalent transformations

1 These transformations map the quadrilateral F on to L, M and N.

Object	Transformations		Image
	First	Second	
F	Reflect in y = 1	Reflect in y = x	L
F	Rotate 180° about (1, 1)	Translate $\begin{pmatrix} 0 \\ 2 \end{pmatrix}$	M
F	Reflect in y = ⁻1	Rotate ⁻90° about (1, ⁻1)	N

> Use axes with:
> ⁻5 ≤ x ≤ 5 and
> ⁻5 ≤ y ≤ 5

a On a new diagram draw and label the images L, M and N.
b What single transformation maps F on to:
  i L   **ii** M   **iii** N ?

Exercise 10.3
Transformations

Each tile is a transformation of tile P.

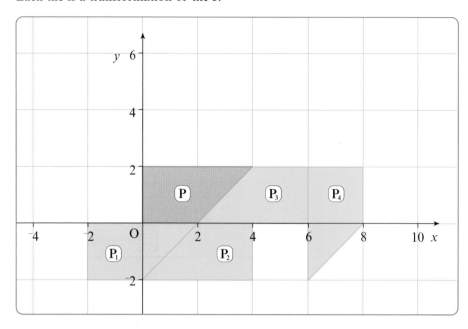

1 **a** Draw these tiles on axes with $^-4 \leqslant x \leqslant 10$ and $^-4 \leqslant y \leqslant 8$.
   b Describe a single transformation that maps P on to:
      i P_1 **ii** P_2 **iii** P_3

2 In this table each pair of transformations maps tile P on to P_4.
   a For each mapping describe the second transformation fully.

	Object	Image	Transformations	
			First	Second
i	P	P_4	Rotate $^-90°$ about (2, 0)	
ii	P	P_4	Rotate 180° about (1, 4)	
iii	P	P_4	Reflect in y = x	

   b Describe another pair of transformations that maps P on to P_4.

3 These transformations map tile P on to P_5, P_6 and P_7.

	Transformations		
Object	First	Second	Image
P	Rotate $^-90°$ about (2, $^-2$)	Reflect in x = 5	P_5
P	Reflect in y = x	Translate $\begin{pmatrix} ^-2 \\ 0 \end{pmatrix}$	P_6
P	Rotate $^+90°$ about (0, 2)	Reflect in x = 1	P_7

   a On your diagram draw the images P_5, P_6 and P_7.
   b Describe a pair of transformations that map P_5 on to P.

Enlargements

Exercise 10.4
Enlargements

1 These tiles are arranged in the shape of a Greek cross.

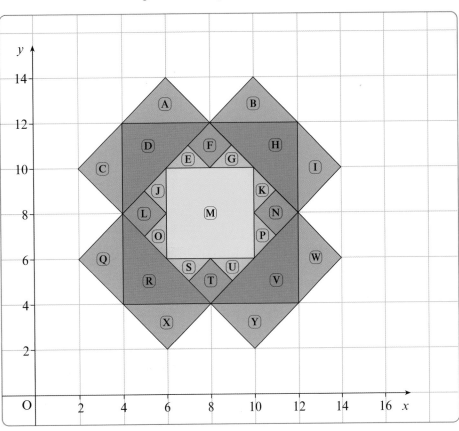

You could put tracing paper over your drawing for each question.

If you draw lines through corresponding points on the object and image, they will meet at the centre of enlargement.

a Copy the diagram and label the tiles A to Y.

b What is the image of E after an enlargement with centre (4, 8) and SF 2?

c Find the scale factor and centre for each of these enlargements.

Object	Image	SF	Centre
S	Y		
Y	U		
E	A		
Q	W		

d Explain why tile T will not map on to M with just an enlargement.

For an enlargement give the scale factor and the coordinates of the centre.

For a translation give the vector.

For a reflection give the equation of the mirror line.

For a rotation give direction and angle of rotation and the coordinates of the centre.

e This table gives a pair of transformations for three mappings. Describe fully the second transformation for each of these mappings.

	Object	Image	Transformations First	Second
i	G	W	Enlarge SF 2 with centre (8, 8)	
ii	Q	E	Rotate ⁻90° about (6, 6)	
iii	A	S	Enlarge SF $\frac{1}{2}$ with centre (4, 8)	

Exercise 10.5
Drawing enlargements

1   Draw the triangle A on axes with:
$$^-6 \leqslant x \leqslant 10$$
$$^-6 \leqslant y \leqslant 10.$$

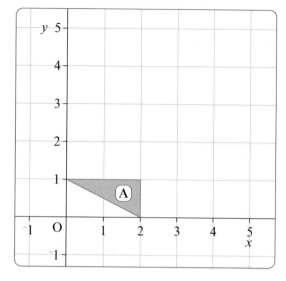

> For an enlargement:
> the distance from the centre to a point on the object multiplied by the scale factor gives the distance from the centre to the corresponding point on the image.

2   These transformations map the triangle A on to B₁, B₂, B₃ and B₄.

Object	First transformation	Second transformation	Image
A	Enlarge SF 2 with centre (0, 0)	Translate $\begin{pmatrix} 1 \\ 2 \end{pmatrix}$	B₁
A	Rotate ⁻90° about (2, 0)	Enlarge SF 2 with centre (⁻1, 0)	B₂
A	Enlarge SF 2 with centre (⁻1, 0)	Translate $\begin{pmatrix} 4 \\ 4 \end{pmatrix}$	B₃
A	Rotate ⁺90° about (0, 1)	Enlarge SF 2 with centre (⁻3, ⁻2)	B₄

a   On your diagram draw and label the images B₁, B₂, B₃ and B₄.
b   Describe a single transformation that will map B₁:
   i on to B₂   ii on to B₃   iii on to B₄.
c   What single transformation maps A:
   i on to B₁   ii on to B₃.

3   In this table each pair of transformations maps B₂ on to A.
   For each mapping describe the second transformation fully.

	Object	Image	First transformation	Second transformation
a	B₂	A	Rotate ⁺90° about (5, 0)	
b	B₂	A	Rotate ⁺90° about (5, 2)	

4 Each tile in this pattern is also a transformation of A.

   a Copy this pattern on axes with:
$$^-6 \leqslant x \leqslant 10$$
$$^-6 \leqslant y \leqslant 10$$

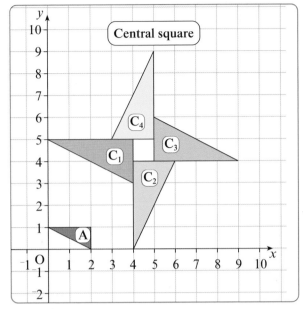

   b In a table show what transformations map A on to each triangle in this pattern.

   c **i** Make another pattern using four triangles.

      ii In a table to show what transformations map A on to each triangle in your pattern.

      iii Pass your table to a partner and ask them to draw your pattern.

> You do not need more than two transformations for each mapping.

5

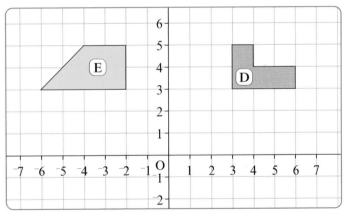

   a Copy these shapes on axes with: $^-12 \leqslant x \leqslant 12$
$$^-7 \leqslant y \leqslant 10$$

   b On your diagram, draw and label the images D_1 and E_1.

	Transformations		
Object	**First**	**Second**	**Image**
D	Enlarge SF 2 with centre (0, 1)	Rotate 180° about (0, 1)	D_1
E	Enlarge SF $^-1.5$ with centre (0, 1)	Enlarge SF $^-1.5$ with centre (0, 1)	E_1

   c Describe a single transformation that maps:

      i D on to D_1 **ii** E on to E_1.

   d Describe a single transformation that maps:

      i D_1 on to D   **ii** E_1 on to E.

Thinking ahead to ...
inverse transformations

A a Draw hexagon R on axes with:
$^-7 \leqslant x \leqslant 7$ and $^-7 \leqslant y \leqslant 7$.

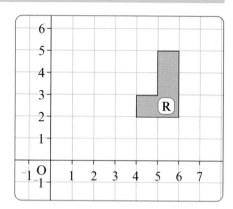

b Describe the effect on R of each of these pairs of transformations.

| | Transformations | |
Object	First	Second
R	Enlarge SF $^-2$ with centre (2, 1)	Enlarge SF $^-0.5$ with centre (2, 1)
R	Rotate $^-90°$ about (1, 0)	Rotate $^-270°$ about (1, 0)

Inverse transformations

♦ If a combination of two transformations maps the object on to itself then each transformation is the **inverse** of the other.

Exercise 10.6
Inverse transformations

1 Describe the inverse transformation of:

a
> Translation
> $\begin{pmatrix} 1 \\ ^-2 \end{pmatrix}$

b
> Rotation
> $^-90°$
> about
> (1, 0)

c
> Enlargement
> SF 2
> with centre
> ($^-1$, 2)

2 a Describe the inverse transformation of:
> Reflection
> in
> $y = ^-x$

b What is special about the inverse transformation of any reflection?

3 a Draw the triangle S on axes with:
$^-1 \leqslant x \leqslant 5$
$^-5 \leqslant y \leqslant 5$.

b On your diagram, draw and label the images S_1 and S_2.

> S_1 Rotation 180° about (3, 0)

> S_2 Enlargement SF $^-1$ with centre (3, 0)

c Describe two inverse transformations of   Rotation 180° about (x, y)

End points

You should be able to ...   ... so try these questions

A   Use combined transformations

A1 **a** Draw shape E on axes with:
$^-12 \leqslant x \leqslant 6$ and $^-6 \leqslant y \leqslant 6$.

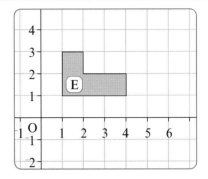

b On your diagram, draw and label the images K, L and M.

Transformations			
Object	First	Second	Image
E	Enlarge SF $^-2$ with centre ($^-1, 0$)	Enlarge SF 0.5 with centre (3, $^-4$)	K
E	Reflect in $y = ^-x$	Reflect in $y = 0$	L
E	Rotate 180° about (0, 0)	Rotate 180° about (0, $^-2$)	M

c What single transformation maps E on to:
i K   **ii** L   **iii** M ?

d These transformations map K on to L, M and E.
Describe the second transformation.

	Transformations			
	Object	Image	First	Second
i	K	L	Rotate $^-90°$ about ($^-1, ^-3$)	
ii	K	M	Reflect in $x = 0$	
iii	K	E	Translate $\begin{pmatrix} 2 \\ 2 \end{pmatrix}$	

e **i** What single transformation maps K on to L ?
ii Describe two single transformations that each maps K on to M.

B   Identify inverse transformations

B1 Describe the inverse transformation of each of these.

a
Enlargement
SF 0.25
with centre
(3, $^-1$)

b
Rotation
$^-270°$
about
(0, 2)

c
Translation
$\begin{pmatrix} 0 \\ ^-3 \end{pmatrix}$

B2 Describe the inverse transformation of: Reflection in $y = x + 1$

Toujours Paris

Ile de la Cité

This boat-shaped island in the River Seine is where Paris was first inhabited by Celtic tribes over 2000 years ago. It is where Notre Dame is situated. This cathedral is a superb example of French medieval architecture and is particularly known for its wonderful stained glass rose windows.

The width of this South Window is 13 metres.

In the Ile de la Cité you will also find Point Zéro. This is a geometer's mark from which all distances in France are measured.

Each side of the shape is 12 cm long.

Paris au Quotidien

Arrondissements: Il faut le savoir, Paris est divisé en 20 arrondissements se déroulant en spiraleà partir du 1er (le quartier du Louvre).

Banques: Ouvertes en général du lundi au vendredi de 9h à 16h30, quelques (rares) agences le samedi. Les Caisses d'Epargne ouvrent plus souvent le samedi et ferment le lundi.

Change: On ne peut pas tout prévoir à l'avance; vous pourrez changer vos devises dans les gares, les aéroports, les grandes agences de banque, les points change (ouverts tard le soir), ainsi qu'à notre bureau d'accueil des Champs-Elysées.

Daily Life in Paris

Districts: You should know that Paris is divided into 20 districts numbered in a circular direction, starting with the 1st district (the Louvre area).

Banks: They are generally open from Monday to Friday from 9 am to 4.30 pm, some (rare) branches on Saturday. The savings banks are more often open on Saturday and closed on Monday.

Exchange: You cannot foresee everything; you can therefore change your foreign currency in railway stations, airports, major bank branches, exchange offices (open late in the evening), as well as in the visitors' office on the Champs-Elysées.

Eiffel Tower Factfile – 1996

- Built in 1889 for the Universal Exhibition
- Built by Gustave Eiffel (1832–1923)
- Built from pig iron girders
- Total height 320 metres
- The world's tallest building until 1931
- Height to 3rd level is 899 feet
- There are 1652 steps to the third level
- Two and a half million rivets were used
- The tower is 15 cm higher on a hot day.
- Its total weight is 10100 tonnes
- 40 tons of paint are used every 4 years
- On a clear day it is possible to see Chartres Cathedral, 72 km away to the South West.
- The tower is visited by about $5\frac{1}{2}$ million people every year

Admission charge   56 Francs

DAY TRIPS BY EUROSTAR
Waterloo Station (London) to Paris
Celebrate that special occasion in style with a day trip to Paris!

ADULT   £
CHILD (4–11 YRS) £

Entry fees in Paris – 1996

Eiffel Tower	56 FF
Louvre	45 FF
Pompidou Centre	35 FF
Picasso Museum	28 FF
Museum of Modern Art	27 FF
Versailles Palace	45 FF
Parc de la Villette	45 FF
Cluny Museum	28 FF

Paris Lucky dip – Superb value !

In the hat are four tickets to the:
Eiffel Tower,
Picasso Museum,
Versailles Palace and
the Museum of Modern Art.
Pick two tickets at random from the four.
Entry fee – only 83 Francs.

83 FF

Datafile
Population of Paris (in 1982)   2 188 918
In 1996, £1 sterling was equivalent to 7.54 French Francs.
1 metre = 3.281 feet
1 kilometre = 0.62 miles

Give answers to 3 significant figures where appropraite.

1 **a** How many lines of symmetry has the South Window of Notre Dame?
   b What is the order of rotational symmetry of the South Window?
   c Draw a window shape where the number of lines of symmetry is not equal to the order of rotational symmetry.
   d Calculate the area of the South Window inside the frame.

The window is surrounded by a frame with the cross-section below.

   e Calculate the area of the frame's cross-section.
   f Calculate the approximate volume of the frame in cubic metres.

2 For Point Zéro in the Ile de la Cité, the outer polygon is a regular octagon.
   a Calculate the size of an exterior angle.
   b Calculate the size of an interior angle.
   c Calculate the distance across the octagon from one flat face to the opposite one.
   d Calculate the total area of Point Zéro.

3 **a** How many tons of paint will have been used on the Eiffel Tower from when it was built up to the year 2000?
   b How much higher than the third level is the total height of the tower?
      Give your answer to the nearest metre.
   c From a point 2000 metres away what is the angle of elevation to the topmost point on the Eiffel Tower, to the nearest degree?
   d The spire of Notre Dame reaches 90 metres from the ground and is 4.3 km as the crow flies from the Eiffel Tower.
      What is the angle of depression from the third level of the Eiffel Tower to the tip of Notre Dame's spire? Give your answer to 2 sf.
   e The ratio of steps to the third level, to steps to the first level is about 9 to 2.
      About how many steps are there to the first level?
   f Calculate the approximate percentage that the tower grows on a hot day.

4 What is the approximate bearing of Paris from Chartres?

5 **a** In 1996, what was the Eiffel Tower entry fee equivalent to in £ Sterling?
   b By 1997 one French Franc had changed in value to 10.6 pence. What effect did this change have on the entry fee in £ sterling?

6 **a** Compare the French and English text in the extract on Daily Life in Paris.
      What is the relative frequency of a vowel in each language? (Vowels are a, e, i, o, and u.)
   b Compare the French and English extracts. Which language uses the longest words? Explain how you decided.

7 For the Paris Lucky Dip use the following shorthand:
   E – Eiffel Tower   *P* – Picasso Museum
   V – Versailles Palace *M* – Museum of Modern Art
   a What is the probability that a pair of tickets is picked which includes the Versailles Palace?
   b What is the probability of picking P and M?
   c Give the probability of picking a pair of tickets
      i worth more than the entry fee
      ii worth less than the entry fee.
   d Is the seller likely to make a profit or loss on every hundred entries? Give your reasons.

8 These two bills were for Eurostar day trips to Paris.

Paris Special

Enclosed are tickets for:
2 adults and 3 children
Total charge £465

Paris Special

Enclosed are tickets for:
3 adults and 1 child
Total charge £386

Calculate:
a the cost of an adult's ticket **and** a child's ticket
b the total cost for 1 adult and 2 children.

Starting points
You need to know about ...

... so try these questions

A Solving equations in one unknown

- where the unknown is on both sides of the equation

$$5c - 4 = 3c - 8$$

[−3c] $2c - 4 = {}^-8$

[+4] $2c = {}^-4$

[÷2] $c = {}^-2$

- where brackets are involved

$$3(4p + 5) = 5(3p - 4)$$

$$12p + 15 = 15p - 20$$

[−15] $12p = 15p - 35$

[−15p] ${}^-3p = {}^-35$

[÷ ${}^-3$] $p = \frac{35}{3} = 11.66 \ldots$

- where fractions are involved

$$\tfrac{2}{3}(w + 3) = 4w - 3$$

[× both sides by 3] $2(w + 3) = 12w - 9$

                   $2w + 6 = 12w - 9$

[+9] $2w + 15 = 12w$

[−2w] $15 = 10w$

          $w = 1.5$

A1 Solve these equations:
- **a** $7d - 8 = 3d + 14$
- **b** $3y + 9 = 2y - 5$
- **c** $5(2x + 1) = 41 + x$
- **d** $3(3p + 4) = 2(p + 27)$
- **e** $5(4 - x) = 3(2x + 1)$
- **f** $3(k - 1) = 2(1.5 - 3k)$
- **g** $8(n + 5) = 4(3n - 8)$
- **h** $15(g - 3) = 10(2g + 1)$

A2 Solve these equations:
- **a** $\tfrac{2}{3}c - 1 = 4$
- **b** $\tfrac{3}{4}x + 1 = 2x$
- **c** $3 - \tfrac{1}{2}x = x - 15$
- **d** $\tfrac{3}{5}(v + 4) = 3v$
- **e** $\tfrac{1}{2}(w - 3) = 2(2w + 1)$
- **f** $\tfrac{1}{3}(4a + 2) = 2(a - 6)$
- **g** $\tfrac{2}{3}(x - 1) = 2(2x - 6)$
- **h** $\tfrac{3}{8}y + 2 = \tfrac{1}{3}y - 3$

B Factorising expressions

- when a numerical factor can be identified

     factorise $12a - 9x + 18y$

     i.e.   **$3(4a - 3x + 6y)$**

- when an algebraic factor can be identified

     factorise $a^2b + ab^2 - ac$

     i.e.   **$a(ab + b^2 - c)$**

- when more than one factor can be identified

     factorise $15xy - 20x^3 + 5xy^2 + 10x^2y^3$

     i.e.   **$5x(3y - 4x^2 + y^2 + 2xy^3)$**

B1 Factorise these expressions:
- **a** $6bc - 15ax + 3by$
- **b** $18a^2 + 24b^2c$
- **c** $3a^2x - 5ay^2 + 6ab - ac$
- **d** $axy - a^2x^2 + ax^2y - abx$
- **e** $6c^2d - 15bcd$
- **f** $8axy^2 + 12abx - 20a^2x + 16ax$

C Dealing with powers and roots

- when powers are involved

            $x^2 = 3a^2b - 4c$

[√ both sides]   **$x = \sqrt{(3a^2b - 4c)}$**

- when roots are involved

            $\sqrt{c} = 3xy + b$

[square both sides]   **$c = (3xy + b)^2$**

C1 Write each of these as an equation in x:
- **a** $x^2 - 3 = 4a$
- **b** $3x^2 = 5c + 1$
- **c** $5 + \sqrt{x} = 3a - 2$
- **d** $\sqrt{(ax)} = 7$
- **e** $5\sqrt{x} = 4a$

Thinking ahead to ...
changing the subject
of formulas

A A cook book gives this formula to find the time to cook a piece of lamb.

Allow 30 minutes per pound and an extra 20 minutes.

a How long would it take to cook 6 pounds of lamb?

b What weight of lamb would be cooked in 1 hour and 50 minutes?

Changing the subject of formulas

The subject of a formula is the variable that is to be calculated.

The formula that links cooking time (T) with weight (W) can be written as:

$$T = 30W + 20$$ T is the subject of this formula

♦ With the formula you to calculate a value for T for a value of W.

♦ To calculate W for a value T, we need to make W the subject of the formula.

Flowchart method for changing the subject of a formula

Addition 'undoes' subtraction and vice versa. For example:

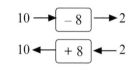

♦ Draw a flowchart for the formula.

$$W \xrightarrow{} \boxed{\times 30} \xrightarrow{30W} \boxed{+20} \xrightarrow{30W+20} T$$

♦ Reverse the flow chart to rearrange the formula.

$$W \xleftarrow{\frac{T-20}{30}} \boxed{\div 30} \xleftarrow{T-20} \boxed{-20} \xleftarrow{} T$$

$$W = \frac{T-20}{30}$$

Multiplication 'undoes' division and vice versa. For example:

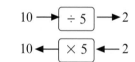

Algebraic method for changing the subject of a formula

♦ T is the subject

♦ W is the subject $W = \dfrac{T-20}{30}$

Exercise 11.1
Changing the subject
of formulas

1 Make y the subject of each of these formulas:

a $5x = 3y - 4$	**b** $9x + 2y = 8$	**c** $5x - 4 = 4y + 5$
d $3x - 4 = 5y - 8$	**e** $3xy + 4 = 2a$	**f** $2x + 2xy = 3a$
g $4x = 3(2y + 1)$	**h** $3(4y - 2) = 5x$	**i** $2(3 - 4y) = 5x$
j $2(3x - y) = 5x - 4$	**k** $5a^2 + 3 = 4 - 2y$	**l** $4(3y - 1) = x^2 + 2$
m $2(3a - 5y) = a - 9x$	**n** $2(3 - 4y) = x^2$	**o** $2x(3 - 4y) = 5$
p $a^2(b + 2y) = 5$	**q** $x^2 - 4 = 3a(y - a)$	**r** $3\pi + 2ay = a^2r$

2 The formula that gives the cost in pence (c) of placing an advertisement in a local paper, where n is the number of words is:

$$c = 15n + 50$$

a Calculate the cost of a 65 word advert.

b **i** Make n the subject of the formula.

ii How many words are in an advert that costs £19.85?

c For £10, what is the maximum number of words in an advert?

3   A formula for the sum (S) of the interior angles of a polygon is:
$$S = 180(n - 2) \text{ where } n \text{ is the number of sides}$$

   a   Calculate the sum of the interior angles of a heptagon.
   b   **i**   Make n the subject of the formula.
       ii   The sum of the interior angles of a polygon is 3240°.
          How many sides does the polygon have?
   c   Explain why it is not possible to draw a polygon where the sum of the interior angles is 600°.

4   When a metal rail of length w metres is increased in temperature by $t°$ C
it increases in length. The new length x metres is given by the formula:
$$x = w(1 + kt), \quad \text{where } k \text{ has a value of } 0.0008$$

   a   The temperature of a rail 55 metres in length is increased by 21° C.
     i   Calculate the length of the rail after the temperature increase.
     ii   With an increase in temperature of 21° does the length of the rail
        increase by more that 15%. Explain your answer.
   b   **i**   Make t the subject of the formula.
       ii   What increase in temperature increases the rail length
          by 1.342 metres?

5   The surface area (S) of a cylindrical axle is given by the formula:
$$S = 2\pi r(r + h) \text{ where } r \text{ is the radius, and } h \text{ the length.}$$

   a   Calculate the value of S, to 4 sf, when $r = 22.5$ cm and $h = 2.2$ metres.
   b   **i**   Make h the subject of the formula.
       ii   An axle has a radius of 15 cm, and a surface area of 3016 cm².
          Calculate the length of the axle to 2 sf.

Changing the subject of formulas that involve fractions

Example 1

♦ An approximate formula to convert kilometres to miles is: $m = \dfrac{5}{8}k$

  ❖ Making k the subject gives a formula $m = \dfrac{5}{8}k$
    for converting miles to kilometres.

                      [× 8] $8m = 5k$

                      [÷ 5] $\dfrac{8m}{5} = k$

  ❖ So $k = \dfrac{8m}{5}$

Example 2

♦ A formula that links t and a is given as: $\dfrac{3t}{4} = \dfrac{5}{a - 1}$

  ❖ for subject a: [× both sides by 4] $\times 4 \left(\dfrac{3t}{4} = \dfrac{5}{a-1} \right) \times 4$

                                    $3t = \dfrac{4 \times 5}{a - 1}$

          [× both sides by $(a - 1)$] $3t(a - 1) = 20$
                                 $3at - 3 = 20$
           [+3] $3at = 23$
           [÷3t] $a = 23 \div 3t$

                                    $a = \dfrac{23}{3t}$

> Multiplying both sides by 4,
> and then $(a - 1)$ produces an
> equation with no fractions.
> In this way manipulation is
> easier.

This is just one way to rearrange the above formula so that it reads $a = \dots$.
Different rearrangements may have more, or fewer, steps.

Exercise 11.2
Rearranging formulas
with fractions

For these questions, round
each answer to 2 dp.

Remember manipulation is
made easier if you can
produce an equation with
no fractions involved.

1 A formula for converting kilograms (k) to pounds (p) is: $p = \frac{11}{5}k$
  a How many pounds are equivalent to 8 kilograms?
  b Make k the subject of the formula.
  c Convert 3 pounds to kilograms.

2 The formula for the area (A) of a triangle with base length b and height h is:
$$A = \frac{1}{2}bh$$
  a Make h the subject of the formula.
  b Find the height of a triangle with area $100\,cm^2$ and base length $2.5\,cm$.

3 Temperature in °F can be converted to °C using this formula:
$$C = \frac{5(F - 32)}{9}$$
  a Convert 68°F to °C.
  b Rearrange the formula to give a formula to convert ˚C to °F.
  c Convert 24°C to °F.

4 Make y the subject of each formula:
  a $z = \frac{3}{4}y$ **b** $m = \frac{1}{3}xy$ **c** $d = \frac{1}{2}(y + 4)$ **d** $k = \frac{4}{7}(y - h)$

5 When d metres are travelled in t seconds,
a formula for average speed (s) in km/h is: $s = \frac{18d}{5t}$
  a In 1992, Linford Christie ran 100 metres in 9.96 seconds.
    What was his average speed in $km\,h^{-1}$?
  b Make d the subject of the formula.
  c Make t the subject.

6 When the temperature at ground level is $G°C$ and the height above the ground
in metres is h, the approximate temperature $T(°C)$ is given by:
$$T = G - \frac{h}{300}$$
  a The temperature at ground level is 26°C. Calculate the temperature
    outside a jet flying at 15 000 metres above ground.
  b Make h the subject of the formula.
  c Calculate h when $G = 20$ and $T = ^-30$.

7 A formula for the area (A) of a
trapezium is given as: $A = \frac{h(b + c)}{2}$.

Calculate the value of c when:
$A = 250.25$, $b = 12.40$, and $h = 17.50$.

8 Make w the subject of each formula:
  a $\frac{5}{3w} = 2x$ **b** $\sin 32° = \frac{3}{4w}$ **c** $\frac{w}{3} - 5a = 4b$
  d $t = \frac{a}{w - b}$ **e** $\frac{a^2}{2w} = 0.5b$ **f** $\frac{c^2 - b}{2w} = 2ab$
  g $\frac{3x}{2w + 3} = 4$ **h** $\frac{3x}{w - 1} = 2$ **i** $\frac{\tan 50°}{2w + 1} = 3$
  j $\frac{2a}{w - 3} = 5$ **k** $\frac{w + 4}{5} = 2a$ **l** $\frac{3w - 2}{4} = l$
  m $\frac{2w + 3}{2} = 3a - 1$ **n** $\frac{2}{w} = \frac{3}{a}$ **o** $\frac{3w}{x} = \frac{4a}{5}$
  p $\frac{2a}{w - 3} = 4$ **q** $\frac{2}{3}(w - 3) = 5a + 1$ **r** $3a + 1 = \frac{5a}{w + 2}$

125

Rearranging formulas when factorising is involved

Example

♦ A formula that links b, c, and w is:

$$2b + 3 = \frac{b + c}{w}$$

❖ Make b the subject: [× both sides by w]

$$w(2b + 3) = b + c$$
$$2bw + 3w = b + c$$
$$2bw - b = c - 3w$$

[Factorise]

$$b(2w - 1) = c - 3w$$

[÷ both sides by $(2w - 1)$]

$$\boldsymbol{b = \frac{c - 3w}{2w - 1}}$$

Exercise 11.3
Using factorising

1 A formula for the surface area (S) of this cuboid is: $S = 2bw + 2ab + 2aw$

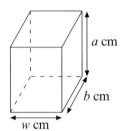

a cm

b cm

w cm

   a Make w the subject of the formula.
   b Make a the subject of the formula.
   c When $w = 4.50$ cm and $a = 6.40$ cm the surface area is 136.08 cm². Calculate the value of b in this cuboid.

2 The diagram shows a circular play area centre O and radius w metres. Part of the area is to be fenced, shown in the diagram as a red line.
   A formula for the length of fencing (P) is:

$$P = 2w + \frac{\pi w}{2}$$

O

w metres

   a Rearrange the formula so that w is the subject.
   b The length of fencing used was 89.27 metres. Calculate, to 2 sf, the diameter of the play area.

3 This is a block of packaging material with a rectangular slot cut through it.
   A formula for the volume V of packaging material in the block is: $V = abc - 2abd$

2a

d

a

b

c

   a **i** Rearrange the formula to make b the subject.
       ii Calculate the value of b when:
           $V = 1602.25$ cm³, $a = 6.50$ cm, $c = 25.00$ cm, and $d = 4.00$ cm.
   b Calculate the value of a when:
       $V = 4212.00$ cm³, $b = 18.00$ cm, $c = 32.50$ cm, and $d = 6.50$ cm.

4 Rearrange each of these formulas to make h the subject:

   a $3ac = 4ah - hy$ **b** $3h = 4x + 2ah$ **c** $3xh + 5 = 2x + ah$
   d $ah + b^2 - c^2h = 4$ **e** $3h - 5 + hx = 2$ **f** $ah + bh - 4 = 5$
   g $3ah + y + hx = 2$ **h** $3ah + 4 = h - 1$ **i** $4 - 3ah = 5bh + 1$
   j $3 - 4ah + by = h + 1$ **k** $3 - hy + hx = 5$ **l** $3(2ah + 1) - hx = 2$

   m $3(ah + 1) = 2(bh - 2)$ **n** $\dfrac{ah}{4} = 5x$ **o** $\dfrac{3}{h} + 4 = a$

   p $2(3ah - 4) = \frac{1}{3}$ **q** $\frac{2}{3}a = 4(xh + b)$

Rearranging formulas with squares and roots

Example 1

Four square photographs, of side x, are placed in a square mount of side c as shown in the diagram.

a Write a formula for the area (A) of mount that is still visible.

b Rearrange the formula to make x the subject.

a A formula for the area (A) is: $A = c^2 - 4x^2$

b The area is: $A = c^2 - 4x^2$

  [$+ 4x^2$] $4x^2 + A = c^2$

  [$-A$] $4x^2 = c^2 - A$

  [÷ both sides by 4] $x^2 = \dfrac{(c^2 - A)}{4}$

  [√both sides] $x = \sqrt{\dfrac{(c^2 - A)}{4}} = \dfrac{\sqrt{(c^2 - A)}}{\sqrt{4}} = \dfrac{\sqrt{(c^2 - A)}}{2}$

> To square both sides, you square the *expression* on each side. This is not simply squaring each *term* on both sides.

Example 2

Make y the subject of the formula: $\sqrt{(y + 3a)} = a - 2$

  [square both sides] $y + 3a = (a - 2)^2$

  $y + 3a = a^2 - 4a + 4$

  [$-3a$] $y = a^2 - 7a + 4$

Exercise 11.4
Dealing with squares and roots

1 When an object is dropped, a formula for the approximate distance (d metres) travelled in a time of t seconds is:
$$d = \left(\tfrac{49}{10}\right)t^2$$
The Sears tower in Chicago is 443 metres high.
About how long will it take an apple to fall from the top to the ground?

2 A formula for velocity (v) is : $v^2 = u^2 + 2as$
a Show why a formula for u is: $u = \sqrt{(v^2 - 2as)}$
b Calculate the value of u, to 1 sf, when: $v = 14$, $a = 3.5$, and $s = 18$

3 The formula for the volume (V) of a right cone of radius r, and height h is: $V = \left(\tfrac{1}{3}\right)\pi r^2 h$.
Rearrange the formula to make r the subject.

4 A formula for the volume (V) of a sphere of radius r is : $V = \left(\tfrac{4}{3}\right)\pi r^3$.
a Make r the subject of the formula.
b Calculate the radius of a sphere which has a volume of $100\,\text{cm}^3$.

> $p^3 = p \times p \times p$
>
> If $y = p^3$ then the **cube root** of y is p.
>
> $\sqrt[3]{y} = p$

5 A formula for the area (A) of a triangle is: $A = \sqrt{s(s - a)(s - b)(s - c)}$

Rearrange the formula to make b the subject.

6 Rearrange each formula to make b the subject:
a $b^2 + 3a - 4 = y^2$ b $3y = x - 2ab^2$ c $b^2 x = y - 1$
d $b^2 - 3x = 4 - 2x$ e $4x = 2(b^2 - 5)$ f $3x + 4a = 2(1 - b^3)$
g $b^2 = \dfrac{x - 1}{b}$ h $b^2 = \dfrac{b^2 - c}{2a}$ i $\sqrt{(3b - 1)} = a$
j $2a = \sqrt{(b - 2)}$ k $w = \sqrt{(ab^2 + 3)}$ l $bc = \sqrt{(b^2 + 1)}$
m $2\sqrt{(a^2 - b^2)} = xy$ n $\pi\sqrt{(a + b)} = r$ o $k = 2\pi\sqrt{\dfrac{b}{y}}$
p $\sqrt{(2b - x)} = \sqrt{(a + c)}$ q $c - 3 = \sqrt{(2b + 1)}$ r $2\sqrt{(b - x)} = x - 2$

Evaluating non-linear formulas

- ◆ For the formula, $a = (b + 5)(b - 1)$, find the value of a when $b = 3$.
$$a = (3 + 5) \times (3 - 1)$$
$$= 8 \times 2$$
$$= 16$$

- ◆ For the formula, $y = x^2 + 4x + 1$, find the value of y when $x = 7$.
$$y = 7^2 + (4 \times 7) + 1$$
$$= 49 + 28 + 1$$
$$= 78$$

Exercise 11.5
Evaluating non-linear
formulas

Accuracy

For these questions, give answers correct to 2 dp when no other degree of accuracy is stated.

To calculate the greatest volume think about using a graph, or a spreadsheet.

1 Stopping distance is the distance a vehicle travels as it brakes to a halt. A formula that gives the stopping distance of a car on a dry road is:
$$d = \frac{v^2}{200} + \frac{v}{5},$$
where d is the stopping distance (metres) and v the speed (km h^{-1}).
Calculate the stopping distance of a car travelling at 110 km h^{-1} on a dry road.

2 The net for a square-based box is made by cutting four square corners from a 12 cm square piece of card as shown.
A formula for the volume ($V \text{ cm}^3$) of the box is:
$$V = 4x(x^2 - 12x + 36)$$
where x is the length shown on the diagram.
a Find the volume of the box when $x = 1.5$.
b Calculate V when $x = 4$.
c What value for x gives the box with the greatest volume?

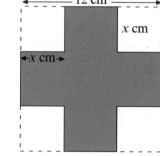
12 cm
x cm
x cm

3 **A** $\boxed{y = x^2 + 5x - 8}$ **B** $\boxed{y = x^2 + 3x + 2}$ **C** $\boxed{y = x^3 - 3x^2 - x + 2}$

D $\boxed{y = (x + 1)(x + 2)}$ **E** $\boxed{y = (x - 2)(x + 9)}$ **F** $\boxed{y = (x + 3)(x + 1)(x - 3)}$

For each formula find the value of y when:
a $x = 5$ **b** $x = {}^-5$ **c** $x = 2$ **d** $x = {}^-2$ **e** $x = 2.5$ **f** $x = {}^-2.5$
Comment on any patterns in your results.

4 The formula $v = \sqrt{(u^2 + 2as)}$ gives:
the velocity of an object (v) in m/s, for an initial velocity of u m/s,
an acceleration (a) in m s^{-2}, and a distance (s) travelled in metres.
a Calculate to 1 dp the value of v when:
   i $u = 30$, $a = 5$ and $s = 6.8$ **ii** $u = 20$, $a = 9.8$ and $s = 2.4$
b Calculate to 2 sf the value of u when:
   i $s = 15.40$, $v = 120.00$ and $a = 3.60$
   ii $v = 100$, $a = {}^-14.50$, $s = 250$
   iii $a = 3\frac{1}{2}$, $v = 18\frac{1}{4}$, and $s = 6\frac{1}{3}$

5 The volume (V) of a sphere of radius r is given by the formula $V = \frac{4}{3}\pi r^3$.
The Earth is an approximate sphere of radius 6.4×10^6 metres.
a Calculate the volume of the Earth, correct to 4 sf.
b Rearrange the formula to give r in terms of V.

End points

You should be able to ...   ... so try these questions

A Rearrange a formula

A1 Rearrange each formula to make x the subject:
   a $3x - a = 5$
   b $a - 4x = 2x + 3$
   c $2(3x + y) = 5$
   d $3(a - xy) = b + 2xy$
   e $3(2 - 3x) = 3(x + bc)$

B Handle formulas where fractions are involved

B1 Make v the subject of each formula:
   a $\frac{3}{4}v = a - x$ **b** $2v + 1 = \frac{3}{5}(a - 3)$

   c $\frac{2a + 3}{v} = 3a^2$ **d** $\frac{2v + 5}{4} = ax + 2y$

   e $\frac{3v + 2a}{3} = \frac{a + v}{5}$ **f** $\frac{3}{b - 2v} = c^2$

   g $\frac{1}{w} + \frac{2}{v} = \frac{3}{x}$

C Recognise when you need to factorise when rearranging a formula

C1 Rearrange each formula to give c in terms of the other variables:
   a $ax^2 + cx = 3$
   b $3x + 2ac = ac - 5x + cy$
   c $2a(a + 3c) = a(1 + c)$
   d $a^2b - a^2c = 3 + 2a$
   e $(w - cx^2) = \frac{2}{3}$
   f $2 + a^2c + cx = ax + 1$

D Deal with powers and roots in formulas

D1 In each formula rearrange the terms to make y the subject:
   a $\sqrt{xy} = 5$
   b $(a + x) = \sqrt{(1 + y)}$
   c $\frac{2}{\sqrt{y}} = 2x - 1$

   d $3\sqrt{\frac{y}{a}} = b$

   e $5 = 2\sqrt{(a^2 - y)}$
   f $\sqrt{(1 - ay + by)} = 3$
   g $3 - y^2 = 4a + x$
   h $2(3y^2 - 4) = 5x$
   i $3y^2 = 6ax - 9$

E Evaluate formulas

E1 A formula for the surface area (S) of a cylinder is:
$S = 2\pi rh + 2\pi r^2$, where r is the radius and h the height.
   a Calculate the value of S when: $r = 5.7$ cm and $h = 12.5$ cm. Give your answer to 3 sf.
   b Calculate the value of h when: $r = 5$ cm and $S = 424$ cm^2. Give your answer to 1 dp.

E2 Given the formula $p = \dfrac{a + b^2}{3a}$,

calculate to 2 sf the value of b when: $a = 3.5$, and $p = 5.5$.

Starting points
You need to know about ...

... so try these questions

A Writing ratios

- A **ratio** compares the size of two or more quantities.

  $$3:4 \qquad 1:4:2 \qquad 3\tfrac{1}{2}:\tfrac{1}{2}$$

- In the ratio $3:4$, the **number of parts** are 3 and 4.

A1 Roughcast is used to cover walls. It is a mix of 3 parts mortar to 1 part gravel.
Write this mix as a ratio of:
  a mortar to gravel
  b gravel to mortar.

B Equivalent ratios

- The ratios $3:4$ and $6:8$ are **equivalent ratios**.

  3 : 4

  6 : 8

- To write an equivalent ratio:
  - multiply or divide each number of parts by the same number.

  $$\div 2 \overset{6:8}{\underset{3:4}{\frown}} \div 2 \qquad \times 5 \overset{2:3:7}{\underset{10:15:35}{\frown}}$$

- A ratio in its **simplest terms**, or **lowest terms**, is written with the smallest whole numbers possible.

  $$\times 4 \overset{1:\frac{1}{4}:3}{\underset{4:1:12}{\frown}} \qquad \div 3 \overset{15:24}{\underset{5:8}{\frown}} \div 3$$

B1 Copy and complete these sets of equivalent ratios.
  a $4:1$ **b** $2:5:4$ **c** $9:12$
  $\quad 12:?$ $\quad 1:?:2$ $\quad ?:4$
  $\qquad\qquad\qquad\qquad\qquad 6:?$

B2

$2:5$	$1:3:2$	$10:20$
$10:25$	$2\tfrac{1}{2}:5$	$1:2:3$
$3:9:6$	$2:1$	$1:2\tfrac{1}{2}$

List the sets of equivalent ratios.

B3 Write each of these ratios in its simplest terms.
  a $9:6$ **b** $14:21$
  c $4:8:2$ **d** $5:\tfrac{1}{2}$
  e $2:1\tfrac{1}{2}:3$

C Unitary ratios

- Two or more ratios can be compared by writing each one as a **unitary ratio** in the form $n:1$ or $1:n$.

A   3.2″   4″
B   4″   5″
C   4.8″   6″

The ratio of **width to height** for each of these photographs is:

A	$4:3.2$	B	$5:4$	C	$6:4.8$
	$\mathbf{1.25:1}$		$\mathbf{1.25:1}$		$\mathbf{1.25:1}$
	or $\mathbf{1:0.8}$		or $\mathbf{1:0.8}$		or $\mathbf{1:0.8}$

The ratios are equivalent so the photographs are **in proportion**.

C1

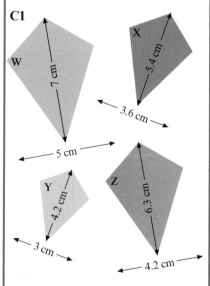

Which of these kites are in proportion?

D Writing ratios as fractions, decimals and percentages

- A ratio that compares **two** quantities can be written as a fraction, as a decimal, and as a percentage.

The **width-to-height ratio** is 5 : 4 or:

$$\frac{\text{width}}{\text{height}} = \frac{5}{4} = 1.25 = 125\%$$

4″

5″

- ❖ the width is $\frac{5}{4}$ of the height
- ❖ the width is 1.25 times the height
- ❖ the width is 125% of the height.

E Sharing in a given ratio

- An amount can be shared in a given ratio.

Example Share £140 in the ratio 2 : 1 : 4
- ❖ find the total number of parts
  2 + 1 + 4 = 7
- ❖ find the amount for one part
  £140 ÷ 7 = £20
- ❖ multiply each number of parts by the amount for one part.

	2	:	1	:	4	Total
						7
	×£20		×£20		×£20	×£20
	£40	:	£20	:	£80	£140

F Similar triangles

- Triangles that have the same three angles are similar.

- ❖ $\hat{A}$ and $\hat{X}$ are **corresponding angles** because they are equal.
- ❖ AC and XZ are **corresponding sides** because they are opposite corresponding angles.
- Triangles that are enlargements of each other are similar.

G Reciprocals

- Two numbers which multiply together to equal 1 are **reciprocals** of each other.

0.8 is the reciprocal of 1.25 $\frac{4}{5}$ is the reciprocal of $\frac{5}{4}$

1.25 is the reciprocal of 0.8 $\frac{5}{4}$ is the reciprocal of $\frac{4}{5}$

- The reciprocal of a number n is $\frac{1}{n}$ or $1 \div n$.

$$\frac{1}{0.8} = 1.25 \qquad \frac{1}{1.25} = 0.8$$

D1 Write each of these ratios as:
  i   a fraction
  ii a decimal
  iii a percentage.

  a 5 : 8   b 9 : 5
  c 7 : 12   d 15 : 11
  e 11 : 18   f 17 : 24

E1 Amy, Ben and Zoe are left £150 by their grandmother. They share the money in the ratio of their ages: 5, 3, and 2. Calculate how much each gets.

E2 Liz trains for the 100 m hurdles. She splits her time 3 : 5 between speed work and technique. Calculate how long Liz spends on:
  a technique in 2 hours training
  b speed work in 4 hours training

F1 EFG and JKL are similar.

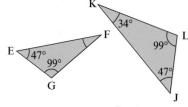

  a Explain why $\hat{F}$ is equal to 34°.
  b Give the corresponding angle to $\hat{G}$.
  c Give the corresponding side to:
    i EG   ii KL

G1 Give the reciprocal of:
  a 2   b 0.25
  c 3   d $1\frac{1}{3}$

Keeping in proportion

◆ When adjusting a recipe, you need to keep the ingredients in proportion.

Example   This recipe for Swiss Hot Chocolate serves 2 people.
How much of each ingredient is needed for 5 people?

Swiss Hot Chocolate
- *600 ml milk*
- *140 g drinking chocolate*
- *80 ml whipped cream*

Milk		Chocolate		Cream		Serves
600 ml	:	140 g	:	80 ml		2
×2.5		×2.5		×2.5		×2.5
1500 ml	:	350 g	:	200 ml		5

You can keep the multiplier in your calculator memory.

◆ find the **multiplier:**
$5 \div 2 = 2.5$

◆ multiply each amount by the multiplier.

Exercise 12.1
Recipes

1 This recipe serves 6 people. How much of each ingredient do you need for 9 people?

Chilled Chocolate Drink
230 g caster sugar • 300 ml water
50 g cocoa • 1200 ml chilled milk

2 This recipe for chocolate fudge makes 36 pieces.
a How much cocoa is needed to make 72 pieces?
b How much milk is needed to make 18 pieces?
c Calculate how much of each ingredient you need to make 24 pieces.

Chocolate Fudge
- *450 g white sugar*
- *150 ml milk*
- *150 ml water*
- *75 g butter*
- *30 g cocoa*

3 This recipe makes 24 sweets.
a Calculate how many drops of peppermint essence are needed to make 42 sweets.
b How much chocolate is needed for 42 sweets?

Chocolate Peppermint Creams
- *230 g icing sugar • 1 egg white*
- *4 drops peppermint essence*
- *100 g plain chocolate*

◆ When you use an equivalent ratio to solve a problem, you are keeping the number of parts in proportion.

Example

An orange dye is a mix of red and yellow in the ratio 2 : 3.
a What amount of red is mixed with 480 ml of yellow?
b How much orange dye is produced?

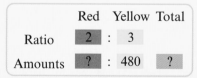

	Red		Yellow	Total
Ratio	2	:	3	
Amounts	?	:	480	?

◆ find the multiplier,
480 ml ÷ 3 = 160 ml

◆ multiply the other number of parts by the multiplier

◆ find the total of the amounts.

Red		Yellow	Total
2	:	3	
×160 ml		×160 ml	
320 ml	:	480 ml	800 ml

Exercise 12.2
Using equivalent ratios

1 Calculate:

a the amount of yellow dye to mix with 210 ml of red dye

b how much orange dye is produced.

2 Walls can be covered with mortar to protect them from the weather.

a For a clay wall how much cement is mixed with 1500 kg of sand?

b For a concrete wall:
   i write the mortar mix as a ratio in its simplest terms
   ii calculate how much concrete is produced with 400 kg of cement.

Wall surface	Mortar mix Cement : Lime : Sand
Clay	1 : 1 : 6
Concrete	$1 : \frac{1}{2} : 4\frac{1}{2}$

3 On a map, 4.8 cm stands for a distance of 240 m.

a What length on the map represents a distance of 315 m?

b Give the map scale as a unitary ratio.

c Explain why the total number of parts has no meaning in this ratio.

♦ When one shape is an enlargement of another, each dimension has been multiplied by the same number to keep it in proportion.

Example I′J′K′L′ is an enlargement of IJKL. Find the height K′L′.

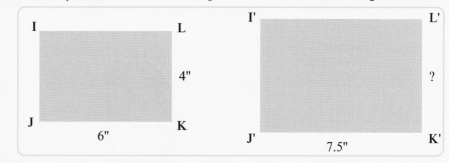

The multiplier is the scale factor of the enlargement.

♦ find the multiplier,
$7.5 \div 6 = 1.25$

♦ multiply the height KL by the multiplier.

The shapes have the same width-to-height ratio, so they are in proportion.

Width		Height			$\frac{\text{Width}}{\text{Height}}$
6″	:	4″		IJKL	$\frac{6}{4} = 1.5$
×1.25		×1.25			
7.5″	:	**5″**		I′J′K′L′	$\frac{7.5}{5} = 1.5$

Exercise 12.3
Enlargement

1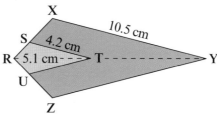

Kite RXYZ is an enlargement of kite RSTU.

a Calculate the scale factor of the enlargement.

b Find the length RY.

c Calculate the ratio:
   i $\frac{RT}{ST}$ ii $\frac{RY}{XY}$

d Explain why the ratios are equal.

Similar shapes

◆ Two shapes are **similar** if:
  ❖ all corresponding angles are equal, **and**
  ❖ all ratios of lengths of corresponding sides are equal.

These ratios are greater than 1 because lengths in the larger shape have been divided by lengths in the smaller shape.

A ratio is less than 1 if you divide lengths in the smaller shape by lengths in the larger shape.

$$\frac{AB}{PQ} = \frac{BC}{QR} = \frac{CD}{RS} = \frac{AD}{PS}$$
$$= 0.\dot{6}$$

For shapes ABCD and PQRS:

❖ corresponding angles are equal:

$\hat{A} = \hat{P}, \quad \hat{B} = \hat{Q}, \quad \hat{C} = \hat{R}, \quad \hat{D} = \hat{S}$

❖ ratios of lengths of corresponding sides are equal:

$$\frac{PQ}{AB} = \frac{1.8}{1.2} = 1.5 \qquad \frac{RS}{CD} = \frac{2.7}{1.8} = 1.5$$

$$\frac{QR}{BC} = \frac{3.6}{2.4} = 1.5 \qquad \frac{PS}{AD} = \frac{3.9}{2.6} = 1.5$$

So ABCD and PQRS are similar.

Exercise 12.4
Similar shapes

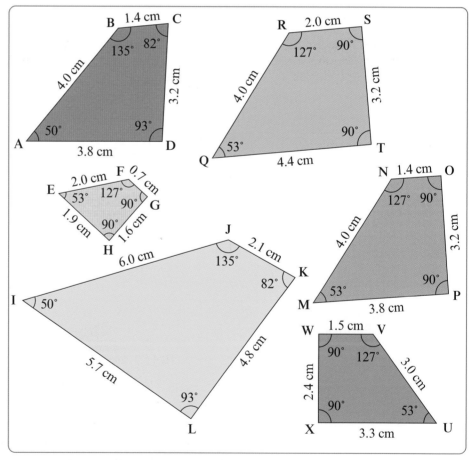

1 a Which shape is similar to EFGH?
  b Explain why.

2 a List all the pairs of similar shapes.
  b Give a ratio of the lengths of corresponding sides for each pair.

Finding lengths in similar shapes

- You can use a ratio to find a length in the **larger** of two similar shapes.

Example   ABC and PQR are similar triangles.
Find the length PQ.

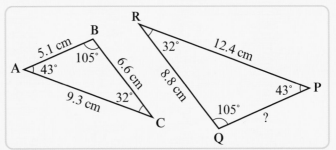

Dividing a length on the larger shape by a length on the smaller shape gives the ratio greater than 1:
$$\frac{PR}{AC} = \frac{12.4}{9.3} = 1.\dot{3}$$

The ratio less than 1 is:
$$\frac{AC}{PR} = \frac{9.3}{12.4} = 0.75$$

- Calculate the ratio greater than 1 for any two corresponding lengths.
$$\frac{PR}{AC} = \frac{12.4}{9.3} = 1.\dot{3}$$

- Multiply AB, the corresponding length to PQ, by the ratio.

AB $\xrightarrow{\times 1.\dot{3}}$ PQ
5.1 cm → **6.8 cm**

- To find a length in the **smaller** of two similar shapes:
  - use the same method with the ratio less than 1.

Exercise 12.5
Finding lengths in similar shapes

1

DEF and STU are similar.
Explain why this calculation is wrong.

To find DF: $\frac{TU}{FE} = \frac{8}{6.4} = 1.25$

So DF = US × 1.25 = 7 cm × 1.25
= 8.75 cm ✗

2

GHIJ and WXYZ are similar.
Find the length:
a YX   b IJ

3   LMN and LJK are similar triangles.
a   Find the length JM.
b   Explain why JK and MN are parallel.

4   KLNP and QMNO are similar.
Find the length LN.

Similar triangles

♦ You need to recognise when triangles are similar.

Example In this diagram, PQ is parallel to ST.

> If two triangles have the same three angles then they must be similar.
>
> All ratios of corresponding lengths, therefore, are equal.

a Explain why triangles PQR and TSR are similar.
b Find the length PR.

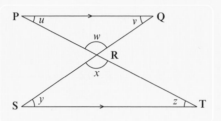

u and z are alternate angles,
v and y are alternate angles,
w and x are opposite angles, so
$u = z$, $v = y$, $w = x$

The triangles have the same three angles, so they are similar.

b The ratio is: $\dfrac{QR}{RS} = \dfrac{6}{7.5} = 0.8$

$$\begin{aligned} \mathbf{PR} &= RT \times 0.8 \\ &= 9.2\,\text{cm} \times 0.8 \\ &= \mathbf{7.36\,cm} \end{aligned}$$

Exercise 12.6
Similar triangles

1 a Explain why ABD and CAD are similar triangles.
   b Give the corresponding side to:
     i AC   **ii** AD
   c Find the length:
     i AB   **ii** BC

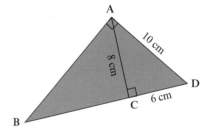

2 a Calculate the ratio:
     i $\dfrac{KM}{NM}$ **ii** $\dfrac{OM}{LM}$
   b Explain why KMO and NML are similar triangles.

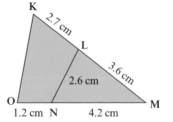

3 a Explain why DEF and GHF are similar triangles.
   b Find the length GH.

4 Explain why enlarging GHF, using centre of enlargement F, does **not** give DEF.

Proportionality

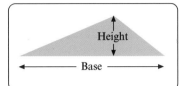

◆ All the shapes in a set of similar shapes must be in proportion.

Example   This logo is made up of four similar triangles.
The dimensions of the triangles,
in centimetres, are:

	W	X	Y	Z
Base (b)	4	5	6	4.8
Height (h)	1	1.25	1.5	1.2

b	4	5	6	4.8
	×0.25	×0.25	×0.25	×0.25
h	1	1.25	1.5	1.2

This ratio is a **constant** because it is the same for each pair of values.

All the ratios $\frac{h}{b}$ are the same, 0.25, so h is **proportional to** b.

The symbol $\propto$ means 'is proportional to'.

◆ If one variable, y, is proportional to another variable, x, you can write:

$$y \propto x$$

Exercise 12.7
Proportionality

1 a Draw a graph of h against b.

The four points lie on a straight line.

 b Explain why the line, when extended, passes through (0, 0).
 c What is the link between the constant ratio and the gradient of the line ?
 d Give an equation connecting b and h in the form $h = \ldots$.

2 a For each of the four similar triangles, calculate the ratio $\frac{b}{h}$.

 b Give an equation connecting b and h in the form $b = \ldots$.

This angle is the angle between the base of each triangle and the horizontal.

3 a Draw a graph of a against b.
 b Is a proportional to b?
  Explain your answer.

	W	X	Y	Z
Base (b)	4	5	6	4.8
Angle ($a°$)	24°	48°	72°	84°

4 a Copy and complete this table.
 b Draw a graph of A against h.
 c Is $A \propto h$?
  Explain your answer.

	W	X	Y	Z
Height (h)	1	1.25	1.5	1.2
Area (A)				

5 a Copy and complete this table.
 b Draw a graph of A against h^2.
 c Is $A \propto h^2$?
  Explain your answer.

	W	X	Y	Z
h^2				
A				

6 These are the dimensions of another four triangles.

 a Draw a graph of h against b.
 b Describe the shape of the graph.
 c Calculate ratios to show that h is not proportional to b.

	A	B	C	D
b	4	4.8	5	6
h	2.5	2.7	2.75	3

7 **a** Each of these five triangles has an area of 3 cm².
    i Draw a graph of h against b.
    ii Is $h \propto b$?
    Explain your answer.

	P	Q	R	S	T
Base (b)	3	4	5	6	8
Height (h)	2	1.5	1.2	1	0.75

  b **i** Copy and complete this table.
    ii Draw a graph of h against $\frac{1}{b}$.
    iii Is $h \propto \frac{1}{b}$?
    Explain your answer.

	P	Q	R	S	T
$\frac{1}{b}$					
h	2	1.5	1.2	1	0.75

Direct and inverse proportion

- If two variables, x and y, are proportional to each other, $y \propto x$, then they are in **direct** proportion.

When two variables are directly proportional, an **increase** in one matches an **increase** in the other.

The relationship between the variables can be given as: $y = kx$, where k is a constant.

Example

$$b \quad 4 \quad 5 \quad 6 \quad 4.8$$
$$\times 0.25 \quad \times 0.25 \quad \times 0.25 \quad \times 0.25 \qquad h = 0.25\,b$$
$$h \quad 1 \quad 1.25 \quad 1.5 \quad 1.2$$

- Two variables, x and y, are in **inverse** proportion when one of the variables is in direct proportion to the reciprocal of the other: $y \propto \frac{1}{x}$

When two variables are inversely proportional, an **increase** in one matches a **decrease** in the other.

The relationship between the variables can be given as: $y = \frac{k}{x}$ or $xy = k$, where k is a constant.

Example

b	3	4	5	6	8
h	2	1.5	1.2	1	0.75
bh	6	6	6	6	6

$h = \dfrac{6}{b}$ or $bh = 6$

Exercise 12.8
Direct and inverse proportion

1 The dimensions of these metric paper sizes, given in millimetres, are in direct proportion.

	A4	A3	A2	A1	A0
Width (w)	210	297	420	594	841
Height (h)	297	420	594	841	1189

  a Calculate the height to width ratio, $\dfrac{h}{w}$, for each size.
  b Explain why these ratios are not exactly equal to $\sqrt{2}$.
  c Give an equation connecting w and h.

2 The dimensions of the sticky labels in this packet, given in centimetres, are inversely proportional.

Width (w)	18	12	9	7.2	6
Height (h)	2	3	4	5	6

  a What is the area of each of the labels?
  b Give an equation connecting w and h in the form:
    i $h = \ldots$ **ii** $wh = \ldots$ **iii** $w = \ldots$.

Lucky Labels

3 The mass of glaze, g grams, needed to glaze a plate is in direct proportion to the square of the plate's diameter, d.

a Copy and complete this table.

d	5	7	9	10	14
d^2					
g	10	19.6	32.4	40	78.4

b Give an equation connecting d and g in the form $g = kd^2$.

Finding the constant

♦ To give an equation connecting two variables, you need to find the constant.

Example w is directly proportional to the square of f, and $w = 45$ when $f = 5$.
Give an equation connecting w and f.

Write down the relationship.

Substitute $w = 45$ and $f = 5$ into the formula.

Rearrange the formula to find the constant.

$$w \propto f^2 \text{ so}$$
$$w = kf^2$$
$$45 = k \times 5^2$$
$$45 = 25k$$
$$\frac{45}{25} = k$$

This gives $k = 1.8$, so $\mathbf{w = 1.8f^2}$

♦ For two variables in inverse proportion, it is easier to use the formula $xy = k$ to find the constant.

Example d is inversely proportional to the positive square root of z, and $d = 2.5$ when $z = 36$.
Give d in terms of z.

$$d \propto \frac{1}{\sqrt{z}} \text{ so}$$
$$d\sqrt{z} = k$$
$$2.5 \times \sqrt{36} = k$$
$$2.5 \times 6 = k$$

This gives $k = 15$, so $\boldsymbol{d = \dfrac{15}{\sqrt{z}}}$

Exercise 12.9
Finding the constant

1 m is inversely proportional to v, and $m = 6$ when $v = 9$.
a Write down the relationship between m and v.
b Find the constant.
c Give an equation connecting m and v.
d Calculate m when $v = 4.5$.
e Explain what happens to m when v is halved.

2 s is directly proportional to the positive square root of q, and $s = 28$ when $q = 16$.
a Write down the relationship between s and q.
b Give an equation connecting s and q.
c Calculate s when $q = 36$.

3 p is inversely proportional to the square of t, and $p = 2.5$ when $t = 6$.
a Give an equation connecting p and t in the form $p = \dots$.
b Calculate p when $t = 3$.
c Explain what happens to p when t is halved.
d Rearrange your equation to give t in terms of p.
e Calculate t when $p = 3.6$.

4 The number of plates, n, that can be glazed with one bag of glaze powder is inversely proportional to the square of the diameter, d, of the plate. One bag glazes 800 side plates, diameter 5″.

   a Write down the relationship between n and d.
   b Find the constant.
   c Give an equation connecting n and d.
   d Calculate how many plates one bag of powder will glaze for:
     i 10″ dinner plates   ii 14″ serving plates.

5 The area of cardboard needed to make a box for a basketball, $A\,\text{cm}^2$, is directly proportional to the square of the diameter of the ball, d cm. A 26 cm basketball box needs 2366 cm² of cardboard.

   a Write down the relationship between A and d.
   b Find the constant.
   c Give A in terms of d.
   d Calculate how much cardboard is needed for a 19 cm basketball box.

6 The length of time, t seconds, that a basketball bounces when dropped is directly proportional to the square root of the height, h cm, from which it is dropped. The ball bounces for 16 seconds when dropped from 1 m.

   a Give an equation connecting t and h.
   b Calculate the bounce time, to the nearest 0.1 seconds, from a height of 50 cm.

> You need to decide whether to work in centimetres or metres.

7 The f/stop on this camera lens is inversely proportional to the aperture diameter, a mm. $f8$ has an aperture of 5.25 mm.

   a Write down the relationship between f and a.
   b Find the constant.
   c Give f in terms of a.
   d Calculate the aperture diameter for $f16$.

> The aperture is the adjustable opening in the lens that lets the light in when you take a photograph.

8 The brightness ratio, r, of a camera lens is in inversely proportional to the square of the f/stop. $f4$ has a brightness ratio of 0.25.

   a Give an equation connecting r and f.
   b Calculate the brightness ratio for $f16$.
   c Find the f/stop that has a brightness ratio of 1.

> The brightness ratio compares how much light is let in at two different apertures.
> For example: an aperture with a brightness ratio of 0.5 lets twice as much light in as an aperture with a brightness ratio of 0.25.

9 Chocolate Chunks are cubic pieces of chocolate. The mass of one piece, m grams, is directly proportional to the cube of the width, w cm. The 1.5 cm chunk has a mass of 10.8 grams.

   a Give m in terms of w.
   b Calculate the mass of a 3 cm chunk.
   c The width of two chunks is in the ratio 1:2. Give the ratio of the mass of the two chunks.

w cm

End points

You should be able to ...   ... so try these questions

A Keep amounts in the same proportion

A1 This ice-cream recipe serves 8 people.
  a Calculate how much of each of these ingredients you need to serve 20 people.
  i caster sugar   **ii** boiling water

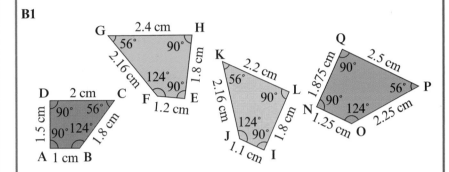

Chocolate Ice Cream
- *150 g caster sugar*
- *20 g cocoa • 4 eggs*
- *410 g can evaporated milk*
- *4 tablespoons boiling water*

  b How many eggs are needed to serve 6 people?

B Identify similar shapes

B1

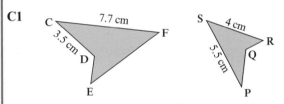

Which of these shapes are similar to ABCD?

C Find lengths in similar shapes

C1

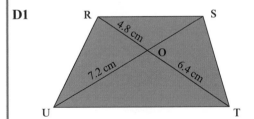

CDEF and PQRS are similar. Find the length:
  a PQ **b** EF

D Recognise and use similar triangles

D1

RSTU is a trapezium.
  a Explain why triangles ROS and TOU are similar.
  b Find the length OS.

E Understand direct and inverse proportion

E1 The length of time, s seconds, that a tennis ball bounces when dropped is in direct proportion to the square root of the height, h cm, from which it is dropped.
The ball bounces for 18 seconds when dropped from 64 cm.
  a Give an equation connecting s and h.
  b Calculate the bounce time from a height of 1 m.

E2 w varies inversely as q, and $w = 1.2$ when $q = 5$.
  a Give w in terms of q.
  b Calculate w when $q = 10$.
  c Explain what happens to w when q is doubled.
  d Calculate q when $w = 7.5$.

Starting points
You need to know about ...

... so try these questions

A Prisms and pyramids

- This solid has a cross-section which is the same all through the solid. This is known as a **uniform cross-section**.

- Solids with a uniform cross section are known as **prisms**.

- These are other examples of prisms.

Triangular prism   Pentagonal prism

- A **pyramid** is a solid with a polyhedral base with triangular sides which meet at one vertex.

- These are two examples of pyramids.

Hexagonal pyramid   Square pyramid

B The area of a plane shape

- Area of a triangle $= \frac{1}{2}bh$

- Area of a parallelogram $= bh$

- Area of a trapezium $= \dfrac{h(a + b)}{2}$

where h is the perpendicular height.

C The area and circumference of a circle

- Area of a circle $= \pi r^2$

- Circumference of circle $= 2\pi r$ or πd

A1 Each of the solids is either a prism or a pyramid.
a List all the prisms.

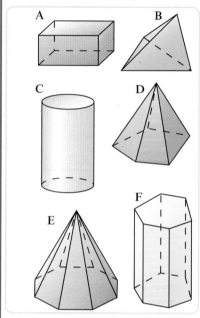

b Name each solid.

B1 Calculate the areas of these shapes.

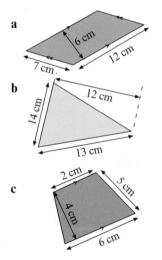

a 6 cm, 7 cm, 12 cm

b 14 cm, 12 cm, 13 cm

c 2 cm, 5 cm, 4 cm, 6 cm

C1 Calculate the area of a circle with a diameter of 2.4 m.

C2 A circle has a circumference of 52 cm. What is its radius?

C3 Write an expression for the area and circumference of a circle with radius $2y$.

D Volumes and surface areas of prisms

◆ The volume of any prism = Area of uniform cross-section × Depth

Depth

Example What are the volume and surface area of this prism?

The uniform cross-section is trapezium-shaped.

Area of trapezium = $\dfrac{5 \times (3 + 6)}{2}$

$= 22.5\,\text{cm}^2$

Volume of prism = 22.5 × 12
$\qquad\qquad\qquad = \mathbf{270\,cm^3}$

◆ The surface area is the total of the areas of **all the exterior faces**.

To find the area of face A you need to know its width PQ.

By Pythagoras' rule:
$$PQ^2 = PT^2 + TQ^2$$
$$PQ = \sqrt{3^2 + 5^2} = \sqrt{34}$$
$$PQ = 5.83 \text{ (2 dp)}$$

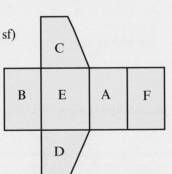

Area of face A = 5.83 × 12 = 70 cm² (2 sf)
Area of B = 5 × 12 = 60 cm²
Area of top C = 22.5 cm²
Area of bottom D = 22.5 cm²
Area of back E = 6 × 12 = 72 cm²
Area of front F = 3 × 12 = 36 cm²

Surface area of prism = 283 cm² (3 sf)

E The volume and surface area of a cylinder

◆ Volume of cylinder = $\pi r^2 h$

◆ Area of curved surface = $2\pi rh$ or πdh

◆ Total surface area = $2\pi r^2 + 2\pi rh$

Top
Area = πr^2

Bottom
Area = πr^2

r

h

$2\pi r$

Curved surface

h

Area = $2\pi rh$

D1 Calculate the volume and surface area of each of these prisms.

1.5 cm

4.2 cm

9.5 cm

1.8 cm

4.2 cm

A

2.7 cm

8.0 cm

3.6 cm

2.4 cm

3.0 cm

2.4 cm

8.5 cm

3.6 cm

C

E1 Calculate the volume and total surface area of this cylinder.

3.5 cm

D

8.5 cm

E2 A cylinder has a radius of 8 cm and a length of 12 cm.
Write an expression in π for:
a the volume of the cylinder
b the total area of the cylinder.

The area of composite shapes

Composite shapes are made up from more than one shape.
Sometimes you can find the area by adding areas; at other times it is easier to subtract.

Example 1

Find the area of ABCDEF.

The area (A) of ABCDEF can be given by:
$$A = (12.4 \times 4.5) + (4.6 \times 4.8)$$
$$= 55.8 + 22.08$$
$$= 77.9 \ (1 \ dp)$$

The area of ABCDEF is 77.9 cm²

or

The area (A) of ABCDEF is given by:
A = Area of large rectangle – Area cut out for L-shape
$$A = (12.4 \times 9.3) - (4.8 \times 7.8)$$
$$A = 115.32 - 37.44$$
$$\mathbf{A = 77.9 \ (1 \ dp)}$$

Example 2

Find the shaded area.

The area of the shaded part (A) is given by:
A = Area of square – Area of circle
$$A = (8.6 \times 8.6) - (\pi \times 4.3^2)$$
$$A = 73.96 - 58.09 \ldots$$
$$\mathbf{A = 15.9 \ (1 \ dp)}$$

> The answer is rounded at the end of the calculation.

The shaded area is 15.9 cm².

Exercise 13.1
Working with composite shapes

1 Calculate the surface area of each shape.

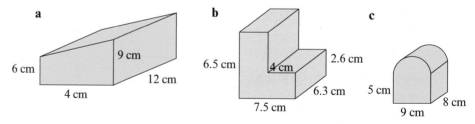

a

6 cm · 9 cm · 12 cm · 4 cm

b

6.5 cm · 4 cm · 2.6 cm · 6.3 cm · 7.5 cm

c

5 cm · 9 cm · 8 cm

2 This shows an open-topped magazine holder which is made from card.
The front is cut away so magazines can be removed easily.

a Calculate the area of side R.
b Calculate the total area of card used to make the box.

8 cm · Side R · 30 cm · 14 cm · 9 cm · 22.5 cm

3 This surround is used to frame photographs. A circle of radius 4 cm is cut from a rectangle of card. Gold lines are printed 1 cm from the edge of the circle and the card as shown.

  a Calculate the area of card after the cut out.
  b Is the area of photograph showing more or less than $\frac{1}{4}$ of the area of the surround? Explain your answer.
  c Calculate the length of gold line on the card.

18 cm

13 cm

4 This diagram shows the net of a box for playing cards. The net was cut from a rectangle of card that it just fitted.

  a What were the original dimensions of the piece of card?
  b Calculate the area of the glue flap on the right.
  c The box opens at either end. Find the area of an opening end.
  d Calculate the total area of the net.
  e Roughly, what fraction of the card is wasted? Explain how you decided.

55 mm

58 mm

16 mm

Type 21

Playing Cards

Playing Cards

Glue flap

88 mm

80 mm

Type 21

6 mm

8 mm

5 This logo design for a company that makes helmets uses two parts of a circle in a red square.

  a Calculate the area of the visor in the logo (the blue part).
  b Find the area of the helmet in the logo (the yellow part).
  c What percentage of the logo is red?

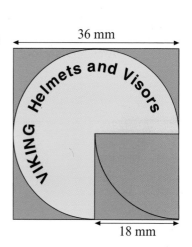

36 mm

VIKING Helmets and Visors

18 mm

6 These are diagrams of filters used in spotlights. Blue and yellow filters can give blue, yellow and green light.

Each filter is in a square frame of length x.

Give an expression in x for:

  a the area of the blue filter
  b the non-coloured area in the yellow filter frame
  c the area of green where the two filters overlap.

x

Blue filter   Yellow filter   Both filters

Parts of a circle

For some problems you need to calculate the area of a sector of a circle or the length of an arc.

For both of these the ratio of the angle x to a full circle (360°) is used.

◆ Area of sector $= \dfrac{x}{360} \times$ area of circle

$$= \dfrac{x}{360} \pi r^2$$

◆ Arc length $= \dfrac{x}{360} \times$ circumference

$$= \dfrac{x}{360} \pi d$$

Example A piece of cheese of angle 56° is cut from a round cheese of radius 15 cm. Find its area and perimeter.

Area of sector $= \dfrac{56}{360} \times \pi r^2$

$= \dfrac{56}{360} \times \pi \times 15^2$

$= \mathbf{110.0\ cm^2}$ (to 1 dp)

Arc length $= \dfrac{56}{360} \times \pi d$

$= \dfrac{56}{360} \times \pi \times 30$

$= 14.7\ cm$

Perimeter $= 15 + 15 + 14.7 = \mathbf{44.7\ cm}$

Exercise 13.2
Arcs and sectors

1   In each case calculate the area of the sector and its perimeter.

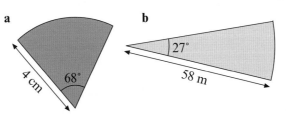

a

b

2   In each case calculate the area of the sector and its perimeter. Give each answer in terms of π.

a

b

3   A baby's bib is made from towelling and is designed around two arcs of circles with the same centre.

a   Calculate the area of towelling in the bib.

b   The bib is edged all round with piping. What length of piping is used?

Calculating volumes and surface areas

Exercise 13.3
Volumes and surface
area problems

1 Calculate the volume and surface area of each shape.

a

12 cm   8 cm   5 cm

b

6.5 cm   4.3 cm   9.4 cm   10.5 cm

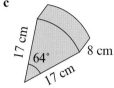

c

17 cm   64°   8 cm   17 cm

d A cylinder of diameter 13.5 cm and height 15.4 cm.

2 This collecting box is in the shape of a cylinder.
The circumference of its base is 29.2 cm
and its capacity is 1120 cm³.
Calculate the height of the box.

h cm

3 In a childrens' play area this space under the
swings is dug to a depth of 0.3 m and filled
with bark chippings.

a Calculate the volume of bark chippings
needed.

b Forestry Products sell bark chippings in
bags. Each bag costs £5.12 and
contains 0.07 m³ of chippings.

   i How many bags of chippings
should be bought?

   ii What is the total cost of
chippings?

12.2 m   8.0 m   10.5 m

4 The diagram shows the uniform cross-section of an open-air swimming pool.

25 m   1.4 m   12.5 m   3.2 m

The width of the pool is 12 m.
The depth of water in the shallow end is to be 1 m.

a Calculate the area of the cross-section.
b What is the total capacity of the swimming pool?
c Calculate the volume of water in the pool.
d The amount of chlorine added to the water
in this pool is 1 millilitre per cubic metre
of water.
How much chlorine, in litres, will be added?

The surface area of a solid
is the **total** area of all its
exposed faces, including
curved ones.

5 A solid spigot is made from a cylinder of
diameter 6 cm and height 4 cm which is fixed
on to a cylinder of diameter 12 cm and
height 8 cm.
Calculate the surface area of the spigot.

8 cm   6 cm   12 cm   4 cm

6 Kevin usually makes a fruit cake in a 20 cm square cake tin.
The finished cake has a depth of 8 cm.
Just to be different, he makes a cake of the same volume
in a round tin with a diameter 24 cm.
What is the expected depth of this cake?

7 This competition appeared in a puzzle magazine.

> ### WIN A BOX OF POUND COINS !!
> - A cuboid-shaped box is full of pound coins.
> - The areas of the three different rectangular faces
>   are 120 cm², 96 cm² and 80 cm².
> - Each edge measures a whole number of centimetres.
>
> ### FIND THE VOLUME OF THE BOX AND WIN THE MONEY !

a Find the volume of the box described in the competition.
b A pound coin has a diameter of 2.2 cm and a thickness of 0.3 cm.
Estimate how much money is in the box.

8 A concrete post to support a handrail has this symmetrical uniform
cross-section. The post is 16 cm thick.

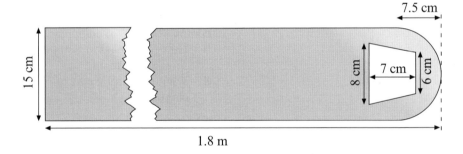

Calculate the volume of concrete in the post.

9 A piece of cheese is cut from a large cylinder of cheddar.
Each cut passes vertically down through the centre of the end circle.
The piece has an angle of 54°.

a Calculate the area of one end of the
cheese piece.
b Calculate the area of the curved surface.
c What is the total surface area of the
piece of cheese?
d If no other pieces have been cut, what is
the surface area of the remainder of the
cylinder of cheese?

Beware: you will need to
calculate a further
dimension before you can
do part b.

10 A tunnel is cut through a hillside.
The cross-section of the tunnel is shown
where the arc **AB** is a semicircle.
The tunnel is 540 metres long.

a Calculate the volume of soil which
must be removed.

b All the interior surfaces are lined with a
skin of concrete.
Calculate the internal surface area of
the tunnel.

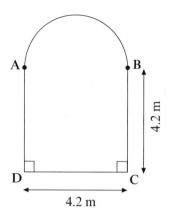

11 The diagram shows a two
kilogram weight.
The weight is made from
a hollow cylinder of metal
from which a sector of
angle 30° is cut out.
This cut-out allows the
weight to be slid on to
a pole.

a Calculate the volume
of the weight.

b Calculate the mass of
metal which is cut
out from the hollow
cylinder.

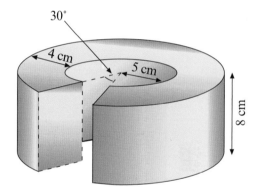

12 A solid is made from a cuboid with
dimensions x, y and z.
A hole of radius r is drilled right through
from one side as shown.

Write and simplify an expression for:

a the volume of the solid

b the surface area of the solid.

13 In a solid cylinder the height is half the radius.
Write an expression for the radius R in terms of the volume V and the
surface area S.

Capacity, volume and density

- ◆ For liquids, volume or capacity is often measured in litres (l) or millilitres (ml).

  1 litre = 1000 millilitres
  1 millilitre is equivalent in volume to 1 cm³.

- ◆ Mass (often called weight) is measured in kilograms (kg) or grams (g).

  1 kilogram = 1000 grams
  1 ml of water weighs 1 gram.

- ◆ Density can be measured in grams per cubic centimetre (g/cm³).

  $$\text{Density} = \frac{\text{mass in grams}}{\text{volume in cm}^3}$$

Exercise 13.4
Capacity, volume and density

1 Write down one choice from each bracket to complete the sentence.
  a The volume of an orange is about (30 cm³, 300 cm³, 3000 cm³).
  b The capacity of a wine glass is about (75 litres, 7.5 litres, 75 millilitres).
  c The weight of an apple is about (17 grams, 170 grams, 1.7 kilograms).

2 A dairy plans to sell cartons containing 550 ml of milk.

Milk carton designs – External dimensions

  a Which of these cartons do you think the dairy should use?
  The waxed cardboard used for the cartons is 1 mm thick.
  b Which carton do you now think they should use?
  c What is the capacity of carton C?
  d What percentage of the capacity of carton C would be airspace if 550 ml of milk were added?
  e What volume of waxed card is used to make carton C? Ignore the flaps.
  f Find the mass of C if the density of cardboard is 0.86 g/cm³.

> Question 2 shows the difference between volume and capacity.
> Carton A has a **volume** of 8.2 × 7.6 × 12.1 cm³, but its **capacity** is less than this because of the thickness of the cardboard.

3 A milk tank is a cylinder of radius 1.2 m and length 4.8 m.
  Calculate the volume of the tank in:
  a cm³   b litres.

4 Each of these pieces of cheese has a uniform cross-section.

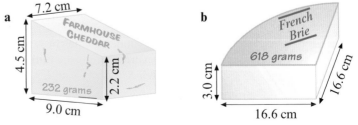

Calculate the volume and density of each piece.

Planes of symmetry

Some solids have **plane symmetry**.
For example, this solid has plane symmetry.

In the mirror, look at half of the solid like this and you see the other half.

So the mirror shows the position of a **plane of symmetry**.

This mirror shows the position of another **plane of symmetry**.

This solid is said to have two **planes of symmetry**.

Exercise 13.5
Properties of solids

1 Each of these solids is made from four cubes.

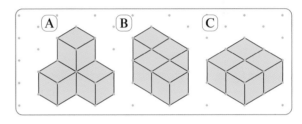

a Which of these solids are prisms?
b How many planes of symmetry has solid B?
c Which solid has exactly 3 planes of symmetry?

2 Draw a prism made from four cubes that has:
a 2 planes of symmetry   b 5 planes of symmetry.

3 Each of these nets A to D is for a prism or a pyramid.

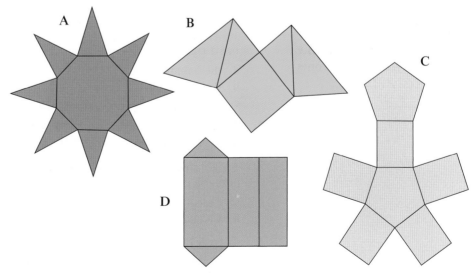

a Which of the nets is for:
   i a prism   ii a pyramid?
b How many planes of symmetry would each assembled solid have?

151

Pyramids and cones

- For any pyramid:
  - **Volume = $\frac{1}{3}$ Base area × Perpendicular height**

- A cone can be considered as a pyramid but with a circular base (i.e. a polygon base with an infinite number of sides). The base area of a cone of radius r is πr^2.

- So for a cone:
  - **Volume of a cone $= \frac{1}{3}\pi r^2 h$**
  - **Curved surface area $= \pi \times r \times$ Slant height**

> A right cone or right pyramid is one where the vertex lies directly over the centre of the base.

Example Find the volume and surface area of a right cone with a base diameter of 12 cm and a perpendicular height of 14 cm.

Volume of cone $= \frac{1}{3}\pi r^2 h$

$= \frac{1}{3} \times \pi \times 6^2 \times 14$

$= \textbf{528 cm}^3$ (nearest integer).

To find the slant height (s)

Using Pythagoras' rule: $s = \sqrt{14^2 + 6^2}$
$= 15.23$ cm

Curved surface area $= \pi \times r \times s$
$= \pi \times 6 \times 15.23$
$= 287$ cm^2 (nearest integer).

Surface area = Curved surface area + Area of base
$= 287 + (\pi \times 6^2)$
$= \textbf{400 cm}^2$ (nearest integer).

Exercise 13.6
Pyramids and cones

1 For a right cone of height 10 cm and base radius of 4 cm, calculate:
   a the volume
   b the curved surface area
   c the surface area.

2 A pyramid has a perpendicular height of 2.4 m and a square base of length 0.8 m. Calculate the volume of the pyramid.

3 A right hexagonal pyramid has a base which is a regular hexagon of side 4 cm and a perpendicular height of 12 cm.
   a Calculate the area of its base.
   b Calculate its volume.

4 Cone A has a base radius of 5 cm and a height of 10 cm.
   Cone B has a base radius of 10 cm and a height of 5 cm.
   Which cone has the larger volume?

The sphere

Archimedes, a Greek mathematician and inventor, was famous for his marvellous machines which were used against the invading Roman army. He was killed in 212 BC by the Romans while defending his home town of Syracuse.

What seems obvious now that a curved surface can have an area was first put forward by Archimedes in about 250 BC. He also discovered the formulas for the surface area and volume of a sphere.

♦ For a sphere of radius r

  ❖ **Volume = $\frac{4}{3}\pi r^3$**

  ❖ **Curved surface area = $4\pi r^2$**

Example Calculate the volume and curved surface area of a basketball which has a diameter of 26 cm.

> **Volume of basketball** = $\frac{4}{3}\pi r^3$
>
> $= \frac{4}{3} \times \pi \times 13^3$
>
> $= 9203 \, \text{cm}^3$ (nearest integer).
>
> **Curved surface area** $= 4\pi r^2$
>
> $= 4 \times \pi \times 13^2$
>
> $= 2124 \, \text{cm}^2$ (nearest integer)

Exercise 13.7
Volumes and surface areas of spheres

1 Ball bearing A has a diameter of 1 cm and ball bearing B one of 2 cm.

  a Calculate the surface area of each ball bearing, leaving your answers in terms of π.

  b How many times larger is the surface area of B than A?

  c Calculate the volumes of each one, leaving your answers in terms of π.

  d How many times larger is the volume of B than A?

2 **a** A ball has a surface area of 3632 cm².
     What is its diameter to the nearest centimetre?

  b A different ball has a volume of 3632 cm³.
     Find its diameter to the nearest millimetre.

3 Saturn has a diameter of 1.2×10^5 km.
   Write an expression for its surface area in terms of π.

4 What are the dimensions of a square piece of card which has the same surface area as a sphere of diameter 14 cm?

5 An Eiffel Tower paperweight is shaped like a hemisphere with a radius of 55 mm.

55 mm

  a What is its volume?

  b What is the external surface area of the clear plastic part?

Archimedes had the diagram in Question **6** carved on his tomb because of its special properties. That's real pride in your work!

6 A sphere of diameter 15 cm fits exactly into a cylinder of height 15 cm and diameter 15 cm.

   Calculate:

  a the curved surface area of the cylinder

  b the curved surface area of the sphere.

15 cm

15 cm

7 A sphere, diameter d, fits exactly inside a cylinder of diameter d and height d.
   Show why both always have the same curved surface area regardless of the value of d.

Parts of solids and composite solids

A cone or pyramid which has had its vertex cut off by a plane parallel to its base is known as a frustum.

Example What is the volume of this frustum of a cone ?

3 cm radius
12 cm
5 cm

Volume of frustum = Vol. of 12 cm cone – Vol. of 7 cm cone

To calculate the volume of the 7 cm cone you need to know its base radius b.
The easiest way to find this is to consider the similar triangles ABE and ACD.

$$\frac{BE}{CD} = \frac{AB}{AC} \quad so \quad \frac{b}{3} = \frac{7}{12}$$

$$b = \frac{3 \times 7}{12} = 1.75 \, cm$$

A
7 cm
12 cm
B b E
5 cm
C 3 cm D

Vol. of frustum $= (\frac{1}{3}\pi \times 3^2 \times 12) - (\frac{1}{3}\pi \times 1.75^2 \times 7)$

$= (\frac{1}{3}\pi \times 108) - (\frac{1}{3}\pi \times 21.4375)$

$= \frac{1}{3}\pi (108 - 21.4375)$

$= \mathbf{90.6 \, cm^3}$ (to 1 dp)

◆ Cones, pyramids and spheres can be parts of composite solids.

Example A perfume spray fits tightly inside a clear plastic cube of side 12 cm. The shape of the spray is a hemisphere that sits on a cylinder. Calculate the volume of air between the spray and the cube.

Vol. spray $\quad=$ Vol. hemisphere + Vol. cylinder

$= (\frac{1}{2} \times \frac{4}{3} \pi r^3) + \pi r^2 h$

$= (\frac{4}{6} \times \pi \times 6^3) + (\pi \times 6^2 \times 6)$

$= 144\pi + 216\pi$

$= 360\pi$

$= 1131 \, cm^3$ (nearest integer)

Vol. airspace $=$ Vol. cube – Vol. spray

$= 12^3 - 1131$

$= 1728 - 1131$

$= \mathbf{597 \, cm^3}$ (nearest integer)

12 cm
12 cm
12 cm

Exercise 13.8
Volume of complex solids

1 A cylindrical pencil is 17.6 cm long and has a radius of 3 mm. It has 1.5 cm of its length shapened to a point. Calculate:

    a its volume   **b** its surface area.

2 A hemispherical hollow of radius 2 cm is made in the top of an 8 cm cube.:

    a Calculate the volume of the solid
    b Calculate the total surface area of the shape.

2 cm
8 cm

3 Calculate the volume and total surface area of each solid.

a

8.5 cm

Radius 4.6 cm

b

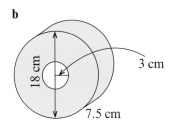

18 cm

3 cm

7.5 cm

c

10 cm

radius
3 cm

10 cm

12 cm

d

Diameter

3 cm

12.5 cm

1.5 cm

16 cm

15 cm

4 An ice lolly mould is shaped like an inverted cone of height 9 cm.

Green juice is poured into the mould until it reaches half the height, then red juice is added to the top.

a What volume of red juice is added?
b What percentage of the volume of the lolly is green?

3 cm

9 cm

> Note that the formula for the volume of a cone still applies to cones which are not right cones, i.e. sloping ones.

5 A model of a clock tower is made from one piece of card.

It is shaped like a square-based pyramid on a square-based prism.

A scale of 1 : 50 is used.

a What is the volume of the clock tower in m³?
b What is the volume of the model in cm³?
c Sketch a possible net for the model.
d Calculate the area of card needed for your net (ignore tabs and other fixings).

7.31 m

20 m

13 m

3 m   3 m

6 Three spheres of diameter 4 cm sit inside a cuboidal tin with internal dimensions of 12 cm, 16 cm and 14 cm.
The space in the tin is filled with water and this water is then poured out into a measuring cylinder of radius 4 cm.
How high up the cylinder does the water reach?

7 This frustum was made by cutting the top off a right cone.
Let h be the height of the original cone in cm.

a Write an expression for the height of the part which was cut off.
b Use similar triangles to show why $5h = 48$, and hence calculate the height of the original cone and the part which was cut off.
c Calculate the volume of the frustum.

3 cm

6 cm

8 cm

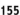

Thinking ahead to ...
the ratio of lengths areas
and volumes

A Cube A has a side length of 1 cm and cube B has a side length of 2 cm.

    a Calculate the surface areas of both cubes.

    b Calculate the volumes of both cubes.

    c The ratio of the dimensions of the cubes is $1:2$.
       Calculate:

       i the ratio of the surface areas

      ii the ratio of the volumes.

The ratio of lengths, areas and volumes

♦ As an object is enlarged the ratio of its lengths obviously increases. Less obviously, the area and volume will also increase but not in the same ratio as the lengths.

♦ Areas involve multiplying a length by a length, so if the all corresponding lengths on an object increase x times, **any** area on the object will increase $x \times x$ or x^2 times.

♦ Volumes involve multiplying a length by a length by a length, so if all the corresponding lengths on an object increase x times, **any** volume on the object will increase $x \times x \times x$ or x^3 times.

♦ This may seem obvious as cubes or cuboids are enlarged. It also applies to any **similar** objects such as spheres, cones, or irregular or compound shapes.

Example Two similar wine bottles have base areas of 30.8 cm² and 50.3 cm².

Large   Small

a Calculate the ratio of the heights of the two bottles in the form $1:n$.

b The large bottle has a height of 30 cm. Calculate the height of the small bottle.

c If the large bottle is a standard bottle, is it true to call the small bottle a 'half bottle'?

a The ratios of the base areas is:
$30.8 : 50.3 = 1 : 1.633\,1169$ (to 7 dp)

so the ratio of corresponding lengths will be $1 : \sqrt{1.633\,1169}$
$$= 1 : 1.277\,9346$$

The ratio of the heights of the bottles is $1:1.2779$ (to 4 dp)

b **The height of the small bottle** $= \dfrac{30}{1.2779} = \textbf{23.5 cm}$ (to 3 sf)

c The ratio of lengths is $1 : 1.277\,9346$
so the ratio of the volumes will be $1 : (1.277\,9346)^3$
$$= 1 : 2.087$$

so the large bottle has roughly twice the capacity of the small one.
so the small bottle can justifyably be called a 'half bottle'.

> It is best not to round these ratios too much because squaring and cubing numbers tends to exaggerate any errors.

Exercise 13.9
Ratio of areas and volumes

1 Two similar cones have heights of 4 cm and 12 cm.

    a The volume of the larger cone is 353 cm³.
       Calculate the volume of the smaller cone.

    b The surface area of the small cone is 13.8 cm².
       Calculate the surface area of the large one.

2

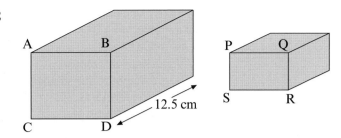

These cuboids are similar.
The area of ABCD is 36.5 cm², the area of PQRS is 22.5 cm²

a Give the ratio of their surface areas in the ratio 1:n.

b Calculate the ratio of the lengths of the cuboid in the form 1:n.

c Calculate the length of the smaller cuboid.

d For these cuboids, give the ratio of the volumes in the ratio 1:n.

3 Two cylinders are similar.
Cylinder A has a length of 8.5 cm.
Cylinder B has a length of 14.5 cm.

a Give the ratio of the base area of the cylinders in the ratio 1:n.

b The volume of cylinder A is 153 cm³.
Find the volume of the larger cylinder.

4 Two pyramids are similar.
The ratio of the dimensions of the bases is 2:5.
Give the ratio of the volumes of the pyramids in the form 1:n.

5 Two cuboidal tanks have volumes in the ratio 1:4.5
Give the ratio of the dimensions of the tanks in the form 1:n.

6 Two cylinders are similar. Their volumes are in the ratio 1:5.5.
The diameter of the smaller cylinder is 8 cm.
Calculate the diameter of the larger cylinder.

7 A scale model of a object is built to a scale of 1 to 32.

a The surface area of the model is 125.4 cm².
What would you expect the surface area of the real object to be? Explain your answer.

b The volume of the model is 238 cm³.
What do you expect to be the volume of the real object? Explain your answer.

8 Two similarly shaped weights have masses of 5 kg and 2 kg.
The 5 kg weight has a base
which is 9 cm across.

a Write the ratio of volumes of
the larger weight to the smaller
weight in the form $n : 1$.

b How wide is the base of
the 2 kg weight?

9 A newspaper displayed
this chart as part of a
feature on how two
companies donated
money to charity.

a The newspaper
believe they have
displayed the data
accurately, but why is
the chart misleading?

b The £ sign for Cyclone UK is 36 mm tall.
How should the newspaper change Denopt System's £ sign to accurately
reflect the companies' contributions?

10 This irregular solid of end area 16 cm² and
volume 132 cm³ is enlarged by certain scale factors.
Calculate the following with the
stated scale factors:

a End area, SF 2   b Volume, SF 3   c End area, SF $\frac{1}{3}$

d End area, SF $1\frac{3}{4}$ e Volume, SF $\frac{2}{3}$ f Volume, SF 2.

11 A barn with a curved roof has a maximum height of 6 metres and
holds 1740 tons of straw.
A similarly shaped but smaller barn holds half as much straw.

Calculate the maximum height of the smaller barn.

12 Three similar plane shapes, A, B and C, are enlarged.
When A is enlarged by SF 4, B by SF $\frac{1}{2}$ and C by SF 2, the images all
have the same area.

Calculate the scale factor which would enlarge:

a shape A on to shape C   b shape B on to shape C
c shape A on to shape B   d shape B on to shape A
e shape C on to shape A   f shape C on to shape B.

Formulas for length, area and volume

In calculations with length, area and volume:

- a length added to or subtracted from a length gives a length
- an area added to or subtracted from an area gives an area
- a volume added to or subtracted from a volume gives a volume
- a length multiplied by a length gives an area
- a length multiplied by a length multiplied by a length gives a volume
- the square root of an area gives a length
- to add, subtract, multiply or divide by a number that is not a length does not change whether an expression gives a length, area or volume.

For example, if the letters a, b and c represent lengths:

$3a + b$ represents a **length**: the lengths $3a$ and b add to give a length

$\frac{1}{2}a(b - c)$ represents an **area**: the expression $(b - c)$ is a length; the lengths $(b - c)$ and a multiply to give an area

$5a(b^2 + 3c^2)$ represents a **volume**: the areas b^2 and $3c^2$ add to give an area; the length a and the area $(b^2 + 3c^2)$ multiply to give a volume.

Exercise 13.10
Formulas for length, area and volume

1 In the following expressions, l and w each represent a length.
For each expression, decide if it represents a length, area or volume.
a $4(l + w)$ **b** $4lw^2$ **c** $lw + w^2$

2 One of these expressions gives the volume of the prism.

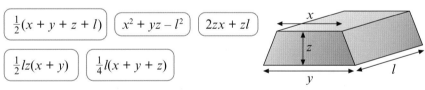

$\frac{1}{2}(x + y + z + l)$ $x^2 + yz - l^2$ $2zx + zl$

$\frac{1}{2}lz(x + y)$ $\frac{1}{4}l(x + y + z)$

a Which is the correct expression for the volume of the prism?
b Give reasons for your answer.

3 One of these expressions gives the perimeter of this shape and one gives the area.

$\pi a^2 b$ πab $\pi b^2 a^2$ $\pi(a + b)$ $\pi b^2(a + 4)$

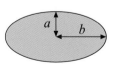

π is a number, not a length.

Which is the correct expression for:
a the perimeter **b** the area?

4 In the following expressions, r and h each represent a length.
For each expression, decide if it represents a length, area or volume.
Give reasons for each answer.
a $\frac{1}{4}rh$ **b** $\sqrt{r^2 + h^2}$ **c** $3(r + h) + \pi h$
d $r^2(r + h)$ **e** $\frac{4}{3}\pi r^3$ **f** $\pi r(r + h)$

5 The letters x, y and z represent lengths.
Explain why $xy + xyz + y(x - z)$ cannot represent a length, area or volume.

End points

You should be able to ...

... so try these questions

A Calculate areas of composite shapes

A1 Calculate the area of this shape.

B Understand about planes of symmetry

B1 This solid is made from six cubes.

How many planes of symmetry does it have?

C Calculate volumes, capacities and surface areas of solids

C1 This is a section through a plastic closed tank which holds heating oil. The tank is shaped like a cylinder with a hemisphere at each end. The thickness of the plastic can be ignored.

Calculate:
a the capacity of the tank in m³
b surface area of the tank in m²
c how many litres of oil there are in a full tank.

D Understand the effect of scale on area and volume

D1 A large dumb-bell solid has a surface area of 852 cm². A smaller similar solid has a surface area of 284 cm².

a The length of the small solid is 15 cm. What is the length of the larger one?

b The volume of the large solid is 3742 cm³. What is the volume of the smaller one?

E Decide if a formula could be for length, area or volume

E1 Amy knows that some of the following formulas could give the curved surface area (A) of a solid but she has forgotten which ones they are. s and r are lengths on the solid.

a $A = 4\pi r^2 s$ **b** $A = \pi(3r - s)$ **c** $A = 2\pi(r^2 + s^2)$

d $A = 4\pi r s^2$ **e** $A = 3\pi r s$ **f** $A = \dfrac{15\pi r^3}{3s}$

Which formulas cannot be for the surface area?

Some points to remember

◆ The volume of a cone with base radius r and height h is given by: $V = \frac{1}{3}\pi r^2 h$

◆ The curved surface area of a cone of slant height s is given by: $A = \pi r s$

◆ The volume of a sphere of radius r is given by: $V = \frac{4}{3}\pi r^3$

◆ The surface area of a sphere of radius r is given by: $A = 4\pi r^2$

Starting points
You need to know about ...

... so try these questions

A Theoretical probability

♦ Theoretical probability can be calculated just by examining possible outcomes.

♦ It is usually given as a fraction (it must be less than 1).

Example 1
What is the probability that this spinner will stop on B?
There are twelve sections of equal size.
Four sections have B on them.
So the probability that the spinner stops on B is $\frac{4}{12} = \frac{1}{3}$.

This can be written as $P(B) = \frac{1}{3}$.

Example 2
In the same way, $P(A \text{ or } B) = \frac{7}{12}$.

♦ Probabilities can be shown on a probability scale from 0 to 1.

$P(B)$ $P(A \text{ or } B)$

B The probability of a non-event

If you know the probability of something happening, then you can also calculate the probability of it **not** happening.

Example
$P(B)$ on the spinner above is $\frac{1}{3}$.

$P(\text{not } B)$ is $1 - \frac{1}{3} = \frac{2}{3}$.

C Multiplication of fractions

In probability, sometimes you need to multiply fractions.

You can think of $\frac{3}{4} \times \frac{2}{5}$ like this:

$$\boxed{3 \times 2 = 6}$$
$$\frac{3}{4} \times \frac{2}{5} = \frac{6}{20} = \frac{3}{10}$$
$$\boxed{4 \times 5 = 20}$$

$\frac{2}{5}$ of $\frac{3}{4} = \frac{2}{5} \times \frac{3}{4}$

♦ Multiply the numerators.
♦ Multiply the denominators.
♦ Then reduce to the simplest terms if you need to.

A1 What is the probability that the wheel will stop on:
  a A   **b** E   **c** D?

A2 What are these probabilities for the wheel?
  a $P(B \text{ or } F)$
  b $P(E \text{ or } A)$
  c $P(A, B \text{ or } C)$
  d P(a letter after D in the alphabet)
  e P(a letter of the alphabet)
  f P(the letter N)

A3 Draw a probability scale and label the positions of $p(A)$, $P(C)$, $P(D)$, and $P(A \text{ or } B \text{ or } E \text{ or } F)$.

A4 For a 1 to 6 dice what is the probability that for one roll you will get:
  a a multiple of 3
  b a prime number
  c a factor of 12?

B1 The probability of getting a red colour on a spinner is $\frac{4}{5}$. What is the probability of not getting red?

B2 In a game $P(2 \text{ points})$ is $\frac{1}{4}$ and $P(3 \text{ points})$ is $\frac{1}{8}$. What is $P(\text{not } 2 \text{ nor } 3 \text{ points})$?

C1 Multiply these fractions. Give each answer in its simplest terms.
  a $\frac{3}{4} \times \frac{1}{4}$
  b $\frac{5}{8} \times \frac{2}{5}$
  c $\frac{2}{3} \times \frac{6}{7}$
  d $\frac{1}{9} \times \frac{3}{4}$

D Relative frequency

- ◆ Relative frequency is a way of **estimating** a probability.

- ◆ It can be used both in equally likely situations or when outcomes are not equally likely.

- ◆ It is found by experiment (**experimental probability**), by survey, or by looking at data already collected (**empirical probability**).

- ◆ It is can be given as a decimal, a fraction or a percentage.

Example

This data shows the colour of cars passing a factory gate one morning.

Estimate the probability that, at a random time, a car passing will be red.

Colour	Frequency
Red	68
Black	14
Yellow	2
Green	34
Blue	52
Grey	35
Other	23
Total	228

The relative frequency of red cars is $\frac{68}{228} = 0.30$ (to 2 dp).

So the probability of a red car is 0.30 or 30%.

- ◆ This estimate of the probability can then be used to predict the number of red cars that will pass the gate on a different morning.

E Tree diagrams for combined events

- ◆ A tree diagram can help to organise data when calculating the probability of several events happening together.

- ◆ To find the probability of a particular joint outcome you can multiply the probabilities along the branches that lead to it.

This is a tree diagram for spinning a fair coin and rolling a fair 1 to 6 dice.

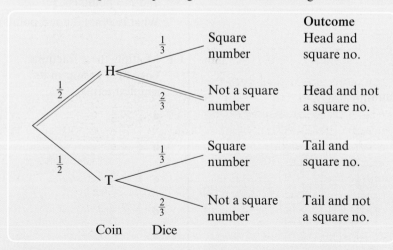

Example
To find the probability of a head **and** a non-square number you multiply the probabilities along the red branches.

Probability of a head and non-square no. is $\frac{1}{2} \times \frac{2}{3} = \frac{2}{6}$

D1 What is the relative frequency of blue cars in the survey? Give your answer to 2 dp.

D2 Estimate the probability that, at a random time, a car passing will be:
   a not blue
   b either yellow or green
   c neither green nor red
   d either black, grey or blue.

D3 For which of these are the outcomes not equally likely.

   The probability that:
   a a dropped matchbox will land face up
   b a person will catch measles before they are ten
   c the next snowtorm will be in December.

E1 What is the probability of a head and a square number?

E2 What is the probability of a tail and a non-square number?

E3 A red 1 to 6 dice and a blue 1 to 6 dice are rolled.

   a Draw a tree diagram to show the probability of a triangle number on the red dice and an even or odd number on the blue one.

   b What is the probability of getting a non-triangle number on the red with an even number on the blue dice?

Ways of pairing things

Exercise 14.1
Pairing

When people come down to breakfast in France the custom is that each person shakes hands with everyone else.
This can mean a large number of handshakes, but exactly how many depends on the number of people.
Two people shaking hands counts as one handshake.

There are five members of the Leblanc family: Angeline, Bruno, Charles, Danielle and Emmelle.
Here are three of the handshakes that are made: AB, AD, BE.

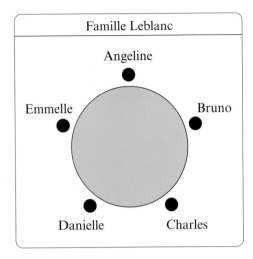

Famille Leblanc

Angeline

Emmelle

Bruno

Danielle

Charles

1 **a** List all the handshakes for the Leblanc family above.
  b Arrange your list so you can be sure you have every handshake.
  c How many handshakes in total?

2 A guest, Frederic, stays overnight with the Leblancs.

  a When they all come down to breakfast list the handshakes made.
  b How many handshakes are made?

3 **a** Draw up a table like this.

No. of people	1	2	3	4	5	6
No. of handshakes	0	1				

  b Describe any patterns you can see in the table.
  c Use your pattern to predict how many handshakes there will be for seven people. Check your prediction.

4 Emmelle is going on a trip. She wishes to take two books. Her bookshelf has five books she has not read. She picks two books at random.

  a List all the different pairs of books she might pick.
  b What is the probability that she picks two books by Sartre?
  c What is the probability that she picks two books by the same author?
  d What is the probability that she picks at least one blue book?
  e Give the probability of picking two books of different colour.

5 Bruno has eight books on his shelf, four of which are by Sartre.
He picks two books at random.
What is the probability that they are both by Sartre?

Dependent and independent events

If one cube is pulled from this bag at random, **replaced**, then another cube is chosen the probability of getting a red is $\frac{3}{9}$ on both occasions.

The same applies to the probability of other colours. This can be represented on a tree diagram like this:

When replacing cubes — Outcomes

			Outcomes
	$\frac{3}{9}$ R	$\frac{3}{9}$ R	RR
		$\frac{5}{9}$ B	RB
		$\frac{1}{9}$ Y	RY
	$\frac{5}{9}$ B	$\frac{3}{9}$ R	BR
		$\frac{5}{9}$ B	BB
		$\frac{1}{9}$ Y	BY
	$\frac{1}{9}$ Y	$\frac{3}{9}$ R	YR
		$\frac{5}{9}$ B	YB
		$\frac{1}{9}$ Y	YY

First pick   Second pick

The probability of getting two reds is therefore $\frac{3}{9} \times \frac{3}{9} = \frac{1}{9}$.

In this case the probability for the second pick **does not depend** on the first. Events of this type are known as independent **events**.

Two or more events or outcomes are independent if the happening of one of them has no effect on the other.

Two events or outcomes are dependent if the happening of one of them directly affects the other.

Suppose that when a cube has been picked it is **not replaced** for the second pick. If a red cube is picked first there will be 8 cubes left and only 2 of them will be red. For the second pick the probability of a red will be $\frac{2}{8}$.

The probabilities on the tree diagram will now look like this.

When not replacing cubes — Outcomes

			Outcomes
	$\frac{3}{9}$ R	$\frac{2}{8}$ R	RR
		$\frac{5}{8}$ B	RB
		$\frac{1}{8}$ Y	RY
	$\frac{5}{9}$ B	$\frac{3}{8}$ R	BR
		$\frac{4}{8}$ B	BB
		$\frac{1}{8}$ Y	BY
	$\frac{1}{9}$ Y	$\frac{3}{8}$ R	YR
		$\frac{5}{8}$ B	YB
		$\frac{0}{9}$ Y	YY

First pick   Second pick

The probability of getting two reds has now changed to $\frac{3}{9} \times \frac{2}{8} = \frac{1}{12}$.

In this case the probabilities for the second pick **do depend** on the first. Events of this type are known as dependent **events**.

Exercise 14.2
Probabilities for dependent events

1   For the problem above, what is the probability of getting:

 a   two blues when cubes are replaced
 b   two blues when cubes are not replaced
 c   a yellow and a red when cubes are replaced
 d   a yellow and a red when cubes are not replaced?

2   A washing line has these socks hanging on it.

Andy the thief steals two socks from the line at random.

a   What is the probability that the first sock he takes has a white stripe?

b   If the first sock has a white stripe, what is the probability that the second will also have a white stripe?

c   Draw a tree diagram to show white stripes or no white stripes when two socks are taken from the line.

d   From your diagram calculate the probability that neither sock the thief takes has a stripe.

Andy has a pang of conscience and puts the socks back on the line. His friend, Lisa, then steals two socks from the twelve, also at random.

e   What is the probability that Lisa steals:
i   two green socks
ii   a blue sock and a yellow sock
iii   a pair of the same colour (ignore the stripes)?

3   A card is picked at random from a pack of nine number cards. It is not replaced then a second card is picked. The cards are numbered 2, 3, 4, 5, 6, 7, 8, 9, 10.

a   Copy and complete the reduced tree diagram for picking cards with prime numbers.

b   Calculate the probability that both cards show prime numbers.

c   What is the probability that only one card will have a prime number?

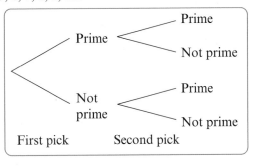

d   Draw a different tree diagram to help you calculate the probability that the product of the two numbers will be even.

4   Three stable hands decide who mucks out the horses by drawing straws. There are 3 short straws and 2 long ones. When a straw has been picked it is not replaced. Any person picking a short straw must help with mucking out.

What is the probability that:

a   all three people have to muck out
b   no one has to muck out
c   only one person mucks out
d   exactly two people muck out?

Note that these are dependent events. Even if the thief takes both socks at exactly the same instant, in probability terms this is the same as taking one then the other.

Even though a tree diagram can get crowded when dealing with four colours, it can still provide a visual way to organise the data.

For instance you could use a reduced tree diagram such as this for question **2e** part **i**.

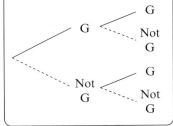

5 A charity decides to raise funds by using a scratch card with ten hidden numbers. There are always five 1's, three 3's and two 4's but they are in different positions on each card.
You win if you uncover a total of 5. More than 5 and you lose.

a List all the winning combinations.

A tree diagram has been started to show the winning combinations.

b Why do you think the ends of some of the branches are crossed out and others are ticked?

Note that not every branch need always be shown on a tree diagram. You only need to draw those useful to you.

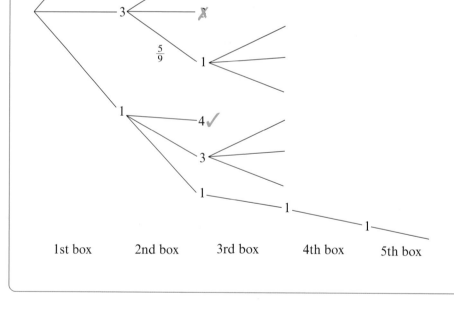

c Copy and complete the tree diagram and the probabilities to show winning combinations.
d Calculate the probability of getting a total of 5 by uncovering:
    i 5 squares   **ii** 3 squares   **iii** 2 squares.
e Is it true to say there is 'Over 50% chance of winning' with one card? Explain your answer.
f If the charity sells 500 cards, what profit or loss are they likely to make?

Conditional probability

The probability of something happening may depend on what happened earlier. For instance, the probability that a student will be absent from school on one day may be affected by whether the same student was absent the day before. These probabilities are often estimates based on relative frequencies.

> The probability that Jenny goes to the cinema on Friday night is an example of **conditional probability**.

Example

The probability that Jenny goes to the cinema on Friday is 0.27 based on her usual behaviour, but if she buys a video the probability goes down to 0.12. The probability that she buys a video is 0.3

Draw a tree diagram and calculate the probability that Jenny goes to the cinema.

The probabilities in blue have been calculated from the knowledge that the probabilities at any point must total 1.

Probability that Jenny goes to the cinema = (0.7 × 0.27) + (0.3 × 0.12)

= 0.189 + 0.036

= **0.225**

Exercise 14.3
Conditional probability

1 The probability that a new road needs repair after one year is 0.14.
If the road is not repaired in the first year, the probability that it needs repair in the second year is 0.45.
If it is repaired, the probability drops to 0.33 in the second year.
   a Draw a tree diagram to show the probabilities of repair over the two years.
   b Calculate the probability that the road:
      i does not need repair over the two years
      ii needs repair in the second year.

2 If it is a sunny day, the probability that the following day is sunny is 0.53.
If it is not sunny, the probability for sun the following day drops to 0.13.
Amy has her holiday on Monday, Tuesday and Wednesday.
It is sunny on Monday.

   What is the probability that Amy has:
   a three days of sun   b only one day of sun   c two days of sun?

3 The probability that a person chosen at random is left-handed is 0.08.
If they are left-handed, the probability that they are also left-footed is 0.91.
If they are not left-handed, the probability of being left-footed is 0.01.

   Use a tree diagram to calculate the probability that a person chosen at random catches a ball with one hand but kicks it with the other.

When can you add probabilities?

Exercise 14.4
Adding probabilities

This shows the set of males with criminal records in the town of Humbleton.

> Give your probabilities as fractions and do not cancel them down.

1   What is the probability that a male criminal in Humbleton has:
    a   a beard   **b**   a necklace   **c**   a beard or a necklace?

2   Compare your answers for the probabilities in Question **1**.
    What link can you find between them?

3   What is the probability that a male criminal in Humbleton has:
    a   an earring   **b**   a moustache?

4   **a**   Predict the probability of a criminal having either an earring or a
         moustache.
    b   Use the full set above to find the probability that a criminal has
         either an earring or a moustache.
    c   Why do you think your prediction may not be the
         same as the true answer?

5   What is the probability that a criminal, chosen at random, has:
    a   a hat   **b**   a beard   **c**   a beard or a hat?

Venn diagrams are named after the mathematician John Venn, who invented them in 1881 for his work on logic.

You can use Venn Diagrams to help you see why you can sometimes add probabilities, but at other times you must not.

Look at those criminals who have:
- ◆ dark hair ◆ earrings.

All those with dark hair are in the red loop and all those with an earring are in the blue loop.

From this you can see that the probability of having dark hair is $\frac{7}{16}$

and of having an earring is $\frac{5}{16}$.

The probability of having either is $\frac{12}{16}$ (which is $\frac{7}{16} + \frac{5}{16}$).

The outcomes 'dark hair' and 'earrings' in Hambleton are said to be mutually exclusive.

But now look at those with:
- ◆ a beard ◆ a moustache.

This time the loops overlap because Alf, Liam and Jim have both beards and moustaches.

The probability of having a beard is $\frac{4}{16}$

and of having a moustache is $\frac{7}{16}$.

The probability of having either is $\frac{8}{16}$ (which is **not** $\frac{4}{16} + \frac{7}{16}$).

A beard and a moustache in Hambleton are not mutually exclusive outcomes.

You can only add probabilities when outcomes are mutually exclusive.

Mutually exclusive outcomes are ones that cannot happen together. For instance, if you are born in January in England you cannot also be born in a summer month.

Outcomes which are not mutually exclusive can happen together. For example, if you are born in January you can be a teenager.

Exercise 14.5
Probability and Venn diagrams

1 **a** Draw a Venn diagram to show the criminals with a necklace and those with fair hair.
   b Can you add the separate probabilities to find the probability that a criminal has either a necklace or fair hair? Explain your answer.

2 Use your diagram to decide the probability that a criminal has:
   a **either** a necklace **or** fair hair
   b **both** a necklace **and** fair hair
   c **neither** a necklace **nor** fair hair
   d a necklace but not fair hair
   e fair hair but not a necklace.

3 Draw Venn diagrams to help you decide on the probabilities of having:
   a either a hat or an earing
   b either a necklace or dark hair
   c either glasses or fair hair
   d neither glasses nor dark hair.

4 For each of these, describe whether the two parts are mutually exclusive – the probability of:
   a a girl playing hockey in a school or a girl playing basketball
   b a boy playing basketball in a school or a girl playing hockey
   c a driver or a passenger
   d a bus driver or a tall woman
   e a dancer or a mechanic.

Outcomes from a biased dice

This table shows the probabilities of getting each number on a biased 0–9 dice.

Outcome	0	1	2	3	4	5	6	7	8	9
Probability	0.13	0.21	0.05	0.10	0.01	0.25	0.13	0.07	0	0.05

A biased dice is one where each outcome is not equally likely.

Other probabilities can be found from these probabilities.

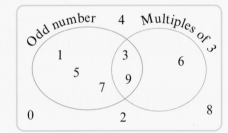

Example

What is the probability of getting a number less than 4 in one roll of the dice?

There are four numbers (0, 1, 2, and 3) less than 4.
There is no overlap between them (you can't get a 3 and a 1 in the same roll).
So you can add the probabilities for 0, 1, 2 and 3.

So the probability of a number less than 4 is 0.13 + 0.21 + 0.05 + 0.1 = 0.49.

Take care with some probabilities where outcomes are not mutually exclusive.

Example   What is the probability of getting either a multiple of 3 or an odd number?

Here you can get a multiple of 3 **and** an odd number in the same roll of the dice.

The numbers 3 and 9 come in both sets but must only be counted once.

So the probabilities to add are those for:
1,   5,   7,   3,   9 and 6.

0.21 + 0.25 + 0.07 + 0.1 + 0.05 + 0.13

So the probability of a multiple of three or an odd number is 0.81.

Exercise 14.6
Outcomes from a biased dice

Note that 0 is counted as the first even number.

1   What is the probability, with this dice, of getting:

  a   a number greater than 6
  b   an even number
  c   a prime number
  d   a number which is not prime
  e   a number which is a multiple of 3 **and** an even number?

2   Use the Venn diagram to calculate the probability of getting in one roll:

  a   a multiple of three **and** an odd number
  b   a number which is **neither** a multiple of 3 **nor** an odd number
  c   a number which **is not** a multiple of 3 but **is** an odd number.

3   Use a Venn diagram to find the probability of getting a number greater than 5 or an even number.

4   **a**   Why can you add all the probabilities when you find the probability that in one roll you get a number less than 5 or a number greater than 7?
  b   Calculate this probability.
  c   What is the probability of **not** getting a number less than 5 **nor** a number greater than 7?

Using Venn diagrams to find probabilities

Venn diagrams can be very useful when you have to find, for instance, the probability of: (one event **and** another event), (one event **or** another event), (**neither** one event **nor** another) or (one event **but not** another event).

Example On Saturday night 20 young people went into town. 12 of these visited Kingston's club, 9 went to Night Owls, and 3 decided not to go to any club.

Calculate:

a *P*(Kingston's or Night Owls)   **b** *P*(Kingston's and Night Owls)

c *P*(Kingston's but not Night Owls).

This problem seems strange at first. You know only 20 people went out but 12 + 9 + 3 appears to make 24 people in town that night.

This must mean 4 people have been counted twice – in other words, they went to both clubs.

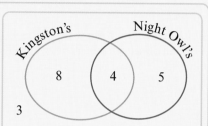

The Venn diagram would therefore look like this.

Therefore:

$$P(\text{Kingston's or Night Owls}) = \frac{(8 + 4 + 5)}{20} = \frac{17}{20}$$

$$P(\text{Kingston's and Night Owls}) = \frac{4}{20}$$

$$P(\text{Kingston's but not Night Owls}) = \frac{8}{20}$$

Exercise 14.7
Venn diagrams and
probabilities

1 Liam carried out a survey into what people had for breakfast.

He found that, of the 44 people asked, 20 had English breakfast(E), 6 of these had both cereal(C) and English breakfast, and 5 people had neither English breakfast nor cereal.

a Draw a Venn diagram to show the information.

b Calculate the following probabilities:

   i *P*(cereal but not English breakfast) **ii** *P*(cereal or English breakfast)

  iii *P*(cereal)   **iv** *P*(not cereal nor English breakfast)

c Explain why *P*(E) + *P*(C) ≠ *P*(E or C).

> The symbol ≠ means
> is not equal to …

2 Two hundred TV viewers were asked about the soaps they watched on Monday night. These are some of the findings where E stands for Eastenders, C for Coronation Street and N for Neighbours.

26 watched only N, in total 100 watched E, 8 watched all three, 35 watched E and C, 20 watched E and N but not C, 22 watched C and N, and 29 watched none of the soaps.

a Copy the Venn diagram and fill in the numbers in each region.

b Calculate these probabilities:

   i *P*(E and N)

  ii *P*(C)

 iii *P*(E or N)

  iv *P*(E and C but not N).

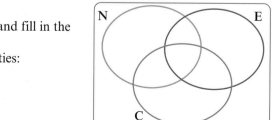

End points

You should be able to ...   ... so try these questions

A Calculate probabilities for dependent events

A1 A box contains 7 coach bolts, 4 machine bolts and 2 galvanised bolts. No other bolts are in the box.
 Two bolts are taken at random from the box at the same time.
 a If one of the bolts taken is a machine bolt, what is the probability that the other one is also a machine bolt?
 b Draw a tree diagram to show the probabilities when two bolts are taken.
 c What is the probability that:
  i both are coach bolts
  ii the two bolts are of different types?

B Understand the effect of conditional probability

B1 The probability that Claire gets up before 7 am is 0.26.
 If she does get up before 7 am, the probability that she has a bath is 0.68.
 If not, the probability of a bath drops to 0.24.
 a Draw a tree diagram with the probabilities to show the situation.
 b Calculate the probability that Claire has a bath in the morning.

C Decide when you can find a probability by adding the separate probabilities

C1 For each of these, describe whether the two parts are mutually exclusive.
 The probability of:
 a a 1 to 6 dice giving a multiple of 3 or a square number
 b a 1 to 10 spinner giving a square number or a prime number
 c a 1 to 6 dice giving a prime number or an even number
 d a 1 to 6 dice giving a square number or a triangular number.

D Use Venn diagrams to help find probabilities

D1 Amongst a group of 34 jugglers, 12 wore green hats and 19 had red trousers. The number of jugglers who had neither green hats nor red trousers was twice the number who had both red hats and green trousers.
 a Draw a Venn diagram to display the information.
 b What was the probability that a juggler, chosen at random, had:
  i a green hat but no red trousers
  ii a green hat or red trousers
  iii a green hat and red trousers?

Some points to remember

- ◆ With combined probability questions it is often helpful to draw a tree diagram.
 A reduced tree diagram may be necessary where there are many outcomes at each stage.

- ◆ With combined probability questions first establish if the events are dependent or independent.

- ◆ Where two objects are picked at the same time it is equivalent to two dependent events where one happens then the other.

- ◆ Before you add separate probabilities check that there is no overlap between the sets.
 A Venn diagram can sometimes help you decide this.

Starting points
You need to know about ...

... so try these questions

A Finding the median and the interquartile range

♦ You can find the median and interquartile range of a set of ungrouped data by listing the data in order.

♦ For a distribution with a large total frequency, using cumulative frequencies is quicker than listing the data.

1996 Open Golf Championship – Top 40 finishers
1st & 2nd round scores

Score	65	66	67	68	69	70	71	72	73	74	75	76	77
Frequency	3	3	14	13	11	15	9	4	5	0	1	1	1
Cumulative Frequency	3	6	20	33	44	59	68	72	77	77	78	79	80

	20th	21st		60th	61st	
Lower quartile	67	68		71	71	Upper quartile
	67.5				71	

80
|
20
+
20
+
20
+
20
|

Interquartile range = Upper quartile – Lower quartile
= 71 – 67.5
= **3.5**

Median score = **69** (40th) 69 ⦙ 69 (41st)
69

B Calculating the standard deviation of a distribution

♦ To calculate the standard deviation of a frequency distribution:

1996 Open Golf Championship – Top 40 finishers
2nd round scores

Score	65	66	67	68	69	70	71	72	73
Frequency	2	3	6	8	6	8	3	3	1

❖ calculate the mean of all the values

❖ calculate the square root of the mean squared deviation.

Score x	Frequency f	Total score fx	Squared deviation $f(x-\bar{x})^2$
65	2	130	28.125
66	3	198	22.6875
67	6	402	18.375
68	8	544	4.5
69	6	414	0.375
70	8	560	12.5
71	3	213	15.1875
72	3	216	31.6875
73	1	73	18.0625
	40	2750	151.5

$\frac{2750}{40}$ = 68.75 $\sqrt{\frac{151.5}{40}}$ = **1.95** (to 3 sf)
Mean score ($\bar{x}$)   Standard deviation

1996 Open Golf Championship

	Frequency			Frequency	
Score	3rd round	4th round	Score	3rd round	4th round
64	1	0	70	11	7
65	0	1	71	3	6
66	2	1	72	3	6
67	0	5	73	3	3
68	5	4	74	3	2
69	6	2	75	3	3

A1 Find the median and interquartile range of:
a the 3rd round scores
b the 4th round scores.

A2 Find the median and interquartile range of the 3rd and 4th round scores combined.

1996 Open Golf Championship
Top 40 finishers

1st round Score	Frequency	Score	Frequency
65	1	72	1
66	0	73	4
67	8	74	0
68	5	75	1
69	5	76	1
70	7	77	1
71	6		

B1 a Calculate the mean and standard deviation of the 1st round scores.

b Copy and complete this table using your answer to part a.

	1st round	2nd round
Mean		68.75
Standard deviation		1.95

C Comparing sets of data

- You can compare sets of data using two types of statistic:
an average, and a measure of dispersion.

	3rd round	4th round
Mean	70.55	70.4
Standard deviation (to 3 sf)	2.52	2.56

The 4th round scores are slightly lower on average.
The amount of variation in the scores is almost identical.

- When you compare data which has extreme values, the median
and the interquartile range can give a better comparison.

D Grouped data

- Data that is collected in groups, or grouped to make it easier to
present, is called a **grouped frequency distribution**.

1996 Open Golf Championship – Top 40 finishers
1st round scores

Score	64 – 66	67 – 69	70 – 72	73 – 75	76 – 78
Frequency	1	18	14	5	2

- Each group of data is a **class**: the size of a class is the **class interval**.
  - the 64-66 class has a class interval of 3.

- You can present grouped data on
a **grouped frequency diagram**.

- The class with the highest frequency
is called the **modal class**:
  - the modal class here is 67–69.

1996 Open Golf Championship
Top 40 finishers – 1st round scores

E Estimating the mean of grouped data

- To calculate an estimate of the mean of a grouped frequency
distribution:
  - find the **mid-class value** for each class
  - estimate the total for each class
  i.e. multiply the mid-class value by the frequency
  - divide the sum of the estimated totals by the total frequency.

1st round score	Frequency f	Mid-class value m	Total score estimate fm
64 –66	1	65	65
67 – 69	18	68	1224
70 – 72	14	71	994
73 – 75	5	74	370
76 – 78	2	77	154
	40		2807

Estimate of mean score ($\bar{m}$) = $\frac{2807}{40}$ = 70.175

C1 Use the statistics in your table
from Question **B1b** to compare
the 1st and 2nd round scores.

C2 a Copy and complete this
table using your answer
to Question **A2**.

	1st & 2nd rounds	3rd & 4th rounds
Median	69	
Interquartile range	3.5	

  b Compare the two sets of
data.

D1 Use the ungrouped data above
Question **A1**, and classes
64–66, 67–69, 70–72, 73–75,
to create a grouped frequency
distribution for:
  a the 3rd round scores
  b the 4th round scores.

D2 For each distribution:
  a draw a grouped frequency
diagram
  b give the modal class.

D3 Use the ungrouped data above
Question **A1**, and a class
interval of 2 to group the
3rd round scores.

E1 Use your grouped frequency
distribution from Question **D1a**
to calculate an estimate of the
mean of the 3rd round scores.

E2

4th round Score	Frequency f	Mid-class value m
64 – 65	1	64.5
66 – 67	6	66.5
68 – 69	6	
70 – 71	13	
72 – 73	9	
74 – 75	5	
	40	

Copy and complete this
working to calculate an
estimate of the mean.

Histograms

* A grouped frequency diagram can also be represented by a **histogram**.
* Data can be collected, or presented, in groups with **unequal** class intervals.

To draw a histogram for a distribution with unequal class intervals:

* find the class interval for each class
* calculate the **frequency density** for each class
  i.e. the frequency divided by the class interval
* use the frequency density as the height of each bar.

Example Draw a histogram for this grouping of the day 2 scores.

Points, p	Frequency	Class interval	Calculation	Frequency density
$400 \leqslant p < 700$	9	300	$9 \div 300$	0.03
$700 \leqslant p < 800$	10	100	$10 \div 100$	0.10
$800 \leqslant p < 850$	13	50	$13 \div 50$	0.26
$850 \leqslant p < 950$	8	100	$8 \div 100$	0.08
$950 \leqslant p < 1100$	10	150	$10 \div 150$	0.0$\dot{6}$

Exercise 15.1
Histograms

1

1996 Olympic Games – Decathlon (Day 1)
Points scored in each of the 5 events by the top 10 decathletes

Points	700 – 799	800 – 849	850 – 899	900 – 949	950 – 999	1000 – 1099	Total
Frequency	8	10	13	8	8	3	50

a Using 2 mm graph paper, draw a histogram for this distribution.
b The frequencies for three of the classes are the same.
Explain why the height of the bar for the 700–799 class is only half the height of the bars for classes 900–949 and 950–999.

2

Alex Kruger (GB) retired on Day 1 of the Decathlon because of a knee injury.

1996 Olympic Games – Decathlon
Total points scored by each decathlete

Points	6500 – 7499	7500 – 7799	7800 – 7999	8000 – 8099	8100 – 8199	8200 – 8299	8300 – 8999
Frequency	2	3	4	3	6	4	6

Draw a histogram for this distribution.

Discrete and continuous data

◆ There are two types of numerical data:
  ❖ **discrete** data can only be certain definite values

> **1996 Olympic Games – Decathlon**
> Dan O'Brien (US) – Points scored in each event
>
> 975   952   830   868   967   991   845   910   842   644

This data is discrete because it is not possible to score fractional numbers of points such as 873.5 in a decathlon event.

  ❖ **continuous** data can take any value on the real number line, including fractional values.

> Tessa Sanderson was taking part in her sixth Olympic Games in 1996. She won the Javelin Gold Medal in 1984.

> **1996 Olympic Games – Women's Javelin**
> Tessa Sanderson (GB) – Qualifying throws
>
> 58.86 m   56.80 m   56.64 m

This data is continuous because the distance thrown can be any value, but it is measured and rounded down to the nearest centimetre.

◆ Some data may appear to be continuous, but is actually discrete.

> Steve Smith won the Bronze Medal with his jump of 2.35 m.

> **1996 Olympic Games – Men's High Jump**
> Steve Smith (GB) – Clearances in Final
>
> 2.25 m   2.32 m   2.35 m

This is discrete data because the bar is only set at certain heights in a high jump competition. For example, in the men's final it was not possible to set a height of 2.30 m.

Exercise 15.2
Discrete and continuous data

1 A

1996 Olympic Games – Women's Long Jump
Fiona May (GB) – Distances jumped in Final

6.68 m   7.02 m   6.78 m   6.73 m   6.76 m   6.88 m

> Fiona May won the Silver Medal with her jump of 7.02 m.
>
> Great Britain won the Silver Medal in the men's 4 × 400 m relay, and set a new European record time.

B

1996 Olympic Games – Pole Vault
Jean Galfione (GB) – Heights cleared in Final

5.60 m   5.80 m   5.86 m   5.92 m

C

1996 Olympic Games
4 × 400 m Men's Relay Final

Great Britain
400 m split times (seconds)

Iwan Thomas	44.91
Jamie Baulch	44.19
Mark Richardson	43.62
Roger Black	43.87

For each set of data:

a   decide whether the data are discrete or continuous
b   explain your decision.

2   Gail Devers and Merlene Ottey were given the same time in the final of the women's 100 m.
Their times, to 3 dp, could have been any value between 10.930 and 10.940 seconds.

Explain why it is appropriate in athletics events to round times **up** to the nearest unit, and distances **down** to the nearest unit.

Women's 100 m Final

Time (s)

Devers	10.94
Ottey	10.94
Torrence	10.96
Sturrun	11.00

3 a Calculate the mean age of these athletes.

 b Explain why the exact mean age could be
    0.5 years greater than your answer.

 c When age data is given in years, do you
    think it is discrete or continuous ?
    Explain your answer.

Great Britain's Men's 4 × 400 m Relay Team Ages at 20th July 1996	
Jamie Baulch	23
Roger Black	30
Mark Richardson	23
Iwan Thomas	22

Using continuous data

◆ When you group continuous data, you need to decide what happens to
  values at the ends of the classes, the **class limits**.

> $16.5 \leqslant x < 18.0$
> $18.0 \leqslant x < 18.5$ ←——— 18.0 ———→ $16.5 < x \leqslant 18.0$
> $18.0 < x \leqslant 18.5$

A distance of 18.0 m goes into different classes in each grouping
because of the different ways the classes are defined.

◆ A common way of showing classes such as:
  $16.5 \leqslant x < 18.0$, $18.0 \leqslant x < 18.5$, etc. is $16.5 -$, $18.0 -$, $18.5 -$, etc.
  When grouping data using unequal class intervals, you should also show
  the upper class limit of the final class, e.g. 21.0

1996 Olympic Games – Women's Shot Final					
Distance (metres)	16.5 –	18.0 –	18.5 –	19.0 –	19.5 – 21.0
Frequency	5	13	10	9	4

◆ When age data is given in its usual form, in completed years, you can
  group it in the same way as discrete data.

Exercise 15.3
Using continuous data

1

1996 Olympic Games – Great Britain's Athletics Team				
Age	18 – 23	24 – 26	27 – 29	30 – 32	33 – 41
Frequency	18	18	19	18	9

> The width of the 18 – 23
> class is 6 years, and the
> mid-class value is 21.

Draw a histogram for this distribution.

2

1996 Olympic Games – Men's Shot Final					
Distance (metres)	19.0 –	19.5 –	20.0 –	20.5 –	21.0 – 22.0	Total frequency
Frequency	5	11	17	8	1	42

 a Draw a histogram for this distribution.
 b The mid-class value of the 19.0 – class is 19.25
    List the mid-class values for the other four classes.
 c Calculate an estimate of the mean distance

> You can use the same
> method to estimate the
> mean as you used before
> for discrete data.

3 For the data from the women's shot final above:

 a draw a histogram
 b use the statistical function on your calculator to estimate the mean.

4 Use your answers to Questions **2** and **3** to compare the men and women.

5   This data shows the reaction times of athletes in the sprint events.

The reaction time is the length of time between the starter's gun firing and the rear foot leaving the starting block.

s is the abbreviation for seconds.

Linford Christie (GB), the 100 m Gold Medal winner in 1992, was disqualified after a second false start when his recorded reaction time was 0.086 s.

Scientists believe a reaction time under one-tenth (0.100) of a second is impossible.

Men's 100 m Final

	Reaction time (s)
Bailey	0.174
Fredericks	0.143
Boldon	0.164
Mitchell	0.145
Marsh	0.147
Ezinwa	0.157
Green	0.169
Christie	DISQ

Men's 200 m Final

	Reaction time (s)
Johnson	0.161
Fredericks	0.200
Boldon	0.208
Thompson	0.202
Williams	0.182
Garcia	0.229
Stevens	0.151
Marsh	0.167

110 m Hurdles Final

	Reaction time (s)
Johnson	0.170
Crear	0.124
Schwarthoff	0.164
Jackson	0.133
Valle	0.179
Swift	0.151
Vander-Kuyp	0.167
Batte	0.160

Women's 100 m Final

	Reaction time (s)
Devers	0.166
Ottey	0.166
Torrence	0.151
Sturrup	0.176
Trandenkova	0.151
Voronova	0.133
Onyali	0.174
Pintusevych	0.176

Women's 200 m Final

	Reaction time (s)
Perec	0.174
Ottey	0.194
Onyali	0.231
Miller	0.172
Malchugina	0.198
Sturrup	0.165
Cuthbert	0.175
Guidry	0.207

100 m Hurdles Final

	Reaction time (s)
Engquist	0.132
Bukovec	0.164
Girard-Leno	0.133
Devers	0.189
Rose	0.179
Freeman	0.181
Shekhodanova	0.175
Goode	0.160

**1996 Olympic Games – Reaction Times
Semifinals – 100 m, 200 m, 100 m/110 m Hurdles**

Reaction time (s)	0.12–	0.14–	0.15–	0.16–	0.17–	0.18–	0.19–	0.21–0.27	Total
Frequency	7	11	13	16	14	16	9	8	94

a   Group the data for the six finals in the same way as the semifinals data.

b   Draw a histogram for:
   i   the semifinals   ii   the finals.

6   a   Copy your grouped frequency distribution for the finals data, and double each of the frequencies.

b   Draw a frequency polygon to show this distribution by plotting each frequency against its mid-class value.

c   On the same diagram, draw a frequency polygon for the semifinalists.

d   Do you think your frequency polygons give a fair comparison of the reaction times in the finals and semifinals ?
   Explain your answer.

There were exactly twice as many semifinalists as finalists.

7   Use your calculator to estimate the mean reaction time in:

a   the semifinals   b   the finals.

8

'Athletes' reaction times are faster in finals than in semifinals'

a   Do you think this hypothesis is true or false ?
b   Give reasons for your answer.

9   Investigate the effects of grouping the finals data in different ways.

Drawing a cumulative frequency curve

1996 Olympic Games – Decathlon (Day 2)
Points scored in each of the 5 events by the top 10 decathletes

Points	400 – 499	500 – 599	600 – 699	700 – 799	800 – 899	900 – 999	1000 – 1099	Total
Frequency	1	0	8	10	17	10	4	50

♦ To draw a **cumulative frequency curve**:

  ❖ construct a cumulative frequency table

> If you include a cumulative frequency of 0 in your table then you have a point to start the curve from: (400, 0).

Points	<400	<500	<600	<700	<800	<900	<1000	<1100
Cumulative frequency	0	1	1	9	19	36	46	50

  ❖ plot the cumulative frequencies on a graph

  ❖ join the points with a smooth curve.

Exercise 15.4
Drawing cumulative frequency curves

1

1996 Olympic Games – Decathlon (Day 1)
Points scored in each of the 5 events by the top 10 decathletes

Points	700 – 799	800 – 849	850 – 899	900 – 949	950 – 999	1000 – 1099	Total
Frequency	8	10	13	8	8	3	50

a Copy and complete the cumulative frequency table below.

Points	<700	<800	<850	<900	<950	<1000	<1100
Cumulative frequency	0						

b Use your table to draw a cumulative frequency curve.

2

> Steve Backley (GB) won the javelin silver medal with the very first throw of the final.

1996 Olympic Games – Men's Javelin Final

Distance (metres)	76 –	80 –	81 –	82 –	84 –	87 – 89
Frequency	6	6	8	13	13	2

a Copy and complete the following cumulative frequency table.

Distance (metres)	<76	<80	<81	<82	<84	<87	<89
Cumulative frequency	0	6					48

b Draw a cumulative frequency curve for the Men's Javelin final.

3 Using your answers to Question **2**, can you think of a way to find the median distance thrown in the final? Explain your method.

Estimating the median and the interquartile range

There were 48 throws in the final, so the **exact** median distance is halfway between the 24th and 25th longest.

It is impossible to find these distances from the table, so you can only **estimate** the median.

♦ A cumulative frequency table shows which class the median is in.

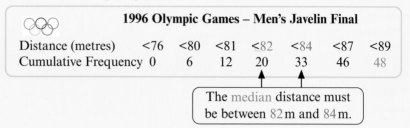

1996 Olympic Games – Men's Javelin Final							
Distance (metres)	<76	<80	<81	<82	<84	<87	<89
Cumulative Frequency	0	6	12	20	33	46	48

The median distance must be between 82 m and 84 m.

As you are only estimating distances within the classes, you can divide the 48 throws into four quarters using the **12th**, **24th**, and **36th** longest (cumulative frequencies 12, 24, and 36).

♦ To estimate the median and quartiles from a cumulative frequency curve:
  ❖ divide the cumulative frequency into four quarters
  ❖ go across to the curve, then go down and read off each value.

Estimate of median distance   = **82.4 m**
Estimate of interquartile range = 84.6 − 81.0
                                = **3.6 m**

Exercise 15.5
Estimating the median and interquartile range

1

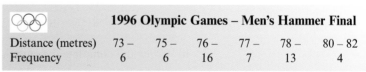

1996 Olympic Games – Men's Hammer Final						
Distance (metres)	73 –	75 –	76 –	77 –	78 –	80 – 82
Frequency	6	6	16	7	13	4

a Copy and complete the following cumulative frequency table.

Distance (metres)	<73		<80	<82
Cumulative frequency	0			52

b Draw a cumulative frequency curve for the Men's Hammer final.

2 Use your cumulative frequency curve to estimate:
  a the median distance thrown   **b** the interquartile range.

3 Compare the distances thrown in the Men's Hammer final and the men's Javelin final.

4 a From page 179, copy the cumulative frequency table and the cumulative frequency curve for the Decathlon (day 2).
  b Estimate the median points score.
  c Estimate the interquartile range of the scores.

Use cumulative frequencies 12.5, 25, and 37.5 to divide the data into four quarters.

Use cumulative frequencies 12.5, 25, and 37.5 to divide the data into four quarters.

5 Use your answers to Exercise 15.4, Question **1** to estimate:

   a the median points score on day 1 of the decathlon

   b the interquartile range of the scores.

6 Compare the points scored on days 1 and 2 of the Decathlon.

7

	1996 Olympic Games – Women's Javelin Final						
Distance (metres)	56 –	58 –	60 –	62 –	64 –	66 – 68	Total frequency
Frequency	7	11	10	10	7	1	46

   a Make a cumulative frequency table for the Women's Javelin final.

   b Draw a cumulative frequency curve.

   c Decide how to divide the data into four quarters.

   d Estimate the median distance thrown and the interquartile range.

Estimating cumulative frequencies

   ◆ You can estimate cumulative frequencies from a cumulative frequency curve.

Example Estimate how many Men's Javelin throws were:

   a less than 81.5 m   **b** greater than 85 m

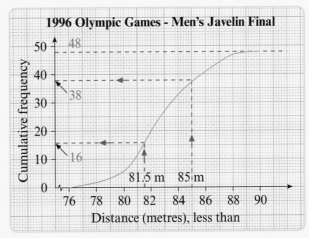

   a Estimated number of throws less than 81.5 m **= 16**

   b Estimated number of throws greater than 85 m = 48 – 38

                                                       = 10

Exercise 15.6
Estimating cumulative frequencies

1 Use the cumulative frequency curve above to estimate how many throws were less than 83 m.

2 The winning throw in the 1988 Men's Javelin final was 84.28 m. Estimate how many throws were greater than this in 1996.

3

Jonathan Edwards (GB) won the Silver Medal in the Triple Jump.

	1996 Olympic Games – Men's Triple Jump Final					
Distance (metres)	15.5 –	16.0 –	16.5 –	17.0 –	17.5 –	18.0 – 18.5
Frequency	1	7	14	6	2	1

   a Draw a cumulative frequency curve for the Men's Triple Jump final.

   b Estimate how many jumps were greater than 16.8 m.

Sampling from a population

♦ A **population** is the name given to any set of data under investigation. If you are investigating a very large population, it may not be possible to collect all the data.

♦ A **sample** is a smaller set of data, chosen from a population, that can be analysed and used to make conclusions about the population.

Exercise 15.7
Sampling from a population

1 The British Team for the 1996 Olympic Games consisted of 500 members. This is the distribution of their ages.

1996 Olympic Games
Ages of Great Britain Team at 20/7/96

Age	16 –	21 –	24 –	27 –	29 –
Frequency	25	54	68	59	63

Age	31 –	34 –	37 –	42 –	52 – 71
Frequency	51	41	47	55	37

Draw a histogram for this age distribution.

2 These are three random samples taken from the 500 members of the Great Britain Olympic Team.

In a random sample, each member of the population has the same chance of being chosen.

One way of choosing a random sample is to:

♦ allocate a number to each member of the population

♦ use a random number table to select the sample.

If the population is listed at random then you could choose a **systematic** sample, e.g. every 10th member on the list is chosen until the sample is complete.

1996 Olympic Games
Great Britain Team

Age	Frequency
19 –	5
24 –	4
29 –	7
39 –	4
49 – 68	5

Sample size 25

1996 Olympic Games
Great Britain Team

Age	Frequency
19 –	8
24 –	13
29 –	12
34 –	3
39 –	5
49 – 68	9

Sample size 50

1996 Olympic Games
Great Britain Team

Age	Frequency
19 –	14
24 –	25
29 –	28
34 –	10
39 –	11
49 –	8
59 – 68	4

Sample size 100

a Draw a histogram for each random sample.
b Compare the shapes of your distributions with your answer to Question **1**.

The estimate of the mean for each sample can be used as an estimate of the mean of the population.

3 For each random sample in Question **2**, use mid-class values of 21.5, 26.5, ... etc. to calculate an estimate of the mean.

4 The actual mean age of the Great Britain Olympic Team was 33.4 years. Use your answers to Question **3** to describe the effect of the size of sample on the estimate of the mean.

5 The Great Britain Team had 312 competitors and 188 support staff.

a Do you think the mean age of these two groups is likely to be the same? Explain your answer.
b When choosing a random sample of 50, what do you think the advantage might be of choosing random samples of 31 from the competitors and 19 from the support staff?

End points

You should be able to ...   ... so try these questions

A Use histograms and frequency polygons

B Calculate an estimate of the mean of a grouped frequency distribution

C Estimate the median and the interquartile range

D Compare grouped frequency distributions

E Estimate cumulative frequencies

1996 Olympic Games – Discus Finals						
Distance (metres)	56 –	60 –	62 –	64 –	66 –70	Total
Frequency Women	7	10	13	13	6	49
(of throws) Men	5	8	16	13	3	45

A1 Draw a histogram to show the distances thrown in the:
   a Women's Discus final   **b** Men's Discus final.

A2 a Draw a frequency polygon for the Women's Discus final.
   b On the same diagram, draw a frequency polygon for the Men's final.
   c Compare the two distributions.
   d Explain why the frequency polygons would not have given a fair comparison if the number of throws in the finals had been 59 and 45.

B1 (Do **not** use the statistical function on your calculator for this question.) For the Men's Discus final, calculate an estimate of the mean distance thrown.

B2 Use the statistical functions on your calculator to estimate the mean of the distances thrown in the Women's Discus final.

1996 Olympic Games – Men's Long Jump Final							
Distance (metres)	6.4 –	7.2 –	7.6 –	7.8 –	8.0 –	8.2 –	8.4 – 8.6
Frequency	2	3	4	13	13	2	1

1996 Olympic Games – Women's Long Jump Final					
Distance (metres)	6.2 –	6.4 –	6.6 –	6.8 –	7.0 – 7.2
Frequency	3	6	9	14	3

C1 a Draw a cumulative frequency curve for the Men's Long Jump final.
   b Use your cumulative frequency curve to estimate:
      i the median distance jumped   **ii** the interquartile range.

C2 Use cumulative frequencies 9, 18, and 27 to estimate the median and interquartile range for the Women's Long Jump final.

D1 Compare the distances jumped in the Women's and Men's finals.

D2 Use your answers to Questions **B1** and **B2** to compare the distances thrown in the Women's and Men's Discus finals.

E1

1996 Olympic Games – Women's Triple Jump Final					
Distance (metres)	13.5 –	13.9 –	14.1 –	14.4 –	14.7 –	15.0 – 15.4
Frequency	10	9	12	8	7	1

   a Draw a cumulative frequency curve for the Women's Triple Jump final.
   b Use your curve to estimate how many jumps were:
      i less than 14.0 m   **ii** greater than 14.5 m.

Some points to remember

♦ When you choose a sample from a population, usually the larger the sample the closer its mean and standard deviation are to those of the whole population.

WHEEL GARDEN CENTRE

OUR WATER WHEEL PRODUCES OVER 60% OF THE ELECTRICITY WE USE

Watering cans - plastic			
5 litre	8 litre	10 litre	12 litre
99p	£1.29	£1.69	£1.99
Watering cans - traditional			
1 gallon	1.5 gallon	2 gallon	2.5 gallon
£4. 99	£6.49	£7.99	£9.99

Visit our Coffee Shop

Rolls of Plastic Sheet

The easy way to stop weeds

15 metres long
and
1650 mm wide

Only £3.75
per roll
while stocks last

Special Offers on Spring bulbs

Traditional Watering Can Roses
Now in stock

£15.99

Cloches

Cloche Frames

56°   56°

100 mm

315 mm

Victorian Bell Cloches

The Super 9 Garden Store – 100% treated timber

0.8 metres   Front   1.5. metres

Two large windows :
• the same size
• fully opening

5.5 metres

Roof angle gives fast run-off of rainwater

2.6 metres

Door   Side

1.9 metres

2.8 metres

Special Features:

• The back of the store has no windows
• One side has no door or window
• The roof has a 10 cm overhang on all sides

£449.99

1 The plastic sheet is 120 microns thick.
(One micron is $\frac{1}{10\,000}$th of a centimetre.)
   a Give the thickness of the sheet in metres as a number in standard form.
   b Give the volume of the plastic sheet on the roll in m^3 in standard form.

2 The plastic sheet is rolled onto a cardboard tube. The inside diameter of the tube is 86 mm and the outside diameter is 94 mm.
   a Calculate the volume of cardboard used to make the tube. Do not round your answer.
   b The outside of the tube is coated with adhesive. The adhesive is applied at a rate of 135 ml/m^2, and is supplied in 5 litre cans.
   How many tubes can be coated with adhesive from one can? (There is no wastage.)

3 Calculate, to the nearest millimetre, the length of wire used to make one cloche frame.

4 A four-frame open-ended cloche 2.5 metres long is made by covering four frames, above ground level, with plastic sheet. At either end, an extra 15 mm of sheet is allowed for a seam.
   a How many cloches can be made from one roll of plastic sheet?
   b Calculate the percentage of each roll of sheet that is wasted making these cloches.

5 A Victorian bell-cloche is in the shape of a cylinder surmounted by a hemisphere. The internal dimensions of the cloche are: diameter 28 cm and height 42 cm.
   a Show that the capacity of the bell-cloche is approximately 23 litres.
   b The bell-cloche is made of 9 mm thick glass. Calculate the volume of glass used to make the cloche.
   c If the internal diameter (cm) of a bell-cloche is $2r$, and the internal height (cm) is h, show that the capacity C of the cloche is given by:

   $$C = \tfrac{1}{3}\pi r^2(3h - r)$$

   d Rearrange the formula for capacity C to give a formula for h in terms of r and C.

6 Wheel Garden Centre has a policy that price increases will never be more than 6%.
Next month they will increase the price of plastic sheet to £3.99 per roll.

Is this increase in line with their policy? Explain.

7 In metres the height h of a bucket, painted red, on the water wheel above the pool is given by the equation:

   $$h = 4 + 3\sin(30t)$$

   where t is the time in seconds after the wheel has been set in motion.
   a Calculate h (to 1dp) for values of t from 0 to 12.
   b Draw a graph to show how the height of the red bucket varies during the first 12 seconds.
   c The floor of the Coffee Shop is 3.7 metres above the pool. In the first 12 seconds when was the red bucket level with the floor of the Coffee Shop?

8 In the Coffee Shop Jim paid £3.29 for three coffees and two teas. Ella paid £4.10 for five teas and 2 coffees.

Write and solve two equations to find the prices of tea and coffee in the Coffee Shop.

9 Packs of spring bulbs are made up with daffodils and tulips in the ratio 5 : 3.

If there are n bulbs in a pack, give the number of tulip bulbs in terms of n.

10 The outside of the Super 9 store is sprayed with timber preservative (excluding the roof). The preserver is sprayed at a rate of 250 ml/m^2.

Will 5 litres of preserver cover one store? Explain your answer.

11 Which traditional watering can is the best value for money in your opinion? Explain your answer.

12 The traditional copper watering can 'rose' is the shape of a truncated right cone.
   a Calculate, in cm^3, to 2 dp the volume of water needed to fill the rose.
   b Calculate, in cm^3, to 1 dp the curved surface area of the rose.

Diameter 18 mm

95 mm

Diameter 62 mm

Starting points
You need to know about ...

... so try these questions

A Linear (straight line) graphs

A linear graph can be identified from its equation.
The equation of all linear graphs is of the form
$$y = mx + c$$ where m is the gradient and
c the intercept with the y-axis

Line A has a gradient of $\frac{3}{4}$, and an intercept with the y-axis at 1.

The equation of line A is
$$y = \frac{3}{4}x + 1$$

Line B has a gradient of $\frac{-5}{2}$, and an intercept with the y-axis at $^-3$.

The equation of line B is:
$$y = \frac{-5}{2}x - 3$$

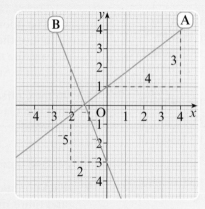

Line A has a **positive gradient** sloping upwards from left to right.
Line B has a **negative gradient** sloping downwards from left to right.

Being able to identify the gradient and intercept with the y-axis from a linear equation enables you to sketch or draw a graph.

To sketch a graph of $y = \frac{2}{3}x - 5$
you can identify that:

the gradient m is $\frac{2}{3}$

the y-intercept c is $^-5$

The sketch shows a graph of
$$y = \frac{2}{3}x - 5$$

(Note this is a sketch, so no accurate plotting or measuring is needed.)

To draw a graph of $y = \frac{2}{3}x - 5$

you can identify that the gradient is $\frac{2}{3}$, and the y-intercept is $^-5$.

To draw the graph:

- draw, graduate, and label a pair of axes
- plot the point (0, $^-5$), i.e. the y-intercept
- from the y-intercept show the gradient,
  i.e. to plot a second point on the graph
- draw a straight line passing through the two points
- label the linear graph with its equation.

(Note this is drawing a graph, so accuracy is essential.)

A1 Identify the gradient and intercept with the y-axis for these linear graphs.
  a $y = 4x + 3$
  b $y = \frac{1}{5}x - 8$
  c $y = 0.8x + 1.5$
  d $y = \frac{7}{4} + \frac{5}{4}x$
  e $y = 1 - 0.25x$
  f $y = 6x$
  g $y = x$
  h $y = 12$

A2 A linear graph has an intercept with the y-axis at (0, 3) and a gradient of 2.5.

  Write the equation of this graph.

A3 A linear graph has a gradient of $^-1$ and an intercept with the y-axis at the point (0, $^-2$).

  Give the equation of this line.

A4 Sketch each of these linear graphs.
  a $y = 3x + 2$
  b $y = 5x - 4$
  c $y = \frac{3}{5}x + 1$
  d $y = \frac{5}{8}x$
  e $y = 3 - 4x$
  f $y = 0.5 - 1.5x$

A5 Draw each of these linear graphs.
  a $y = \frac{1}{2}x + 1.2$
  b $y = \frac{3}{4} - 2x$
  c $y = 4 + 3x$
  d $y = \frac{3}{4}x$
  e $y = 1.5 - 4x$
  f $y = x - 2$

B Rearranging linear equations

Linear equations may have to be rearranged to put them in the form

$$y = mx + c$$

(Note that rearranging an equation is **not** changing the equation; it is producing an equivalent equation.)

- To draw the graph of $3y + 4x = 6$ using the gradient and intercept method, the equation will need to be in the form $y = mx + c$.

Example To rearrange $3y + 4x = 6$

$$3y + 4x = 6$$
[– 4x from both sides] $\quad 3y = {}^-4x + 6$
[÷ both sides by 3] $\quad y = {}^-\frac{4}{3}x + 2$

So $3y + 4x = 6$ and $y = {}^-\frac{4}{3}x + 2$ are equivalent equations.

The graph of $3y + 4x = 6$ has a gradient of ${}^-\frac{4}{3}$ and a y-intercept at $(0,2)$.

- Rearranging the linear equation may involve dealing with brackets.

Example To rearrange $4 = 2(3y - 5x)$

$$4 = 2(3y - 5x)$$
[multiply out bracket] $\quad 4 = 6y - 10x$
[+ 10x to both sides] $\quad 4 + 10x = 6y$
[÷ both sides by 6] $\quad \frac{4}{6} + \frac{10}{6}x = y$

So $4 = 2(3y - 5x)$ and $y = \frac{5}{3}x + \frac{2}{3}$ are equivalent equations.

- Rearranging the linear equation may involve dealing with fractions.

Example To rearrange $\frac{3}{5}x = \frac{1}{2}y - 1$

$$\frac{3}{5}x = \frac{1}{2}y - 1$$
[multiply both sides by 10] $\quad 6x = 5y - 10$
[+ 10 to both sides] $\quad 6x + 10 = 5y$
[÷ both sides by 5] $\quad \frac{6}{5}x + 2 = y$

So $\frac{3}{5}x = \frac{1}{2}y - 1$ and $y = \frac{6}{5}x + 2$ are equivalent equations.

- Rearranging the linear equation may involve fractions and brackets.

Example To rearrange $\frac{3}{4}(2y - 3x) = 2$

$$\frac{3}{4}(2y - 3x) = 2$$
[× both sides by 4] $\quad 3(2y - 3x) = 8$
[multiply out the bracket] $\quad 6y - 9x = 8$
[+ 9x to both sides] $\quad 6y = 9x + 8$
[÷ both sides by 6] $\quad y = \frac{3}{2}x + \frac{4}{3}$

So $\frac{3}{4}(2y - 3x) = 2$ and $y = \frac{3}{2}x + \frac{4}{3}$ are equivalent equations.

(Note that when you are dividing both sides of an equation by a value it is better to write the coefficient of x as a fraction rather than a decimal. In this way you can work with a gradient as a fraction.)

B1 Rearrange each of these equations so that they are in the form $y = mx + c$.

a $\quad 5y = 3x + 15$

b $\quad 2y + 5x = 8$

c $\quad 3y - 4x = 3$

d $\quad 4 - 2y = 3x$

e $\quad 7x - 2y = 1$

f $\quad 2(x - 3y) = 6$

g $\quad 5 = 4(2x + y)$

h $\quad 2(3 - 2y) = 5x$

i $\quad 4(2x - 1) = 2y$

j $\quad \frac{2}{3}y - 1 = 3x$

k $\quad 4 - \frac{1}{2}x = 5y$

l $\quad y = \frac{3}{5}x - 5$

m $\quad 3x + \frac{2}{3}y = 4$

n $\quad 5(x + 2y) = 3$

o $\quad \frac{3}{5}x + 2y = 4$

p $\quad 4(x - 3) = \frac{1}{2}y$

q $\quad 6 = 3(2x - y)$

r $\quad \frac{3}{4} = 3x - y + 1$

s $\quad 2(x - 3) = 3(4 - 2y)$

t $\quad 3(x + 1) = 4(3 - y)$

u $\quad 1 + \frac{1}{3}x = 2y$

v $\quad 3 - \frac{1}{4}y = \frac{1}{2}x$

w $\quad 1 - \frac{1}{2}x = \frac{2}{3}y$

x $\quad \frac{1}{2}(y + 4) = \frac{2}{3}x$

y $\quad \frac{2}{3}(x + 2y) = 1$

z $\quad \frac{5}{8}(y - 2x) = 3$

Solving simultaneous linear equations graphically

When a linear relationship between two variables can be expressed by two or more different equations, you can find the value of each variable by drawing graphs of each equation and finding a point where the coordinates satisfy both equations (i.e. where the line graphs intersect).

Example

Find values of x and y that satisfy the equations:

$$2x + 3y = {}^-5 \dots (1)$$
$$x + y = {}^-1 \dots (2)$$

♦ To draw graphs using the gradient and intercept the equations need to be in the form $y = mx + c$

To rearrange Equation (1)

$$2x + 3y = {}^-5$$

[i.e.]
$$3y = {}^-5 - 2x$$

[i.e.]
$$y = \frac{{}^-5}{3} - \frac{2}{3x}$$

To rearrange Equation (2)

$$x + y = {}^-1$$

[i.e.]
$$y = {}^-1 - x$$

♦ Draw graphs of $y = \frac{{}^-5}{3} - \frac{2}{3x}$ and $y = {}^-1 - x$ on the same pair of axes.

> Linear graphs are of the form $y = mx + c$. This can be rearranged to give:
>
> $$mx = y - c$$
> $$c = y - mx$$
> $$y = c + mx$$
> $$\frac{y - c}{m} = x$$
>
> ...
>
> So, $y = \frac{{}^-5}{3} - \frac{2}{3}x$ is a rearranged form of:
>
> $$y = -\frac{2}{3}x - \frac{5}{3}$$

The graph of
$$y = \frac{{}^-5}{3} - \frac{2}{3x} \text{ has:}$$

a gradient of $\frac{{}^-2}{3}$

a y-intercept at $\frac{{}^-5}{3}$

The graph of
$y = {}^-1 - x$ has:
a gradient of $^-1$
a y-intercept at $^-1$

The two linear graphs both pass through the point $(2, {}^-3)$. The values of x and y at this point must satisfy both equations, i.e. $x = 2$ $y = {}^-3$.

> When the scales for the axes are not given in the question you must decide on appropriate scales.
>
> Having drawn your graphs you may have to extend your axes to find a point that both graphs pass through (point of intersection).

Where the two linear graphs cross, the coordinates give the solution to the equations.
The solutions are $x = 2$ and $y = {}^-3$.

Check the graphical solution by substituting the values in one equation.

Check in Equation (1) for $x = 2$, $y = {}^-3$:
LHS $= 2(2) + 3({}^-3) = 4 - 9 = {}^-5 =$ RHS (solution is correct.)

> It is always a good idea to check the solution to an equation. Finding an error will allow you to rework your solution and not lose marks.

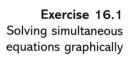

Exercise 16.1
Solving simultaneous equations graphically

1 Solve each pair of equations graphically.

a $x + 4y = 7$
   $2x + 5y = 8$

b $5x - 3y = {}^-7$
   $3x + y = 7$

c $5x + 7y = 4$
   $x + 3y = 4$

d $3x + 2y = 12$
   $4x - y = 5$

e $12x + 5y = 9$
   $5x - y = 13$

f $8x + y = 7$
   $11x + 4y = 7$

2   By drawing two linear graphs find values of x and y that satisfy the two equations $3x + 2y = 5$ and $3y - 3x = 15$.

3   **a**   On a pair of axes draw a graph of $y = 3x - 5$.
    b   Show that $2(y + 5) = 6x$, and $y = 3x - 5$ are equivalent.
    c   Draw another linear graph on your axes and solve these simultaneous equations.
$$2(y + 5) = 6x \ \dots \ (1)$$
$$3x - 2y = 4 \ \dots \quad (2)$$

4   **a**   On a pair of axes draw a graph of $3x + y = 9$.
    b   By drawing another linear graph on the axes solve the simultaneous equations:
$$3x + y = 9 \ \dots \ (1)$$
$$x + 2y = 6 \ \dots \ (2)$$

    c   Use graphs to explain why this pair of equations
$$y - 3x = 5 \ \dots \quad (1)$$
$$2y - 4 = 6x \ \dots \ (2)$$

    cannot be solved simultaneously.

5   A group of male and female students went on a fell walk.
In total, sixty-three students were in the group.
The number of females was nine more than twice the number of males.
Let x be the number of females in the group and y the number of males.

    a   Write two different equations in x and y from the student data.
    b   **i**   Draw and label a pair of axes with values: $0 \leqslant x \leqslant 63$ and $0 \leqslant y \leqslant 63$
        ii   By drawing suitable linear graphs find the number of females and the number of males in the group.

6   A blend of olive oil is made by mixing Extra Virgin and Virgin olive oils.
When making 500 litres of the blended oil the amount of Virgin oil used was 25 litres more than four times the amount of Extra Virgin oil used.
Let x be the number of litres of Extra Virgin oil used and y the number of litres of Virgin oil used.

    a   Write two different equations in x and y from the olive oil data.
    b   **i**   Draw and label a pair of axes with values: $0 \leqslant x \leqslant 500$ and $0 \leqslant y \leqslant 500$.
        ii   Draw two linear graphs to find the amount of each type of oil used when 500 litres of the blended oil are produced.

    The next 500 litres was a different blend, with the amount of Virgin oil being 40 litres more than six times the amount of Extra Virgin oil.

    c   **i**   Write a different equation in x and y from the new data.
        ii   Draw a third linear graph on the axes to find the amount of each type of oil used in this next blend.

7   Two variables x and y are such that:
$$y = \tfrac{1}{2}(x + 7)$$
$$\text{and} \qquad x = \tfrac{1}{3}(29 - 4y)$$

    a   On a pair of axes, draw two linear graphs to show the relationship between x and y.
    b   Find a value for x, and a value for y, that will satisfy both equations.

8   The equation $2y + 2 = 3x$ is solved simultaneously with a second linear equation in x and y. The solution of $x = 4$ and $y = 5$ satisfies both equations. The graph of the second equation has a y-intercept at $(0, 3)$.
Draw graphs to find the second linear equation.

Quadratic graphs

A quadratic expression in one variable (e.g. n) is an expression where the highest power of the variable is 2 (e.g. n^2).

Quadratic graphs are shown on these axes.

The graph of $y = x^2 + 2x$ can be plotted by calculating values of y for chosen values of x.

Example

For $\quad y = x^2 + 2x$

x	−1	0	1	2	3
x^2	1	0	1	4	9
$2x$	−2	0	2	4	6
y	−1	0	3	8	15

i.e. the graph of $y = x^2 + 2x$ passes through the points: (−1, −1), (0, 0), (1, 3), (2, 8), (3, 15) ...

Note that the points should be joined by a smooth curve.

> The smooth curve of a quadratic graph is known as a **parabola**.

From the graphs drawn on the axes you can note that:

- quadratic graphs are symmetrical
  graphs such as $y = x^2$, $y = 2x^2$, $y = 0.5x^2$, are symmetrical about the y-axis (the line $x = 0$).

- the value of any constant, i.e. not a term in any variable, fixes the y-intercept of the graph.
  $y = x^2 + 5$ has a y-intercept at (0, 5); $y = x^2 + 3x − 3$ has a y-intercept at (0, −3).

Exercise 16.2
Quadratic graphs

1 From the graphs above give the line of symmetry of:
   a the graph of $y = x^2 + 2x − 3$ b the graph of $y = x^2 + 2x$.

2 Draw a pair of axes where $^-4 \leqslant x \leqslant 4$, and $^-12 \leqslant y \leqslant 28$.
   a On the axes draw these quadratic graphs.
      $y = x^2$ $y = x^2 + 6$ $y = x^2 − 3x$ $y = x^2 − 3x − 8$
   b Give the line of symmetry of the graph $y = x^2 − 3x$.
   c Give the equation of a quadratic graph that has the same line of symmetry as $y = x^2 − 3x$ but has a y-intercept at (0, −8).

3 Draw a pair of axes where $^-4 \leqslant x \leqslant 4$, and $^-4 \leqslant y \leqslant 32$.
   a On the axes draw these quadratic graphs and compare them.
      $y = x^2 + 2x$ $y = x^2 + 3x$ $y = x^2 − 2x$ $y = x^2 − 4x$
   b What does the coefficient of x tell you about a quadratic graph?

> You might choose to use a graphical calculator when you have to compare a number of graphs.

A sketch graph shows the shape of the graph and known data. This data might show x-intercepts and/or y-intercepts, or maybe the relative steepness or tightness of a graph.

Sketching a graph is not the same as drawing a graph. Points are not plotted and graduations on axes do not have to be accurate.

4 Give the line of symmetry and the y-intercept for each of these graphs.

a $y = x^2 + 4x - 3$ b $y = x^2 - x + 2$ c $y = x^2 + 5x$
d $y = x^2 - 6x + 1$ e $y = x^2 + 6x - 2$ f $y = x^2 + 8x + 3$
g $y = x^2 - 7$ h $y = x^2 - 6x + 8$ i $y = x^2 - 7x + 5$

5 This is a sketch graph of $y = x^2$.

a Make a copy of this sketch.
b On your copy sketch and label these graphs.
   i $y = x^2 + 3$
   ii $y = x^2 - 5x$
   iii $y = x^2 - 4x - 5$

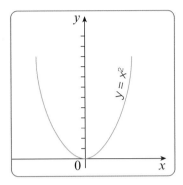

6 On a pair of axes, sketch these graphs and label them.

a $y = x^2 - 5x - 6$
b $y = x^2 + x + 4$

We have considered the effect of the coefficient of x, and the constant value in a quadratic expression, on its graph.

The coefficient of x^2 will also have an effect on a quadratic graph.

Example

When the coefficient of x^2 is not 1.

For the graph of $y = 2x^2$

	when $x = 0$,	$y = 0$
	$x = 1$,	$y = 2$
	$x = 2$,	$y = 8$
	$x = {}^-1$,	$y = 2$
	$x = {}^-2$,	$y = 8$
	... ,	...

So, on the same axes the graph of $y = 2x^2$ is a tighter curve than the graph of $y = x^2$

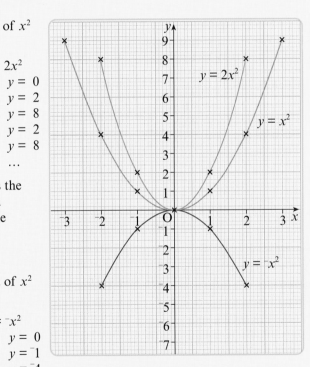

Example

When the coefficient of x^2 is negative.

For the graph of $y = {}^-x^2$

	when $x = 0$	$y = 0$
	$x = 1$,	$y = {}^-1$
	$x = 2$,	$y = {}^-4$
	$x = {}^-1$,	$y = {}^-1$
	$x = {}^-2$,	$y = {}^-4$
	... ,	...

When we say the graph is inverted, we could say that it is upside down. We might also say that, in this case it is a reflection in the x-axis, i.e. the line $y = 0$.

So, the graph of $y = {}^-x^2$ is inverted compared with the graph of $y = x^2$.

7 Draw a pair of axes where ${}^-3 \leqslant x \leqslant 3$, and $10 \leqslant y \leqslant {}^-30$.

On the axes draw these quadratic graphs.

a $y = {}^-3x^2$ b $y = 2 - 4x - x^2$ c $y = 3x - 2x^2$ d $y = 6x - 8 - 2x^2$

Solving quadratic equations graphically

This is the graph of $y = x^2 + 5x - 6$, for values of x from $^-8$ to $^+6$.

We can use the graph to solve the equation $x^2 + 5x - 6 = 0$.

The graph of $y = x^2 + 5x - 6$ crosses the graph of $y = 0$ where:
$$x = {}^-6 \quad \text{and} \quad \text{where} \quad x = 1$$

At $x = {}^-6$, and $x = 1$ the two equations must be equal.
So we can write:
$$x^2 + 5x - 6 = 0$$

From the graphs, the values of x that satisfy the equation are:
$$x = {}^-6 \text{ or } x = 1$$

$y = 0$ is the equation of the x-axis.

You can be fairly confident of these values of x as solutions because they are both integer values.

If you are in any doubt, substitute in the equation to check each value.

For this graph:

when $x = {}^-8$ $y = 18$
$x = {}^-7$ $y = 8$
$x = {}^-6$ $y = 0$
$x = {}^-5$ $y = {}^-6$
$x = {}^-4$ $y = {}^-10$
$x = {}^-3$ $y = {}^-12$
$x = {}^-2$ $y = {}^-12$
$x = {}^-1$ $y = {}^-10$
$x = 0$ $y = {}^-6$
$x = 1$ $y = 0$
$x = 2$ $y = 8$
$x = 3$ $y = 18$
$x = 4$ $y = 30$
$x = 5$ $y = 44$
$x = 6$ $y = 60$

These values of x, from the graph, are not integer values. The values are not exact, they are a good approximation. They answer the question, from the graph.

For more accurate solutions, use the values from the graph as a starting point for the trial-and-improvement method.

The graph of $y = x^2 + 5x - 6$ can be used to solve many more equations.

Example From the graph solve $x^2 + 5x - 6 = 5$.
The graph of $y = x^2 + 5x - 6$ crosses the graph of $y = 5$ so we can say: $x^2 + 5x - 6 = 5$
The two equations are equal where $x \approx {}^-6.6$ and where $x \approx 1.6$

The solutions for $x^2 + 5x - 6 = 5$ are: $x \approx {}^-6.6$ and $x \approx 1.6$

Example From the graph solve $x^2 + 5x - 6 = {}^-8$.
The graph of $y = x^2 + 5x - 6$ crosses the graph of $y = {}^-8$ so we can say: $x^2 + 5x - 6 = {}^-8$

The solutions for $x^2 + 5x - 6 = {}^-8$ are: $x \approx {}^-4.6$ and $x \approx {}^-0.4$

Exercise 16.3
Solving quadratic
equations graphically

1   The graph of $y = x^2 + 5x - 6$ can also be used to solve the equation:
$$x^2 + 5x - 6 = 10$$
  a   What other graph would you draw on the axes to solve $x^2 + 5x - 6 = 10$?
  b   Explain how you would use the two graphs to solve the equation.
  c   From the graph on page 192, solve $x^2 + 5x - 6 = 10$.

2   The graph on page 192 can be used to solve these equations:
$$x^2 + 5x - 6 = 0$$
$$x^2 + 5x - 6 = 5$$
$$x^2 + 5x - 6 = 8$$
$$x^2 + 5x - 6 = 1$$
  a   Give two other equations you think can be solved from the same graph.
  b   Explain how you would solve your equations.

3   Asif used the same graph to solve $x^2 + 5x - 6 = 22$,
  and only found one solution.
  a   Explain why.
  b   Give the solution you think Asif did find from the graph.
  c   Is the other solution greater or less than $x = {}^-8$? Explain.

4   Draw the graph of $y = x^2 - 5x + 6$ for values of x from $^-2$ to 6.
  a   Use your graph to solve $x^2 - 5x + 6 = 0$.
  b   On your axes draw and label the graph of $y = 4$.
  c   Use your graphs to solve $x^2 - 5x + 6 = 4$.
  d   Use the graph solve $x^2 - 5x + 6 = 10$.

5   Draw the graph of $y = x^2 - 4x - 5$ for values of x such that $^-3 \leqslant x \leqslant 7$.
  a   Use the graph to solve:
    i $x^2 - 4x - 5 = 0$ ii $x^2 - 4x - 5 = 11$
  b   From the graph solve $x^2 - 4x - 5 = {}^-9$.

6   a   i   Draw the graph of $y = x^2 - 4x + 3$ for x such that $^-3 \leqslant x \leqslant 5$.
      ii Use the graph to solve $x^2 - 4x + 3 = 0$.
    b   i   For values of x such that $^-3 \leqslant x \leqslant 5$ draw the graph of $y = x^2 + 3$.
      ii On the same axes draw and label a graph of $y = 4x$.
      iii Show that the solutions to $x^2 + 3 = 4x$ are $x = 1$ and $x = 3$.

7   In each of the following draw a graph and solve the equation.
    a   For x: $^-6 \leqslant x \leqslant 2$ draw the graph of $y = x^2 + 5x - 4$, and solve:
      i $x^2 + 5x - 4 = 0$ ii $x^2 + 5x - 4 = {}^-6$ iii $x^2 + 5x = 4$
    b   For x: $^-4 \leqslant x \leqslant 2$ draw the graph of $y = x^2 + 3x - 1$, and solve:
      i $x^2 + 3x - 1 = 0$ ii $x^2 + 3x + 1 = 0$ iii $x^2 + 3x - 1 = 0.5$
    c   For x: $^-2 \leqslant x \leqslant 5$ draw the graph of $3 + 4x - x^2$, and solve:
      i $4x - x^2 + 3 = 0$ ii $4x + 3 - x^2 = 4$ iii $4x - x^2 + 1 = 0$
    d   For x: $^-4 \leqslant x \leqslant 2$ draw the graph of $y = 1 - 3x - 2x^2$, and solve:
      i $2x^2 = 1 - 3x$ ii $^-3 = 1 - 3x - 2x^2$
    e   For x: $^-2 \leqslant x \leqslant 3$ draw the graph of $y = 5x - 2x^2$, and solve:
      i $5x - 2x^2 = 0$ ii $5x - 2x^2 + 2 = 0$

8   Draw a suitable graph and solve the equation $(x + 2)^2 - 5 = 0$.

9   For x: $^-2 \leqslant x \leqslant 3$, solve $3x(x - 2) + 1 = 0$ by drawing a graph.

10 a   Draw a graph to show that if $x(x + 4) = 6$, then $x \approx {}^-5$ or $x \approx 1$.
    b   Use graphs to explain that the equations $x(x + 4) = 6$ and $x(x + 4) - 6 = 0$
       have the same solutions.

For x: $^-6 \leqslant x \leqslant 2$ is a
notation that can be
interpreted in this way:

for values of x such that,
x is greater than or equal
to $^-6$, and less than or
equal to 2.

In some cases to use a graph to solve an equation is only possible if you can decide on an additional graph to draw on the axes.
Rearranging the equation is one way to decide on additional graphs.

Example

Draw the graph of $y = 2x^2 + x - 4$ for $x: {}^-2 \leqslant x \leqslant 2$.
Use the graph to find approximate solutions to:
a $2x^2 + x - 4 = 0$ **b** $2x^2 + x = x + 3$ **c** $2x^2 + 1 = x + 2$

The graph of $y = 2x^2 + x - 4$
is drawn.

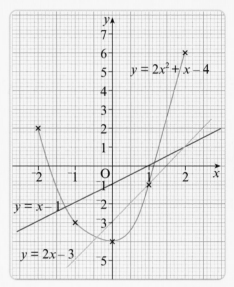

a To solve $2x^2 + x - 4 = 0$
From the graph:
$x \approx {}^-1.7$, or $x \approx 1.2$

b To solve $2x^2 + x = x + 3$
the equation must be rearranged.

The LHS is $2x^2 + x$.
By subtracting 4 from the LHS
we have $2x^2 + x - 4$ (graph drawn)

So, to solve $2x^2 + x = x + 3$
we subtract 4 from both sides.

$2x^2 + x - 4 = x + 3 - 4$
i.e. $2x^2 + x - 4 = x - 1$

On the axes draw the graph of $y = x - 1$.
Where the curve $2x^2 + x - 4$ and the line $x - 1$ intersect is the solution to the equation $2x^2 + x = x + 3$.

The solution to $2x^2 + x = x + 3$ is $x \approx {}^-1.2$, or $x \approx 1.2$

c To solve $2x^2 + 1 = x + 2$

The LHS is $2x^2 + 1$.
By subtracting 5 and adding x LHS is $2x^2 + 1 - 5 + x = 2x^2 + x - 4$.

So, to solve $2x^2 + 1 = x + 2$, we subtract 5 and add x to both sides.

$2x^2 + 1 - 5 + x = x + 2 - 5 + x$
i.e. $2x^2 + x - 4 = 2x - 3$

On the axes we draw the graph of $y = 2x - 3$.
Where the curve $2x^2 + x - 4$ and the line $2x - 3$ intersect is the solution to the equation $2x^2 + 1 = x + 2$.

The solution to $2x^2 + 1 = x + 2$ is $x \approx {}^-0.5$, or $x = 1$.

11 **a** Draw the graph of $y = x^2 - 4x - 2$, for $x: {}^-3 \leqslant x \leqslant 6$.
b Use the graph to find approximate solutions to $x^2 - 5x - 5 = x - 10$.
c Find approximate solutions to $x^2 - 2x + 3 = 8 - x$ from the graph.

12 **a** Draw the graph of $y = 9 - 2x - x^2$, for $x: {}^-5 \leqslant x \leqslant 3$.
b Find approximate solutions to $12 - x = 13 - 5x - x^2$.
c Find approximate solutions to $7 + 2x - x^2 = 3 + x$.

13 If you had drawn the graph of $y = 12 - 4x - x^2$, find the equation of each additional line you would draw to solve these.
a $10 - x^2 = 5x + 6$ **b** $7 - 6x = 15 - 6x - x^2$

14 **a** For x: $^-8 \leqslant x \leqslant 3$ draw the graph of $y = 12 - 4x - x^2$.

b Use the graph to find approximate solutions to $1 - x = 8 - 7x - x^2$.

c Find approximate solution to $4 - 3x - x^2 = 1 - 2x$ from the graph.

d Use the graph to find approximate solutions to $2x + 7 = 4 - x^2 - 2.5x$.

The graph of $y = 12 - 4x - x^2$ was used to solve an equation and the approximate solutions were given as $x \approx 1.7$ or $x \approx ^-4.7$.

e Show from the graph that the equation solved was $9 - 4x = 17 - x^2 - 7x$.

15 **a** For x: $^-7 \leqslant x \leqslant 3$, draw the graph of $y = x^2 + 5x - 8$.

Use the graph to find approximate solutions to these equations.

b $x(x + 5) = 8$

c $5(x - 1) + x^2 = 0$

d $x^2 + 5x = 10$

e $x(x + 7) - 3 = 1 + 7x$

f $3(x - 2) = x(x + 11) - 12$

Graphs of reciprocal curves

If a number could be divided by zero the answer would be infinite.

So $8 \div 0$ is said to be ∞.

Think about $\frac{8}{x}$.

If $x = 1$, $\quad \frac{8}{x} = 8$

$x = 0.01$, $\quad \frac{8}{x} = 800$

$x = 0.001$, $\quad \frac{8}{x} = 8000$

as x approaches zero $\frac{8}{x}$ will approach ∞.

If $x = ^-1, ^-0.01, ^-0.001, \dots$ then $\frac{8}{x}$ approaches $^-\infty$.

An asymptote to a curve is a straight line to which a curve continuously draws nearer but without ever touching it.

Displaying this graph on a graphical calculator will help you to investigate how the graph of a curve approaches an asymptote.

Reciprocal graphs can be identified from their equation.

There will be a term in the form $\frac{n}{x}$

Example Draw the graph of $y = \frac{8}{x}$ for x: $^-4 \leqslant x \leqslant 4$

When $x = ^-4$, $\quad y = ^-2$
$x = ^-3$, $\quad y = ^-2.7$ (1dp)
$x = ^-2$, $\quad y = ^-4$
$x = ^-1$, $\quad y = ^-8$
$x = 0$, $\quad y$ is ∞
$x = 1$, $\quad y = 8$
$x = 2$, $\quad y = 4$
$x = 3$, $\quad y = 2.7$ (1dp)
$x = 4$, $\quad y = 2$

From these values, the curve is broken at $x = 0$.

Also, as x becomes very large, $\frac{8}{x}$ becomes very small, but

$\frac{8}{x}$ will never equal zero.

So the graph will get very close to each of the axes, but it will never touch either of them.

Here the x-axis ($y = 0$) and the y-axis ($x = 0$) are called asymptotes to the curve.

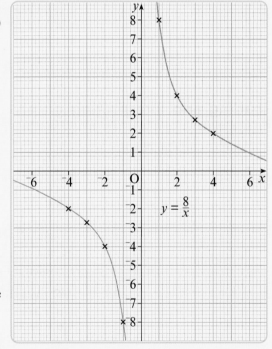

1 **a** **i** For x: $^-5 \leqslant x \leqslant 5$, draw the graph of $y = \frac{5}{x}$.

ii Give the equation of any asymptotes to the graph of $y = \frac{5}{x}$.

b On the same axes draw and label the graph of $y = \frac{5}{2x}$.

2 **a** For x: $^-5 \leqslant x \leqslant 5$ draw the graph of $y = \frac{4}{x} + 3$.

b Give the equation of any asymptotes to the graph of $y = \frac{4}{x} + 3$.

3 Give the equation of any asymptotes to the curve $y = \dfrac{6}{x} - 8$.

4 a Sketch the curve of $y = \dfrac{6}{x} + 2$.

One asymptote to the curve is the line $x = 0$.

b On your sketch draw and label the other asymptote with its equation.

5 a For x: $1 \le x \le 12$, draw the graph of $y = \dfrac{12}{x}$.

b Use the graph to find approximate solutions to these equations.

   i $\dfrac{12}{x} = x + 1$ ii $\dfrac{12}{x} = x - 3$ iii $x^2 = 12$

6 Draw graphs of $y = \dfrac{20}{x}$, and $y = x$ on the same axes.

From your graphs show that $\sqrt{20} \approx \pm 4.5$.

7 a For x: $1 \le x \le 10$, draw the graph of $y = \dfrac{10}{x} - x$.

b As the value of x increases, explain what value y will approach.

c Give the equation of two asymptotes to the graph of $y = \dfrac{10}{x} - x$.

8 Explain why $y = {}^-2x$ is an asymptote to the graph of $y = \dfrac{25}{x} - 2x$.

Include a labelled sketch graph in your explanation.

9 For x: ${}^-5 \le x \le 4$, draw the graph of $y = \dfrac{6}{x - 4}$.

Reading and interpreting graphs

When a graph is read or interpreted, it is important to remember that any values taken from the graph can only be approximate, say to 1 dp.

Example For x: $1 \le x \le 10$ draw the graph of $y = \dfrac{15}{x} + x - 5$.

Use the graph to find:
a the minimum value for y
b the values of x when $y = 5.2$.

For the graph, calculate values for y from values for x
i.e. when $x = 1$, $y = 11$
     $x = 2$, $y = 4.5$
     $x = 3$, $y = 3$
     ... ,   ...

From the graph:
a the minimum value for y is approximately 2.7
b when $y = 5.2$, the values of x are: $x \approx 1.8$, and $x \approx 8.4$

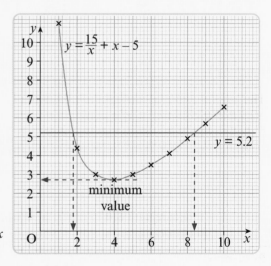

1 For x: $1 \le x \le 10$, draw the graph of $y = \dfrac{12}{x} + x - 10$. From the graph find:

   i the minimum value of y ii values of x when $y = {}^-2.5$

2   Draw the graph of $y = 4 - 3x - x^2$.

    a Use the graph to find an approximate maximum value for y.

    b Give two values of x for which $y = 2.5$.

3   For x: $^-6 \leqslant x \leqslant 2$, draw the graph of $y = 9 - 5x - x^2$.

    a From your graph give the approximate maximum value of y.

    b When $y = 11.5$, give approximate values for x.

    c Solve the equation $6 - 2x = 9 - 5x - x^2$.

    d **i** Explain why, by drawing the graph of the line $y = x + 15$, you should be able to find approximate solutions to $5x + 8 = 2 - x - x^2$.

        ii Find approximate solutions to $5x + 8 = 2 - x - x^2$.

    e On the same axes draw the graph of $y = x^2 + x + 5$.

        i What is the approximate minimum value of y?

        ii Use your graphs to solve $x^2 + x + 5 = 9 - 5x - x^2$.

        iii Give an equation for the line joining the points where the two curves intersect.

4   Draw the graph of $y = \frac{1}{2}(x^2 - 3x - 5)$ for x: $^-3 \leqslant x \leqslant 4$.

    a From the graph:

        i give an approximate minimum value of y

        ii find approximate values for x when $y = ^-1$.

    b On the same axes draw the graph of $y = \frac{4}{x} - 6$.

    c Explain why neither of the curves intersect with the line $y = ^-6$.

5   On the same axes draw the graphs of $y = \frac{2x}{3 - x}$, and $y = \frac{1}{2}x^2 + 2$.

Use x: $^-4 \leqslant x \leqslant 4$.

    a Use the graphs to solve the equation $2x = (0.5x^2 + 2)(3 - x)$.

    b Only one curve will intersect with the line $x = 3$. Which curve will not intersect? Explain why.

Graphs of higher-order polynomial equations

An equation of higher order than a quadratic has a highest power of the variable greater than 2, as in the following polynomial equations.

$$3a^3 + 4a \qquad a^3 + a^2 - 1 \qquad y^5 - 4y = 3 \qquad k^6 = 1$$

Example

Draw the graph of $y = x^3 + 2$ for x: $^-3 \leqslant x \leqslant 3$.

When	$x = ^-3$,	$y = ^-25$
	$x = ^-2$,	$y = ^-6$
	$x = ^-1$,	$y = 1$
	$x = 0$,	$y = 2$
	$x = 1$,	$y = 3$
	$x = 2$,	$y = 10$
	$x = 3$,	$y = 29$

The graph can be used to solve $x^3 + 2 = 0$
From the graph if $x^3 + 2 = 0$ then $x \approx ^-1.3$

$x^3 + 2 = 0$ is known as a **cubic** equation.

> The graph, when drawn, will be a smooth curve.

> Remember values read from the graph will only be approximate.

Exercise 16.6
Graphs of polynomial equations

1   On the same axes draw graphs of $y = x^3 + 4$ and $y = 4 - x^3$.
   a   Describe any common features of the graphs.
   b   Describe any differences between the graphs.
   c   For each graph:
      i   describe what happens as x becomes increasingly large
      ii describe what happens as x becomes increasingly negative.

2   For x: $^-4 \leqslant x \leqslant 3$ draw the graph of $y = x^3 + 2x^2$.
   a   From your graph solve the equation $x^3 + 2x^2 = 0$.
   b   By drawing an additional graph, find an approximate solution to the equation $12x + 5 = 2x^2 + x^3$.
   c   i   On the same axes draw the graph of $y = 4x^2 - x^3$ for x: $^-2 \leqslant x \leqslant 4$.
      ii Use your graph to solve $4x^2 - x^3 = 0$.
      iii Find approximate values for x when $y = 7$.
      iv Find an approximate value for y when $x = ^-1.5$.

3   Draw the graph of $y = x^3 - 3x^2$ for values of x from $^-3$ to 4.
   a   Use your graph to find an approximate value for x when $y = 8$.
   b   Find values for x when $x^3 - 3x^2 = ^-4$.
   For x: $^-3 \leqslant x \leqslant 4$, the equation $x^3 - 3x^2 = n$ is satisfied by only one value of n.

4   Draw the graph of $y = \frac{1}{2}(x^3 - 3x - 8)$ for values of x from $^-4$ to 4.
   Use the graph to find:
   a   an approximate value for y, when $x = 3.4$
   b   an approximate value for x when $y = ^-9$
   c   an approximate solution to the equation $\frac{1}{2}(x^3 - 3x - 8) = 0$
   d   three approximate values of x that satisfy $\frac{1}{2}(x^3 - 3x - 8) = 5x - 2$.

5   Draw the graph of $y = x^3 - x^2 - 4x + 4$ for x: $^-3 \leqslant x \leqslant 4$.
   a   Use the graph to solve $x^3 - x^2 - 4x + 4 = 0$.
   b   When $x = ^-1.5$ give an approximate value for y.
   c   Find three approximate values for x that give $x^3 - x^2 - 4x + 4 = 2$.

6   The width of a rectangle is given as w (cm), and the length as $w + 8$ (cm). An expression for the area A (cm^2) of the rectangle is $A = w(w + 8)$.
   a   Draw a graph of $A = w(w + 8)$ for values of w from zero to 8. (Plot w on the horizontal axis.)
   b   From the graph find approximate dimensions of the rectangle when the area is:
      i   55 cm^2 ii   18 cm^2 iii   100 cm^2
   c   What is the approximate area of the rectangle when $w = 3.8$ cm?
   d   If the rectangle has an area of 75 cm^2, find the approximate value of w.

7   The dimensions of a rectangle of area A (cm^2) are given in this way.
   ◆   let the width of the rectangle be w (cm)
   ◆   the length is 4 cm less than twice the width of the rectangle.
   a   Write an expression for the area of the rectangle.
   b   Draw a graph of A against w, for values of w: $0 \leqslant w \leqslant 8$.
   c   From the graph, give the approximate dimensions of the rectangle when the area is:
      i   35 cm^2 ii   62 cm^2 iii   80 cm^2
   d   What is the approximate area of the rectangle when the width is 5.6 cm?
   e   Give the dimensions of the rectangle (to 1 dp) when the area is 44 cm^2.

Sketching graphs by completing the square

If you can write a quadratic expression as a complete square, it can help to sketch the graph.

Example

Sketch the graph of $y = x^2 + 4x + 1$.

Completing the square gives:
$$y = (x + 2)^2 - 4 + 1$$
i.e. $y = (x + 2)^2 - 3$

> A full explanation of completing the square can be found on page 105 of this book.

For the graph of $y = (x + 2)^2 - 3$
$(x + 2)^2$ cannot be negative,
so the minimum value of y
is when $(x + 2) = 0$, i.e. $x = {}^-2$

When $x = {}^-2$, $y = {}^-3$, so,
the minimum point is $({}^-2, {}^-3)$.

The intersect with the y-axis
is where $x = 0$ i.e.
when $x = 0$, $y = 1$
so, the y-intercept is at $(0, 1)$.

The graph can now be sketched.

Exercise 16.7
Sketching graphs by completing the square

1 For the graph of $y = x^2 + 6x - 2$:

    a Rearrange the equation by completing the square.
    b What is the minimum value of y? Explain your answer.
    c Give the coordinates of the intercept with the y-axis.
    d Sketch the graph of $y = x^2 + 6x - 2$.

2 For the graph of $y = x^2 + 10x + 4$:

    a Show that the minimum value of y is $^-21$.
    b Sketch the graph of $y = x^2 + 10x + 4$.

3 Sketch the graph of $y = x^2 + 14x - 5$.

4 Sketch the graph of $y = x^2 - 8x - 6$.

5 **a** On the same axes sketch the graphs of $y = x^2 + 8x + 4$, and $y = x - 9$.
    b Explain, with the help of your sketch graphs, why you cannot find a value for x that satisfies $x^2 + 8x + 4 = x - 9$.

6 The diagram shows a sketch of a quadratic graph in the form:
$$y = ax^2 + bx + c$$
Find an equation for the graph that is sketched and list values for a, b, and c.

End points

You should be able to ...

... so try these questions

A Solve simultaneous linear equations graphically

A1 By drawing suitable graphs solve these equations for x and y.

a $5x - 3y = 13$
$2x + 5y = {}^-1$

b $2x - 3y = 3$
$7x - 2y = 19$

A2 Two groups of people bought tickets on the Cliff Railway. The first group of five adults and two children paid a total of £32. The second group of two adults and three children paid a total of £20.50.

By drawing suitable linear graphs, find the charges for adult and child tickets for the Cliff Railway.

B Work with, and solve equations from quadratic graphs

B1 Give the equation of the line of symmetry of the graph $y = x^2 - 4x$.

B2 Solve these quadratic equations by drawing suitable graphs.

a $x^2 + 2x - 8 = 0$
b $x^2 - 3x - 7 = 3$
c $x^2 - x + 12 = 16$
d $2x^2 - 2x - 12 = 0$

B3 **a** Draw the graph of $y = 2x^2 + x - 5$.

Use the graph of $y = 2x^2 + x - 5$ together with any additional graphs you choose to draw to solve these equations.

b $2x^2 + 4x - 9 = 5x - 5$
c $5x + 7 = 2x^2 + 5x + 1$
d $2x - 5 = 2x^2 + 5x - 7$

C Draw and interpret reciprocal graphs

C1 For x: $^-5 < x < 5$ draw the graph of $y = \dfrac{6}{x} - 2$.

C2 For x: $^-6 \leqslant x \leqslant 4$ draw the graph of $y = \dfrac{2}{x} + 5$.

Give the equation of any asymptotes to the graph of $y = \dfrac{2}{x} + 5$.

C3 Sketch the curve of $y = \dfrac{5}{x} + 4$.

On your sketch draw and label any asymptotes.

D Read and interpret graphs

D1 For x: $1 \leqslant x \leqslant 10$, draw the graph of $y = \dfrac{12}{x} + x - 8$.

a From the graph find an approximate minimum value for y.
b Give approximate values for x when $y = {}^-0.6$.

D2 For x: $^-6 \leqslant x \leqslant 2$ draw the graph of $y = 8 - 5x - x^2$.

a From the graph give an approximate maximum value for y.
b When $y = 3.8$ give two approximate values for x.
c Use the graph and any suitable additional graph find values of x that satisfy the equation $2x + 4 = 9 - x - x^2$.

D3 The width of a rectangle is given as w (cm) and the length as $w + 6$ (cm). An expression for the area A (cm^2) of the rectangle is given as $A = w(w + 6)$.

a Draw a graph of $A = w(w + 6)$ for values of w from zero to 6. (Plot w on the horizontal axis.)

b From the graph find approximate dimensions of the rectangle when the area is:

   i 58 cm^2 **ii** 32 cm^2.

c Calculate the approximate area of the rectangle when $w = 5.4$ cm.

d If $A = 35$ cm^2, calculate a value for w correct to 1 dp.

E Sketch graphs and use completing the square

E1 On the same axes sketch and label these graphs.

   a $y = x^2 + 3x + 1$

   b $y = 2x + 3$

E2 Sketch and label these graphs on the same axes.

   a $y = x^2 - 4$

   b $y = 4 - x^2$

   c $y = 4 - 3x - x^2$

E3 On the same axes sketch and label these graphs.

   a $y = \dfrac{9}{x} + 1$

   b $y = x^3 + 4$

   c $y = 4 - x^3$

E4 For the graph of $y = x^2 + 8x - 7$.

   a Show that the graph has a minimum value of $^-23$.

   b Sketch the graph of $y = x^2 + 8x - 7$.

E5 The diagram shows a sketch of a quadratic graph in the form

$$y = ax^2 + bx + c$$

Find an equation for the graph and list values for a, b, and c.

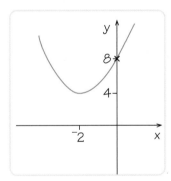

Some points to remember

- The equation of any graph gives you data about the graph before you plot any points or sketch a line on a pair of axes. This data can indicate shape, intersects with axes and any maximum or minimum values.

- The graphs of curves should be drawn as a smooth curve, with axes clearly graduated, points accurately plotted and the final curve labelled with its equation.

- Data that you read from a graph is only an approximation. For more exact values use trial and improvement starting with any approximate value read from a graph.

Starting points
You need to know about ...

... so try these questions

A Trigonometric ratios

◆ These are definitions of three trigonometric ratios (trig ratios).

$$\sin \theta = \frac{\text{opp}}{\text{hyp}} \qquad \cos \theta = \frac{\text{adj}}{\text{hyp}} \qquad \tan \theta = \frac{\text{opp}}{\text{adj}}$$

$$\text{opp} = \text{hyp} \times \sin \theta \qquad \text{adj} = \text{hyp} \times \cos \theta \qquad \text{opp} = \text{adj} \times \tan \theta$$

◆ These trig ratios can be used to calculate sides or angles in right-angled triangles.

Example In $\triangle ABC$ $AB = AC = 5\,\text{cm}$ and $BC = 7\,\text{cm}$.
Calculate the angle $C\hat{A}B$.

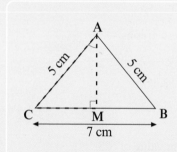

$\triangle ABC$ is isosceles.
$$CM = MB = 3.5\,\text{cm}$$
$$C\hat{A}M = B\hat{A}M$$

In $\triangle AMC$:
$$\sin C\hat{A}M = \frac{CM}{AC} = \frac{3.5}{5} = 0.7$$
$$C\hat{A}M = 44.42 \ldots °$$
$$C\hat{A}B = 88.9° \text{ to 1 dp.}$$

B Graphs of $y = \sin x$ and $y = \cos x$

◆ This diagram shows the graphs of $y = \sin x$ and $y = \cos x$ for values of x from 0° to 90°.

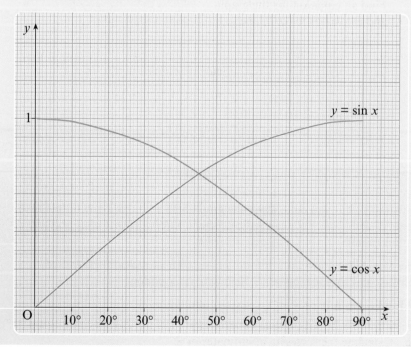

A1 The points B and C lie on the circumference of a circle with centre O.

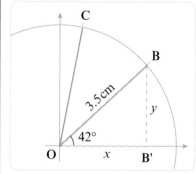

   a Calculate, correct to 2 dp:
     i the coordinates of B
     ii the area of $\triangle OBB'$
   b C is the point (0.88, 3.39).
     Calculate the angle between OC and the horizontal axis, correct to 1 dp.

A2 Calculate the area of a regular pentagon of side 8 cm.

A3 If $\tan \theta = \frac{3}{4}$ find the value of:
   a $\cos \theta$ **b** $\sin \theta$.
   Do not use a calculator.

Use the graphs of $y = \sin x$ and $y = \cos x$ to answer Questions **B1 – B3**.

B1 Estimate the value of:
   a $\cos 40°$
   b $\sin 40°$

B2 Estimate the angle x for each of these:
   a $\sin x = 0.4$
   b $\cos x = 0.4$

B3 Find the angle x for each of these:
   a $\sin 20° = \cos x$
   b $\cos 48° = \sin x$
   c $\cos x = \sin x$

Notation for trigonometric ratios

♦ $y = \cos 4x$ can also be written as $y = \cos (4x)$ to show that you need to find the value of $4x$ before finding the cosine.

When $x = 10$

$$y = \cos 4x$$
$$= \cos (4 \times 10)°$$
$$= \cos 40°$$
$$= 0.766 \text{ (3 sf)}$$

♦ $y = 4 \cos x$ can also be written as $y = 4 \times \cos x$

When $x = 10$

$$y = 4 \cos x$$
$$= 4 \times \cos 10°$$
$$= 3.94 \text{ (3 sf)}$$

♦ In the same way
$y = \sin 3x$ can be written as $y = \sin (3x)$ and
$y = 3 \sin x$ can be written as $y = 3 \times \sin x$

Exercise 17.1
Evaluating trigonometric functions

1 Evaluate these expressions, correct to 2 dp, when $x = 20$.

    a $2 \sin x$ **b** $\sin 3x$ **c** $\cos 2x$

    d $3 \cos 2x$ **e** $2 \sin 4x$ **f** $5 \cos 3x$

2 If $y = 4 \cos 3x$:

    a find the value of y when
        i $x = 5$ **ii** $x = 7.5$ **iii** $x = 12.35$

    b for what value of x does
        i $y = 0$ **ii** $y = 2$?

Polar and cartesian coordinates

θ is a Greek letter pronounced 'theta'. It is used commonly to indicate angles.

♦ Polar coordinates give the position of a point in a plane by stating:
    ❖ its distance, r from a fixed point, the pole
    ❖ the angle, θ measured anticlockwise, between a line drawn from the pole to the point and a fixed line, the polar axis.
    These are written (r, θ) the distance followed by the angle, for example $(4, 50°)$.

♦ Cartesian coordinates give the position of a point in a plane by stating
    ❖ its distance from two perpendicular axes, for example $(6, 5)$.

Example This diagram shows the position of a boat at S on a radar screen with rings 10 km apart.

The cartesian coordinates for R are $(20, 20)$
In $\triangle ORR'$
$\hat{ROR}' = 45$
$OR = \sqrt{800}$ (by Pythagoras)
$= 28.28$ (2dp)
So the polar coordinates for R are $(28.28, 45°)$.

Exercise 17.2
Using polar and cartesian coordinates

1 The polar coordinates of S are $(20, 150°)$.

    a Explain why the cartesian coordinates for S are $(^-20 \cos 30°, 20 \sin 30°)$.

    b Calculate the cartesian coordinates of S.

2 Each of the points A to D on the radar screen shows the position of an aeroplane. The rings are 10 km apart.

AOD and BOC are straight lines.

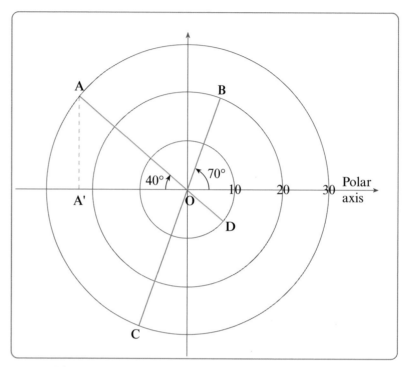

a Explain why the polar coordinates for the point A are (30, 140°).

b Calculate these distances, correct to 2 dp.

   i OA′   **ii** AA′.

c Give the cartesian coordinates of A.

d For each of the points B, C and D:

   i give the polar coordinates

   ii calculate the cartesian

       coordinates correct to 2 dp.

> For the cartesian coordinates each distance is given correct to 2 dp.

> It may help to mark each position on a sketch.

3 For three other aeroplanes the polar coordinates and cartesian coordinates are given below. For two more aeroplanes only the cartesian coordinates are given.

a Match each of the polar coordinates to its cartesian coordinates.

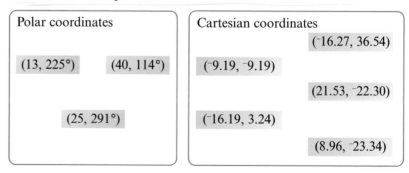

b Calculate the missing polar coordinates, to the nearest whole number.

4 The cartesian coordinates of point A are (x, y), and the polar coordinates are (r, θ).

   a Write an expression for r in terms of x and y.

   b Write the cartesian coordinates in terms of r and θ.

   c If $r = 1$, what are the cartesian coordinates in terms of θ?

Trigonometric functions for any angle

> A unit circle is a circle of radius 1 unit.

◆ For any angle the values of sin θ and cos θ are defined as the cartesian coordinates of the point on a unit circle with polar coordinates (1, θ).

Example Find the value of cos 128° and sin 128°.

The point A lies on a unit circle so the coordinates of A are (cos 128°, sin 128°).

So   cos 128° = ⁻OA′
      sin 128° = AA′

In △ OAA′:
       OA′ = 1 × cos 52°
           = cos 52°
           = 0.616
       AA′ = 1 sin 52°
           = sin 52°
           = 0.788
So the coordinates of A are (⁻0.616, 0.788)

So, cos 128° = ⁻0.616 and sin 128° = 0.788

Exercise 17.3

Evaluating trigonometric functions for any angle

1   Find another angle whose cosine = ⁻0.616.

2   Use the sketch to help you find the value of:
    a   cos 308°   **b**   sin 308°.

3   Use diagrams to explain why:
    a   sin 21° = sin 159°   **b**   sin 201° = ⁻sin 21°
    c   cos 5° = cos 355°   **d**   cos 185° = ⁻cos 5°.

4   The value of cos 36° is 0.809 (3sf). What is the value of:
    a   cos 144°   **b**   cos 324°   **c**   cos 216°?

5   **a**   Sort these into pairs that have the same value.

sin 52°	sin 232°	sin 128°
cos 233°	cos 128°	sin 308°

    b   Find the value for each pair correct to 3 sf.

6   For what values of θ, from 0° to 360°, is:
    a   cos θ < 0   **b**   sin θ < 0

7   A negative angle is measured clockwise from the polar axis.
    a   Draw a diagram to find the value of cos θ and sin θ for:
        i   θ = ⁻90°   **ii**   θ = ⁻52°
    b   Find a negative value for θ which satisfies:
        i   sin θ = sin 54°   **ii**   sin θ = sin 100°   **iii**   cos θ = cos 200°

8   **a**   Explain why cos 450° = 0.
    b   Give three values of θ for which sin θ = 1.

> It may help to sketch a unit circle for each question.
>
> For example for **3b**:
>
>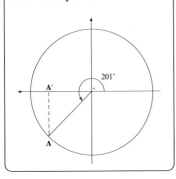

Graphs of $y = \sin x$ and $y = \cos x$

♦ The diagram shows the graphs of $y = \sin x$ and $y = \cos x$ for $0° \leqslant x \leqslant 360°$

♦ If you use your calculator to find $\sin x$ for values of x from $0°$ to $90°$, you can use the symmetry of the graph to find other solutions.

Example **Solve $\sin x = \sin 20°$ and $\sin x = {}^-\sin 20°$ for $0° < x < 360°$**

From a calculator $\sin 20° = 0.34$ (2 dp), so $^-\sin 20° = {}^-0.34$ (2dp).

The graph shows that at the points A and B the value of $\sin x$ is 0.34. This corresponds to the angles $20°$ and $160°$.

In the same way at P and Q $\sin x = {}^-0.34$ for angles of $200°$ and $340°$ respectively.

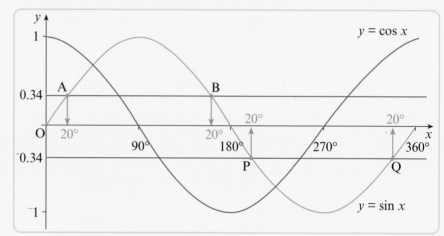

Solve $\sin x = \sin 20°$	Solve $\sin x = {}^-\sin 20°$
From a calculator:	From a calculator:
$\sin 20° = 0.34$ (2 dp)	$\sin 20° = 0.34$ (2 dp)
$\sin x = 0.34$	so $^-\sin 20° = {}^-0.34$ (2dp)
From the graph:	From the graph:
$x = 20°$	$x = 180° + 20°$
or $x = 180° - 20°$	$x = 200°$
$x = 160°$	or $x = 360° - 20°$
	$x = 340°$

Exercise 17.4
Using the graphs of
$y = \sin x$ and $y = \cos x$

1 What is the maximum and minimum value for:

   a $\sin x$ **b** $\cos x$?

2 Use the graph of $\sin x$ to estimate for which values of x, between $0°$ and $360°$, $\sin x = 0.5$. [Check your answers using a calculator]

To avoid marking the page put tracing paper over the graph each time you use it.

3 Solve each of these for values of x between $0°$ and $360°$.

   a i $\cos x = \cos 40°$ **ii** $\cos x = {}^-\cos 35°$ **iii** $\sin x = {}^-\sin 72°$

   b i $\sin x = 0.9$ **ii** $\cos x = {}^-0.9$

   c i $\cos x < 0.5$ **ii** $\sin x < {}^-0.5$ **iii** $\cos x = \sin x$

      iv $\cos x < \sin x$

4 Two solutions for $\cos x = 0.5$ are $x = 60°$ and $x = 300°$.

   a Find two other solutions with $x > 300°$.

   b Give another solution with $x \leqslant 0°$.

5 One solution for $\sin x = 1$ is $x = 90°$.

   Find another solution with:

   a $x > 90°$ **b** $x \leqslant 0°$.

An example which shows that a statement is false is called a counter-example.

Finding a value for which a statement is true does not prove that it is true for all values of x.

6 Three of these statements are false for some values of x.
a Give a counter-example for the three statements that are false.

A $\sin (180° - x) = \sin (180° + x)$
B $\cos x = \sin (90° + x)$
C $\sin (x + x) = \sin x + \sin x$
D $\cos x = \cos (90° + x)$
E $\cos x = \cos (360° - x)$

b Explain how you know that the other two statements are true for all values of x.

Transformations of the graphs of $y = \sin x$ and $y = \cos x$

Exercise 17.5
Drawing trigonometric graphs

We say the movement is modelled by this equation because it does not describe the movement exactly but it is reasonably accurate.

These are some values for $h = 9 \cos \theta$.

$t = 0$ $h = 9 \times \cos 0°$
$\qquad = 9$

$t = 60$ $h = 9 \times \cos 60°$
$\qquad = 4.5$

1 The movement of the tip of the needle in this sewing machine can be modelled by the equation

$$h = 9 \cos t$$

where:

t is the time in milliseconds (thousandths of a second) that the machine has been running.
h is the height above the footplate in millimetres.

Foot plate

a Copy and complete this table for values of $h = 9 \cos t$ over the first 600 milliseconds.

t (ms)	0	60	120	180	240	300	360	420	480	540	600
h (mm)	9	4.5									

b i Explain why the graph should be a smooth curve.
   ii Draw the graph of $h = 9 \cos t$.
c At what height above the footplate did the tip of the needle start?
d Each time the tip of the needle returns to its maximum height above the footplate it completes one stitch.
   i How long does the machine take to complete one stitch?
   ii For how long is the needle below the footplate on each stitch?
e How many stitches will the machine complete in one second?

Use the same pair of axes as you used for Question **1b**.

2 The movement of the tip of the needle on another sewing machine can be modelled by the equation

$$h = 12 \cos t$$

a Sketch the graph of $h = 12 \cos t$
b Does this machine complete stitches at the same rate?
c What is the difference between the two machines?

◆ Each of the graphs below is a transformation of the graph of $y = \sin x$.

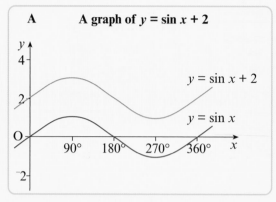

A   **A graph of $y = \sin x + 2$**

B   **A graph of $y = 2 \sin x$**

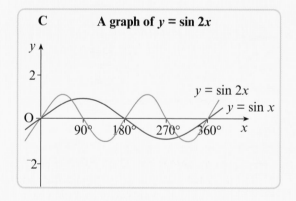

C   **A graph of $y = \sin 2x$**

Exercise 17.6
Sketching and using
trigonometric graphs

It may help to sketch the
graph of $y = \cos x$ first.

1   Using the diagrams above:
   a   state the maximum and minimum values of y on each graph
   b   describe the link between the graphs of $y = \sin x$ and:
      i $y = \sin x + 2$ **ii** $y = 2 \sin x$ **iii** $y = \sin 2x$.

2   **a**   For the values $0 \leqslant x \leqslant 360°$ sketch the graphs of:
      i $y = \cos x - 2$ **ii** $y = 3 \cos x$ **iii** $y = \cos 3x$.
   b   For each graph state the maximum and minimum values of y.

3   What are the maximum and minimum values of y for:
   a $y = \sin 4x$ **b** $y = 5 \cos x$ **c** $y = \sin x - 4$
   d $y = \cos 2x + 1$ **e** $y = 2 \sin x - 2$ **f** $y = 3 \sin 2x + 2$.

4   On one pair of axes sketch the graph of:
   a $y = \sin 3x$ **b** $y = 2 \sin 3x$ **c** $y = 2 \sin 3x - 4$.

5 Each of these graphs is a transformation of $y = \sin x$ or $y = \cos x$.

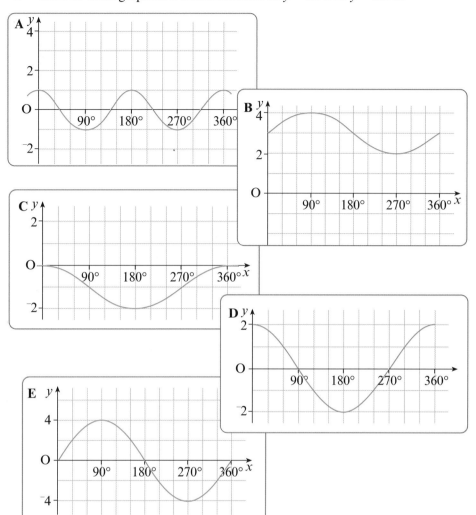

These are the five equations for the graphs above.

> In each equation a is a constant.

$$y = a \sin x \qquad y = \cos x + a \qquad y = a \cos x$$

$$y = \sin x + a \qquad y = \cos ax$$

For each graph:

a write down the matching equation

b find value of a in its equation.

> These are some values for
> $y = \cos (x + 45°)$:
>
> | x | $y = \cos (x + 45°)$ |
> |---|---|
> | 0 | $\cos (0 + 45°) \approx 0.71$ |
> | 45 | $\cos (45° + 45°) = 0.00$ |

6 For the graph of $y = a \sin bx + c$, where a, b and c are constants, write an expression for the maximum value of y.

7 Sketch the graphs of:

a $y = \cos (x + 45°)$ **b** $y = \cos (x - 45°)$.

8 Explain why the graph of $y = \sin (x + 90°)$ and $y = \cos x$ are the same.

9 Which of these gives the same graph as $y = \cos x$?

A $y = \sin (x + 90°)$ B $y = \sin x - 90°$ C $y = \cos (x + 360°)$

D $y = \sin x + 90°$ E $y = \sin (x - 90°)$ F $y = \cos x + 1$

The graph of $y = \tan x$

♦ You can write $\tan x$ in terms of $\sin x$ and $\cos x$.
For values of x in the first quadrant

$$\frac{\sin x}{\cos x} = \frac{opp}{hyp} \div \frac{adj}{hyp}$$

$$= \frac{opp}{hyp} \times \frac{hyp}{adj}$$

$$= \frac{opp}{adj}$$

$$= \tan x$$

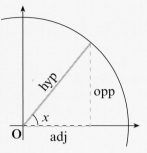

So $\dfrac{\sin x}{\cos x} = \tan x$ for $0 \leqslant x < 90$

This can be extended to values of x in the other quadrants.

♦ This is a graph of $y = \tan x$ for $^-90° < x < 450°$

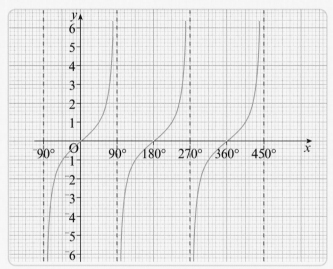

Exercise 17.7
Using the graph of
$y = \tan x$

1 Explain why the value of $\tan 100°$ is negative.

2 Solve each of these for values of x between 0° and 360°.
 a i For what acute angle x does $\tan x = 1$?
  ii Give another value of x that satisfies this equation.
 b Give two values of x that satisfy the equation $\tan x = ^-1$.

3 Explain why:
 a $\tan 56° = \tan 236°$ b $\tan 304° = \tan (^-56)°$.

4 a Use your calculator to find a value for x such that $\tan x \approx 1.1918$.
 b Use the graph to find other values of x which satisfy this equation.

5 Give three values of x between $^-90°$ and 450° for which:
 a $\tan x = \tan 60°$ b $\tan x = ^-\tan 25°$ c $\tan x = ^-\tan 32°$

6 a Use your calculator to find the value of:
  i $\tan 89°$ ii $\tan 89.5°$ iii $\tan 89.9°$ iv $\tan 89.99°$
 b Use your calculator to find the value of:
  i $\tan 91°$ ii $\tan 90.5°$ iii $\tan 90.1°$ iv $\tan 90.01°$
 c Why do you think your calculator does not give a value for $\tan 90°$?
 d Lines drawn at $^-90°$, 90°, 270° and 450° are called asymptotes.
  At what value of x would the next asymptote occur?

End points

You should be able to ...   ... so try these questions

A Solve trigonometric equations	**A1** Solve each of these for $0° \leqslant x \leqslant 360°$.

A1 Solve each of these for $0° \leqslant x \leqslant 360°$.
  a $\cos x = \cos 70°$
  b $\cos x = {}^-\cos 70°$
  c $\tan x = {}^-\tan 40°$
  d $\sin x = {}^-\sin 28°$.

A2 Sort these into pairs that have the same value.

  $\cos 41°$ $\cos 139°$

  $\cos 229°$ $\cos 319°$

  $\cos 131°$ $\cos 221°$

B Transform trigonometric graphs

B1 Sketch the graph of:
  a $y = 3 \cos x$
  b $y = \sin 3x$
  c $y = \sin x + 4$
  d $y = 2 \cos x - 3$

B2 Which of these
equations matches
this graph?
  A $y = \sin 2x$
  B $y = \cos x + 2$
  C $y = \cos (x + 2°)$
  D $y = \sin (x + 90°) + 2$
  E $y = 2 \cos x + 2$

Give reasons for your
answers.

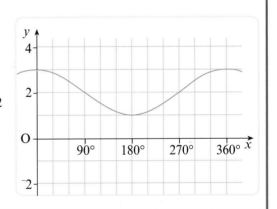

Some points to remember

♦ The graphs of $y = \sin x$ and $y = \cos x$

♦ The graph of $y = \tan x$

211

Starting points

You need to know about ...

... so try these questions

A Inequalities that describe a set of integers or range of values

◆ The inequality signs: > **greater than**
                       <   **less than**
                       ≥   **greater than or equal to**
                       ≤   **less than or equal to**
can be used to define a range of values for a variable.
For instance $^-3 < c \leqslant 4$ means the variable c can have any value greater than $^-3$ but less than or equal to 4.
Values for c such as $^-2$, 3.2, $^-1\frac{1}{2}$ are all acceptable.
This is sometimes called the **solution set** for c.

◆ The solution set
$^-3 < c \leqslant 4$
can be shown on a
number line like this.

Empty circle   Solid circle
$^-3$ **is not** included   4 **is** included

◆ Sometimes only integer values are considered. Two different inequalities can then describe the same set of integers.

For instance, both these solution sets have the integers
0, 1, 2, 3, 4, 5

A1 a Show the inequality
$^-2 \leqslant x < 5$ on a number line.
  b Which of these values for x
satisfy the inequality:
2, $^-5$, 5, $^-2$, 1.634, $^-4$, $4\frac{3}{4}$?

A2 For each of these, what integer
values of n satisfy the
inequality?
  a $4 < n \leqslant 9$
  b $^-2 \leqslant n \leqslant 3$
  c $71 > n \geqslant 68$
  d $^-4 \geqslant n > ^-12$

A3 Which one of these inequalities
describe a different set of
integer values from the others?
$^-4 \leqslant h < 6$, $^-5 < h < 6$,
$^-4 \leqslant h \leqslant 5$, $^-4 < h < 6$,
$^-5 < h \leqslant 5$

A4 Write two different inequalities
involving g which are satisfied
by these integers: $^-3$, $^-2$, $^-1$, 0, 1.

A5 Write a single inequality to
show those integers common to
all three of these inequalities.
$^-5 < f \leqslant 8$ $^-24 \leqslant f < 7$
$^-3 \leqslant f \leqslant 7$

B Identifying and showing simple regions on a graph

◆ The conditions satisfied by two or more inequalities can be shown
by a region on a graph.

Example
Sketch the region where $x > 4$ **and** $^-5 \leqslant y \leqslant 2$.

◆ The region where $x > 4$ is shown by the red shaded area and
where $^-5 \leqslant y \leqslant 2$ by the blue one. Where both regions overlap
both conditions are satisfied.

◆ Sometimes the region which meets
the condition is shaded in (as here).
At other times you will be asked to
shade in the region not wanted.
Check carefully.

B1 Sketch graphs to show the
regions satisfied by each pair
of inequalities.
  a $2 \leqslant x < 5$ $y \geqslant 3$
  b $x < ^-4$ $3 \leqslant y < 7$
  c $^-3 < x \leqslant 3$ $^-8 \leqslant y \leqslant ^-1$

B2 What two inequalities are
satisfied by the shaded region
on this sketch graph?

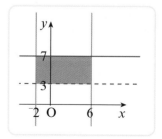

◆ Note that the red boundary line for x is dotted because points where
$x = 4$ are not included in the inequality $x > 4$.

The blue lines for y are solid because $y = 2$ and $y = ^-5$ are included
in $^-5 \leqslant y \leqslant 2$.

C The graphical link between a linear equation and an inequality

Example

Show the region on a graph where both the inequalities $y > 10 - 2x$ and $y \leqslant 2x - 1$ are satisfied.

- Lightly draw the linear graphs of $y = 10 - 2x$ and $y = 2x - 1$ to show the **boundaries** of the regions.

- Decide if the lines should be dotted or solid.

  $y = 2x - 1$ is solid since points on the line are included in $y \leqslant 2x - 1$.

  $y = 10 - 2x$ is dotted since points on the line are not included.

- For each boundary line in turn, choose a point P on one side of it, e.g. (6, 7). Substitute P's coordinates into the inequality and check if the inequality is true or not for that point.

  Substituting into $y \leqslant 2x + 1$ gives $7 \leqslant (2 \times 6) + 1$
  $\qquad 7 \leqslant 13$ true:
  so for this side of the line $y \leqslant 2x + 1$ is true.

  Then choose a point to check which side of its boundary line the other inequality applies to.

- Shade out the regions where the inequalities are **not true**.

  The part of the graph **not shaded** meets both conditions.

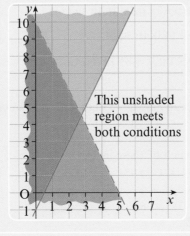

This unshaded region meets both conditions

C1 Use inequalities to describe the shaded region on each graph.

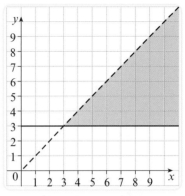

C2 Show the region on a graph where both the inequalities $y \geqslant x + 1$ and $y < 8 - \frac{1}{2}x$ are satisfied. Shade out the regions **not required**.

C3 Use a graph to show the region where all of these inequalities are satisfied:
$\qquad y < x + 2$
$\qquad y \geqslant x$
$\qquad {}^-1 \leqslant x < 4$

C4 What two inequalities describe the unshaded region?

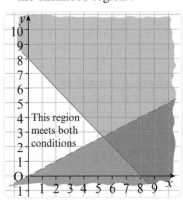

This region meets both conditions

Thinking ahead to ...
solving inequalities

A Start with the inequality **8 > 4** which is true.
Do each of the following operations to the inequality and state if the result is still true.

a	Add 7 to both sides.	**b**	Subtract 5 from both sides.
c	Multiply both sides by 8.	**d**	Divide both sides by 2.
e	Add ⁻8 to both sides.	**f**	Multiply both sides by ⁻3.
g	Divide both sides by ⁻2.		

Rearranging and solving inequalities

♦ An inequality can have an unknown on both sides – for instance:

> ### Danfield Nurseries
> We sold 5 trays of roses and 3 single rose plants on Monday.
> On Tuesday we sold 3 trays and 13 single rose plants.
> We sold more rose plants on Monday than on Tuesday.

> How many rose plants are on a tray?

As an inequality this can be written as $5x + 3 > 3x + 13$
where x is the number of rose plants on a tray.

♦ To solve an inequality you can treat it like an equation.

Example 1

Solve this inequality:	$5x + 3 > 3x + 13$
Subtract $3x$ from both sides:	$2x + 3 > 13$
Subtract 3 from both sides:	$2x > 10$
Divide both sides by 2:	$x > 5$

So the number of rose plants on a tray must be greater than 5, i.e. at least 6.

♦ **The only difference from solving an equation is that if you multiply or divide both sides of an inequality by a negative value the inequality signs will reverse.**

You can avoid having to do this by keeping the coefficient of x positive.

Example 2

Solve this inequality	$3x - 8 \leqslant 5x - 2$
Subtract $3x$ from both sides	$^-8 \leqslant 2x - 2$
Add 2 to both sides	$^-6 \leqslant 2x$
Divide both sides by 2	$^-3 \leqslant x$
So	$x \geqslant {}^-3$

So x can have any values greater than or equal to ⁻3.

> When you rearrange an inequality try to keep the number in front of the variable positive. (i.e. try to keep the coefficient of x positive).
>
> **Example**
>
> Solve
> $$3x - 8 \leqslant 5x - 2$$
>
> Subtract $3x$ from both sides. Do not subtract $5x$ or you will get $^-2x - 8 \leqslant {}^-2$ and will have the problem of dividing through by ⁻2 and changing the sign.

Exercise 18.1
Solving inequalities

1 Solve each of these inequalities.

a	$3y + 6 < 27$	**b**	$13 \geqslant s + 5$	**c**	$5p - 3 \geqslant 27$
d	$10 < 2b + 3$	**e**	$2 \geqslant 6a + 50$	**f**	$5x - 2 > 40$
g	$8 - 3k \geqslant {}^-6$	**h**	$22 \leqslant 4a - 6$	**i**	$13 - 4d > 33$
j	$^-32 \geqslant 3a + 7$				

Where there are brackets, multiply them out first.

For inequalities like $^-9 < 2x + 1 < 5$ treat them as two separate inequalities, e.g. $^-9 < 2x + 1$ and $2x + 1 < 5$

So $^-5 < x < 2$

2 Solve each of these inequalities.

a $2a - 5 \geqslant 6 - a$ b $2k - 6 > 7k + 8$

c $3x + 7 > x - 11$ d $2n - 2 \leqslant 4n - 9$

e $3q + 5 < 1 - 2q$ f $6 < 2(2k - 1)$

g $7h + 3 > 13h + 5$ h $2(3c - 2) < 11$

i $7h - 4 < 5(4 - 3h)$ j $2 - 4(2 - 3p) \geqslant 5(p + 2)$

3 Rearrange these inequalities into the form $A < x < B$, where A and B are integers.

a $^-3 < x + 1 < 2$ b $^-7 < 2x - 3 < 7$

c $^-14 < 1 - x < 2$ d $6 < 2 - 4x < 14$

Inequalities with squared terms

◆ Where an inequality involves an index power, the range of values for the variable may be continuous or have several separate parts.

Example 1 For which values of x is $x^2 < 9$ true?

Since $x^2 = 9$ has two solutions $x = 3$ and $x = ^-3$ the inequality $x^2 < 9$ has two values between which x must lie $^-3 < x < 3$. This is a continuous range between $^-3$ and 3.

$^-3 < x < 3$

Example 2 For which values of x is $x^2 > 9$ true?

Here the inequality $x^2 > 9$ has two values outside of which x must lie so $x < ^-3$ or $x > 3$
This is not a continuous range but two separate parts.

$x < ^-3$ $x > 3$

Exercise 18.2
Inequalities with squared terms

1 Solve each of these inequalities to give the range of values for the variable.

a $d^2 \geqslant 36$ b $17 > g^2$

c $a^2 + 7 \leqslant 56$ d $4 + 2h^2 > 36$

e $64 - 3t^2 < 16$ f $14 - 4c^2 \geqslant 6 - 2c^2$

g $3c^2 - 8 \geqslant 1 - 6c^2$ h $2(f^2 + 2) < 4(2f^2 - 5)$

2 What set of integers satisfies each of these inequalities?

a $k^2 \leqslant 36$ b $5 + b^2 < 30$

c $1 - 2d^2 > d^2 - 47$ d $5 \geqslant 4(x^2 - 5)$

e $7s^2 - 45 < 5(s^2 - 6.5)$ f $3(x^2 - 3) \geqslant 2(3x^2 - 7)$

3 Why is there no value of h which satisfies $2h^2 + 40 < 0$?

4 Which of these inequalities has no solution?

a $34 + 2d^2 > 6$ b $34 - 2d^2 > 6$

c $34 + 2d^2 < 6$ d $34 - 2d^2 < 6$

5 What set of integers satisfies the inequality $14p - 4p^2 > 0$?

Linear programming (An extension activity)

The optimum solution is the best possible solution which meets all the conditions imposed.
It is often the solution which gives the maximum profit.

Some mathematical problems can be described by a set of inequalities and the optimum solution found by examining regions on a graph.
This is known as linear programming.

Example

A poultry keeper wants to keep ducks and turkeys in the same run.
The keeper wants fewer than 20 birds and no more than 4 turkeys.
She wants to spend £60 or more for a discount from her supplier.
At discount prices, a duck costs £3.60 and a turkey costs £4.80.
Let d the number of ducks and t be the number of turkeys.

a Write three different inequalities from the conditions above.
b Draw a graphs of t against d to show the inequalities.
c The profit from a duck is £3 and from a turkey is £7.
How many of each bird should she buy for maximum profit?

a For the number of turkeys: $\qquad$ $t \leqslant 4$ $\qquad$ ... (1)

For the total number of birds: $\qquad$ $d + t < 20$ $\qquad$ ... (2)

For the cost: $\qquad\qquad\qquad\qquad$ $360d + 480t \geqslant 6000$
divide both sides by 120 $\qquad\qquad$ $3d + 4t \geqslant 50$ $\quad$ ... (3)

b The regions for these inequalities can be drawn by looking at where each boundary line crosses the t and d axes.
$\qquad$ For (2), when $d = 0$, $t = 20$ $\quad$ and when $t = 0$, $d = 20$
$\qquad$ For (3), when $d = 0$, $t = 12.5$ and when $t = 0$, $d = 16.7$

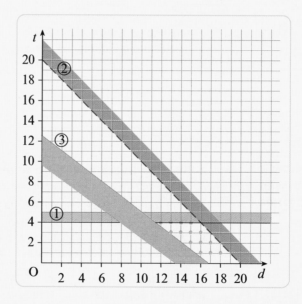

The largest or smallest values of the profit will lie at one vertex (corner) of the region which meets the other conditions. This means it is only necessary to test points nearest the vertices.

c At the point (19, 0) the profit is $(19 \times £3) + (0 \times £7) = £57$
At the point (17, 0) the profit is $(17 \times £3) + (0 \times £7) = £51$
At the point (15, 4) the profit is $(15 \times £3) + (4 \times £7) = £73$
At the point (12, 4) the profit is $(12 \times £3) + (4 \times £7) = £64$

So 15 ducks and 4 turkeys gives the greatest profit.

Exercise 18.3

Linear programming

1 For the turkey and duck problem:

   a Why is the point (19, 1) not in the solution set, i.e. not shown as a gold dot?
   b Why is the point (16.5, 2.5) not in the solution set?
   c The point (13, 3) appears to be in the solution set.
   How can you be certain that it is in the solution set?
   d What profit is represented by the point (17, 2)?

2 Seascape Ferries have two types of ferry, Viking and Neptune.
   They have 7 Vikings and 8 Neptunes in their fleet.
   A Viking carries 80 cars and 3 lorries and a Neptune 50 cars and 6 lorries.
   On one day Seascape must transport at least 600 cars and at least 45 lorries.

   a If v Vikings and n Neptunes are used, explain why:

   i for lorries: $3v + 6n \geq 45$ or $v + 2n \geq 15$ **ii** for cars: $8v + 5n \geq 60$

   b Give two other inequalities which apply.
   c Draw a graph of v against n and show the region which meets all
   the conditions.
   Mark with dots all the possible combinations in the solution set.
   d What is the smallest number of ferries that can be used?
   How many of each type could be used?

3 Canfield Exhibition Hall hire out stands to exhibitors.
   There are prominent stands by the entrance, each with an area of $8\,m^2$,
   and stands in the centre with an area of $10\,m^2$.
   The charge is £280 a day for an entrance stand and £120 for a centre one.
   The total area for all stands is $120\,m^2$ and the rental per day must be at
   least £1680.
   The manager has calculated the ratio of centre stands to entrance stands.
   Let E be the number of entrance stands and C the number of centre stands.

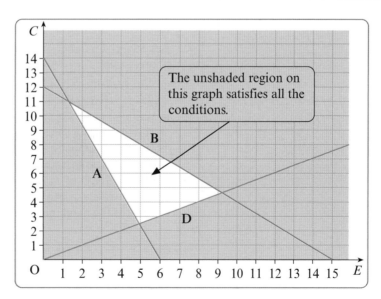

The unshaded region on this graph satisfies all the conditions.

   a From the information given, write an inequality which applies to:
   i the stand areas   **ii** the rental.
   b What do you think are the equations of lines A and B on the graph?
   c Line D shows the boundary of the ratio of large stands to entrance stands.
   Write an inequality which describes this ratio.
   d The number of visitors to the hall is in direct proportion to the
   number of stands. How many centre stands and entrance stands should
   there be for the maximum number of visitors?

End points

You should be able to ...   ... so try these questions

A Find integer values which satisfy an inequality

A1 For each of these what integer values of g satisfy the inequality?

a $^-2 < g < 0$ b $^-5 \leqslant g < 4$
c $7 \geqslant g \geqslant 4$ d $^-56 \geqslant g > ^-60$
e $d^2 < 16$ f $4c^2 - 6 \geqslant 6c^2 - 32$

B Solve an inequality to find the range of values for x

B1 Solve these inequalities.

a $5x \leqslant 30$ b $12 < 4f$
c $4a + 5 \geqslant 53$ d $5k + 28 > 3$
e $3(4s - 2) \leqslant 42$ f $7d - 10 > 5 - 3d$
g $x^2 > 100$ h $2x^2 - 6 \leqslant 2$

C Draw a region to illustrate where several inequalities are satisfied

C1 On a graph with values of x and y between 0 and 12 show the region where the inequalities $y \geqslant x + 3$ and $y \leqslant 12 - 3x$ are both satisfied.

D Use linear programming to find an optimum solution to a problem

D1 Cinema 2 can seat up to 200 people and the owners need takings per performance of at least £720 to make a profit.

The majority of seats are standard grade at £4 each and the remainder are luxury grade at £5 each. For different performances there are different numbers of standard and luxury seats, but there are never more than three times as many standard seats as luxury seats.

Let S be the number of standard seats and L the number of luxury seats.

a Which of these conditions fits the data given?
$S < L$ $S \leqslant L$ $S = L$ $S > L$ $S \geqslant L$
b Write an inequality for:
  i   the seating capacity of the cinema
  ii the seats that have to be sold to make a profit
  iii the ratio of standard to luxury seats.
c Draw a graph of L against S with axes from 0 to 200 to show the region which satisfies all the conditions.
d What is the maximum possible takings on one performance?

Some points to remember

- Always check carefully to see if $\geqslant$ rather than $>$, or $\leqslant$ rather than $<$, is used.

- When you solve an inequality you can treat it like an equation except that:
  - if you multiply or divide both sides by a negative value you must reverse the signs.

- Often in linear programming you have to find the optimum solution to a further condition. In this case test the points nearest to the vertices of the region which matches the other conditions.

Starting points
You need to know about ...

... so try these questions

A Writing fractions as decimals and percentages

- To write a fraction as a decimal:
  - ❖ divide the numerator by the denominator.

$$\tfrac{3}{8} = 3 \div 8 = 0.375 = 37.5\%$$ $$\tfrac{5}{6} = 5 \div 6 = 0.8\dot{3} = 83.\dot{3}\%$$

B Calculating a percentage of a given amount

To calculate a percentage of a given amount:

- Multiply the amount by the appropriate decimal.
  For instance, to calculate **65%** of 420 kg

$$420 \times 0.65 = 273$$

So 65% of 420 kg is 273 kg

C Writing one number as a percentage of another

Compare the numbers 18 and 36:
- ◆ 18 is half of 36 or 18 ÷ 36 = 0.5
- ◆ 18 is 50% of 36 or 0.5 × 100 = 50%

As a single calculation: (18 ÷ 36) × 100 = 50%

This method can be used with any two numbers p and t

To **calculate p as a percentage of t: $(p \div t) \times 100$**

Example

Jenny and Bruce walked from John O'Groats to Lands End, a distance of 868 miles. By the end of Day 4 they had walked 113 miles. What percentage of the total distance is this?

To calculate **113** as a percentage of 868

$$(113 \div 868) \times 100 = 13.018 \dots$$

They had travelled 13.0% (1 dp) of the total distance.

D Interpreting a calculator display in calculations with money

Interpreting a calculator display correctly, is important.
When you calculate 24% of £15 the display shows:

The calculation is in pounds so the answer is **£3.60**

When you calculate 24% if £1.50 the display shows:

The calculation is in pounds so the answer is **£0.36**
It is more likely that the answer will be given as **36 pence**.

A1 Write each of these as a decimal and as a percentage:

  a $\tfrac{3}{4}$ **b** $\tfrac{5}{8}$ **c** $\tfrac{8}{5}$ **d** $\tfrac{5}{4}$

  e $\tfrac{6}{5}$ **f** $\tfrac{13}{20}$ **g** $\tfrac{8}{32}$ **h** $\tfrac{19}{6}$

B1 Calculate:
- **a** 55% of 650 miles
- **b** 72.5% of £400
- **c** 46% of 3450
- **d** 28% of £415
- **e** 4.5% of 360 metres
- **f** 38% of £4.50
- **g** 0.5% of £25
- **h** 8% of 3 miles.

C1 Calculate, giving your answer correct to 2 dp:
- **a** 52 as a percentage of 80
- **b** 85 as a percentage of 184
- **c** 1.5 as a percentage of 12
- **d** 15 as a percentage of 12
- **e** 0.75 as a percentage of 25.

C2 Of a total bill for £65.70, only £9.20 of this was for parts.

Calculate the charge for parts as a percentage of the total bill (correct to 2 sf).

D1 In each of these, interpret your calculator display appropriately.
- **a** Calculate 16% of £85 (answer in pounds)
- **b** Calculate 14% of 4 cm (answer in millimetres).
- **c** Find 44% of 3.5 kg (answer in grams).
- **d** Find 9% of £2.27 (answer in pence).
- **e** What is 78% of 65 mm:
  - **i** in millimetres
  - **ii** in centimetres?

Thinking ahead to ...
percentage changes

Often percentages are used to describe
a change in an amount.
For example, in supermarkets special offers
can be shown as:

Extra 15% FREE !

For the customer:

A How much extra do you get free?
Is it more or less than a quarter of the
amount for the normal price?

B What fraction would you use to
describe the extra free amount?

C How many ml of the product are in the special offer pack?

Percentage changes

For an increase by a certain percentage, a final value can be found in this way.

Example
Toothpaste is sold in tubes containing 150 ml.
In a special offer, 12% extra toothpaste is in the tube for the same price.
How much toothpaste is in the special offer tube?

> Think of the toothpaste in this way: 100% of the contents is 150 ml.
>
> The special offer tube has 12% extra, so it must contain: 112% of 150 ml.
>
> 112 % as a decimal is 1.12
>
> To calculate 112% of 150: $150 \times 1.12 = 168$
>
> The special offer tube contains **168 ml** of toothpaste.

Similarly you can decrease by a given percentage.

Example
A fast food store decided to decrease by 18% the weight of packaging for
their regular meals, which weighed 40 grams.
Calculate the weight of the new packaging.

> Think of the packaging in this way: 100% of the contents weighs 40 g.
>
> The new packaging weighs 18% less, so it must weigh 82% of the 40 grams.
>
> 82% as a decimal is 0.82
>
> To calculate 82% of 40: $40 \times 0.82 = 32.8$
>
> The new regular meal packaging weighs **32.8 grams**.

Exercise 19.1
Percentage changes

1 In a special offer, the 440 gram of coffee in a jar is to be increased by 15%.

  a What percentage of the 440 grams of coffee are in the special offer jar?
  b Calculate the amount of coffee in the special offer jar.

2 **a** Increase 350 kg by 18%.   **b** Increase 447 km by 16%.
    c Increase 4.50 metres by 22%.   **d** Increase £35 000 by 8%.
    e Increase £27.50 by 32%.   **f** Increase 25800 tonnes by 17%.
    g Increase 3 500 000 litres by 9%.   **h** Increase 0.6 cm by 15%.

> Depreciate means to lose value.

3 A manufacturer buys a machine for £56 800. The machine is expected to depreciate by 12% in the first year and by 8.5% each future year.
What will be the value of the machine after ten years to the nearest £1?

4 Baz paid £2685 for a new keyboard. The salesman told him to expect that, at the end of every year, the value of the keyboard would fall by 15% of its value at the start of that year.

What do you expect to be the value of the keyboard at the end of five years?

5 Last year a company spent £3.4 million on advertising. Next year they have set a target of saving 3.5% on advertising spending.

Next year, how much do they expect to spend on advertising?

6 In 1997 Wyvern Water lost water from their underground pipes at the rate of 600 litres per minute. Between 1998 and the end of 2004 they have a programme of repairs that will save, on average, 4.8% per year, on water loss.

In total, how much water do Wyvern Water expect to lose in 2005?

7 Each year for five years, a company plans to use 20% less paper.
Will they use no paper in five years time? Explain your answer.

Percentages and VAT

To calculate the total price of goods or services including VAT is the same as: increasing the cost price by the percentage VAT.

Example A garden shed is advertised for: **£114.99** + VAT at 17.5%
Calculate the total charge for the shed.

> This example is with VAT at 17.5%.
>
> In all questions that involve VAT you must use the standard rate of VAT at the time.
>
> If you are unsure, ask for the rate of VAT.

Think of the total charge (cost price + VAT) for the shed in this way:

The total charge for the shed is: **117.5%** of its cost price

To calculate 117.5% of £114.99:
$$114.99 \times 1.175 = 135.113$$

The total charge for the shed (including VAT) is:

£135.11 (to the nearest penny)

Exercise 19.2
Calculating with VAT

1 The cost of these items is given without VAT (ex VAT).
Calculate the charge, including VAT, for each item.

a camera £16	**b** trainers £44.25	**c** bike £185
d toaster £19.40	**e** pen 72 pence	**f** TV £368.42
g fridge £262	**h** mower £24.55	**i** CD £9.35
j video £188.70	**k** battery 34 pence	**l** pencil 11 pence

> Traders have to charge VAT. The VAT is then paid by the traders to the Customs and Excise.
>
> These payments are made every three months.

2 To hire a coach for a hockey tour cost £675 + VAT.
The cost of the coach was shared equally by the 23 people on the tour.

Calculate to the nearest fifty pence how much each person on the tour had to pay for the hire of the coach.

3 Fraser needs four new tyres for his car. He has a maximum of £150 in total to spend on the tyres. All tyre prices are given ex VAT.

To the nearest 10 pence, what is the most Fraser can pay for a tyre ex VAT?

Reverse percentages

When you divide by 117.5, you are calculating 1%.

You then multiply by 100% to calculate the 100%.

This is for VAT at 17.5%

Check on the current rate of VAT to find the number to divide by to calculate 1%.

Calculating the original value of something, before an increase or decrease took place, is called 'calculating a reverse percentage'.

Example   The total price of a bike (inc. VAT at 17.5%) is £146.85
Calculate the cost price of the bike ex VAT.

The total price of the bike = 117.5% of the ex VAT price
$$146.85 = 117.5 \times \text{ex VAT price}$$
$$146.85 \div 1.175 = \text{the ex VAT price}$$
$$124.978... = \text{the ex VAT price}$$

The price of the bike ex VAT is £124.98 (to the nearest penny)

Exercise 19.3
Calculating reverse percentages

1   These prices include VAT, calculate each price ex VAT.
Give your answers correct to the nearest penny.
    a   CD player £135.50   b   camera £34.99   c   ring £74.99
    d   trainers £65.80   e   TV £186.75   f   phone £14.49
    g   calculator £49.99   h   PC £799.98   i   tent £98.99

2   Ella bought a pair of climbing boots for £45.60 in a sale that gave '20% off!'.
    a   What was the non-sale price of the boots?
    b   How much did Ella save buying the boots in the sale?

3   When Mike sold his bike for £35, he said he made a profit of about 45%.
    To the nearest pound, how much did Mike pay for the bike?

4   A 675 gram box of cereal is said to hold 35% more than the regular box.
    How many grams of cereal are in the regular box?

5   The Bay Point Hotel charges £65.45 per person per night for bed and breakfast. This charge includes VAT.
    How much does the hotel take per person per night, at this charge?

6   In 1997 Reynards Fast Foods made a profit of £146 455.
    The profits for 1997 were 6.5% above the profits made in 1996.
    Calculate the profit made in 1996, correct to the nearest £5.

7   A light-bulb manufacturer makes clear and pearl light-bulbs.
    Each week they make 45 360 clear bulbs, which is 64% of the total production of the bulbs made in a week.

    a   What is the total number of bulbs produced in a week?
    b   How many pearl bulbs are produced in a week?
    c   For each week give the ratio in its lowest terms, of clear bulbs made : pearl bulbs made.

8   Asif and Nina make and sell vegetarian snack foods. They sell at prices to give them a profit of 315%. Last year their total sales were £26 855.

    a   To the nearest pound, how much profit did they make last year?
    b   Write a formula that they might use to calculate their profit (p) from their total sales (s).

9   In 1996, a total of 126 788 people visited the Butterfly Sanctuary.
    This was estimated to be 14% fewer visitors than 1995.
    Give an estimate of the total number of visitors in 1995.
    Explain the degree of accuracy you worked to.

10 Write a formula to calculate the cost of an item without VAT (c) from the price of the item with VAT (p).

Percentages and interest

Interest is explained in the *Oxford Mathematics Study Dictionary* in this way:

> Interest The interest is the amount of extra money paid in return for having the use of someone else's money.

When you borrow, or save money with a Bank, Building Society, the Post Office, a Credit Union, or a finance company, interest is *charged* or *paid*.

Interest is: *charged* on money you borrow and *paid* on money you save.

Interest is: *charged* or *paid* pa, at a fixed rate, e.g. 6% pa.

> pa means *per annum*, or each year.

Simple interest is a type of interest not often used these days.

♦ Simple interest is fixed to the sum of money you originally borrow or save.

Simple interest can be calculated using this *simple interest formula*:

In words, the formula is:

$$I = P \times R \times T \qquad Interest = Principal \times Rate \times Time$$

Principal is the amount of money you borrow or save.
Rate is the interest rate pa. **as a decimal**.
Time is for how long, usually in years.

Example
Calculate the interest charged on a loan of £750, for 4 years at 7% pa.
Using the formula gives:
$$I = P \times R \times T, \text{ with } P = 750, R = 0.07 \ (7\% = 0.07) \text{ and } T = 4$$
$$I = 750 \times 0.07 \times 4$$
$$I = 210$$
The interest charged on this loan is £210.

(If the £750 had been saved for 4 years at 7% pa,
the interest paid on the savings would be £210.)

Exercise 19.4
Calculating with simple interest

1   Calculate the simple interest charged, or paid for each of these:
   a £450 borrowed for 6 years with interest at 12% pa
   b £280 saved for 8 years with a rate of interest of 3% pa
   c £1500 saved for 15 years at 6% pa interest
   d £6000 borrowed for 10 years at an interest rate of 17% pa

2   To buy new kit a band borrows £3500 over 10 years at 17% interest pa.
   a Calculate the amount of interest paid on the loan.
   b At the end of the loan, how much in total will have been paid for the kit?

3   A new bridge will cost an estimated £44 million, and take six years to build. If, at the start, all £44 million is borrowed at a simple interest rate of 8.5%, estimate the total cost of the bridge.

4   A sum of £350 was saved for six years. Over this time the simple interest earned was a total of £96.60. Calculate the rate of interest paid.

Compound interest

> Compound interest is used by banks, building societies, credit card companies and high street shops.

Compound interest is either *charged* or *paid*, but not just on the original sum.

Example

Calculate the interest on £100 saved for 2 years at 4%.

♦ At the end of year 1, the total is £104 (£100 + £4 interest)
♦ At the end of year 2, the total is £108.16 (£104 + £4.16 interest)

In short, compound interest includes interest on interest already *paid* or *charged*.

Working year-by-year, you can calculate compound interest and see that it builds to a greater total than simple interest over the same period of time.

Example

Calculate the interest on £480 saved for 3 years at 7%.

♦ Interest paid at the end of year 1 is: **£33.60** (£480 × 0.07)
  Interest for year 2 will be calculated on £513.60 (£480 + £33.60)
♦ Interest paid is: **£35.95** (£513.60 × 0.07)
  Interest for year 3 will be calculated on £549.55 (£513.60 + £35.95)
♦ Interest paid is: **£38.47**
  The total interest paid is: £33.60 + £35.95 + £38.47 = **£108.02**

Exercise 19.5
Calculating with compound rates

1 Calculate the total interest paid on these savings at compound interest:

a £350 for 3 years at 9% pa
b £1400 for 4 years at 3% pa
c £3600 for 5 years at 6% pa
d £12 250 for 3 years at 4% pa
e £4050 for 2 years at 12% pa
f £35 250 for 2 years at 9.5% pa
g £565 for 3 years at 10.5% pa
h £185 for 4 years at 0.3% pa
i £45 000 for 4 years at 7.2% pa
j £1224 for 2 years at 2.3% pa.

2 Shelley won £5000, and put it in a savings scheme for five years.
The savings scheme pays interest at 6.8% pa compound.

a Calculate the total interest paid on her savings.
b At the end of five years what was the total in Shelley's saving scheme?

3 Roughly how long must a sum of money be saved at 8% pa compound, for the value of the savings to double? Explain your answer.

4 On average, the price of new cars has increased by 3.8% pa over the last five years. At this rate, what would you expect a model that cost £18 955 five years ago to be priced at today to the nearest £1?

5 The world population of a species of bird is estimated to be decreasing at the rate of 18% pa. There were estimated to be 4200 birds in 1995.

a If the rate of decrease remains the same, estimate the year in which the species would become extinct. Explain your answer.

In 1995 a programme was put in place to halt the decrease, and increase the world population of the species by 4% pa.

b If this rate remains the same, when would you expect the population of this species to reach 6000? Explain your answer.

> Check that your formula works by using it with Questions **2**, **3**, and **4** above.

6 The sum of £A is saved in a scheme that pays interest at r% pa compound. Write, and simplify, an expression for the total vaule of the savings at the end of five years.

There is a compound interest formula.

Here the rate of interest is: given as a percentage but used as a **decimal** for calculations.

♦ For a principal of £150, invested at a rate of 6% for a period of 4 years

At the end of year 1, the value of the principal is:
$$150 \times 1.06$$

At the end of year 2, the value of the principal is:
$$150 \times 1.06 \times 1.06 \quad \text{or} \quad 150 \times 1.06^2$$

At the end of year 3:
$$150 \times 1.06^2 \times 1.06 \quad \text{or} \quad 150 \times 1.06^3$$

At the end of year 4:
$$150 \times 1.06^3 \times 1.06 \quad \text{or} \quad 150 \times 1.06^4$$

The total for the interest £I is therefore: $I = (150 \times 1.06^4) - 150$

For any principal, a general formula can be used. This is based on:

Interest £I, on a principal sum £P, invested at $r\%$, for n years.

The compound interest can be found by using this formula:

$$I = [P \times \left(1 + \frac{r}{100}\right)^n] - P$$

Exercise 19.6
Using the compound interest formula

1 Calculate the total interest paid on a principal of £8500 invested for twelve years at a rate of 4% pa compound.

2 W&J claim that the value of their Unit Trust is likely to grow by 8.5% pa compound for the next five years.

If you invest £15 250 with the W&J Unit Trust, what would you expect your investment to be worth at the end of five years?

3 Two sisters, Rhian and Celine, were each left £2500 in a will.

Rhian decided to spend £5 per week on the National Lottery, and at the end of three years she had won a total of £1216.50.

Celine decided to invest her share at an interest rate of 7.5% pa compound.

Who do you think made the best decision? Explain your answer.

4 A building society offered the following terms for a minimum saving of £25 000 over a 10-year period.

For the first three years interest is paid at 5.8% pa compound
For the next four years interest is paid at 6.6% pa
For the remaining time interest is paid at 7.2% pa.

At the end of ten years, what will be the value of a £25 000 investment?

5 A village is given a grant of £185 000 to build a new village hall. Once the grant is given it cannot be invested for more than five years.

The village hall committee decide to invest the grant in total for five years, at the end of which they would need **at least** £232 000 in the account.

Problems involving compound growth or reduction such as Question 6 can be calculated in a similar way to compound interest.

a What is the lowest rate of interest (1 dp) they need for this investment? Explain your answer.
b How will your figures change for a maximum period of four years?

6 There are 436 rabbits in a colony and their population increases by 8% per year. What will be the size of the colony after 16 years?

Buying on credit

Here the deposit is an amount you must pay in cash.

The deposit paid can be an amount of money (£30), or a percentage of the full price, e.g. 20% deposit.

There are rules for buying on credit. These can be changed by governments, and it may be possible to buy on credit with no deposit.

If you buy on credit, you pay a deposit on purchase and the remainder you pay off with a loan.
The total for the loan is paid off in a number of equal *instalments*.

Example

This advert is for a colour television.

only £179.99

CREDIT PLAN: **You pay £20 deposit the balance at 23% compound interest in 24 equal instalments (2 years)**

Calculate the monthly instalment for this credit plan.

The amount of the loan is £159.99 (i.e. £179.99 – £20 deposit)
With interest the total to be repaid on the loan is £242.05 (£159.99 × 1.23^2)
With 24 instalments, each instalment $= £242.05 \div 24$
$= £10.085 \ldots$
The monthly instalment will be £10.09 (to the nearest penny)

Exercise 19.7
Buying on credit

1 With the same Credit Plan as for the television above, calculate the monthly instalment for a washing machine costing £399.99 over three years.

2 Eric bought a camcorder advertised for £469.99.
He paid no deposit, was charged interest at 26% pa compound, and had the loan over 4 years (48 equal instalments).
   a Calculate the total Eric will pay for the camcorder.
   b Calculate the monthly instalment.

3 Dinah decides to buy a second-hand car priced at £6995.
She is allowed £1150 for her old car and takes out a loan for the difference.
The interest rate is 13.5% pa compound, and the loan is over 30 months.
   a Calculate her monthly instalment.
   b How much, in total, will this *new* car have cost Dinah?

4 An extension to an hotel has to be carpeted.
The total floor area is 586m^2, and the carpet costs £34.99 ex VAT per m^2.
The hotel pays a deposit of £8 500, and borrows the remainder of the money over five years at an interest rate of 14.2% pa compound.
   a How much in total will the hotel pay for the carpet?
   b What will the hotel have paid for each square metre of carpet?

5 Copy and complete this repayment table for up to 60 months.

Amount borrowed	Repayments (months)				
	12	24	36	48	60
£100					
£500					
£1000					
£2000					
£5000					
£10000					

Repayment table Interest rate 9.6% pa (compound)

End points

You should be able to ...   ... so try these questions

A Calculate percentage changes	**A1** Increase 480 km by 16%.
	A2 A CJ regular size cola is 380 ml. CJ decide to increase the size of their regular cola by 12%. To the nearest millilitre, give the size of the larger regular cola.
	A3 Decrease £55.80 by 6%. Give your answer to the nearest penny.
	A4 In 1992, there were a total of 42 154 breakdowns on a motorway section. In 1993 the total number of breakdowns fell by an estimated 7%. Estimate the number of breakdowns in 1993, on this motorway section.
B Work with VAT	**B1** A fridge/freezer is advertised for £849.99 ex VAT. Calculate the price of the fridge/freezer with VAT.
	B2 To the nearest penny, the VAT (at 17.5%) added to a bill was £84.88. Calculate the total for the bill including VAT.
C Calculate reverse percentages	**C1** In 1996 Buslinks *UK* made a profit of £2.42 million pounds. This was a increase of 6.5% on the profits for 1995. Calculate the profits for 1995 correct to 4 sf.
	C2 Jetstream have been providing charter flights to Spain for three years. In their third year they flew a total of 425 620 passengers to Spain. This was an increase of 8% on their second year, which was an increase of 3.5% on their first year. Estimate the total number of passengers they flew to Spain in their first year.
D Calculate simple interest	**D1** Calculate the simple interest on £235 invested at 4.5% for 7 years.
	D2 Asif had savings of £650 for a period of 5 years. He was paid simple interest, and at the end of the 5 years he had £796.25 in the account. Calculate the rate of interest he was paid.
E Calculate compound interest	**E1** Calculate the interest paid on a principal of £45 250 invested for 6 years at 4.25% pa compound.
F Calculate with buying on credit	**F1** Lauren buys an electric guitar priced at £499.95. She pays £100 and pays off the rest at 18% p.a. compound interest, with monthly instalments over 2 years. **a** How much are the monthly instalments? **b** How much will Lauren have paid in total for her guitar?

Some points to remember

- Working with a calculator it is easier if you think of, and use, percentages as decimals.
- Check that your answer to a calculation is of the right size, and to a sensible degree of accuracy.
- When you are calculating interest, paid or charged, make sure you know whether it is at a rate of simple interest, or compound interest.

Starting points
You need to know about ...

... so try these questions

A The terminology for parts of a circle

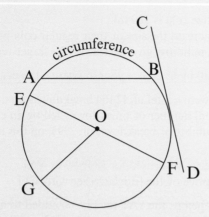

In this circle with centre O:

AB is a **chord**	A chord is a straight line that joins two points on the circumference of a circle.
CD is a **tangent**	A tangent to a circle is a straight line which touches the circle at one point only.
EF is a **diameter**	A diameter is a chord that passes through the centre.
Circumference	The circumference is the distance measured around the curved edge of a circle.
OG is a **radius**	A radius is any straight line from the centre to the circumference.

The curved part of the circle between A and B is known as an **arc**.
There are two **arcs** AB:
the larger is the **major arc**
the smaller is the **minor arc**.

The chord AB divides the circle into two **segments**.
There are two segments created by the chord AB: the **major segment** and the **minor segment**.

AB, PR, and GH are all chords.
The **perpendicular bisector** of each chord has been drawn to show that:
The perpendicular bisector of any chord passes through the centre of its circle.

A1 ◆ Draw a circle, centre O with a radius of 4 cm.
◆ Mark any point P on your page 8 cm from O.
◆ From P draw two tangents to the circle.
◆ Label the point where one tangent touches the circle A, and where the other tangent touches B.

a Measure the distance PA and PB.
b What do you notice?
c Is this the case for other points P?
◆ Join PO.
d Measure angles APO and BPO.
e What do you notice?
f Is this always the case for other points P?
◆ Draw in the lines OA and OB.
g Measure angles OAP and OBP.
h What do you notice?
i Is this always the case?
◆ Draw in the chord AB.
j Is OP the perpendicular bisector of AB? Give reasons for your answer.

A2 Draw any circle centre O. The chord AB is such that the ratio
minor arc AB : major arc AB
is 1 : 2.
a Mark a position for A and B on your circle.
b Explain how you were able to fix points for A and B.

A3 a Draw around a circular object. By drawing and bisecting chords find the centre of the circle you have drawn.
b Two straight lines meet at right angles at B so that AB = 4 cm and BC = 6 cm. AB and BC are chords of the same circle, centre O. Find the distances OA, OB and OC.

The angle subtended at the centre

For a chord AB and any point C on the circumference of a circle, joining A to C, and B to C gives angle ACB.

Angle ACB is said to be subtended by the chord AB.

In this circle, centre O, AB is a chord and C is a point on the circumference.

Angle ACB is:

♦ subtended by the chord AB
♦ at the circumference of the circle.

Angle AOB is:

♦ subtended by the chord AB
♦ at the centre of the circle.

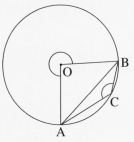

A geometrical property of the circle is that:
the angle AOB is twice the angle ACB ($\hat{AOB} = 2 \times \hat{ACB}$).

The general statement is:
For the same chord, the angle subtended at the centre is twice the angle subtended at the circumference in the major segment.

When the angle subtended at the centre is in the minor segment:

The general statement is:
For the same chord, the angle subtended at the circumference is half the reflex angle subtended at the centre.

Proof:

When you show a proof or answer questions on circle theorems you need to give reasons at each stage – see the statements in brackets here.

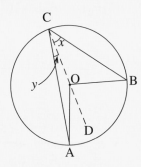

let $\hat{BCO} = x$ and $\hat{ACO} = y$
In $\triangle$ OCB, $\hat{OCB} = x$ (isoscoles $\triangle$)
So $\hat{BOC} = (180° - 2x)$ (angle of sum $\triangle$)
In $\triangle$ OCA, $\hat{OAC} = y$ (isoscoles $\triangle$)
So $\hat{AOC} = (180° - 2y)$ (angle sum of $\triangle$)

Angle $\hat{BOD} = 180° - \hat{BOC}$ (angle sum of straight line)
            $= 180° - (180° - 2x)$
            $= 2x$

Angle $\hat{AOD} = 180° - \hat{AOC}$ (angle sum of straight line)
            $= 180° - (180° - 2y)$
            $= 2y$

So $\hat{AOB} = 2x + 2y$
Also $\hat{ACB} = x + y$
So $\mathbf{\hat{AOB} = 2 \times \hat{ACB}}$

Angles in the same segment

In this circle, AB is a chord. The points C, D, and E are other points on the circle.

The angles ACB, ADB, and AEB are all:

- subtended by the chord AB
- at the circumference of the circle
- in the same segment
  (in this case the major segment).

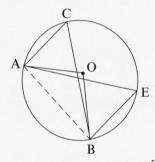

A geometrical property of the circle is that:
the angles ACB, ADB, and AEB are all equal in size.
The general statement is:
Angles subtended at the circumference by the same chord in the same segment are equal.

Proof:

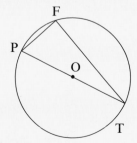

O marks the centre of the circle.

$$A\hat{O}B = 2 \times A\hat{C}B \qquad \text{(angle at the centre is } 2 \times \text{angle at circum.)}$$

Also $A\hat{O}B = 2 \times A\hat{E}B$

So $2 \times A\hat{C}B = 2 \times A\hat{E}B$

So **$A\hat{C}B = A\hat{E}B$**

Similarly $A\hat{C}B = A\hat{D}B$

Angles in a semicircle

When a chord becomes a diameter, then each segment is a semicircle. The angle subtended at the circumference in a semicircle is a right angle.

In this case $P\hat{G}T = P\hat{F}T = 90°$

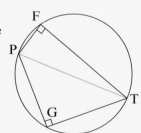

The general statement is:
Any angle subtended at the circumference in a semicircle is a right angle.

Proof:

PT is a diameter and passes through the centre O.

$$P\hat{O}T = 180° \qquad \text{(straight line)}$$

$$P\hat{F}T = \tfrac{1}{2}P\hat{O}T \qquad \text{(angle at centre = } 2 \times \text{angle at circum.)}$$

So **$P\hat{F}T = 90°$**

Secant

Any straight line that cuts across a circle at two points is called a **secant**.

A tangent is a special case of a secant as the two cuts become a single point of contact.

The two cuts are said to become **coincident**, giving a single point.

Tangents to a circle

From any point P, outside the circle, two tangents to the circle can be drawn; the distance from P to the point of contact being the same for each tangent, i.e. PS = PT.

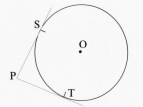

The angle between a radius, drawn to the point of contact of a tangent, and the tangent is a right angle, i.e. $P\hat{S}O = P\hat{T}O = 90°$.

Any chord (ST) drawn in a circle creates two segments. One of these two segments can be described as being **alternate** to the other.

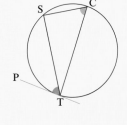

When a tangent (PT) is drawn at one end of the chord, then an angle is created between the tangent and the chord ($P\hat{T}S$).

This angle, measured on one side of the chord, is equal to the angle in the alternate segment ($S\hat{C}T$).

In this case $P\hat{T}S = S\hat{C}T$

The general statement is:
The angle between a chord and the tangent, at its point of contact is equal to the angle subtended at the circumference in the alternate segment.

Proof:

Let CT be the diameter.

$$T\hat{S}C = 90°$$ (angles in a semicircle)

So $S\hat{C}T + S\hat{T}C = 90°$ (angle of sum △)

Also $P\hat{T}C = 90°$ (tangents meet diameter at 90°)

So $P\hat{T}S + S\hat{T}C = 90°$

So $S\hat{C}T = P\hat{T}S$

For the general case when CT is not the diameter, imagine point C moves to the new position C'.
$S\hat{C'}T = S\hat{C}T$ since angles in the same segment are equal.
So $P\hat{T}S$ always equals $S\hat{C}T$ for all positions of C in that segment.

231

Using circle theorems

Example 1

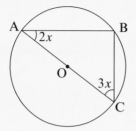

AC is a diameter and O is the centre.
Find the value of x.

$$ABC = 90° \qquad \text{(angle in a semicircle)}$$
$$\text{So } 2x + 3x = 90° \qquad \text{(angle sum of } \triangle \text{)}$$
$$5x = 90°$$
$$x = 18°$$

Example 2

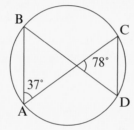

Calculate $C\hat{D}B$ and $A\hat{C}D$.

$$C\hat{D}B = 37° \qquad \text{(} C\hat{D}B \text{ and } C\hat{A}B \text{ are in the same segment on chord } BC\text{)}$$
$$A\hat{C}D = 180° - 37° - 78° \qquad \text{(angle sum of } \triangle \text{)}$$
$$= 65°$$

Example 3

Calculate $D\hat{B}C$.

$$B\hat{O}D = 2 \times 64° \qquad \text{(angle at centre)}$$
$$= 128°$$
$$\text{So reflex } B\hat{O}D = 360° - 128°$$
$$= 232°$$

$$B\hat{C}D = \tfrac{1}{2} \text{ of reflex } B\hat{O}D \qquad \text{(angle at centre)}$$
$$= \tfrac{1}{2} \times 232 = 116°$$

Triangle BCD is isoscele so $D\hat{B}C = B\hat{D}C$.
$$\text{So } D\hat{B}C = \tfrac{1}{2}(180 - 116) \qquad \text{(angle sum of } \triangle \text{)}$$
$$D\hat{B}C = 32°$$

Exercise 20.1

Using circle theorems

1 Find the angles shown by letters in each diagram giving your reasons. (In each case O is the centre.)

a

b

c

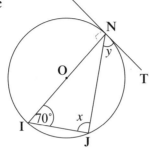

TN is a tangent at N.

d

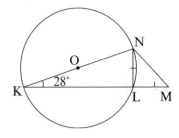

Find KŃM.

2 **a** Name two angles subtended at the circumference by the chord AC.
b Name two angles subtended at the circumference by the chord CD.
c What is the size of CÂD?
d What is the size of CÊA?
e BC is a tangent to the circle.
What is the size of BĈA?
Explain the reason for your answer.

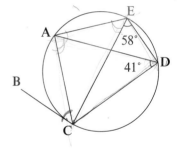

3 In this diagram, the circle has centre O. BE is a chord, AB a tangent, and BD̂E = 37°.

a What is the size of EÔB?
Explain your answer.
b What is the size of BĈE?
c What is the size of AB̂O?
Explain the reason for your answer.
d What is the size of OB̂E?
Explain the reason for your answer.
e What is the size of EB̂A?

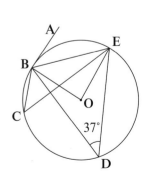

4 In the diagram, the circle has centre O. ED is a chord.

a Name an angle at the circumference in the major segment subtended by ED.
b Calculate the size of EÔD (reflex).
c Calculate the size of DF̂E.
d Calculate the size of OÊD.
Give the reason for your answer.

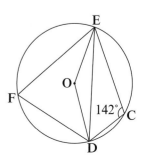

5 In the diagram, the circle has centre O.
DE is a diameter, FE is a chord, and FC a tangent.

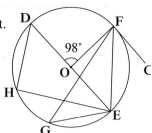

  a Calculate the size of $\hat{FGE}$.
    Explain the reasons for your answer.
  b Calculate the size of $\hat{OEF}$.
    Explain the reasons for your answer.
  c Explain why $\hat{EFC}$ is 41°.
  d DEH is 29°. Calculate the size of $\hat{HDE}$.
    Explain your answer.

6 In the diagram, the circle has centre O.
GC is a diameter and DF a tangent.

DF = 7.2 cm and CF = 2.8 cm.

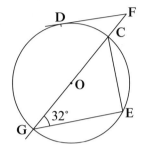

  a Calculate the length GF.
  b Calculate the length CE.
  c Calculate the area of triangle GCE.

7 In the diagram, the circle has centre O and BC is a tangent.
The radius of the circle is b cm.

  a Write an expression in a for:
    i $\hat{DOC}$ **ii** $\hat{OCD}$
  b By considering the angles at O:
    i Write an equation in a for the
      sum of the angles at the centre.
    ii Solve your equation, and
      calculate the size of $\hat{CAD}$, $\hat{DOC}$ and $\hat{ODC}$.
  c Write an expression in b for the length OB.
  d Calculate the size of $\hat{CFD}$. Explain your calculation.

8 In the diagram the circle has centre O and FB this is a tangent.
DE is a diameter.

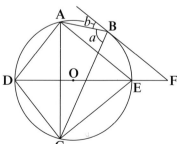

  a Give an expression for each of
    these angles:
    i $\hat{AEC}$ **ii** $\hat{ACB}$ **iii** $\hat{AOC}$
  b Write an expression for $\hat{CAB}$.
  c Write an expression for $\hat{ADC}$.
    Explain your answer.
  d AE = EC. Write an expression for $\hat{BCE}$.
  e AD = DC. Write an expression $\hat{DCA}$.

The cyclic quadrilateral

RSTU is a cyclic quadrilateral.
A quadrilateral is said to be cyclic when:

♦ the four vertices of the quadrilateral lie
on the circumference of the same circle.

The other property all cyclic quadrilaterals
have is that:

♦ the angles at opposite vertices are
supplementary.

> Supplementary angles are a pair of angles that, when added together, give a total of 180°.

As RSTU is cyclic then:

$$R\hat{S}T + T\hat{U}R = 180°$$
and $$S\hat{R}U + U\hat{T}S = 180°$$

Proof:

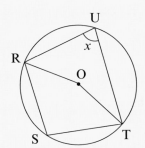

Let $R\hat{U}T = x$
So obtuse angle $R\hat{O}T = 2x$ **(angle at centre)**
So reflex angle $R\hat{O}T = 360° - 2x$
But angle $R\hat{S}T = \frac{1}{2}$ of reflex $R\hat{O}T$
   (angle at centre)

So $R\hat{S}T = \frac{1}{2}(360° - 2x)$

$\phantom{So R\hat{S}T} = 180° - x$

So $R\hat{S}T = 180° - R\hat{U}T$

or **$R\hat{S}T + R\hat{U}T = 180°$**

Exercise 20.2
Cyclic quadrilaterals

1   Explain why all rectangles are cyclic quadrilaterals.

2   Is it possible to draw a parallelogram that is cyclic?
Explain your answer.

3   Apart from the rectangle, what other quadrilateral is always cyclic?
Explain your answer with diagrams.

4   CDEF is a cyclic quadrilateral with angles
of v, w, x and y degrees as shown by the diagram.

If $p = 15°$, explain why:
$v + x = 12p$

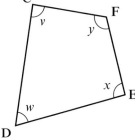

5   In the diagram the circle has centre O.
The size of $N\hat{K}L$ is given as a.

Use circle properties to explain why
$N\hat{K}L$ and $L\hat{M}N$ are supplementary.

6 In the diagram the circle has centre O.
EOG is the diameter.
Calculate FĜH.

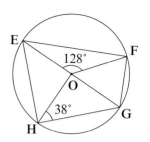

7 In the diagram the circle has centre O.
A tangent is drawn to the circle at G.
FH = GF.

   a Write and solve an equation in x to find
the size of angles:

     i HÊG   **ii** HF̂G.
     Explain your answer.

   b Calculate the size of GÔH.

   c Could HOGF be a cyclic quadrilateral?
Give two reasons for your answer.

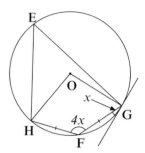

8 In the diagram, O is the centre of the circle and
FB is a chord.
The ratio BĈE : BF̂E is 3 : 5.

   a Calculate the size of:

     i BĈE   **ii** BF̂E   **iii** FB̂C

   b Calculate the size of FÔC.
Explain your answer.

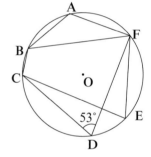

9 In the diagram O is the centre of the circle.
AB is a chord and DC = DA.
Angle AÔB is v degrees.

   a Write an expression in v for each of these angles:

     i BĈA   **ii** OB̂A   **iii** DĈB

   b Explain why an expression for DÂB is:

     $135° - \frac{1}{2}v$

   c Show that an expression for DÊB is:

     $\frac{1}{2}(90° + v)$

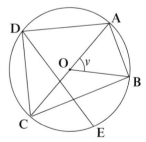

10 In the diagram O is the centre of the circle.
BD is a tangent to the circle.

   a Give the size of CÊA.
Explain your answer.

   b Calculate CD̂E.
Give reasons to support your calculations.

End points

You should be able to ...   ... so try these questions

A Identify angles in the same segment

A1 **a** What is the size of $D\hat{A}B$?
 b What is the size of $E\hat{A}C$?

A2 Give an angle that is the same size as:
 a $E\hat{A}D$ **b** $C\hat{E}B$

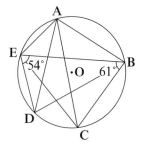

B Link angles at the centre and at the circumference on the same chord

B1 Calculate the size of:
 a $A\hat{B}C$ **b** $A\hat{D}C$

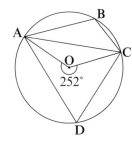

C Work with angles in a semicircle

C1 In the circle the centre is O and $C\hat{A}B = 28°$
Calculate the size of $A\hat{C}B$.
Explain your calculation.

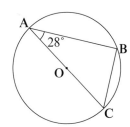

D Solve problems when tangents are involved

D1 Calculate the size of $D\hat{A}E$.
Explain your working.

D2 Calculate the size of $D\hat{E}A$.
Give reasons for your answer.

D3 Calculate the size of $D\hat{A}O$.
Explain your answer.

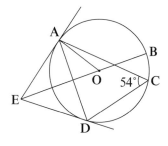

E Use the properties of cyclic quadrilaterals

E1 List the properties of all cyclic quadrilaterals.

E2 The angles of a cyclic quadrilateral are given as $3k$, $4k$, $5k$, and $6k$.
 a On a diagram show possible positions of these angles.
 b Write and solve an equation in k to find the size of each angle.

Southampton Evening Chronicle   *Monday 15 April 1912*

TRAGEDY AT SEA

IT IS WITH great regret that we bring you the news that last night at 10:40 pm the 'unsinkable liner' the Titanic hit an iceberg on her way to New York. The Titanic later sank at 2:20 am with the loss of many lives. It was the liner's maiden voyage and on board were 331 first class passengers, 273 second class, 712 third class and a full crew – only 32.2 % of those on board survived. Each first-class passenger had paid £870 for the privilege of making the voyage in this luxury floating palace. To reassure the passengers the orchestra was still playing as the liner was going down and many passengers were so sure the ship could not sink that they refused to board the lifeboats.

The captain had been given repeated warnings of icebergs ahead but chose to steam on at 22.5 knots. It was calm weather with good visibility but the lookouts had not been issued with binoculars. The iceberg is thought to have had a height of about 100 feet showing above the water and a weight of about 500 000 tons. The sea water temperature was only 28° Fahrenheit and this took its toll on those jumping overboard. It is thought that the capacity of the lifeboats was insufficient for the number of people on board.

Survivors were picked up by the liner Carpathia which had heard the SOS when it was 58 miles away. The Carpathia steamed at a staggering 17.5 knots to reach the sinking Titanic. The ship's engineer said this was 25% faster than her usual speed.

HOW FAIR WAS THE RESCUE?

Reports coming in give the final casualty figures from the Titanic. There was not enough lifeboat space for all on board because the Titanic was considered to be the first unsinkable ship. The owners White Star admit that lifeboats could only hold 33% of the full capacity of the liner and 53% of those on board on that fateful night. Breaking the survival figure down by class we find 203 first-class, 118 second-class and 178 third-class passengers were rescued. Nearly a quarter of all crew were saved. Analysis of these figures is taking place to see if all people on board had an equal chance of being rescued.

Strange BUT *true*

Fourteen years before the disaster, and before the Titanic had been built, a story was published which described the sinking of an enormous ship called the Titan after it had hit an iceberg on its maiden voyage.

The comparisons between ships is even more amazing.

	Titan (Fiction 1898)	*Titanic* (True 1912)
Flag	British	British
Month of sailing	April	April
Displacement (tons)	70 000	66 000
Propellers	3	3
Max. speed	24 knots	24 knots
Length	800 feet	882 feet
Watertight bulkheads	19	15
No. of lifeboats	24	20
No. on board (inc crew)	2000	2208
What happened?	Starboard hull split by iceberg	Starboard hull split by iceberg
Full capacity	3000	

Distances at sea are measured in nautical miles and ships' speeds are given in knots.
1 nautical mile is 1852 metres.
1 knot is a speed of 1 nautical mile/hour.

1   Calculate approximately how many people died in the tragedy.

2   If all those who survived were in lifeboats, what was the mean number of people per boat?

3   In 1912 the price of a small house was about £200. In 1996 the same house would cost about £68 000. If fares on a cruise liner increased in the same ratio what would have been the first class ticket price in 1996?

4   About $\frac{1}{9}$th of the volume of an iceberg is above water level.
    The part of the iceberg showing above the water line can be approximated to a cone with base diameter of 85 metres.
    a   Estimate the volume of the iceberg showing in cubic metres. Take 1 foot as 0.305 metres.
    b   The density of an iceberg is about 950 kg per metre³.
        Estimate the total mass (in tonnes) of the iceberg that the Titanic hit.

5   a   What was the Carpathia's usual speed?
    b   At 17.5 knots, how long would it take the Carpathia to steam the 58 nautical miles to the Titanic?
    c   The Carpathia received the SOS message at 12:30 am. Approximately how long after the Titanic sank did she arrive at the scene?

6   You can convert a temperature from °Celsius (C) to °Fahrenheit (F) with this formula:
    $$F = \frac{9}{5}C + 32$$
    a   Make C the subject of the formula.
    b   Calculate a water temperature of 28 °F in degrees Celsius.
    c   An approximation to convert °F to °C is "Subtract 30 from the temperature in °F then halve the result."
        For a temperature of 28°F find the percentage error that this approximation gives.

7   Show, with working, that the statement

    Nearly a quarter of all crew were saved

    is correct.

8   a   How many people could the lifeboats have held in total?
    b   Use your answer to part a to calculate an approximate value for the full capacity of the Titanic.

9   Calculate the relative frequency of survival for:
    a   first-class passengers
    b   second-class passengers
    c   third-class passengers.

10 Calculate the total percentage of the passengers aboard who were rescued.

11 What is the displacement of the Titanic to 1 sf?

12 A nautical mile is defined as "the length of arc along the equator subtended by an angle of $\frac{1}{60}$ of a degree at the centre of the Earth". The Earth has a diameter of about 12 756 kilometres.

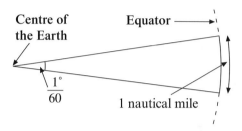

Show that a nautical mile is about 1850 metres.

13 The Titanic had cranes, known as "derricks", for lifting the cargo on to the ship. This diagram shows a derrick in one position. The tower and part of the cable are vertical.

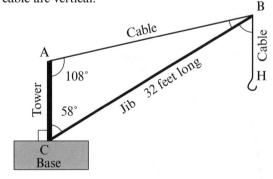

    a   What is the angle ABH? Give your reasons.
    b   Calculate the length AB on the derrick.
    c   Calculate how high point B is above point A?

At the enquiry after the sinking, White Star, the owners, said that in the previous ten years they had carried 21 79 594 passengers with the loss of only 2 lives.

14 Give the number of passengers carried to:
    a   1 sf   b   4 sf

15 In the ten years between 1981 and 1990 about 1.2×10^7 people from the UK crossed the Atlantic by plane. With the same death rate as White Star gave, roughly how many people would have died in that time?

239

Starting points

You need to know about ...

... so try these questions

A Bearings

- All bearings are:
  - measured clockwise from North
  - written using three figures.

Example

The bearing of B from A is 105°.
The bearing of A from B is 285°.

- You can fix a position by:
  - giving a bearing and distance from one point
  - giving a bearing from two different points.

Example

The point B is on a bearing of 105° from A and is 10 km from A.

Example

The point C is on a bearing of 078° from A and on a bearing of 320° from B.

B Pythagoras' rule

- In any right-angled triangle, the area of the square on the hypotenuse is equal to the sum of the area of the squares on the other two sides.

AB is the hypotenuse,
so $AB^2 = AC^2 + BC^2$

i.e. $AB = \sqrt{(AC^2 + BC^2)}$

C Trigonometric ratios

- The trigonometric ratios can be used to calculate sides or angles in right-angled triangles.

- Each trigonometric ratio can be written in different ways.

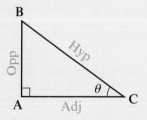

$\sin \theta = \dfrac{\text{Opp}}{\text{Hyp}}$	$\cos \theta = \dfrac{\text{Adj}}{\text{Hyp}}$	$\tan \theta = \dfrac{\text{Opp}}{\text{Adj}}$
$\text{Opp} = \text{Hyp} \times \sin \theta$	$\text{Adj} = \text{Hyp} \times \cos \theta$	$\text{Opp} = \text{Adj} \times \tan \theta$

A1 This diagram shows some towns on a radar screen positioned at H.

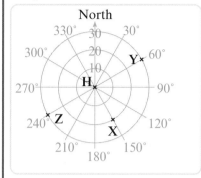

a What is the bearing of:
 i Y from H
 ii H from Y
 iii Z from Y?

b Estimate the bearing of X from Y.

c The rings on the screen are 10 km apart. Point P is due North of X and on a bearing of 030° from H. How far from H is P?

B1 **a** From the radar screen above sketch and label △XHY.

b Calculate the distance XY to the nearest 0.1 km.

C1 Using triangle XHY above calculate the angle HX̂Y to the nearest degree.

C2 Z is south and west of H.

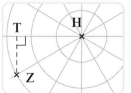

Calculate, to the nearest km:
a how far Z is west of H
b how far Z is south of H.

D Sine and cosine of angles from 0° to 180°

♦ Graph $y = \sin x$ and $y = \cos x$ from 0° to 180°

D1 Solve each of these for:
$0 \leqslant \theta \leqslant 180°$.

Give the answer to the nearest degree.

a **i** $\sin \theta = 0.5$
    ii Explain why there are two possible values.
b $\cos \theta = {}^{-}0.2$
c $\cos \theta = 0.2$
d $\cos \theta = \sin \theta$

E Constructing triangles

♦ To construct a triangle with sides of a cm, b cm and c cm.

  ❖ draw one line as the base e.g. a
  ❖ with one end of the base as centre:
  ❖ draw an arc of radius b
  ❖ with the other end of the base as centre draw an arc of radius c
  ❖ join the ends of base to the intersection of the arcs to give the triangle.

♦ To construct a triangle when you know two sides v and t, and one non-included angle 54°.

  ❖ draw one side as the base e.g. v
  ❖ at one end of the base measure and draw an angle of 54°
  ❖ with the other end of the base as centre draw an arc of radius t
  ❖ where the arc and the line at 54° to the base intersect is the third vertex of the triangle.

(Note:- the triangle depicted is only one of two possible triangles).

E1 **a** Construct a triangle with sides of length 6 cm, 4 cm and 8 cm.
    b Measure the largest angle.

E2 **a** Construct two different triangles ABC with $A = 42°$ AB = 8 cm and BC = 6 cm.
    b For each of your triangles measure the angle B.

F Triangles

♦ When sides of a triangle are labelled, it is normal to use a small letter that matches the label of the opposite vertex.

For example:
side ST is labelled w.

♦ The largest side is always opposite the largest angle.

For example:
largest angle SWT, longest side w, or ST.

♦ Angle SWT is called:
the **included angle** between sides SW and WT.

F1 In triangle PQR $p = 8$ cm, $q = 4$ cm and $R = 90°$. Calculate the size of the smallest angle to the nearest degree.

F2 In triangle DEF $f = 5$ cm, $d = 6$ cm and $E = 58°$. Calculate, to the nearest millimetre, the shortest distance from F to the line DE.

The area of a triangle

The included angle for two sides of a triangle is the angle between those two sides.
Example

B

A

C

$\hat{A}$ is the included angle for sides AB and AC.

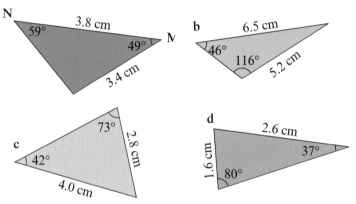

♦ The area of any triangle can be written in terms of two sides and the included angle.

Area of $\triangle ABC = \frac{1}{2}ah$

Using $\triangle CAO$ $h = b \sin C$

So the area of $\triangle ABC = \frac{1}{2}ab \sin C$

In the same way you can write:

Area of $\triangle ABC = \frac{1}{2}bc \sin A$ (*A* is the included angle for sides BA and CA)

Area of $\triangle ABC = \frac{1}{2}ca \sin B$ (*B* is the included angle for sides CB and AB)

Exercise 21.1
The area of a triangle

Accuracy
For this exercise:
♦ give each length and area correct to 2 sf
♦ give each angle to the nearest degree.

1 Calculate the area of each of these triangles.

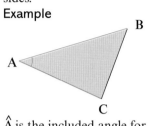

2 Triangle DEF is isosceles with DE = EF = 4 cm and $D\hat{E}F = \theta$.

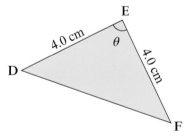

a Find the area of $\triangle DEF$ when $\theta = 48.5°$.

b **i** For what values of θ is the area $4\,\text{cm}^2$?
   ii Explain why there are two possible values for θ.

c What value of θ gives the maximum area of $\triangle DEF$?

3 In triangle JKL, JK = 5 cm, KL = 6 cm.

a For what values of *K* is the area of $\triangle JKL = 10.8\,\text{cm}^2$?
b Calculate the maximum area of $\triangle JKL$?

4 Jamie drew $\triangle PQR$ with PQ = 3.4 cm, PR = 2.8 cm and QPR = 52°.
He drew lengths to the nearest millimetre and angles to the nearest degree.

a Find the maximum and minimum length of PQ.
b Calculate the maximum and minimum area possible for $\triangle PQR$.

Sine rule

♦ The **sine rule** links the sides and angles of a triangle. This is one way to prove the **sine rule**.

In $\triangle ABD$ $h = c \sin A$
In $\triangle BCD$ $h = a \sin C$
Therefore $a \sin C = c \sin A$

This can be rearranged to give the **sine rule**.

$$\frac{a}{\sin A} = \frac{c}{\sin C} \quad \text{and} \quad \frac{\sin A}{a} = \frac{\sin C}{c}$$

In the same way you can show that:

$$\frac{b}{\sin B} = \frac{c}{\sin C} \quad \text{and} \quad \frac{\sin B}{b} = \frac{\sin C}{c}$$

and $$\frac{a}{\sin A} = \frac{b}{\sin B} \quad \text{and} \quad \frac{\sin A}{a} = \frac{\sin B}{b}$$

Exercise 21.2
The sine rule

1   a   Which of these expressions is true for $\triangle PQR$?

   (A) $\dfrac{p}{\sin Q} = \dfrac{q}{\sin P}$ (B) $r = \dfrac{\sin P \times q}{\sin Q}$

   (C) $p \sin P = q \sin Q$ (D) $p \sin R = r \sin P$

2   Copy and complete these statements for $\triangle LMN$.

   a $m = \dfrac{3.4 \times \sin \square}{\sin \square}$

   b $\sin N = \dfrac{\square \times \sin \square}{\square}$

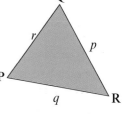

♦ The sine rule can be used to calculate the length of a side in a triangle, given any two angles and the length of one side.

> It may help to label the sides from the vertices first.

> In some triangles you will need to calculate the missing angle before you can use the sine rule.

Example   In triangle RST calculate the length of RS.

♦ Use the angle sum of a triangle for the missing angle.
$S = 180° - (53° + 48°) = 79°$
♦ Use the sine rule to calculate a side.

$$\frac{t}{\sin T} = \frac{s}{\sin S}$$

$$t = \frac{s \times \sin T}{\sin S} = \frac{6.5 \times \sin 48°}{\sin 79°} = 4.9 \text{ to 1 dp}$$

So the length of RS is 4.9 cm (1 dp).

Exercise 21.3
Calculating lengths using the sine rule

1   a   Find the sequence of key presses on your calculator to calculate the length of RS.

   b   Calculate the length of ST correct to 1 dp.

Accuracy
For this exercise give each answer correct to 1 dp.

2 In these triangles calculate the length of the side marked with a letter.

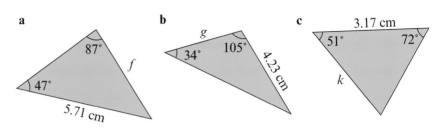

3 Triangle PQR is isosceles with PQ = 8 cm and QPR = 56°.

a Draw two different triangles, and show that QR has two possible lengths.
b Calculate the two possible lengths for QR.

Use the full calculator value for each calculation

4 In triangle TUV the angle $T = 104°$, $U = 37°$ and TU = 5 cm. Calculate the area of $\triangle$ TUV.

5 To construct $\triangle$ XYZ Eamonn drew XZ, to the nearest millimetre, and angles X and Z to the nearest degree.

a What is the largest possible value of X?
b Explain why the smallest possible value of Y is 79°.
c Calculate the maximum possible length of YZ.

On some formula sheets the sine rule is only given as:

$$\frac{a}{\sin A} = \frac{b}{\sin B} = \frac{C}{\sin C}$$

For each problem use one pair of expressions.
For instance

$$\frac{a}{\sin A} = \frac{c}{\sin C}$$

can be rearranged to give:

$$\frac{\sin A}{a} = \frac{\sin C}{c}$$

♦ With the sine rule, given two sides and one opposite angle, a second angle in the triangle can be calculated.

Example Calculate angle B in $\triangle$ ABC
❖ Use the sine rule with the two sides given.

In $\triangle$ ABC $\frac{\sin C}{3.7} = \frac{\sin 24°}{4.8}$

$\sin C = \frac{3.7 \times \sin 24}{4.8}$

$\sin C = 0.313\,52° \ldots$
$C = 18.2718° \ldots$

❖ Calculate the required angle:
$B = 180° - (24 + 18.2718 \ldots)°$
$B = 137.73°$ (2 dp)

Exercise 21.4
Using the sine rule to calculate angles

Accuracy
For this exercise give each answer correct to 1 dp.

1 Calculate the angle θ in each of these triangles.

2   This pentagon is right-angled at A and E.

  a   The angle $B\hat{D}C = 37°$.
      Calculate the angle $A\hat{B}C$.

  b   Calculate the area of ABCDE.

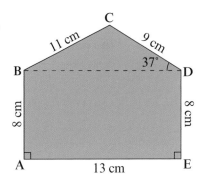

> Use the full calculator value in each calculation.

3   In triangle ABC, AC = 6.2 cm, AB = 5.1 cm and **C** = 28°.
     This diagram shows that in $\triangle$ ABC, there are two possible
     positions for **B,** shown as B_1 and B_2.

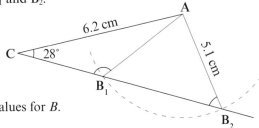

  a   Use the sine rule to find
      the value of sin B.

  b   Calculate two possible values for B.

4   **a**   Sketch two possible triangles for each of these.

>   **i**   In triangle XYZ XZ = 8.3 cm, XY = 7.3 cm and Z = 58°

>   **ii**   In triangle XYZ XZ = 9.2 cm, YZ = 8.0 cm and X = 43°

  b   Give two possible values for Y in each of these triangles.

Cosine rule

♦   The cosine rule links an angle and three sides of a triangle.
    This is one way to prove the **cosine rule**.

In $\triangle$CAD $h^2 = b^2 - p^2$

In $\triangle$BCD $a^2 = h^2 + (c - p)^2$
$$a^2 = b^2 - p^2 + (c - p)^2$$
$$a^2 = b^2 - p^2 + c^2 - 2cp + p^2$$
$$a^2 = b^2 + c^2 - 2cp$$
$$a^2 = b^2 + c^2 - 2c \times b \cos A \qquad (\text{in } \triangle\,\text{CAD, } p = b \cos A)$$

This gives the **cosine rule**:
$$a^2 = b^2 + c^2 - 2bc \cos A$$

The cosine rule gives an expression for one side in terms of
the opposite angle and the other two sides of the triangle.

♦   The cosine rule can be rearranged to give an expression
    for the cosine of one angle in terms of the lengths of the sides.

$$a^2 = b^2 + c^2 - 2bc \cos A$$
$$2bc \cos A = b^2 + c^2 - a^2$$
$$\cos A = \frac{b^2 + c^2 - a^2}{2bc}$$

Exercise 21.5
The cosine rule

1 **a** Copy and complete these for $\triangle DEF$.

   i $d^2 = e^2 + f^2 - 2ef \cos \square$

   ii $f^2 = e^2 + \square - 2e \square \cos \square$

  b Which of these is true for $\triangle DEF$?

   i $\quad e^2 = d^2 + f^2 - 2de \cos E$

   ii $\quad e^2 + d^2 - f^2 = 2de \cos F$

   iii $\quad \cos D = \dfrac{e^2 + f^2 - d^2}{2ef}$

   iv $\quad \cos E = \dfrac{e^2 + f^2 - d^2}{2df}$

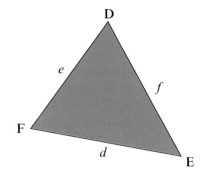

2 In this diagram AB is the diameter of the circle.

Use the cosine rule to explain why:

  a $AB^2 > AC^2 + CB^2$
  b $AB^2 = AD^2 + DB^2$
  c $AB^2 < AE^2 + EB^2$

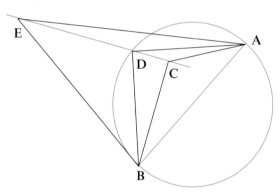

♦ The cosine rule can be used to calculate the length of a side in a triangle given the length of two sides and the included angle.

Example

Calculate the length of PQ in triangle PQR.

From the vertices label the sides p, q and r.

Use the cosine rule to calculate the length of the side.

$$r^2 = p^2 + q^2 - 2pq \cos R$$
$$r^2 = 4.35^2 + 5.84^2 - 2 \times 4.35 \times 5.84 \times \cos 106°$$
$$r^2 = 67.032\,683 \ldots$$
$$r = 8.2 \; (1\text{dp})$$

♦ Given the lengths of all three sides, any angle of a triangle can be calculated using the cosine rule.

Example Calculate the angle *F* in triangle EFG.

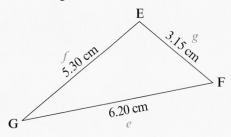

From the vertices label the sides *e*, *f* and *g*.

Use the cosine rule to calculate the angle.

$$\cos F = \frac{e^2 + g^2 - f^2}{2eg}$$

$$\cos F = \frac{6.20^2 + 3.15^2 - 5.30^2}{2 \times 6.20 \times 3.15}$$

$$\cos F = 0.519\,0092 \ldots$$

Therefore *F* = 58.7° (1 dp)

Exercise 21.6
Calculating angles using the cosine rule

1 For triangle EFG above:
  a list the correct sequence of key presses to evaluate *F*.
  b explain why there is only one possible value for *F*.

Accuracy
For this exercise give each length and area correct to 3 sf.

2 In each of these triangles find the side or angle marked in blue.

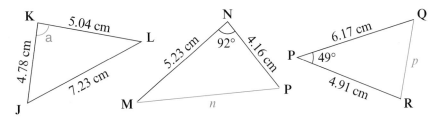

3 Find the largest angle in a triangle with sides of 8 cm, 12 cm, and 15 cm.

4 Calculate the area of a triangle with sides of length 6 cm, 9 cm and 10 cm.

5 Triangle ACE is one triangle that can be drawn by joining the vertices of ABCDE, a regular pentagon of side 4 cm.
  a What is the size of:
    i $A\hat{B}C$
    ii $C\hat{A}B$
    iii $C\hat{A}E$?
  b Calculate the length of AC.
  c Calculate the perimeter of △ACE.
  d Calculate the area of the △ACE.
  e How many different triangles can you draw by joining the vertices of ABCDE?

Use the full calculator value in each calculation.

6 FGHIJKLMN is a regular nonagon. Each side is 6 cm.

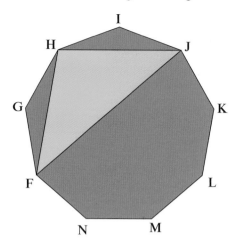

a Calculate the length HF.
b FHJ is one triangle that can be drawn by joining the vertices of the nonagon. Calculate its area and perimeter.
c Calculate the perimeter of triangle FMJ.

The circumcircle of a shape is a circle that passes through all its vertices.
Example
This is the circumcircle of triangle ABC.

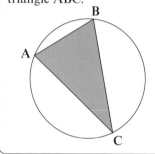

7 Any polygon is cyclic if all its vertices lie on the circumference of a circle.
This circle is called its circumcircle.

This is a regular decagon.

The radius of its circumcircle is 5 cm and its centre is at O.

a Calculate the area of the decagon.
b Calculate the perimeter of the decagon.

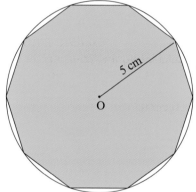

A dodecagon is the name given to a 12-sided polygon.

8 Calculate the area of a regular dodecagon with a circumcircle of radius 8 cm.

9 **a** A regular polygon (with n sides) has a circumcircle of radius r.
Write an expression for the area of the polygon in terms of r and n.
b If the radius of the circumcircle is 1 cm, calculate the area of the regular polygon when:
i $n = 20$ **ii** $n = 40$ **iii** $n = 100$ **iv** $n = 1000$
What do you notice about the area?

10 Find the radius of the circumcircle of a regular hexagon of perimeter 54 cm.

Bearings

Exercise 21.7
Calculating bearings and distances

For questions like this split the route into triangles

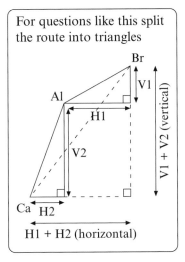

Accuracy
For this exercise:
♦ give each distance correct to 4 sf
♦ round each angle to the nearest degree.

1 This diagram shows the position of three lighthouses.
Braydon is 56 km from Alington on a bearing of 071°.
Caster is 78 km from Alington on a bearing of 216°.

a What is the bearing of Alington from Caster?
b Calculate the direct distance from Braydon to Caster.
c Calculate the bearing of Braydon from Caster.

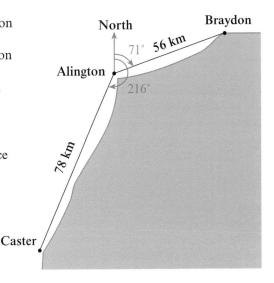

2 This diagram shows the route taken by a boat which starts at P.
The boat sails on a bearing of 143° for 24 km to a buoy at Q, then sails due south for 18 km to a buoy at R.

a What is the bearing of P from Q?
b Calculate:
  i the distance between P and R
  ii the bearing of R from P.
c **i** How far is Q east of P?
  ii How far is Q south of P?
d How far is Q east of PR?

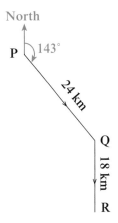

3 A boat starts at A and sails on a bearing of 048° for 12.6 km to B, where it changes course to a bearing of 154° to sail 18.5 km to C.
Calculate how far C is due east of the starting point A.

4 From his boat Salamander Harry fixes the position of two other boats.
Enya is at a distance of 2300 metres on a bearing of 146°.
Cosmos is at a distance of 4200 metres on a bearing of 062°.

a Calculate the distance (in a straight line) between Enya and Cosmos.
b What is the bearing of Cosmos from Enya.

5 The boat Wija sails due north between two headlands A and B. The bearing of B from A is 303°. From W, the bearing of A is 055°, and B 329°.
Wija is 3.4 Km from A and 7.5 km from B, calculate the distance AB.

6 Two boats leave harbour at the same time.
One sails on a bearing of 308° at a speed of 18 knots, the other on a bearing of 204° at a speed of 22 knots.
What is the distance between the boats after 30 minutes?

Angles of elevation and depression

♦ From a point A the angle of elevation of a point B is the angle between the horizontal and the line of sight from A to B.

θ is the angle of elevation of B from A.

♦ From a point A the angle of depression of a point C is the angle between the horizontal and the line of sight from A to C.

β is the angle of depression of C from A.

Example

A man of height 1.6 m is standing on a tower.
From this position he can see a ball which is 30 m from the base of the tower. He measures the angle of depression to the ball as 62°. Calculate the height of the tower.

Angle T$\hat{B}$M = 62 ° **(alternate angles)**

So H = 30 × tan 62°

H = 56.4 m (to 1 d.p.)

So height of tower h = 56.4 – 1.6
= 54.8 m to 1 dp

Exercise 21.8
Angles of elevation and depression

Accuracy
For this exercise round your answers to 2 dp.

1 Jan uses a theodolite at T to measure the distance and the angle of elevation or depression to points A and B.

The angle of depression of A from T is 53.139° and TA is 18.246 metres.
The angle of elevation from T to B is 15.070° and TB is 27.149 metres.

a What is the obtuse angle A$\hat{T}$B?

b Calculate:

  i the distance AB

  ii the angle of depression from B to A

  iii the angle of elevation from A to B.

2 This diagram shows a loading ramp used for ferries. It is supported by cables that are fed out from a tower and fixed half way along the ramp at A.
The ramp must be fixed so that it is horizontal at high tide.
The maximum angle of depression allowed, at low tide, on the ramp is 18°.

a At which of these ports could this ramp be used?

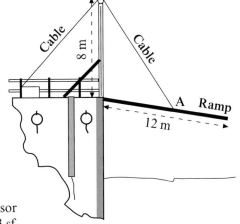

Harbour	Tidal range
Arden	4.28 m
Jameston	2.86 m
Daleen	3.85 m
Palter	3.54 m

b A sensor is to be fitted to the cable sounding an alarm when the slope reaches 18°.
How far from A should the sensor be fixed? Give your answer to 3 sf.

Three-dimensional trigonometry

When you work in 3-D, it is essential to identify angles correctly.

The diagram shows a pyramid.
The vertical height is shown by WY.
(The line WY is perpendicular to the base.)

> Perpendicular indicates that two lines are at right angles to each other.

Identifying angles:

The angle between a side (WCB) and the base is angle WTY where WT is perpendicular to BC.

The angle between the edge CW and the base is angle WCY.

Note that angle WTY and angle WCY are **not** the same size.

Exercise 21.9
Three-dimensional
trigonometry

1 The diagram shows a phone mast and points A and B due west and due south respectively.
The angle of elevation from A to the point T is 35°.
The distance AB is 740 m and the mast is 48 m high

Calculate correct to 2 sf:
a the distance AM.
b the angle of elevation of the top of the mast from point B.

2

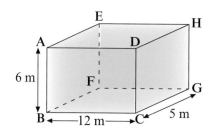

The diagram shows a cuboid with dimensions of 6 m, 12 m and 5 m.

Calculate, correct to 2 sf:
a the distance BG.
b the diagonal distance GA.
c the angle CÊD.

3 The diagram shows an 8 cm cube.
Cutting through the midpoints, B, C and D of three edges forms a pyramid ABCD which has a triangular base.

 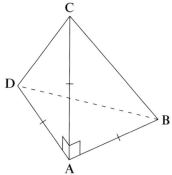

a Calculate the volume of the pyramid cut from the cube
b What is the angle between the edge BC and the base ABD?

The pyramid is placed to stand on the cut face, △ BCD.

c Calculate the length of each side of the base BCD.
d What is the angle BCD?
e Calculate the area of △ BCD.
f Calculate the perpendicular height of the pyramid.
g Calculate the angle between the line AB and the base BCD.

Give your answers correct to 2 s.f.

End points
You should be able to ...   ... so try these questions

A   Use the sine rule

A1   In triangle RST calculate, correct to 2sf:

   a   the length RS
   b   the length of RT.

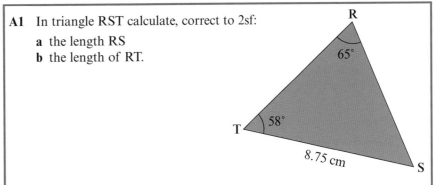

A2   In triangle CDE calculate, to 2sf:

   a   angle DEC
   b   the length of ED.

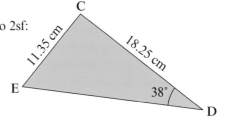

B   Calculate the area of a triangle

B1   In $\triangle$ EFG calculate, to 3 sf:

   a   the size of angle GEF
   b   the length EG
   c   the area of triangle EFG.

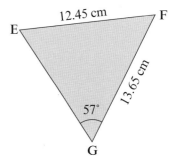

C   Use the cosine rule

C1   Using the cosine rule in $\triangle$ RST, calculate, to 3 sf:

   a   the size of angle TRS
   b   the size of angle RST.

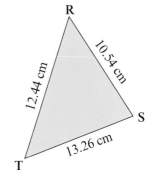

C2   Using the cosine rule in $\triangle$ KLM calculate, to 3 sf:

   a   the length of KL
   b   the size of angle MKL.

D Use bearings

D1 A boat sails from point A for 4.5 kilometres on a bearing of 072° to point B. From B the boat sails on a bearing of 134° to point C. C is 6 kilometres due east of A.

Calculate, correct to 3 sf., how far the boat sailed from point B to point C.

D2 Two boats leave harbour at the same time:

Seeker Me sails at a speed of 15 knots on a bearing of 192°.
Bold Over sails at a speed of 18 knots on a bearing of 316°.

Calculate the distance between the two boats after 150 minutes.

Give your answer correct to 3 sf.

E Use an angle of elevation or depression

E1 From the top of a church tower, an observer notes that the church gate and a signpost are in line.

The gate is 65 metres from the base of the tower and at an angle of depression of 60° from the top of the tower.

The angle of depression of the signpost from the top of the tower is 18°.

Calculate, to the nearest metre, the distance between the gate and the signpost.

E2 A radio mast is 75 metres tall is erected on level ground.

A camera is to be installed, at ground level, 20 metres from the base of the mast.

Calculate, to the nearest degree, the angle of elevation of the camera if it is to monitor the top of the radio mast.

F Solve three-dimensional problems

F1 The diagram is of a growing unit sold by a garden centre.

The unit is in the shape of a square base with four triangular frames on top, in the shape of a pyramid.

When in position the triangular frames are at an angle of 55° to the base.

Calculate, correct to 2 sf, the full height of the growing unit.

21 cm

92 cm

Some points to remember

For any triangle ABC

♦ Sine rule

$$\frac{a}{\sin A} = \frac{b}{\sin B} = \frac{c}{\sin C}$$

$$\frac{\sin A}{a} = \frac{\sin B}{b} = \frac{\sin C}{c}$$

♦ Cosine rule

$$a^2 = b^2 + c^2 - 2bc \cos A$$

$$\cos A = \frac{b^2 + c^2 - a^2}{2bc}$$

♦ Area of $\triangle ABC$

$$\tfrac{1}{2} ab \sin C$$

Starting points
You need to know about ...

... so try these questions

A Investigations using data

♦ The reason for carrying out an investigation using data is to either test a **hypothesis** or answer a **question**.
The start of an investigation into sleep could be:
Hypothesis – most people sleep at least 7 hours a night
Question – how long do people sleep at night?

♦ You can carry out an investigation in four stages:

A, make a hypothesis (or ask a question)
B, collect the data you need
C, analyse the data you have collected
D, use the results of your analysis to decide whether the hypothesis is true or false.

♦ Stage D may give you an idea for a follow-up investigation.
For example, the start of a follow-up into sleep could be:
Hypothesis – people need more sleep in the winter
Question – is there a link between sleep and time of year?

A1 **a** Make your own hypothesis about sleep.
b Decide what data you need to collect to test your hypothesis.

B Collecting data

♦ A **data collection sheet** is any form or table used to collect data.

To the BDA,
10 Queen Anne Street, London W1M 0BD
Tel: 0171-323 1531

A charity helping people with diabetes and supporting diabetes research.

I enclose a cheque/postal order*
payable to the BDA   £ _____
Debit my Access/Visa* card
by the amount of   £ _____
Card number ☐☐☐☐☐☐☐☐☐☐☐☐☐☐☐☐
Expiry data   ☐☐☐☐
    Please send me more information
    and membership details
Name _____
Address _____
Signature _____
*Delete which is inapplicable   Reg. Charity no. 215199

Body Matters			
Name	Length of thumb (cm)	Length of foot (cm)	Height (cm)
Sam			
Wasim			
Liz			
Shane			
Des			
Linda			
Dean			
Nisha			

♦ A **questionnaire** collects data by asking questions.

Sleep Questionnaire

1 What is your name?   _____

2 How old are you?   _____ years

3 What time do you usually go to bed? _____

♦ A data collection sheet or questionnaire is also called a **survey**.

B1 Design a data collection sheet to use for a traffic survey.

255

C Types of question

♦ You can use different types of questions on a questionnaire:

❖ multi-choice questions

> **7** What do you sleep on ?
>
> *Please tick one box only*   ☐ Back   ☐ Front   ☐ Side

❖ multi-choice questions with a scale

> **8** How heavy a sleeper are you ? HEAVY ⟶ LIGHT
>
> *Please tick one box only*   Very Fairly Average Fairly Very
>   ☐   ☐   ☐   ☐   ☐

❖ branching questions

> **9** Do you suffer from regular sleepless nights ?
>
> *Please tick one box only*   ☐ Yes   ☐ No
>
> *If your answer is* NO *then go to Question 12*

❖ questions with more than one answer.

> **12** What helps you get a good night's sleep ? ☐ A hot drink just before bed
> *Put a 1 in the box for the most helpful,*   ☐ Eating just before bed
> *a 2 for the next most helpful,*   ☐ Exercise during the evening
> *and so on*   ☐ Relaxation breathing
>   ☐ Other *(please state)*
>   _____

D Using a scatter diagram

♦ You can use a scatter diagram to investigate if there is a link between two sets of data.

Question – does the time taken to get to sleep depend on the amount of light in the room?

At higher amounts of light, people take a longer time to fall asleep.

At lower amounts of light, people take a shorter time to fall asleep.

The time taken to fall asleep does depend on the amount of light: as the amount of light increases, the time taken to fall asleep also increases.

C1 Design a questionnaire about sleep which includes different types of question.

D1

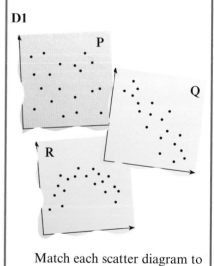

Match each scatter diagram to each pair of sets of data.

a	Time taken to get to sleep	against	Time since drank coffee
b	Amount of sleep	against	Room temperature
c	Amount of sleep	against	Height of bed off floor

Designing and criticising questions

♦ When you create a questionnaire, your questions must be carefully designed to:
  ❖ make them easy to answer
  ❖ make sure the answers give you the data you need.

Poor question | | **Improved question**

How much sleep did you get last night?	This question is **not clear**: the words used need to be more exact. (Different people are likely to have different ideas of what is meant by 'average'.)	How much sleep did you get last night?
☐ Less than average ☐ About average ☐ More than average		☐ Less than 8 hours ☐ About 8 hours ☐ More than 8 hours
Do you agree that we need at least 8 hours sleep each night?	This is a **leading** question: it leads people into giving a certain answer. (The question seems to expect the answer 'Yes'.)	Do you think we need at least 8 hours sleep each night? ☐ Yes ☐ No ☐ Not sure
What do you sleep on?	This question is **ambiguous**: it could have more than one meaning. (The question is meant to be about sleeping position, but could be answered 'a bed'!)	What do you sleep on? ☐ Back ☐ Front ☐ Side

Exercise 22.1
Designing and criticising questions

1 a Explain why this question is not clear.
   b Write an improved question.

When do you usually go to bed? ☐ Early ☐ Late

2 a Explain why this is a leading question.
   b Write an improved question.

You get a worse night's sleep on a soft bed, don't you?

3 a Explain why this question is ambiguous.
   b Write an improved question.

Where do you sleep best?

4
Leisure Centre Survey
1 Do you agree that the town needs a new leisure centre? ☐ Yes ☐ No
2 Would you be a frequent user of the centre? ☐ Yes ☐ No
3 Would you use the courts? ☐ Yes ☐ No
4 How much would you be prepared to pay to use the pool? ☐ Less than £1.50 ☐ More than £2.50

This questionnaire has been written to survey local people about a new leisure centre.

a Criticise each of the questions.
b Write an improved question for each one.

Experiments

♦ A survey asks people to give an opinion about something, or asks about facts which are easy to remember.

Example

> ### TV Survey
>
> 1 What is your favourite TV channel? ☐ BBC1   ☐ BBC2   ☐ ITV
>
> ☐ Channel 4   ☐ Channel 5
>
> 2 Did you watch TV last night?   ☐ Yes   ☐ No

♦ The data needed for some investigations can only be collected:

♦ over a period of time

> How much time do you spend in a week watching each TV channel?

♦ by designing an experiment.

> People take longer to get to sleep the more light there is in the room.

The data collection sheet used for these types of investigation can be called an **observation sheet**.

Exercise 22.2
Experiments

> To design your experiment:
> ♦ decide what data you need
> ♦ decide how to collect it
> ♦ design an observation sheet.

1 Design an observation sheet to collect data on how much time people spend in a week watching each TV channel.

2 Design an experiment to answer this question.

> **Body Matters**
> How many times do people blink in a day?

3 **a** Carry out your experiment.
   b Analyse the data you collect.
   c Interpret your results to answer the question.

4 Design an experiment to test this hypothesis.

> **Body Matters**
> Taller people do not have as good a sense of balance as shorter people.

5 **a** Carry out your experiment.
   b Analyse the data you collect.

6 Do you think the hypothesis is true or false? Explain why.

Thinking ahead to ...
sampling

A Rachel is investigating how much sleep students in her school get each night.

This is the distribution of students in the school.

Yr 7	Yr 8	Yr 9	Yr 10	Yr 11	Total
150	155	161	140	146	752

Rachel decides to take a random sample of 150, i.e. about 20%.

Which of these possible selections do you think will give the best sample? Explain your answer.

Ⓐ
Yr 7
150

Ⓑ
Yr 7	Yr 8	Yr 9	Yr 10	Yr 11
30	30	30	30	30

Ⓒ
Yr 7	Yr 8	Yr 9	Yr 10	Yr 11
30	31	32	28	29

Stratified random sampling

- When you choose a random sample from a population, the sample should model the characteristics of the population as closely as possible.

- If you think there are certain groups, or strata, within the population that are likely to give very different responses, then you can model this by taking a random sample from each group: a **stratified random sample**.

- The size of the sample you take from each group, or stratum, should be proportional to the size of the group in the population.

Example Show how a sample of 150 is chosen from this population, taking into account the students' year group and gender.

	Yr 7	Yr 8	Yr 9	Yr 10	Yr 11	Total
Boys	69	74	85	74	76	378
Girls	81	81	76	66	70	374
Total	150	155	161	140	146	752

Number of Yr 7 girls in sample = $\frac{81}{752} \times 150 = $ **16** to nearest whole number

Number of Yr 11 boys in sample = $\frac{76}{752} \times 150 = $ **15** to nearest whole number

Exercise 22.3
Sampling

1 Copy and complete the following table to show how the stratified random sample is chosen for the example above.

	Yr 7	Yr 8	Yr 9	Yr 10	Yr 11	Total
Boys					15	
Girls	16					
Total						150

2 The Great Britain Team for the 1996 Olympic Games had 500 members: 312 competitors and 188 support staff.
Show how a stratified random sample of 120 members is chosen.

3 The gender breakdown of the Great Britain Olympic Team was:

	Competitors	Support Staff	Total
Male	189	132	321
Female	123	56	179
Total	312	188	500

a Show how a stratified random sample of 120 members is chosen.
b What is the quickest way to calculate how many females would be in a stratified random sample of 75 members?
Explain your answer.

4 a What was the total population of the UK in 1995?
b Calculate how many people from each country would be in a stratified random sample of 500 000.

1995 UK Population (millions)

England	Northern Ireland	Scotland	Wales
48.9	1.7	5.1	2.9

Make sure that the number of people in your sample adds up to 500 000.

Correlation

♦ You can describe the link between two sets of data using the term **correlation**.

Sleep Experiment 1
Does the length of time you take to fall asleep depend on how light the room is?

These results show **positive** correlation: an *increase* in one set of data tends to be matched by an *increase* in the other set.

The result of experiment 2 may not be what you expect. It happens because sleep is part of your daily rhythm of sleeping and waking.

Going to bed late means that you will soon reach your time for waking, and vice versa.

A daily rhythm, like this sleep/wake example, is called a **circadian rhythm**.

Sleep Experiment 2
Does the length of time you sleep depend on the length of time since you last slept?

These results show **negative** correlation: an *increase* in one set of data tends to be matched by a *decrease* in the other set.

Exercise 22.4
Correlation

1

Mean semi-detached house prices in towns near London – 2nd Quarter 1996	
Distance from London (miles)	44 66 41 75 86 47 68 36 62 77 57 53
Mean house price (£000's)	93 78 98 72 63 97 71 104 86 64 78 88

a Draw these axes: horizontal 0 to 90, vertical 50 to 130.
b Plot the house price data on your diagram.
c Is the correlation positive or negative?

2

A negative number of dioptres shows short-sightedness; a positive number of dioptres shows long-sightedness.

Eye Tests for 10 people	
Pressure in eye (mmHg)	12.1 11.7 15.2 19.1 11.2 18.9 15.9 17.3 13.0 16.6
Refractive power of lens (dioptres)	3.6 ⁻3.9 5.1 10.4 ⁻6.4 3.0 ⁻6.9 6.5 ⁻8.4 0.8

a Draw these axes: horizontal 10 to 20, vertical ⁻12 to 12
b Plot the eye test data on your diagram.
c Is the correlation positive or negative?

This is called drawing a line **by eye** or **by inspection**.

3   For each of your scatter diagrams, draw a line through the middle of the plots, like this:

4   Which scatter diagram did you find it easier to draw the line on? Explain why.

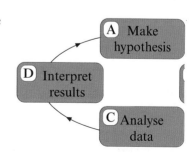

Using a line of best fit

◆ A line drawn through the middle of the plots on a scatter diagram is called a **line of best fit**. The stronger the correlation, the easier it is to draw this line.

This is **moderate** positive correlation because the plots are well scattered around the line of best fit.

This is **strong** negative correlation because the plots are quite close to the line of best fit.

◆ When it is not possible to draw a line of best fit, there is no link between the two sets of data: there is **no correlation**.

Exercise 22.5
Describing correlation

1 Use this scatter diagram to describe the correlation between income and percentage of income given to charity.

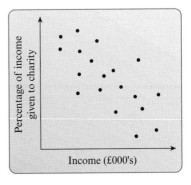

2 Use your scatter diagram from Exercise 22.4 Question **1** to describe the correlation between distance of town from London and mean house price.

3 Use your scatter diagram from Exercise 22.4 Question **2** to describe the correlation between pressure in eye and refractive power of lens.

4 Design an experiment to answer this question:
'Is there any correlation between your fathom and your height?'

5 a Carry out your experiment.
  b Plot the data you collect on a scatter diagram.
  c Draw a line of best fit.
  d Use your scatter diagram to describe any correlation.

> Your fathom is the distance between the ends of your fingers when your arms are stretched as wide as possible. This distance is roughly six feet for an adult.

Estimating values from a line of best fit

◆ It is possible to estimate values from a line of best fit.

Example

a   Estimate the height of a person with head circumference 56 cm.
b   Estimate the head circumference of a person 195 cm tall.

You can extend the line of best fit...

... but not too far or it becomes unreliable!

a   Estimated height of person with head circumference 56 cm = **168 cm**
b   Estimated head circumference of person 195 cm tall = **66 cm**

Exercise 22.6
Estimating values

Use your scatter diagram from Exercise 22.4 Question **1** for Questions **1** to **3**.

1   Estimate the distance from London of a town with a mean house price of:
   a   £90 000   b   £65 000

2   Estimate the mean house price for a town:
   a   70 miles from London   b   55 miles from London

3   Extend your line of best fit to estimate:
   a   the distance from London of a town with a mean house price of £120 000
   b   the mean house price for a town 25 miles from London.

4

Natural Births – Length of Pregnancy & Weight of Baby									
Length of pregnancy (days)	271	287	283	274	271	279	263	276	283	270
Weight of baby (kg)	2.5	4.2	3.8	3.3	4.5	3.4	2.9	4.1	4.3	3.5

This data has been collected to test the hypothesis:
'A longer pregnancy leads to a heavier baby.'
Plot this data on a scatter diagram.

5   a   Draw a line of best fit on your scatter diagram.
   b   Describe the correlation between length of pregnancy and weight of baby.
   c   Use your line of best fit to estimate:
      i   the length of pregnancy for a baby that weighs 3.5 kg
      ii   the weight of a baby with a length of pregnancy of 280 days.

6   Do you think it would make sense to extend this line of best fit?
   Give reasons for your answer.

End points

You should be able to ...

... so try these questions

A Design and criticise questions for a questionnaire

B Design experiments

C Choose a stratified random sample

D Use a scatter diagram and line of best fit to describe correlation

E Estimate values from a line of best fit

A1

> ### *Bypass Survey*
>
> **1** Are you a local ? ☐ Yes ☐ No
>
> **2** What do you think of the traffic in the village ? _____
>
> **3** Do you agree that the village needs a bypass ? ☐ Yes ☐ No

    a Criticise each of these questions.
    b Write an improved question for each one.

B1 Design an experiment to answer this question.

> ### *Body Matters*
> How long can people hold their breath for ?

C1

1991 Population of capital Cities (000's)			
Belfast	Cardiff	Edinburgh	London
279	272	402	2343

Calculate how many people from each capital city would be in a stratified random sample of 10 000.

Petrol Cars – Size of Engine & Petrol Consumption											
Size of engine (litres)	1.6	2.6	1.2	4.0	2.5	1.1	3.2	4.0	3.2	1.8	2.4	3.5
Petrol consumption (mpg)	45	37	40	22	43	48	29	29	33	39	32	25

D1 **a** Draw axes: horizontal 0 to 6.0, vertical 0 to 50
    b Plot the petrol car data on your diagram.
    c Draw a line of best fit.
    d Describe any correlation between size of engine and petrol consumption.

E1 Use your scatter diagram to estimate:
    a the petrol consumption of a car with a 3.0 litre engine
    b the engine size of a car with petrol consumption of 40 mpg.

E2 Extend your line of best fit to estimate:
    a the petrol consumption of a car with a 5.0 litre engine.
    b the engine size of a car with petrol consumption of 20 mpg.

Some points to remember

- ◆ When you choose a stratified random sample, check that the sum of the sample sizes from each stratum equals the total sample size.

- ◆ When you draw a line of best fit on a scatter diagram, make sure the line goes through the middle of the points.

- ◆ In some cases, it does not make sense to extend the line of best fit on a scatter diagram.

Starting points

You need to know about ...   ... so try these questions

A Calculations with time, distance and speed

> **Speed = Distance ÷ Time**
>
> **Time = Distance ÷ Speed**
>
> **Distance = Speed × Time**

Example 1 How long does it take a car travelling at an average speed of 54 mph to cover a distance of 350 miles?

Time = Distance ÷ Speed
= 350 ÷ 54
= 6.48 hours (to 3 sf)
= **6 hours 29 minutes** (to the nearest minute)
(since 0.48 hours is 0.48 × 60 = 28.8 minutes)

Example 2 An arrow from a long bow flew a distance of 196 metres in 2 seconds. What was its average speed in mph?

Speed = Distance ÷ Time
= 196 ÷ 2   = 98 metres per second
= 98 × 60 × 60   = 352 800 metres per hour
= 352 800 ÷ 1000   = 352.8 km per hour
= 352.8 ÷ 1.609   = **219.3 mph** (1 mile = 1.609 km)

A1 What is 0.68 hours to the nearest minute?

A2 A car made the journey from Doncaster to Oxford (135 miles) in 2 hours 52 minutes. What was its average speed? Give your answer to 2 sf.

A3 How long does it take a hot air balloon to fly 100 metres at a speed of 41 m min⁻¹? Give your answer in minutes and seconds.

A4 Convert the following:
  a 14 metres per second into miles per hour
  b 38 miles per hour into metres per second.

B The area of a trapezium

> **Area = $\frac{1}{2}(a + b)h$**

where h is the perpendicular height.

Example Find the area of this trapezium.

First identify the dimensions a, b and h:

$a = 12\,$cm
$b = 25\,$cm
$h = 14\,$cm

Note that the lengths 15 cm and 16 cm are not used.

Area = $\frac{1}{2}(a + b)h$
= $\frac{1}{2} \times (12 + 25) \times 14$
= 0.5 × 37 × 14
= 259

The area of the trapezium is 259 cm².

B1 What is the area of this trapezium?

B2 Calculate the area of this trapezium in square units.

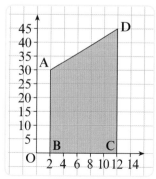

C Using distance–time graphs

This graphs shows journeys made by four people on one day.
They all travelled on the same road.

Joe left home in his Citröen and got back home some time after 4 pm.

Sally took the Jeep and stopped at a friends for lunch then continued her journey.

Ravi drove without a break all day on his Honda motorbike.

Charlie pedalled non-stop on his Claude Butler bike.

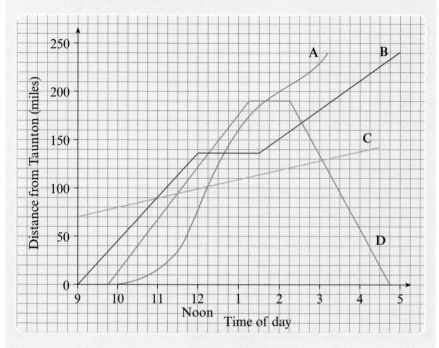

$$\text{Average speed} = \frac{\text{Total distance}}{\text{Total time}}$$

The total time includes any breaks.

Example 1   Calculate the average speed of A over the journey.

$$\text{Average speed} = \frac{240}{(10\text{ am to }3:15\text{ pm})}$$

$$= \frac{240}{5.25} \qquad (5\text{ h }15\text{ min is }5.25\text{ h})$$

$$= \textbf{45.7 mph}$$

Example 2   Calculate the average speed of D over the day.

$$\text{Average speed} = \frac{(190 + 190)}{(9:45\text{ to }4:45)}$$

$$= \frac{380}{7}$$

$$= \textbf{54.3 mph}$$

C1 Identify the line on the graph for each person's journey. Give reasons for your answers.

C2 Which two journeys finished at the same place? Explain your answer.

C3 Which two journeys started at the same time?

C4 At what time did D's journey start?

C5 At noon how far away from Taunton was:
  a A   b B
  c C   d D?

C6 How long did Sally spend at her friend's house? How can you tell?

C7 Who did not start at Taunton? How far was this person from Taunton at 9 am?

C8 How far from Taunton was A when overtaking C?

C9 From the graph:
  D passed C twice.
  a At what times did they pass?
  b What was the difference about the directions on the two occasions?

C10 Calculate C's average speed over the whole journey.

C11 What was B's average speed over the whole journey?

C12 How does B's speed, up to noon, compare with B's speed after 1:30 pm? Give your reasons.

C13 a Who appears to reach the highest top speed at any time on their journey?
  b Roughly when was this?
  c Why is it impossible to tell for certain from the graph?

Finding speeds from distance–time graphs

This distance–time graph shows journeys taken by four people who arrange to meet in Haddington. Julie and Simon are having problems with their cars.

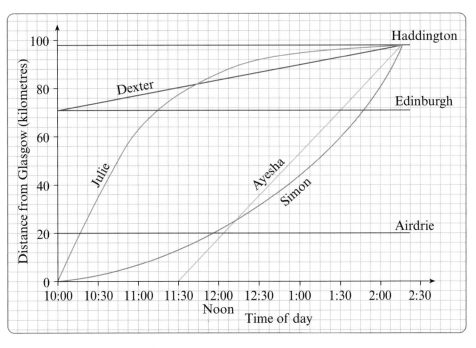

Exercise 23.1
Speeds from graphs

> You may see
> **kilometres per hour**
> in any of these forms
>
> **kph**
> km h^{-1}
> **km/h**

Give answers to 3 s.f. where appropriate.

1 Where does Dexter start from?

2 **a** What was Dexter's average speed in kilometres per hour?
   b How do you think Dexter was travelling?

3 **a** At what time did Ayesha start her journey?
   b What was her average speed in km h^{-1}?

4 Describe how the speeds during Julie's and Simon's journeys differed from each other.

5 What was the average speed over the journey for:
   a Simon
   b Julie?

> For question 7 you need to check where the slope of Ayesha's curve is roughly the same as the slope of Dexter's graph.

6 How did Simon's, Ayesha's and Julie's speeds compare when they passed through Airdrie?

7 At what time was Simon travelling at roughly the same speed as
   a Ayesha
   b Dexter?
   Explain how you decided.

8 How far from Glasgow was Julie when she was travelling at roughly the same speed as:
   a Ayesha
   b Dexter?

9 At roughly what time were Simon and Julie travelling at the same speed?

10 Julie and Simon passed the same point on the road at the same speed. How far from Glasgow is this point?

Exercise 23.2
Drawing and
interpreting graphs

1 Ken and his sister Amy go on a cycling holiday.
The graph shows part of Ken's journey for the first day.

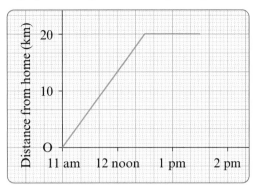

> **Accuracy**
> In this exercise, give all
> average speeds to 1 dp.

a After 1.30 pm he cycles at $15\,km\,h^{-1}$ to reach a camp-site that
is 50 km from home.
i Copy and complete the graph for Ken's first day.
ii Find Ken's average speed for his whole journey.
b Amy leaves their home at 1pm and cycles along the same
route at $22\,km\,h^{-1}$.
i Draw a line on your graph to show Amy's journey.
ii When did she reach the camp-site?
iii At about what time did Amy pass Ken on her way to the camp-site?

2 Alice lives in Cupar and Emily lives 10 miles away in St Andrews.
Alice cycles to St Andrews. This graph shows part of her journey.

a At 1.30 pm, she stops for 10 minutes to buy cakes and then cycles
at a constant speed to reach Emily's house at 2.20 pm.

i Copy and complete the graph for Alice's journey.
ii What is her speed in mph after her stop to buy cakes?
iii Calculate Alice's average speed in mph for her whole journey.

b On the same day, Emily decides to visit Alice. She leaves at 1 pm and
cycles at a speed of 12 mph for 4 miles. She stops for five minutes and
then carries on at a constant speed to reach Alice's house at 1.47 pm.

i How far is Emily from Cupar at the start of her journey?
ii Show her journey on your graph.
iii Find Emily's average speed in mph for her journey to Cupar.
iv Explain why you think Emily did not see Alice on her journey.

c After ringing Alice's door bell for 3 minutes, Emily decides to cycle
home. She reaches St Andrews at the same time as Alice does.

i Show Emily's journey home to St Andrews on your graph.
ii How fast does she cycle home?

The link between distance–time and speed–time graphs

A distance–time graph can give an indication of changing speed when the changing gradient of the curve is considered. It is also possible to draw a speed–time graph from it. Here are two graphs of the same short bicycle journey.

On this distance–time graph some tangents have been drawn to show the speed at these points. It is possible, though, to draw a tangent at any point on the curve. There are an infinite number of tangents possible.

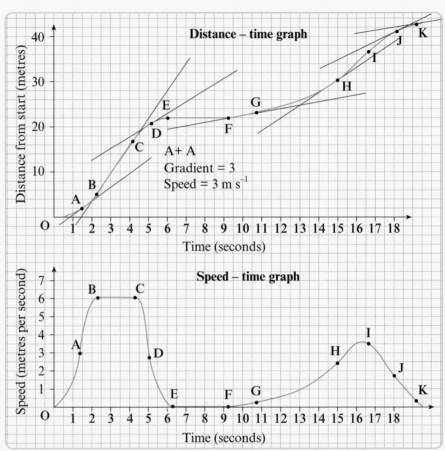

You may see
metres per second
in any of these forms:

m per s
m/s
m s^{-1}

At any point on the distance–time graph a gradient can be drawn and the speed calculated. For example, at point A (after about 1.3 seconds) the speed of the bike is 3 metres per second. Point A can therefore be plotted on the speed–time graph as a speed of 3 m s^{-1} after 1.3 seconds. The more points at which the gradient is found, the more accurate will be the speed–time graph.

Exercise 23.3
Reading a
speed–time graph

1   How can you tell from the distance–time graph that the bike is travelling faster at point B than at point A?

2   What does a horizontal line indicate on:

    a   a distance–time graph   **b**   a speed–time graph?

3   The following questions are about the speed–time graph, but you may need to look at the corresponding points on the distance–time graph.

    a   Why does the graph show a speed of zero between points E and F?
    b   Why are the speeds equal at points B and C?
    c   Why is the second peak on the graph lower than the first peak?
    d   Give two labelled points where the bike is:
        i   accelerating (speeding up)   **ii**   decelerating (slowing down).

End points

You should be able to ...   ... so try these questions

A Interpret distance–time graphs

A1 This graph shows the journey of a car and a cycle.
The cyclist travelled from Leeds to York.
The car driver took the same route to York but returned to Leeds.

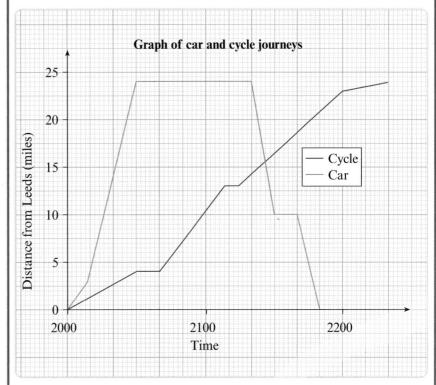

Graph of car and cycle journeys

   a How far did the cyclist travel in the first 20 minutes?
   b How long did it take the car to travel the first 20 miles?
   c How many times did the cyclist stop on her journey to York?
   d What was the cyclist's average speed for this journey in mph correct to 1 dp?

B Interpret a speed–time graph

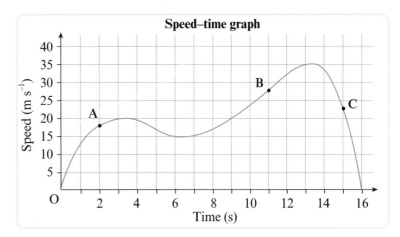

Speed–time graph

B1 **a** At what times was this vehicle travelling at 18 m s^{-1}?

   b Give two times when the vehicle was starting to accelerate.

   c At which times was the vehicle stationary?

   d Describe what the vehicle was doing 4 seconds from the start.

Starting points

You need to know about ...

... so try these questions

A Using vectors to describe a translation

◆ A vector can be used to describe the movement in a translation.

Every point on the triangle has moved 4 squares right and 2 squares down.

The vector which describes this translation is: $\begin{pmatrix} 4 \\ {}^-2 \end{pmatrix}$

B Resultant vectors

◆ The total effect of two or more vectors can be shown as a single vector called the **resultant**.
So if you translate,

first by $\begin{pmatrix} 3 \\ 1 \end{pmatrix}$ then by $\begin{pmatrix} {}^-5 \\ 3 \end{pmatrix}$,

the resultant vector is given by:

$\begin{pmatrix} 3 + {}^-5 \\ 1 + 3 \end{pmatrix} = \begin{pmatrix} {}^-2 \\ 4 \end{pmatrix}$

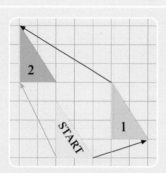

C Using algebra

◆ Expressions that include negative coefficients can be factorised in two ways.
To factorise $6y - 2x$:

$6y - 2x$	or	$6y - 2x$
$= 2(3y - x)$		$= {}^-2({}^-3y + x)$
		$= {}^-2(x - 3y)$

◆ Expressions that include fractional coefficients can be factorised.

To factorise: $\frac{1}{2}x + y$ $\frac{1}{2}(x - y) + x$

$\frac{1}{2}x + y$	$\frac{1}{2}(x - y) + x$
$= \frac{1}{2}(x + 2y)$	$= \frac{1}{2}x - \frac{1}{2}y + x$
	$= 1\frac{1}{2}x - \frac{1}{2}y$
	$= \frac{1}{2}(3x - y)$

D Ratios and fractions of straight lines

◆ A straight line can be divided into two parts, like this:

A — 1 — X — 2 — B

Point X divides line AB in the ratio 1:2, and AX is $\frac{1}{3}$ of the line.

$AX : AB = 1 : 2$ $AX = \frac{1}{3}AB$

A1 Copy triangle ABC and translate it using the vector:

a $\begin{pmatrix} 3 \\ 1 \end{pmatrix}$ b $\begin{pmatrix} 5 \\ 2 \end{pmatrix}$

c $\begin{pmatrix} {}^-2 \\ {}^-3 \end{pmatrix}$ d $\begin{pmatrix} {}^-4 \\ 2 \end{pmatrix}$

B1 Give the resultant vector for each of these combined translations.

a $\begin{pmatrix} 3 \\ 1 \end{pmatrix} \begin{pmatrix} 2 \\ {}^-2 \end{pmatrix}$

b $\begin{pmatrix} {}^-2 \\ {}^-4 \end{pmatrix} \begin{pmatrix} 3 \\ 2 \end{pmatrix}$

c $\begin{pmatrix} 2 \\ 5 \end{pmatrix} \begin{pmatrix} 0 \\ {}^-2 \end{pmatrix} \begin{pmatrix} {}^-3 \\ 1 \end{pmatrix}$

C1 Copy and complete:
a $4x - 2y = 2(\square)$
b $4x - 2y = {}^-2(\square)$
c $9y - 3x = {}^-3(\square)$
d $9y - 3x = 3(\square)$

C2 Factorise:
a $x + \frac{1}{2}y$

b $\frac{1}{3}x - y$

c $x + \frac{1}{2}(x + y)$

d $\frac{1}{3}(x - y) + x$

e $2x + \frac{2}{3}(y - 2x)$

f $2y - \frac{2}{3}(x + y)$

P —— 3 —— Y — 1 — Q

D1 Give these ratios.
a PY : YQ   b QY : YP

D2 What fraction of PQ is:
a YQ   b PY?

Defining vectors

♦ A **vector** can be defined by two quantities:
   ❖ its **size**
   ❖ its **direction**.

♦ A vector can be placed anywhere in a plane, and is usually represented by a straight line:
   ❖ the size of the vector is the length of the line,
   ❖ the direction of the vector is how the line is pointing, in the direction of the arrow.

Other ways of writing the vector **z** include:

$$\underline{z} \quad \underset{\sim}{z} \quad \bar{z} \quad \tilde{z}$$

♦ The **negative** of a given vector is a vector that is:
   ❖ equal in size but
   ❖ opposite in direction.

♦ A **scalar multiple** of a given vector is found by:
   ❖ multiplying its size by a single number
   ❖ leaving its direction unchanged.

♦ When a vector is placed on a coordinate grid, it can also be represented by a **column vector**.

$$\mathbf{z} = \begin{pmatrix} 3 \\ 1 \end{pmatrix} \qquad {}^{-}\mathbf{z} = \begin{pmatrix} {}^{-}3 \\ 1 \end{pmatrix} \qquad {}^{-}2\mathbf{z} = \begin{pmatrix} {}^{-}6 \\ 2 \end{pmatrix}$$

Exercise 24.1
Vectors on a grid

Use these vectors for this exercise.

$$\mathbf{p} = \begin{pmatrix} 1 \\ 3 \end{pmatrix} \qquad \mathbf{q} = \begin{pmatrix} 4 \\ 1 \end{pmatrix} \qquad \mathbf{r} = \begin{pmatrix} {}^{-}1 \\ 2 \end{pmatrix}$$

1 Draw vectors **p**, **q**, and **r** on a coordinate grid.

2 Write each of these as a column vector, and draw it on a coordinate grid.
   a ⁻p **b** 2q **c** 3r **d** ⁻2p **e** ⁻3r

3 This diagram shows the effect of the combined translation, **q** then **p**.
   Give the resultant vector.

4 **a** Draw a diagram to show the combined translation, **q** then **p**.
   b Give the resultant vector.

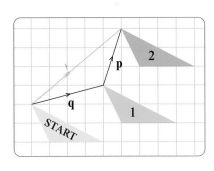

5 Write down what you notice about the effect of combined translations.

6 This diagram shows the effect of the combined translation, **q** then ⁻r.

   a Give the resultant vector.
   b Explain how you can find the resultant from column vectors **q** and **r**.

271

Adding vectors

♦ You can add vectors by combining them end to end, so that their direction 'follow on' from each other.

Example

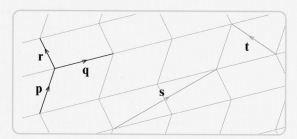

Give **s** and **t** in terms of **p**, **q**, and **r**.

$$s = 2q + r$$

$$t = ^-q + p$$

Exercise 24.2
Adding vectors

1 a This sketch to show **x** = **q** + **r** is incorrect.
Explain why.
b Make a sketch to show the correct **x**.

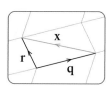

2 Give each of these vectors in terms of **p**, **q**, and **r**.

a   **b**   **c**

Adding vectors is
commutative because,
however you combine them,
the resultant is the same.

3 a Explain why this diagram shows that
adding vectors is commutative:
p + **q** = **q** + **p**
b Make a sketch to show that:
¯**q** + **p** = **p** + ¯**q**

Adding vectors is associative
because, however pairs of
vectors are grouped, the
resultant is the same.

4 a Sketch this diagram.
b Label your sketch to show that
adding vectors is associative:
p + (**q** + **r**) = (**p** + **q**) + **r**

Subtracting vectors

- Adding a negative vector can be written as a subtraction.

- In general, vectors **a** – **b** and **b** – **a** are:
  - ❖ the same in size,
  - ❖ opposite in direction.

Therefore, **b** – **a** is the negative vector of **a** – **b**.

$$\begin{aligned} {}^-(\mathbf{a} - \mathbf{b}) &= {}^-\mathbf{a} + \mathbf{b} \\ &= \mathbf{b} + {}^-\mathbf{a} \\ &= \mathbf{b} - \mathbf{a} \end{aligned}$$

Exercise 24.3
Subtracting vectors

1   Show that **p** – **q** is the negative vector of **q** – **p**:
    a using a sketch   **b** using algebra

2   Make a sketch to show the vector (**p** – **q**) – **r**.

3   Make a sketch to show:
    a **q** – **r**   **b** **p** – (**q** – **r**)

4   Use algebra to explain why subtracting vectors is not associative:
    p – (**q** – **r**) is not equal to (**p** – **q**) – **r**.

5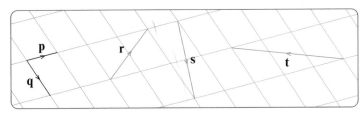

    Give vectors **r**, **s**, and **t** in terms of **p** and **q**.

6   **a** Sketch a large grid like the one in Question **5**.
    b Use your grid to draw:
        i 3**p** – 2**q**   **ii** 2**q** – 3**p**   **iii** 3**p** – **q**   **iv** 6**p** + 2**q**
    c Use algebra to explain why 3**p** – **q** and 2**q** – 6**p** are parallel vectors.

7   These vectors include three pairs of parallel vectors.

    | ⁻2**p** – **q** | 2**p** – **q** | 2**q** – **p** | 2**p** + 4**q** | 2**q** – 4**p** | 2**p** + **q** | **p** + 2**q** |

    List each pair.

8   **a** Give each side of this parallelogram
        of vectors in terms of **p** and **q**.
    b Add your vectors.
    c Explain your answer.

    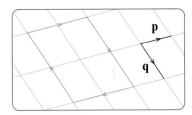

Vectors in space

◆ You can refer to a vector by labelling each end.

Example $\vec{KL}$ is a vector with:

❖ size equal to the distance from K to L
❖ direction from K to L.

$\vec{LK}$ is the same size as $\vec{KL}$, and opposite in direction.

◆ This notation is useful when giving a vector as a **vector sum**.

Example

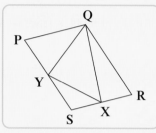

$$\vec{PY} = \vec{PQ} + \vec{QY}$$
$$\vec{PS} = \vec{PQ} + \vec{QR} + \vec{RS}$$
$$\vec{YX} = \vec{YQ} + \vec{QX}$$

etc.

◆ You can use vector sums to give other vectors.

Example

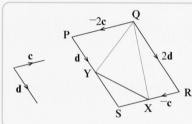

Y is the midpoint of PS;
X is the midpoint of SR.

Give $\vec{QY}$ and $\vec{QX}$ in terms of **c** and **d**.

$$\vec{QY} = \vec{QP} + \vec{PY} \qquad \vec{QX} = \vec{QR} + \vec{RX}$$
$$= {}^-2\mathbf{c} + \mathbf{d} \qquad\qquad = 2\mathbf{d} + {}^-\mathbf{c}$$
$$= \mathbf{d} - 2\mathbf{c} \qquad\qquad = 2\mathbf{d} - \mathbf{c}$$

Exercise 24.4
Vectors in space

1 **a** Give $\vec{YQ}$ in terms of **c** and **d**.

 b Use $\vec{YX} = \vec{YQ} + \vec{QX}$ to show that $\vec{YX} = \mathbf{c} + \mathbf{d}$.

2 **a** Give the resultant vector for:

 i $\vec{EH} + \vec{HD}$

 ii $\vec{EF} + \vec{FG}$

 iii $\vec{HG} + \vec{GD} + \vec{DE}$

 iv $\vec{EF} + \vec{FD} + \vec{DG}$

 b List three vector sums that each give the vector $\vec{FH}$.

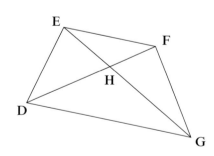

3 **a** Use $\vec{FG} = \vec{FE} + \vec{ED} + \vec{DG}$ to show that $\vec{FG}$ is equal to **q** – **p**.

 b Z is the midpoint of FG, so:
 $\vec{FZ} = \frac{1}{2}(\mathbf{q} - \mathbf{p})$

 i Show that:
 $\vec{EZ} = \frac{1}{2}(3\mathbf{q} - \mathbf{p})$

 ii Give DZ in terms of **p** and **q**.

Using vectors

Plane geometry is the study of the properties and relationships of points and lines in two-dimensional space.

◆ You can use vectors to prove facts in plane geometry.

Example

PQRS is a parallelogram. T is the midpoint of PR: $PT = \frac{1}{2}PR$

Prove that T is also the midpoint of QS.

$\overrightarrow{PR} = \overrightarrow{PQ} + \overrightarrow{QR}$
$= 2\mathbf{c} + 2\mathbf{d}$
$= 2(\mathbf{c} + \mathbf{d})$
So $\frac{1}{2}\overrightarrow{PR} = \mathbf{c} + \mathbf{d}$

Writing $\overrightarrow{QS}$ and $\overrightarrow{QT}$ in terms of $\mathbf{c}$ and $\mathbf{d}$:

$\overrightarrow{QS} = \overrightarrow{QR} + \overrightarrow{RS}$
$= 2\mathbf{d} + {}^-2\mathbf{c}$
$= 2\mathbf{d} - 2\mathbf{c}$
$= 2(\mathbf{d} - \mathbf{c})$

$\overrightarrow{QT} = \overrightarrow{QP} + \overrightarrow{PT}$
$= \overrightarrow{QP} + \frac{1}{2}\overrightarrow{PR}$
$= {}^-2\mathbf{c} + \mathbf{c} + \mathbf{d}$
$= \mathbf{d} - \mathbf{c}$

The distance QS is twice the distance QT so, T must be the midpoint of QS.

Exercise 24.5
Using vectors

1 D is the point so that $PD = 3\mathbf{d} - \mathbf{c}$.
Use $\overrightarrow{QD} = \overrightarrow{QP} + \overrightarrow{PD}$ to prove that D lies on an extension of QS.

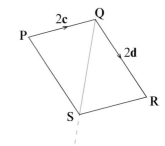

2 In this diagram $DH = \frac{2}{3}DF$.
  a Give these in terms of $\mathbf{p}$ and $\mathbf{q}$.
   i $\overrightarrow{DH}$ **ii** $\overrightarrow{EG}$
  b Prove that $EH = \frac{1}{3}EG$.

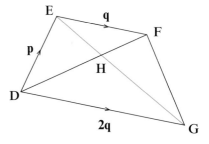

3 OJMN is a parallelogram.
K is the midpoint of JM.
The ratio KL : LN is 1 : 2.
  a Give these in terms of $\mathbf{x}$ and $\mathbf{y}$.
   i $\overrightarrow{KN}$ **ii** $\overrightarrow{KL}$
  b Prove that the ratio OL : LM is 2 : 1.

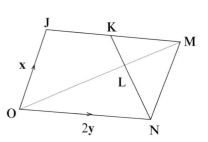

Using parallel vectors

Points are collinear when they all lie in the same straight line.

♦ Other uses of vectors in plane geometry include:
  ❖ proving that lines are parallel,
  ❖ proving that points are collinear.

Example

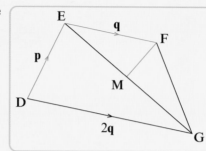

M is the midpoint of EG.

a Prove that MF is parallel to DE.

b If N is the midpoint of DG, prove that N, M, and F are collinear.

$\overrightarrow{GE} = \overrightarrow{GD} + \overrightarrow{DE}$
$= \ ^-2q + p$
$= p - 2q$

So $\frac{1}{2}\overrightarrow{GE}$
$= \frac{1}{2}(p - 2q)$

a $\overrightarrow{MF} = \overrightarrow{ME} + \overrightarrow{EF}$
$= \frac{1}{2}\overrightarrow{GE} + \overrightarrow{EF}$
$= \frac{1}{2}(p - 2q) + q$
$= \frac{1}{2}p - q + q$
$= \frac{1}{2}p$

$\overrightarrow{MF}$ is in the same direction as $\overrightarrow{DE}$, so MF must be parallel to DE.

b $\overrightarrow{NF} = \overrightarrow{ND} + \overrightarrow{DE} + \overrightarrow{EF}$
$= \ ^-q + p + q$
$= p$

$\overrightarrow{NF}$ is in the same direction as $\overrightarrow{MF}$. As point F lies on NF and MF, the points N, M, and F must be collinear.

Exercise 24.6
Using parallel vectors

1 In this diagram,
OV = 2ON and OW = 2OP.
Prove that VW is parallel to NP, and twice its size.

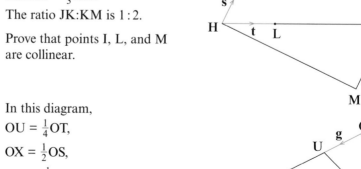

2 HIJK is a parallelogram, and HL = $\frac{1}{3}$HK.
The ratio JK:KM is 1:2.

Prove that points I, L, and M are collinear.

3 In this diagram,
OU = $\frac{1}{4}$OT,

OX = $\frac{1}{2}$OS,

UW = $\frac{1}{2}$US,

V is the midpoint of TS.

Prove that:

a XW is parallel to OT,
b V, W, and X are collinear.

End points

You should be able to ...   ... so try these questions

A Add and subtract
column vectors

$$r = \begin{pmatrix} 2 \\ ^-1 \end{pmatrix} \qquad s = \begin{pmatrix} 1 \\ 4 \end{pmatrix} \qquad t = \begin{pmatrix} ^-2 \\ 2 \end{pmatrix}$$

A1 Write each of these as a column vector, and draw it on squared paper.

   a 2s   **b** ^-3r **c** r + s   **d** s − t   **e** 2t − r   **f** 2s + t

B Add and subtract
vectors in space

B1   **a**   Write CD as a vector sum.
       b   Use your vector sum to give
          CD in terms of **p** and **q**.

B2   M is the midpoint of CD.

      a   Show that BM = $\frac{1}{2}$(4**p** + **q**)
      b   Give AM in terms of **p** and **q**.

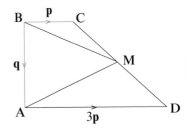

C Recognise when
vectors are parallel

C1 These vectors include two pairs of parallel vectors.

    3r + s   3s − r   2r + 6s   6r + 2s   2r − 6s

List each pair.

C2 Use algebra to explain why 2**s** − **t** and 3**t** − 6**s** are parallel vectors.

D Use vectors to prove
facts in plane geometry

D1 OPQR is a quadrilateral.
EFGH is another quadrilateral, formed
by joining the midpoints of each side.

    a   Give these in terms of **a**, **b**, and **c**.

       i $\vec{RQ}$ **ii** $\vec{PG}$

    b   Prove that $\vec{EH} = \vec{FG}$.

    c   Prove that EFGH is a parallelogram.

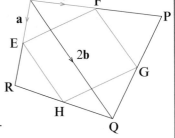

D2 XYZ is a triangle.
L, M, and N are the midpoints of each
of the sides.
The ratio YW:WM is 2:1

    a   Give these in terms of **c** and **d**.

       i $\vec{YM}$ **ii** $\vec{YW}$ **iii** $\vec{YZ}$

    b   Prove that X, W, and N are collinear.

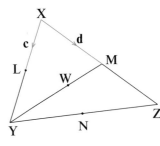

Some points to remember

- A vector can be represented in different ways, for example: $\vec{AB}$ **a** $\begin{pmatrix} x \\ y \end{pmatrix}$

- Adding vectors is:
  - commutative   **a** + **b** = **b** + **a**
  - associative   **a** + (**b** + **c**) = (**a** + **b**) + **c**

- Subtracting a vector has the same effect as adding its negative vector.

Starting points
You need to know about ...

... so try these questions

A Finding a linear rule from a set of data

The speed of a moving object is measured at different times.

Time t (seconds)	0	1	2	3	4	5
Speed v (m s^{-1})	2.4	3.0	3.6	4.0	4.6	5.2

♦ To test for a linear rule, draw a graph of v against t.

♦ The points lie approximately on a straight line.

♦ To 2 significant figures, the gradient is 0.55 and the y-intercept is 2.4.

♦ So a rule that fits the data approximately is:
$v = 0.55t + 2.4$

A1

A
x	0	1	2	3	4
y	4.1	4.3	4.9	5.5	5.6

B
x	2	4	6	8	10
y	2.1	1.9	19	50	97

C
x	1	2	4	5	9
y	12	18	30	36	60

For each table of values:
a Draw a graph of y against x.
b i Decide if y and x could be linked by a linear rule.
ii Find an approximate equation for any linear rule.

B Sketching quadratic graphs

♦ It is easier to find the minimum or maximum point of a quadratic graph when its equation is given in completed square form.

Example Sketch the graph of $y = (x + 3)^2 - 4$.

♦ When $x = {}^-3$, $(x + 3)^2 = 0$, so the minimum value of y occurs when $x = {}^-3$.

♦ When $x = {}^-3$, $y = ({}^-3 + 3)^2 - 4 = {}^-4$, so the minimum point is $({}^-3, {}^-4)$.

♦ The graph of $y = x^2$ is mapped to the graph of $y = (x + 3)^2 - 4$ by a translation of $\begin{pmatrix} {}^-3 \\ {}^-4 \end{pmatrix}$

B1 For each equation, sketch a graph and show clearly the coordinates of the minimum or maximum point and the y-intercept.
a $y = (x + 2)^2 + 3$
b $y = (x - 1)^2 + 5$
c $y = (x + 3)^2$
d $y = (x + 5)^2 - 1$
e $y = (x - 8)^2 - 4$

B2 What translation maps the graph of $y = x^2$ to the graph of $y = (x - 6)^2 + 5$?

C Function notation

♦ A rule that maps one number to another is called a function.

Example $f(x) = x^2 + 6$ is a function.
Calculate the value of $f(3)$.
$f(3) = 3^2 + 6 = 9 + 6 = 15$
We say '3 maps to 15' and '15 is the image of 3'.

C1 A function f is defined so that $f(x) = 3x^2 - 5$.
a Calculate the value of:
  i $f(4)$ ii $f({}^-1)$
  iii $f(2.5)$ iv $f(0)$
b Find a value for x so that $f(x) = {}^-3.31$.

Matching graphs

A symbol that is used for a constant represents a number whose value is fixed.

♦ The equation of this curve is of the form $y = kx^2 + c$, where k and c are constant.

♦ The point $(0, 0.5)$ is on the curve so, for these values of x and y:
$$y = kx^2 + c$$
$$0.5 = k \times 0^2 + c$$
$$0.5 = c$$

So the equation is of the form:
$$y = kx^2 + 0.5$$

♦ The point $(2, 2.9)$ is also on the curve so, for these values of x and y:
$$y = kx^2 + 0.5$$
$$2.9 = k \times 2^2 + 0.5$$
$$2.4 = 4k$$
$$0.6 = k$$

So the equation of the curve is: $y = 0.6x^2 + 0.5$

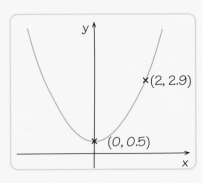

Exercise 25.1
Matching graphs

1

A $(-2.5, 3)$ $(0, -2)$

B $(3, 2.4)$ $(0, 0.3)$

C $(3.5, 19.6)$

D $(1, 2.5)$

E $(3, 2.7)$ $(-2, -0.8)$

F $(-2, -0.25)$

In all equations in this exercise, p, q and k are constants.

$$y = kx^2 \qquad y = kx^2 + p \qquad y = \frac{k}{x} \qquad y = qx^k \qquad y = k\sqrt{x} \qquad y = pq^x$$

Each equation above matches one of the graphs.

    a For each graph:
       i Write down its matching equation.
       ii Find the value of each constant in its equation.
    b Explain why the equation of curve D could not be of the form $y = qx^4$.

2   The equation of a curve is of the form $y = px^2 + q$.
    The curve passes through the points $(1.5, 15.3)$ and $(-0.5, 3.3)$.
    Find the values of p and q.

3   A curve has an equation of the form $y = kq^x$.
    It passes through the points $(1, 2)$ and $(2, 8)$.
    Find the values of k and q.

Looking for relationships

Many different equations give curved graphs; for example:
$C = ar^3 + b$, $C = ar^2 + b$.

For circular tables, the cost could be linked to the area (πr^2) of the table so $C = ar^2 + b$ is a likely rule.

If possible, use the table to check your answers are sensible.

♦ This shows the cost of some circular tables.

Radius r (m)	0.4	0.6	0.8	1.0	1.2	1.4
Cost C (£)	175	210	260	320	395	480

♦ Graph C against r to test for a linear rule.

♦ Points on the graph of C against r lie on a curve, so any rule linking C and r is not linear.

♦ C and r could be linked by an equation of the form $C = ar^2 + b$

♦ Graph C against r^2 to test for a rule of the form $C = ar^2 + b$

r^2	0.16	0.36	0.64	1.0	1.44	1.96
C	175	210	260	320	395	480

$$\frac{120}{0.7} \approx 170$$

♦ The points lie approximately on a straight line.

♦ To 2 significant figures the gradient is 170 and the y-intercept is 150.

♦ So a rule that fits the data approximately is:
$C = 170r^2 + 150$

Exercise 25.2
Finding non-linear rules

1 A stone is dropped and the distance it has fallen is measured at different times.

Time t (seconds)	1	2	3	4	5
Distance fallen d (metres)	5	20	44	78	123

a Draw a graph of d against t^2.
b Explain why your graph shows that a rule of the form $d = kt^2 + p$ approximately fits the data.
c Find a rule of the form $d = kt^2 + p$ that approximately fits the data.
d Use your rule to estimate how far the stone had fallen after 2.5 seconds.
e About how long did it take the stone to fall 100 metres?

2 This table shows the cost of some circular rugs.

Radius r (m)	0.5	1.0	1.5	2.0	2.5	3.0
Cost C (£)	85	145	245	385	565	785

a Draw a graph of C against r^2.
b Use your graph to find a rule that links C and r.
c Estimate the cost of a rug with a radius of 4.5 m.

3 For pendulums of different lengths,
these are the times taken to complete 100 swings.

Length of pendulum l (cm)	Time for 100 swings t (seconds)
5	45
10	63
15	77
20	89
25	100
30	110
35	118
40	126
45	134
50	141

a Draw a graph of t against $\sqrt{l}$.
b Explain why your graph shows that a rule of the form $t = k\sqrt{l}$
approximately fits the data.
c Find the value of k correct to 2 significant figures.
d Estimate how long a pendulum of length 60 cm would take
to complete 100 swings.

4 The table below gives information about the planets in our Solar System.

Planet	Average distance from the Sun, R (millions of miles)	Speed at which it travels through space, V (mph)	Time taken to go once round the Sun, T (days)
Earth	93	66 641	365
Jupiter	484	29 216	4329
Mars	142	53 980	687
Mercury	36	107 132	88
Neptune	2794	12 147	60 150
Pluto	3674	10 604	90 670
Saturn	887	21 565	10 753
Uranus	1784	15 234	30 660
Venus	67	78 364	225

Hypotheses are statements
that are thought to be true
but have not yet been
proved.

These are some hypotheses about relationships between R, V and T,
where p, q and n are constants.

Ⓐ $V \approx \dfrac{p}{\sqrt{R}}$ Ⓑ $V \approx n\sqrt{T}$ Ⓒ $T \approx q\sqrt{R^3}$

a Draw suitable straight-line graphs to show which hypotheses are correct.
b Find the value of the constants in the correct hypotheses.

Transforming graphs

Exercise 25.3
Transforming graphs

Each straight line continues for ever.

1

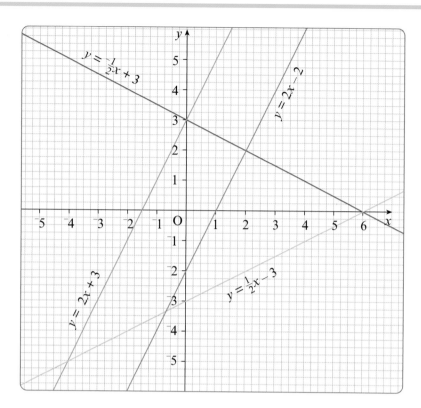

a Which line is the image of $y = 2x + 3$ after a translation of $\begin{pmatrix} 1 \\ -3 \end{pmatrix}$?

b Give three different translations that map $y = 2x - 2$ to $y = 2x + 3$.

c Which line is the image of $y = 2x + 3$ after a rotation of $^-90°$ about $(0, 3)$?

d Describe a reflection that maps $y = \frac{1}{2}x - 3$ to $y = ^-\frac{1}{2}x + 3$.

2 a On a set of axes, draw graphs of:

   i $y = 2x + 1$ **ii** $y = ^-3x - 4$ **iii** $y = \frac{1}{2}x - 1$.

b For each line, find the equation of the image after reflection in the y-axis.

c Without drawing, give the equation of the image of $y = 4x - 3$ after reflection in the y-axis. Explain your method.

3 Give the equation of the image of $y - x = 8$ after reflection in the y-axis.

4 a On a set of axes, draw graphs of:

   i $y = x + 1$ **ii** $y = ^-2x + 3$ **iii** $y = \frac{1}{4}x - 1$.

b For each line, find the equation of the image after reflection in the x-axis.

c Without drawing, give the equation of the image of $y = ^-5x + 1$ after reflection in the x-axis. Explain your method.

5 a Find three different translations that map $y = x - 1$ to $y = x + 5$.

b Describe the link between p and q when $y = x - 1$ is mapped.

to $y = x + 5$ after a translation of $\begin{pmatrix} p \\ q \end{pmatrix}$.

6 What is the equation of the image of $y = 3x + 1$ after a translation of $\begin{pmatrix} v \\ w \end{pmatrix}$?

7 Find the image of $y = kx + l$ after a translation of $\begin{pmatrix} a \\ b \end{pmatrix}$.

♦ If a function f is defined so that $f(x) = x^2$, then $y = x^2$ can be written as $y = f(x)$.

♦ Other equations can be expressed in terms of this function f, and their graphs can be drawn.

Example 1

Draw a graph for the equation $y = f(x) + 2$.

Graph of $y = f(x) + 2$ and $y = f(x)$

x	$y = f(x) + 2$	y
⁻3	$f(⁻3) + 2 = (⁻3)^2 + 2 = 11$	
⁻2	$f(⁻2) + 2 = (⁻2)^2 + 2 = 6$	
⁻1	$f(⁻1) + 2 = (⁻1)^2 + 2 = 3$	
0	$f(0) + 2 = (0)^2 + 2 = 2$	
1	$f(1) + 2 = (1)^2 + 2 = 3$	
2	$f(2) + 2 = (2)^2 + 2 = 6$	
3	$f(3) + 2 = (3)^2 + 2 = 11$	

Example 2

Draw a graph for the equation $y = f(x + 2)$.

Graph of $y = f(x + 2)$ and $y = f(x)$

x	$y = f(x + 2)$	y
⁻3	$f(⁻3 + 2) = f(⁻1) = (⁻1)^2 = 1$	
⁻2	$f(⁻2 + 2) = f(0) = 0^2 = 0$	
⁻1	$f(⁻1 + 2) = f(1) = 1^2 = 1$	
0	$f(0 + 2) = f(2) = 2^2 = 4$	
1	$f(1 + 2) = f(3) = 3^2 = 9$	
2	$f(2 + 2) = f(4) = 4^2 = 16$	
3	$f(3 + 2) = f(5) = 5^2 = 25$	

Exercise 25.4
Using function notation

1   A function g is defined so that $g(x) = 2x - 1$.
    On one set of axes, draw graphs of:

    a $y = g(x)$ b $y = g(x) + 5$ c $y = g(x + 5)$

2   A function h is defined so that $h(x) = x^2 + 3$.

    a   On one set of axes, draw graphs of:
        i $y = h(x)$ ii $y = h(x - 2)$ iii $y = h(x) - 2$
    b   Describe a transformation that maps $y = h(x)$ to $y = h(x - 2)$.

3   This is the graph of a function $y = g(x)$.

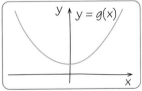

Which of these could be the graph of $y = g(x) - 4$?

4 A function f is defined so that $f(x) = x^2$.

    a On one set of axes, draw graphs of:

        i $y = f(x)$ **ii** $y = f(x + 3)$ **iii** $y = f(x + 3) + 2$

    b Describe a transformation that maps $y = f(x)$ to $y = f(x + 3) + 2$.

5 A student makes the following statement:

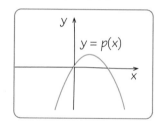

For any function f, a translation of $\begin{pmatrix} ^-4 \\ 5 \end{pmatrix}$ will map the graph of $y = f(x)$ to $y = f(x - 4) + 5$.

    Explain what is wrong with this statement.

6 Two functions are defined so that $g(x) = x^2 + 1$ and $h(x) = x - 4$

    a On one set of axes, sketch graphs of:

        i $y = g(x)$ **ii** $y = h(x)$

        iii $y = {}^-g(x)$ **iv** $y = {}^-h(x)$

    b **i** Describe a transformation that maps $y = g(x)$ to $y = {}^-g(x)$ and also maps $y = h(x)$ to $y = {}^-h(x)$.

        ii Do you think this transformation will map $y = f(x)$ to $y = {}^-f(x)$ for any function f? Explain your answer fully.

7 A function k is defined so that $k(x) = 4x - 5$.

    a On one set of axes, draw graphs of $y = k(x)$ and $y = k({}^-x)$.

    b Describe a transformation that maps $y = k(x)$ to $y = k({}^-x)$.

    c Do you think this transformation will map $y = k(x)$ to $y = k({}^-x)$ for any function k? Explain your answer fully.

8 For $g(x) = x^2$, explain why the graphs of $y = g(x)$ and $y = g({}^-x)$ are the same.

9 This is a sketch of the graph of a function $y = p(x)$.

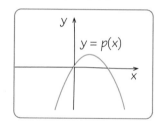

$y = p(x)$

    Which of the sketches below could be the graph of:

    a $y = {}^-p(x)$ **b** $y = p({}^-x)$?

10 A function g is defined so that $g(x) = x^2 - 3$.

    a Draw sketch graphs of:

        i $y = g(x)$ **ii** $y = g(2x)$ **iii** $y = 2g(x)$.

        iv $y = \left(\frac{1}{4}\right)g(x)$ **v** $y = g\left(\frac{1}{4}x\right)$ **vi** $y = {}^-g(2x)$

    b Comment on your results.

11 Sketch $y = f(x)$ where $f(x) = x^2$.
    On separate diagrams, sketch graphs of:

    a $y = {}^-f(x) + 5$ **b** $y = f({}^-3x)$ **c** $y = f\left(\frac{1}{2}x\right) - 4$

Your sketches should show:
- the shape of the graph
- the coordinates of any y-intercepts.

Remember for question 11a
$y = {}^-f(x) + 5$ means
$y = {}^-x^2 + 5$ when
$f(x) = x^2$

12 This is a sketch graph of the function $y = f(x)$ where $f(x) = x^2 - 4x + 5$.

For the following sets of equations and graphs, match each equation to a graph.

a $y = f(\bar{x})$ **b** $y = f(x + 5)$ **c** $y = f(2x)$

d $y = f(\frac{1}{2}x)$ **e** $y = \bar{f}(x) + 10$ **f** $y = f(x - 3) - 2$

Using graphs only

This is part of the graph of a function $y = f(x)$.
From this you can draw other related graphs.

Example Draw the graph of $y = f(2x)$ for $0 \le x \le 5$.

One way to draw the graph is to find values for $y = f(2x)$.

◆ Choose some values for x and find the corresponding y values.

x	$y = f(2x)$	y
0	$f(2 \times 0) = f(0)$	$= 0$
1	$f(2 \times 1) = f(2)$	$= 2$
2	$f(2 \times 2) = f(4)$	$= 1.5$
3	$f(2 \times 3) = f(6)$	$= 2$
4	$f(2 \times 4) = f(8)$	$= 3$
5	$f(2 \times 5) = f(10)$	$= 0$

> In this example, you can only find values for $y = f(2x)$ from the graph of $y = f(x)$.

◆ Plot the points.

◆ Decide how the graph of $y = f(2x)$ is linked to the graph of $y = f(x)$. (Find more values for y if needed: e.g. for $x = 0.5$, $y = f(1) = 2$ for $x = 1.5$, $y = f(3) = 3$.)

> When transforming graphs, draw the transformed graph on axes that use the same scales as the original graph.

◆ Draw the graph.

Exercise 25.5
Transforming graphs

1 Using the graph of $y = f(x)$ above, draw the graph of:

a $y = f(x + 2)$ for $0 \le x \le 5$ **b** $y = 2f(x)$ for $0 \le x \le 5$.

2 The graph of $y = p(x)$ is drawn for $^-2 \leqslant x \leqslant 6$.

  a For $0 \leqslant x \leqslant 3$ draw graphs of:

    i $y = \frac{1}{2}p(x)$

    ii $y = p(x - 2)$

    iii $y = -p(x)$

    iv $y = p(2x)$

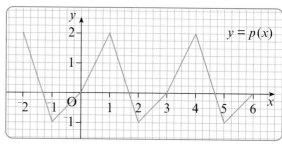

  b Describe the transformation that maps the graph of $y = p(x)$ to $y = {}^-p(x)$.

  c Find two values of x for which $p(x + 2) = 0$.

3 The graph of $y = g(x)$ is drawn for $^-5 \leqslant x \leqslant 5$.

  a For $^-4 \leqslant x \leqslant 4$ draw graphs of:

    i $y = g(x) + 3$

    ii $y = g(x + 1) - 2$

    iii $y = g(-x)$

    iv $y = g\left(\dfrac{x}{2}\right)$.

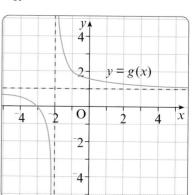

> It may help to work out where the asymptotes will be first.

  b Which transformation maps the graph of $y = g(x)$ to $y = g(x + 1) - 2$?

  c Find a value of x for which $g(x) = {}^-g(x)$.

4 This is the graph of $y = h(x)$.

  a Estimate values of x for which:

    i $h(x) = 2$

    ii $h(^-x) = -2$

    iii $h(x + 3) = 3$.

  b Sketch graphs of:

    i $y = h\left(\dfrac{x}{3}\right)$

    ii $y = {}^-h(x) - 1$

    iii $y = h(x - 1) + 1$.

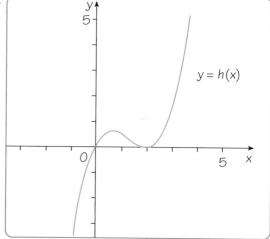

5 The graph of $y = k(x)$ is drawn for $0 \leqslant x \leqslant 4$.

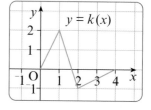

  Write down, in terms of k, the equation of each graph below.

A

B

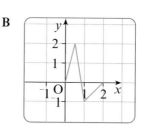

End points
You should be able to ...   ... so try these questions

A Calculate constants in equations from coordinates on graphs

A1 The equation of this curve is of the form $y = pq^x$, where p and q are constants.

Find the value of p and q.

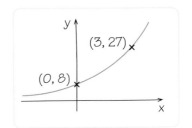

B Find rules by drawing linear graphs

B1 This table shows the cost of some square tablecloths.

Width (x m)	0.6	0.8	1.0	1.2	1.4	1.6
Cost (£ C)	7.50	8.50	9.80	10.40	13.25	15.40

a Draw a graph of C against x^2.
b It is claimed that C and x are linked by a formula of the type:

$$C = ax^2 + b$$

   i Explain why your graph supports this claim.
   ii Estimate the values of a and b.
c Estimate the cost of a tablecloth that is 1.5 m wide.

C Transform graphs of functions

C1 This is the graph of a function $y = f(x)$ for $^-4 \le x \le 6$.

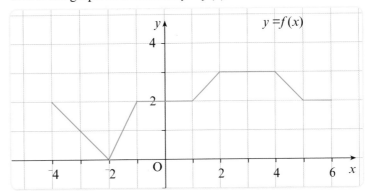

a For $0 \le x \le 4$, draw the graph of:

   i $y = f\left(\dfrac{x}{2}\right)$ **ii** $y = f(x + 1)$ **iii** $f(^-x)$.

b Write down, in terms of f, the equation of this graph.

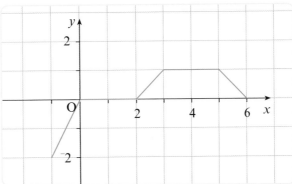

Fractions

1 For each of the following pairs of numbers, find:

   i the highest common factor

   ii the lowest common multiple.

  a 2 and 7   **b** 25 and 30

  c 28 and 63   **d** 10 and 100

  e 36 and 126   **f** 660 and 1260

2 Give each answer as a fraction in its lowest terms. Write fractions greater than 1 as mixed numbers.

  a $\frac{1}{4} + \frac{1}{9}$ **b** $2\frac{1}{2} - 1\frac{1}{3}$ **c** $\frac{3}{5} + \frac{1}{10}$

  d $3\frac{1}{5} - 2\frac{3}{10}$ **e** $\frac{2}{3} - \frac{1}{24}$ **f** $1\frac{1}{2} + \frac{4}{9}$

  g $1\frac{5}{12} + 2\frac{7}{8}$ **h** $\frac{3}{4} - \frac{1}{22}$ **i** $5\frac{1}{4} - 3\frac{5}{8}$

3 Give each answer as a fraction in its lowest terms. Write fractions greater than 1 as improper fractions.

  a $\frac{2}{3} \times 2\frac{1}{2}$ **b** $\frac{5}{6} \div \frac{2}{3}$ **c** $\frac{3}{4} \div \frac{1}{2}$

  d $1\frac{1}{3} \times 2\frac{1}{4}$ **e** $3\frac{4}{5} \div \frac{3}{4}$ **f** $\frac{8}{9} \times \frac{9}{10}$

  g $4\frac{1}{6} \div \frac{3}{5}$ **h** $\frac{1}{2} \times \frac{2}{5} \times \frac{3}{10}$

4 Find the value of these, in fractional form, when

$x = \frac{1}{3}$, $y = \frac{2}{5}$ and $z = \frac{3}{10}$.

  a $5(x + y)$ **b** $\frac{x}{z}$ **c** z^2x

  d $\frac{y - z}{x}$ **e** $\frac{1}{x} + \frac{1}{y}$ **f** $\frac{z}{y - x}$

5 Find the value of these, in fractional form, when

$p = 2$, $q = \frac{1}{4}$ and $r = \frac{2}{3}$.

  a pqr **b** $(r - q)^2$ **c** $q(p - r)$

  d $\frac{q}{p}$ **e** $\frac{1}{p} + \frac{1}{q}$ **f** $\frac{1}{p - q}$

6 If $\frac{1}{f} = \frac{2}{g} + \frac{3}{k}$

what is the value of f, in fractional form, when:

  a $g = 4$ and $k = 8$ **b** $g = 3$ and $k = 5$

  c $g = 6$ and $k = 7$ **d** $g = 5$ and $k = 2$

7 Find two different unit fractions that add to give:

  a $\frac{2}{3}$ **b** $\frac{1}{4}$ **c** $\frac{1}{9}$

8 In a magic square, the sums of the numbers in each row, column and diagonal are equal.

Square A

$\frac{3}{2}$	$\frac{1}{3}$	
$\frac{2}{3}$		
$\frac{5}{6}$		

Square B

$2\frac{1}{4}$	$\frac{1}{2}$	$2\frac{2}{3}$
2	$1\frac{11}{12}$	$1\frac{5}{6}$
$1\frac{1}{6}$	$3\frac{1}{3}$	$1\frac{1}{4}$

  a Copy and complete Square A so that it is a magic square.

  b Square B is not a magic square. How could you change one of the fractions to make a magic square?

9 Find four pairs of equivalent expressions.

  Ⓐ $\frac{x}{x(x + 5)}$ Ⓑ $\frac{x + 5}{x(x + 5)}$ Ⓒ $\frac{2}{x + 5}$

  Ⓓ $\frac{1}{x + 5}$ Ⓔ $\frac{1}{x(x + 5)}$ Ⓕ $\frac{3}{x}$

  Ⓖ $\frac{4}{2(x + 5)}$ Ⓗ $\frac{1}{x}$ Ⓘ $\frac{3x}{x^2}$

10 Write each of these as a single fraction. Give each answer in its simplest from.

  a $\frac{x}{3} + \frac{x}{9}$ **b** $\frac{2}{x} \times \frac{x}{5}$ **c** $\frac{7}{x} - \frac{4}{x}$

  d $\frac{7x}{3} \div \frac{x}{9}$ **e** $\frac{2x}{5} - \frac{x}{10}$ **f** $\frac{3}{x} + \frac{1}{3x}$

  g $\frac{x}{2} + \frac{y}{7}$ **h** $\frac{3}{x} - \frac{1}{x + 4}$ **i** $\frac{x}{4} - \frac{y}{2}$

  j $\frac{5}{x} \times \frac{x}{x - 1}$ **k** $\frac{x}{x + 2} \div \frac{x}{x - 1}$ **l** $\frac{1}{x} + \frac{2}{y}$

  m $\frac{4}{x} + \frac{1}{x - 1}$ **n** $\frac{1}{x} - \frac{x}{y}$ **o** $\frac{1}{x + 4} \div \frac{1}{x - 1}$

  p $\frac{2}{x + 1} + \frac{3}{x + 2}$ **q** $\frac{2}{x + 1} + \frac{3}{x - 2}$

  r $\frac{5}{x + 3} + \frac{1}{x + 3}$ **s** $\frac{2}{x} - \frac{1}{x + 2}$

  t $\frac{1}{x - 1} + \frac{5}{x + 2}$ **u** $\frac{5}{x + 1} + \frac{1}{y + 2}$

11 Copy and complete:

  a $\frac{\square}{x} - \frac{3}{x - 3} = \frac{3(x - 6)}{x(x - 3)}$

  b $\frac{1}{x + 1} + \frac{\square}{x - 1} = \frac{2(5x + 4)}{(x + 1)(x - 1)}$

Properties of shapes

1

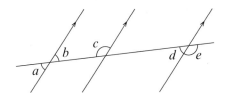

a If $a = 47°$, calculate angles b to e.
b If $a = 51.5°$, calculate the angles b to e.
c If $e = 169°$, calculate angles a to d.

2 These polygons are drawn on a grid of parallel lines. The diagonals of PQRS are marked in red.

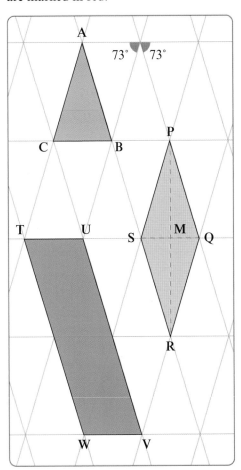

a Work out each interior angle of ΔABC.
b What type of triangle is ABC?
c Work out each interior angle of:
  i PQRS **ii** TUVW
d Explain why PQRS is a rhombus.
e Explain why TUVW cannot be a rhombus.
f The diagonals of PQRS intersect at M.
  Work out each of these angles:
  i PM̂Q **ii** PQ̂M **iii** MQ̂R
  iv QR̂M **v** SR̂M

3 These quadrilaterals are on an isometric grid.

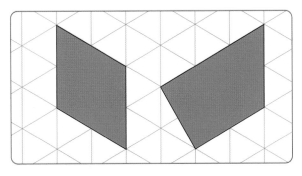

a Show how each of these quadrilaterals will tessellate on its own.
b Show how they will tessellate together.

4 Calculate the angles a to m in the diagram below.

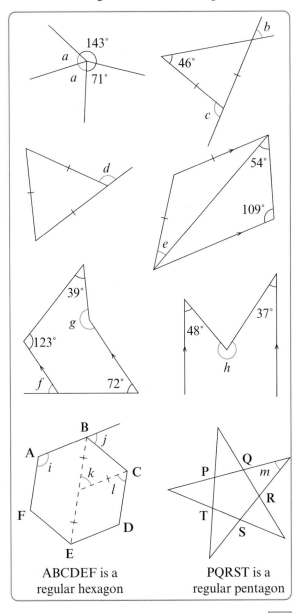

ABCDEF is a regular hexagon

PQRST is a regular pentagon

Manipulation

1 Multiply these terms.

    a $mn \times mn$ **b** $pq \times 4p$ **c** $9b \times 2a^2$

    d $a^3 \times g^3$ **e** $4p \times 5p^2$ **f** $7a^3 \times 4b$

2 Multiply out these brackets.

    a $6(4a - 3b)$ **b** $p(n - p)$ **c** $s(s + t)$

    d $6m(n - m)$ **e** $5x(x + y)$ **f** $u(4u + 3)$

    g $p(5q + 3r)$ **h** $3n(4m + 7n)$ **i** $9a(3b + a)$

3 Simplify these.

    a $8n + 4m - 6n + 3m$ **b** $12a^2 - a + 9a^2$

    c $b^3 + 2b - b^3$ **d** $8x - 4xy - 2y + 6xy$

    e $p + 8q - 5q + 3p$ **f** $8p^2 + 3pq + 5q^2 - pq$

    g $4m^2 + mn - 6n + nm$ **h** $x + 2xy + x - 4xy$

4 Which of these expressions is equivalent to
$4a(2ab + 3a) + a(5b - a) + 4b(2a^2 + 5a)$?

    A $35a^2b + 11a^2$

    B $12a^2b + 14ab + 7a^2$

    C $41ab + 10a$

    D $16a^2b + 11a^2 + 25ab$

5 Multiply these out and simplify

    a $x(6x - 2) + 2x(5x + 3)$

    b $8x(2y + 3x) + x(6x - 3y)$

    c $6(p + 2q) - 3(4p + 2q)$

    d $4(3a + b) - (3a - 2b)$

    e $p(5p - 4) - 2(2p^2 - 3)$

6 Write each of these as a single fraction.

    a $\dfrac{3}{p + 1} + \dfrac{5}{p - 1}$ **b** $\dfrac{5}{p + 4} - \dfrac{3}{p + 2}$

    c $\dfrac{1}{2p + 1} + \dfrac{3}{3p - 2}$ **d** $\dfrac{p + 4}{3} - \dfrac{p - 3}{6}$

7 Write an expression for the width of rectangles A and B.

8 Factorise these fully.

    a $7p + 3pq$ **b** $m + 3mn$ **c** $8pq + 4q$

    d $3y - 12xy$ **e** $2b^2 + 10b$ **f** $18ab + 24bc$

    g $x^2y - 2xy$ **h** $9a^2b + 6ab^2$ **i** $12m^2n - 9mn$

9 Multiply out these brackets and simplify.

    a $(w + 2)(w + 6)$ **b** $(y + 9)(y + 5)$

    c $(x - 3)^2$ **d** $(v - 2)(v - 3)$

    e $(b - 3)(b + 5)$ **f** $(b - 3)(b - 5)$

    g $(h + 5)(h - 5)$ **h** $(t - 3)(t + 3)$

10 Multiply out these brackets and simplify.

    a $(2w - 3)(2w + 3)$ **b** $(2p + 1)^2$

    c $(5x + 6)(3x - 2)$ **d** $(3g - 7)(4g - 5)$

11 $x + 1$ $x + 2$ $x + 3$ $x + 4$ $x + 6$ $x + 12$

Which pair of expressions multiply to give:

    a $x^2 + 7x + 12$ **b** $x^2 + 8x + 12$ **c** $x^2 + 7x + 6$

    d $x^2 + 5x + 6$ **e** $x^2 + 13x + 12$ **f** $x^2 + 6x + 8$?

12 Factorise the following expressions.

    a $x^2 + 4x + 4$ **b** $x^2 + 9x + 20$ **c** $x^2 + 3x - 4$

    d $x^2 + 2x - 15$ **e** $x^2 - x - 6$ **f** $x^2 - 11x + 10$

    g $x^2 - 2x - 8$ **h** $x^2 - 3x + 2$ **i** $x^2 - 4x + 4$

13 Simplify each of these

    a $\dfrac{3x - 6}{x^2 + x - 6}$ **b** $\dfrac{6(x - 3) - 2(x - 3)}{x^2 + 3x - 18}$

14 $x - 6$ $x - 3$ $x - 2$ $x + 1$ $x + 2$ $x + 3$

Which pair of expressions multiply to give:

    a $x^2 + x - 6$ **b** $x^2 - 2x - 3$ **c** $x^2 - 5x + 6$

    d $x^2 - 4$ **e** $x^2 + 5x + 6$ **f** $x^2 - 9$?

15 Factorise these fully.

    a $3x^2 + 13x + 12$ **b** $3x^2 - 15x + 12$

    c $2x^2 - 9x + 4$ **d** $6x^2 - 3x - 3$

    e $3x^2 - 6x$ **f** $9x^2 - 25y^2$

16 Find the values of p and q such that for all values of x:

    a $x^2 - px + 16 = (x - q)^2$ **b** $x^2 - 6x + p = (x - q)^2$

17 Write each of these as a single fraction in its simplest form.

    a $\dfrac{4}{p - 3} + \dfrac{3}{p + 1}$ **b** $\dfrac{2}{(a - b)^2} - \dfrac{3}{2(a - b)}$

    c $\dfrac{15p^2}{8a} \div \dfrac{10p}{12a^3}$ **d** $\dfrac{2}{p + 1} \times \dfrac{3}{p - 1}$

18 **a** Factorise $p^2 - q^2$.

    b In the equation $p^2 - q^2 = 149$,
       p and q are positive integers.

       i Explain why there is only one solution.

       ii Explain why $(p - q)$ must equal 1.

       iii Find the value of p and q.

19 Use the difference of two squares to calculate the exact value of:
$132\,413\,241\,324^2 - 132\,413\,241\,323^2$

20 Copy and complete:

    $\dfrac{\square\square\square}{x + 1} + \dfrac{3}{x} = \dfrac{x^2 + 5x + 3}{x(x + 1)}$

Comparing data

1 These are the round scores from a competition.

| 60 68 52 68 |
| 64 72 64 **Dina** |

| 57 61 59 |
| 68 61 75 **Cian** |

| 58 59 63 65 57 |
| 70 68 74 **Joe** |

For each set of scores, calculate:

a the mean
b the standard deviation.

2 If Joe had scored 15 less in each round, what would the mean and standard deviation of his scores have been?

3 Dina improved each of her round scores by 25% in the next competition.
Give the new mean and standard deviation.

4

| Ring score | 2 | 3 | 4 | 5 | 6 | 7 | 8 | 9 |
| Frequency | 2 | 1 | 3 | 2 | 3 | 6 | 4 | 3 | **Sally** |

| Ring score | 2 | 3 | 4 | 5 | 6 | 7 | 8 | 9 |
| Frequency | 1 | 1 | 3 | 7 | 14 | 13 | 6 | 7 |
| **Gavin** |

a For each distribution, calculate:
  i the mean
  ii the standard deviation
b Compare the two distributions.

5

Peggy

| Ring score | 2 | 3 | 4 | 5 | 6 | 7 | 8 |
| Frequency | 1 | 0 | 2 | 3 | 5 | 4 | 1 |

| Ring score | 3 | 4 | 5 | 6 | 7 | 8 | 9 |
| Frequency | 2 | 4 | 5 | 4 | 6 | 0 | 1 |
Toby

| Ring score | 2 | 3 | 4 | 5 | 6 | 7 | 8 | 9 |
| Frequency | 2 | 1 | 3 | 2 | 3 | 6 | 4 | 3 |
| **Sue** |

a For each distribution:
  i find the median
  ii calculate the interquartile range.
b Compare the three distributions.

| Number of chips | | | | | | | | | |
Restaurant	34	35	36	37	38	39	40	41	Total
P	8	10	14	9	6	5	4	4	60
Q	8	7	5	9	12	11	8	0	60
R	0	3	5	10	12	14	10	6	60

6 For each restaurant:
  a find the median number of chips
  b calculate the interquartile range
  c draw a box-and-whisker plot.

7 a Draw frequency polygons for restaurant P and restaurant R on the same diagram.
  b Compare the two distributions.

8

Explain why each of these diagrams is misleading.

9

𝒲𝒟	**Wilton Dale Theme Parks**		
		1994	**1996**
A	Number of injuries	21	14
B	Number of rides	6	15

Draw a misleading diagram to show each of these sets of data.

Sequences

1   Each diagram shows the first three patterns in a sequence.

Sequence W

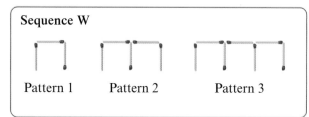

Pattern 1   Pattern 2   Pattern 3

Sequence X

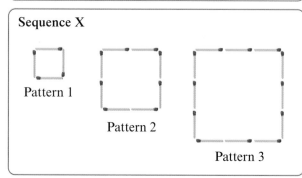

Pattern 1

Pattern 2

Pattern 3

Sequence Y

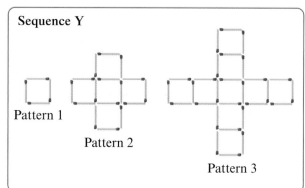

Pattern 1

Pattern 2

Pattern 3

For each sequence:

  a   Draw the 4th pattern.
  b   Find the general term for the sequence. Write it in the form $a_n = \ldots$.
  c   Use the general term to calculate the number of matches in the 10th pattern.

2   Copy and complete each mapping diagram.

a

b
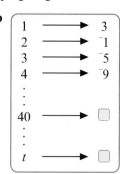

3   These are the first three patterns in a sequence.

Sequence Z

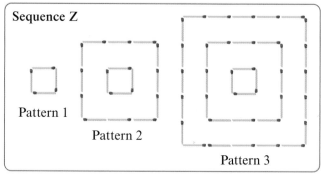

Pattern 1

Pattern 2

Pattern 3

  a   Find a rule for the number of matches in the nth pattern in the form $n \longrightarrow \ldots$.
  b   Show how you found your rule.

4   **A**   1, 4, 7, 10, 13, …
     B   7, 13, 19, 25, 31, …
     C   2, 6, 10, 14, 18, …
     D   7, 12, 17, 22, 27, …
     E   11, 8, 5, 2, ¯1, …
     F   14, 5, ¯4, ¯13, ¯22, …

For each of the sequences A to F:

  a   Find the general term, g_n.
  b   Calculate g_{30}.

5   Give the general term for each of these sequences.

  a   2, 5, 10, 17, 26, …
  b   11, 8, 3, ¯4, ¯13, …
  c   ¯1, 2, 7, 14, 23, …
  d   1, 4, 9, 16, 25, …
  e   6, 12, 22, 36, 54, …
  f   ¯898, ¯895, ¯890, ¯883, ¯874, …

6   For each of the following sequences where $u_1 = 1$:

  a   Calculate u_4.
  b   State if the sequence diverges or converges and any limit it approaches.

  A $u_{n+1} = u_n(u_n + 4)$

  B $u_{n+1} = \dfrac{u_n + 1}{2}$

  C $u_{n+1} = \dfrac{u_n + 2}{u_n}$

  D $u_{n+1} = \dfrac{9u_n + 5}{2u_n}$

Constructions and loci

1 Construct these triangles accurately.
Show all your construction lines.

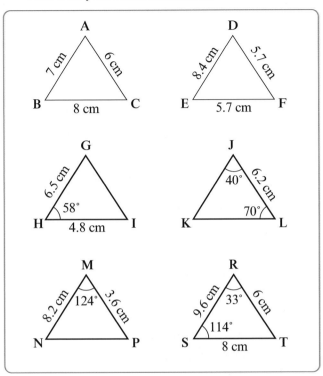

2 Copy each line full size and contruct a
perpendicular bisector of it.

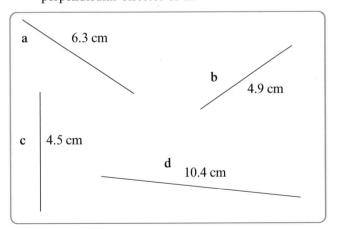

3 Draw each angle accurately and construct its
bisector.

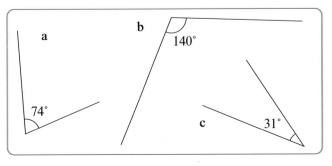

4 For each pair of triangles, state if they are congruent
or not necessarily so and, if congruent, state the case
of congruence.

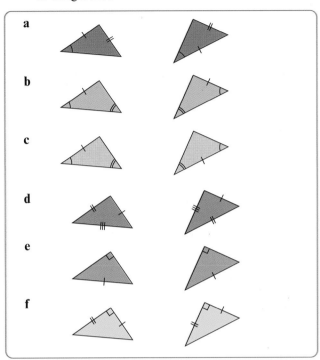

5 A field for the village fete is shaped as a triangle
with these dimensions.

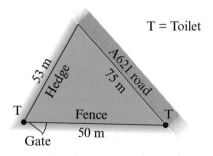

Colonel Briggs Shilton has set out these conditions
for the position of the drinks tent.

Condition 1	The tent must be equidistant from the hedge and the fence.
Condition 2	The distance from each toilet to the tent must be equal.

a Construct a scale drawing of the field to a
scale of 1 to 1000.
b Find by construction the position of the tent.
c Why is this position not a sensible one?
d Give some different conditions which you think
puts the tent in a better position.

Powers and Roots

1 Which of these are not integers?

   a $\sqrt[4]{40}$ **b** $\sqrt[5]{7776}$ **c** $\sqrt[3]{3}$

   d $\sqrt[7]{(-1)}$ **e** $\sqrt[5]{10}$ **f** $\sqrt[9]{1}$

2 Evaluate:

   a $\sqrt[3]{64}$ **b** $\sqrt[6]{0.046656}$

   c $\sqrt[5]{(-243)}$ **d** $\sqrt[5]{1.61051}$

3 Evaluate correct to 1 decimal place:

   a $\sqrt[3]{15}$ **b** $\sqrt[6]{20}$ **c** $\sqrt[4]{24}$

4 Evaluate as a fraction:

   a 4^{-3} **b** $\sqrt[4]{\dfrac{81}{625}}$ **c** $\sqrt[3]{\dfrac{1}{343}}$

5 Find the value of x when:

   a $\sqrt[5]{x} = 1.3$ **b** $\sqrt[x]{10.4976} = 1.8$

   c $\sqrt[x]{512} = 2$ **d** $\sqrt[7]{x} = -0.0000128$

6 Give the answer to each of these using index notation.

   a $4^5 \times 4^3$ **b** $3^2 \times 3^{-3}$ **c** $2^4 \times 2^{-4}$

   d $(2^3)^4$ **e** $(6^7)^{-2}$ **f** $6^5 \div 6^3$

   g $6^3 \div 6^5$ **h** $(6^{-2})^7$

7 To what power must 2^3 be raised to give:

   a 2^9 **b** 2^{-6} **c** $\dfrac{1}{2^3}$?

8 Simplify as far as you can:

   a $y^2 \times y^3$ **b** $(y^6)^5$ **c** $(3y^2)^4$

   d $3y^5 \times 4y^2$ **e** $\dfrac{y^5}{y^4}$ **f** $\dfrac{4y^3}{2y^7}$

   g $\dfrac{2y^3 \times 6y^5}{4y^2}$ **h** $\dfrac{4y \times 3y^4}{6y^7}$ **i** $\dfrac{11y^5}{2y^2 \times 5y^3}$

9 Find two sets of equivalent expressions.

   Ⓐ $3^{\frac{2}{5}}$ Ⓑ $\dfrac{1}{\sqrt{3^5}}$ Ⓒ $3^{\frac{5}{2}}$ Ⓓ $\sqrt[5]{3^2}$

   Ⓔ $\sqrt{3^5}$ Ⓕ $\dfrac{1}{\sqrt[5]{3^2}}$ Ⓖ $(\sqrt{3})^{-5}$ Ⓗ $3^{-\frac{2}{5}}$

10 Evaluate these as integers or in fractional form.

   a $49^{\frac{1}{2}}$ **b** $81^{\frac{1}{2}}$ **c** $27^{\frac{1}{3}}$

   d $343^{\frac{1}{3}}$ **e** $1^{\frac{1}{4}}$ **f** $625^{\frac{1}{4}}$

   g $243^{-\frac{1}{5}}$ **h** $(-1024)^{\frac{1}{5}}$ **i** $32^{\frac{1}{5}}$

   j $16^{-\frac{1}{2}}$ **k** $216^{-\frac{1}{3}}$ **l** $729^{-\frac{1}{6}}$

   m $343^{\frac{2}{3}}$ **n** $256^{\frac{3}{4}}$ **o** $32^{\frac{2}{5}}$

   p $64^{\frac{5}{6}}$ **q** $512^{\frac{2}{3}}$ **r** $625^{\frac{3}{4}}$

   s $32^{\frac{3}{5}}$ **t** $243^{\frac{4}{5}}$ **u** $729^{\frac{5}{6}}$

   v $27^{\frac{4}{3}}$ **w** $64^{-\frac{2}{3}}$ **x** $256^{-\frac{3}{4}}$

   y $243^{-\frac{3}{5}}$ **z** $64^{-\frac{5}{2}}$

11 Solve these equations.

   a $121^{\frac{1}{x}} = 11$ **b** $3^x = \dfrac{1}{27}$

   c $27^x = 3$ **d** $729^{\frac{1}{x}} = 3$

   e $2^{3x+1} = 16$ **f** $3^{2x-1} = \dfrac{1}{81}$

   g $125^x = 25$ **h** $81^x = 729$

   i $x^{\frac{4}{3}} = 16$ **j** $25^x = \dfrac{1}{5}$

   k $343^x = \dfrac{1}{49}$ **l** $x^{-\frac{2}{5}} = \dfrac{1}{16}$

12 Simplify as far as you can:

   a $(\sqrt{6})^2$ **b** $\left(\frac{1}{5}\sqrt{5}\right)^2$

   c $\sqrt{2} \times \sqrt{7}$ **d** $\sqrt{5} \times \sqrt{20}$

   e $(\sqrt{3} + \sqrt{5})^2$ **f** $(\sqrt{7} - \sqrt{2})^2$

   g $\sqrt{14} \div \sqrt{7}$ **h** $(2\sqrt{5} + 1)^2$

   i $(\sqrt{11} - 3)^2$

13 Write each of these recurring decimals as a fraction in its lowest terms.

   a $0.333333\ldots$ **b** $0.363636\ldots$

   c $0.010101\ldots$ **d** $0.126126\ldots$

   e $0.\dot{5}$ **f** $0.\dot{0}\dot{9}$

   g $0.\dot{8}5714\dot{2}$ **h** $0.\dot{2}\dot{7}$

14

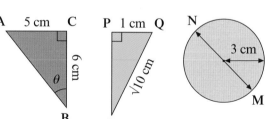

Which of these lengths are rational?

   a AB

   b PR

   c MN

   d the perimeter of triangle ABC

   e the circumference of the circle

Approximation and Errors

1 Round each number to the degree of accuracy stated:

a 5.674   (2 dp)
b 12.652   (1 dp)
c 12.652   (1 sf)
d 2143   (nearest ten)
e 15.77777   (4 sf)
f 93747656   (5 sf)
g 15.986   (2 sf)
h 456.21345   (1 sf)

2 By approximating each number to 1 sf calculate approximate answers to each of these.

a 84.3×452.53
b 4.876×37.71
c 5683.2×0.0372
d 458.12×518
e $734.6 \div 2.316$
f $0.005\,682\,43 \div 7.8931$
g $419\,52 + 77442$
h $\dfrac{34.6296 + 87.3}{0.003\,21}$
i $\dfrac{6834 \times 1939.453}{54.26}$
j $\dfrac{45.95 \times (2.943\,56)^2}{(0.067)^2}$

3 Work out approximate answers by rounding each part first to 1 sf then calculate the percentage error produced by doing this.

a 56.6×21.5
b 4924×3.7
c $246.3 \div 9.67$
d $54.27 \times (21.6)^3$
e $\dfrac{17.63 \times 1839}{(54.64)^2}$

4 State both the upper and lower bound for each number when it is given correct to the degree of accuracy stated.

a 5.6   given to 1 dp
b 54   given to nearest whole number
c 690   given to nearest ten
d 56.372   given to 3 dp
e 65.00   given to 2 dp
f 100   given to 1 sf
g 100   given to 2 sf
h 160 000   given to 4 sf
i 12.9   given to 3 sf
j 16 million   given to nearest ten thousand
k 1000.00   given to 2 dp
l 7.0001   given to 5 sf

5 The dimensions of a large room are shown on this plan and are given correct to the nearest ten centimetres.

a Calculate the range of values that the perimeter could have.
b Calculate the upper and lower bounds for the floor area.
c The floor is to be covered with carpet at £11 per square metre (to the nearest pound). Calculate the range of values for the cost of the carpet used.

6 A scooter covers a distance of 1320 metres (to the nearest ten metres) in 60 seconds (to the nearest 10 seconds).
Calculate the range of values for its speed in metres per second.

7 The volume V of a sphere is given by $V = \frac{4}{3}\pi r^3$ where r is its radius.
A spherical gas tank has a radius of 3.2 metres, to the nearest ten centimetres.

Calculate the upper and lower bounds for the volume of the tank.

8 Convert these numbers into standard form.

a 435 000   **b** 12 million
c 0.000 321   **d** 54.267 45
e 654×10^6 **f** 654×10^{-4}

9 Convert these into ordinary numbers.

a 5.23×10^3 **b** 1.5×10^{-6}
c 1.094×10^{-1} **d** 3×10^{-2}

10 Calculate the value of each of these giving your answers in standard form.

a $(3.42 \times 10^3)^2 \times (1.35 \times 10^{-2})$
b $\dfrac{(4 \times 10^3) + (5 \times 10^2)}{2 \times 10^{-5}}$
c $\dfrac{(4.2 \times 10^{-4}) - (4.2 \times 10^{-5})}{(4.2 \times 10^3) - (4.2 \times 10^2)}$
d $(9 \times 10^{-2})^3 - (9 \times 10^3)^{-2}$
e $(9 \times 10^{-2})^3 - (9 \times 10^{-3})^2$

Solving equations algebraically

1 Solve these equations.

   a $3(2x - 5) = 12$ **b** $4(5x + 1) = 3(4x + 12)$

   c $5(6x + 9) = 12x$ **d** $3(x + 1) = 9(5x - 9)$

   e $\frac{2}{3}(x - 1) = 8$ **f** $\frac{4}{5}(2x + 3) = 14$

   g $\frac{3}{4}(2x - 4) = 2(x + 5)$

   h $\frac{2}{3}(x - 1) = \frac{3}{5}(x + 4)$

   i $\dfrac{5}{2x - 1} = 10$

   j $\dfrac{3}{x - 1} = \dfrac{5}{2x - 3}$

   k $\dfrac{3(2x - 1)}{4} = \dfrac{2(6x + 3)}{5}$

2 The perimeter of a rectangle is 86 cm.
The long side is 9 cm longer than the short side.

   Write and solve an equation to find the dimensions of the rectangle.

3 Remove the brackets from these expressions.

   a $(x + 3)(x - 5)$ **b** $(2x - 1)(x - 3)$
   c $(4 - 5x)(3x + 2)$ **d** $(x - 3)(3 - 4x)$
   e $(x + 4)(x - 4)$ **f** $(2x - 3)(2x + 3)$
   g $x^2(x - 4)$ **h** $2x(x^2 + 3x - 8)$
   i $3x(x^3 + 5x^2 + 4x - 1)$
   j $(x + 3)(x^2 + 6x - 7)$
   k $(x - 5)(3 + 5x - x^2)$
   l $(x^2 + 8x - 15)(4 + x)$
   m $(x + 1)(x + 2)(x - 3)$

4 Solve each pair of simultaneous equations.

   a $2x + 3y = 9$ **b** $4x - 3y = 5$
      $5x - 4y = 11$ $5x + 7y = 17$

   c $6x + 3y = 3$ **d** $8x - 3y = 30$
      $5x + 2y = 3$ $5x - 2y = 19$

   e $7x - 2y = {}^-11$ **f** $3x + 9y = 15$
      $3x + 5y = 7$ $4x + 5y = 6$

   g $2x + 7y = 29$ **h** $3x - 5y = 10$
      $3x - 4y = {}^-29$ $5x - 7y = 6$

   i $4x + y = {}^-11$ **j** $13x - 7y = 66$
      $3x + 5y = {}^-21$ $9x + 15y = 6$

5 Two numbers are such that when you add three times the first number to three times the second number the answer is 3. The difference between the first and second numbers is 9.

   What are the two numbers?

6 Gareth pays for a holiday with a mixture of £5 and £10 notes. the holiday costs £365 and this is paid with a total of 55 notes.

   How many of each type of note were used to pay for the holiday?

7 A shop sells two types of calculator: Scientific and Graphical.
Customer A orders 35 Scientific and 72 Graphical calculators at a total cost of £1228.15
Customer B orders 124 Scientific and 15 Graphical calculators at a total cost of £1242.05

   Calculate the price of each type of calculator.

8 A bag contains a mixture of 5 pence and 20 pence coins. There are 2250 coins in the bag. If the monetary value of the coins in the bag is £183.30, how many of each type of coin is in the bag?

9 A bag contains large and small marbles, and there are 378 marbles in the bag.
Each small marble weighs 2.5 g and each large marble weighs 4.8 g. The total weight of the marbles in the bag is 1.4349 kg.

   Calculate how many of each type of marble is in the bag.

10 Solve these quadratic equations by factorising.

   a $x^2 + 5x - 84 = 0$ **b** $x^2 - 8x + 7 = 0$
   c $x^2 + 3x - 54 = 0$ **d** $x^2 - 15x + 36 = 0$
   e $x^2 + 8x + 12 = 0$ **f** $x^2 - 4x - 320 = 0$
   g $x^2 - 11x - 60 = 0$ **h** $x^2 - 14x + 48 = 0$
   i $x^2 + 6x = 135$ **j** $x^2 - 8x = 65$
   k $x^2 + 20 = 9x$ **l** $x^2 + 28 = 16x$
   m $x^2 = 3x$ **n** $x^2 - 64 = 0$
   o $x^2 - 196 = 0$ **p** $x^2 - 10\,000 = 0$
   q $2x^2 - 5x - 3 = 0$ **r** $2x^2 + 6x - 20 = 0$
   s $3x^2 + x - 2 = 0$ **t** $3x^2 + x - 4 = 0$
   u $6x^2 - x - 2 = 0$ **v** $6x^2 + 35x - 6 = 0$
   w $8x^2 + 14x - 4 = 0$ **x** $18x^2 + 3x - 6 = 0$

11 Solve these equations to 2 dp.

   a $x^2 - 5x + 3 = 0$ **b** $x^2 + 6x - 2 = 0$
   c $x^2 + 8x + 1 = 0$ **d** $x^2 - 3x - 1 = 0$
   e $x^2 + x - 5 = 0$ **f** $x^2 + 2x - 7 = 0$
   g $x^2 - 3x - 2 = 0$ **h** $x^2 + 6x - 8 = 0$
   i $x^2 - 4x - 3 = 0$ **j** $x^2 - x - 3 = 0$
   k $x^2 + 6x + 3 = 0$ **l** $x^2 + x - 1 = 0$
   m $2x^2 + 3x - 6 = 0$ **n** $3x^2 + x - 3 = 0$
   o $4x^2 + x - 1 = 0$ **p** $7x^2 + 3x = 5$

12 Solve these equations using iteration.

   a $x^2 + 6x - 15 = 0$ **b** $x^2 - 6x + 4 = 0$
   c $x^2 - 4x - 30 = 0$ **d** $x^2 + 2x - 16 = 0$

Transformations

1 Draw the pentagon A on axes with: $^-12 \leqslant x \leqslant 6$ and $^-6 \leqslant y \leqslant 6$.

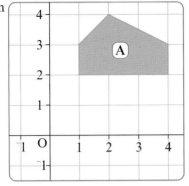

2 Draw the image of A after:

a an enlargement SF $^-2$ with centre ($^-1$, 1)

b an enlargement SF $\frac{1}{2}$ with centre (7, $^-4$).

3 These transformations map A on to B, C, D, E and F.

Object	Transformation	Image
A	Rotate $^+90°$ about (0, 0)	B
A	Rotate $^-90°$ about (1, 1)	C
A	Reflect in x = 5	D
A	Rotate $^+90°$ about (6, 2)	E
A	Reflect in y = ^-x	F

a On a new diagram, on axes with $^-6 \leqslant x \leqslant 10$ and $^-6 \leqslant y \leqslant 6$, draw and label the images B, C, D, E and F.

b Describe the transformation that maps:
  i C on to A   **ii** D on to A.

c Describe the inverse of the transformation that maps:
  i A on to E   **ii** A on to F.

d For each of these mappings which pentagon is the image of B?

	Object	Transformation	Image
i	B	Enlarge SF 1 with centre (0, 1)	
ii	B	Reflect in y = 0	
iii	B	Translate $\begin{pmatrix} 8 \\ 4 \end{pmatrix}$	

e Describe a transformation that maps C on to E.

4

Transformations			
Object	First	Second	Image
A	Rotate $^+90°$ about (0, 1)	Reflect in y = 0	G
A	Reflect in y = 0	Rotate $^+90°$ about (0, 1)	H

a On a new diagram draw the images G and H.

b What single transformation maps G on to H?

c In the table below, each pair of transformations maps G on to H.
Describe each of the second transformations.

	Object	Image	First transformation	Second transforma
i	G	H	Translate $\begin{pmatrix} 6 \\ 0 \end{pmatrix}$	
ii	G	H	Rotate $^-90°$ about (1, $^-2$)	
iii	G	H	Rotate 180° about (0, $^-1$)	

5 These transformations map A on to J, K L and M.

Transformations			
Object	First	Second	Image
A	Enlarge SF 2 with centre (0, 1)	Reflect in y = 1	J
A	Reflect in x = 1	Enlarge SF 2 with centre (5, 0)	K
A	Enlarge SF 2 with centre (5, 0)	Reflect in x = 4	L
A	Enlarge SF $^-2$ with centre (5, 0)	Reflect in x = 2	M

a **i** Draw A on a new diagram with axes: $^-10 \leqslant x \leqslant 12$ and $^-10 \leqslant y \leqslant 8$.
  ii Draw and label images J, K, L and M.

b What single transformation maps:
  i J on to M   **ii** L on to J   **iii** J on to K?

6 Give three different types of transformation that are their own inverse.

Using formulas

1 Rearrange each formula to make x the subject:

a $3x + 5a = 4$	**b** $2(3 - x) = a + 1$
c $3(a - 2x) = b$	**d** $3x - 1 = 2(a - 2x)$
e $3a(x + a) = 2a$	**f** $5(1 - 2x) = 3(x - a)$
g $3a^2x - 1 = n + 2$	**h** $y(2 + ax) = 1 - 3y$
i $ay + ax = 2 - y^2$	**j** $c^2(3a - ac + bx) = 1$
k $wx - wy = 2bc$	**l** $n(2a + ax - c) = ab$
m $b^2(a - 3x) = a^2b$	**n** $\pi(3a - xy) = 2a(\pi - 1)$
o $w(3x - 4) = w - 1$	**p** $3a + 1 = 2a(a - x)$
q $a(1 - ax) = 5a$	**r** $2(3 - 2ax) = a(1 + 3x)$
s $h = ab + 0.5cx$	**t** $ac(w^2 - 3x) = acx$

2 The formula or the cost (£C) of hiring a bicycle for n days is: $C = 5.75 + 2.4n$

Zina paid £32.15 to hire a bike while on holiday. For how many days hire was this?

3 The cost (£C) of hiring a car for n days travelling t miles is: $C = 21n + 0.15(t - 120n)$

a Calculate the cost of hiring a car to travel a total of 1654 miles over four days.
b **i** Make t the subject of the formula.
 ii £145.50 was paid for 6 days hire.
  Calculate the number of miles travelled.
c The hire charge is a fixed price per day, plus so much a mile travelled. A number of free miles are allowed each day. From the formula:
 i What is the fixed price per day?
 ii What is the charge per mile?
 iii How many free miles are allowed a day? Explain your answer.

4 Make n the subject of each formula:

a $\frac{1}{3}n = a + 2$	**b** $\frac{3n}{5} = 2(1 - x)$
c $\frac{1}{n} = \frac{2}{a}$	**d** $\frac{3x - 2}{2n} = 2a$
e $\frac{3n}{a^2 - b} = \frac{1}{2}$	**f** $2x + 3 = \frac{3}{5}(n - 1)$
g $\frac{2}{n - 3} = ax$	**h** $\frac{a}{2n} = \frac{3}{5}$
i $x^2 = \frac{3}{2n - 1}$	**j** $w = \frac{x^2}{3 - n}$
k $\frac{a}{n \cos 30°} = b$	**l** $\frac{a}{x^2} = \frac{3}{2n}$
m $\frac{2}{3n - 4} = a^2$	**n** $\frac{1}{n} = \frac{2}{a + 1}$
o $\frac{a}{b} = \frac{c}{n}$	**p** $\frac{bn}{3n - 2a} = 5$
q $\cos 30° = \frac{3}{n}$	**r** $a = \frac{x}{n - b}$
s $x^2 = \frac{2n - 3}{5}$	**t** $\frac{a}{n} + \frac{1}{n} = w$

5 Given the formula: $\frac{a}{2n} = b + c$

Explain why $n \ne \frac{1}{2}a - \frac{1}{2}(b + c)$.

6 Rewrite each of these as a formula in p.

a $px - py = 3$	**b** $pt^2 = 1 + 3p$
c $3p - 2 = ap + c$	**d** $2(3 - 2p) = a(p - 1)$
e $2(3p - 5) = a^2p$	**f** $\frac{2p + 3}{p + 1} = ab$
g $3 = \frac{p - 2x}{p}$	**h** $ap + ax = b^2p + y$
i $2a(3p - y) = p$	**j** $p \sin x + p \sin y = w$
k $3pw + 1 = p - 3$	**l** $a^2bp + 1 = b^2p$
m $1 + 2cp = ap + b$	**n** $3n(p + b) = a(p - 2b)$
o $3a + \frac{1}{p} = bc$	**p** $\frac{2}{3}(p + 1) = 2(1 - ap)$
q $\frac{1}{4}(2p + 1) = an$	**r** $b(3 + ap) = \frac{1}{3}c^2n$
s $\frac{2}{5}p + a = py$	**t** $a^2p + 2 = \frac{1}{2}(p + 2)$

7 The surface area S of a cylinder is: $S = 2\pi rh + 2\pi r^2$
Rearrange the formula to make π the subject.

8 A formula for the cost (£C) of supplying and laying n paving slabs is:
$C = 1.85n + y(n - 50)$ with a materials fee of y
a Make n the subject of the formula.
b What do you think is the cost of one slab? Explain your answer.

9 Rewrite each formula with v as the subject:

a $\sqrt{v} = (1 + x)$	**b** $3a = \sqrt{(1 - v)}$
c $2x = v\sqrt{3}$	**d** $\sqrt{(2v - 3)} = a - b$
e $a^2 = 3\sqrt{v} - 1$	**f** $2x - 1 = \sqrt{5v}$
g $4 = \sqrt{(v - 3a^2)}$	**h** $x + 3 = \frac{1}{\sqrt{v}}$
i $y^2 = v^2 + 1$	**j** $2v^2 + 1 = ax$
k $3v^2 + av^2 = 4$	**l** $3x - v^2 = v^2y$
m $ab + av^2 = bv^2$	**n** $3(2 - v^2) = a(v^2 - 2)$
o $a^2 + 1 = \frac{1}{v^2}$	**p** $kv^2 + 1 = a^2(v^2 - k)$
q $\frac{1}{3v^2} = 2a - 1$	**r** $\frac{1}{v} = \frac{v}{x + 2}$

10 A formula for the area A of a disc of inner radius r and outer radius R is: $A = \pi(R^2 - r^2)$
a Make r the subject of the formula.
b A disc has an outer radius of 7.5 cm, and an area of 91.8 cm². To 1 sf, what is the inner radius of the disc?

11 A formula linking t, a, and g is given as: $t = 2\pi\sqrt{\frac{a}{g}}$
Make g the subject of the formula.

Ratio and Proportion

1 This recipe makes 25 biscuits.

> **Chocolate Biscuits**
> 50 g icing sugar • 225 g margarine
> 100 g plain chocolate • 225 g flour

Calculate how much of each ingredient is needed to make:

a 45 biscuits **b** 10 biscuits

2 Tropical Fruit Juice is a mix of pineapple and grapefruit in the ratio 5 : 2. Calculate:

a the amount of pineapple juice to mix with 180 ml of grapefruit juice

b how much Tropical Fruit Juice is produced.

3 On a map, 3.6 cm stands for a distance of 108 m.

a What length on the map stands for 87 m?

b Give the map scale as a unitary ratio.

c Explain why the total number of parts has no meaning in this ratio.

4

 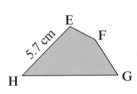

EFGH is an enlargement of JKLM.

a Calculate the scale factor of the enlargement.

b Find the length HG.

c Calculate the ratio: **i** $\dfrac{MJ}{ML}$ **ii** $\dfrac{HE}{HG}$

d Explain why the ratios are equal.

5

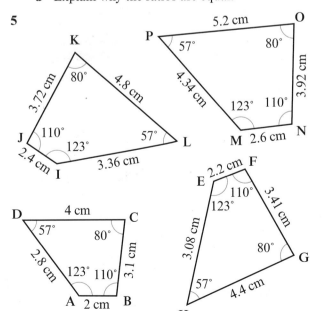

Which of these trapeziums are similar to ABCD?

6

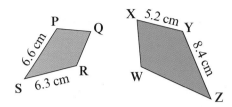

PQRS and WXYZ are similar.
Find the length: **i** QR **ii** WZ

7

AB and DC are parallel.

a Explain why ABE and BDC are similar triangles.

b Give the corresponding side to: **i** AB **ii** AE

c Find the length BE.

8

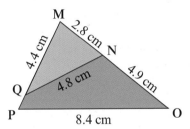

a Calculate the ratio: **i** $\dfrac{PO}{QN}$ **ii** $\dfrac{MO}{QM}$

b Explain why MOP and MQN are similar triangles.

c Find the length PQ.

9 z is in direct proportion to the square of p, and $z = 21.6$ when $p = 6$.

a Write down the relationship between z and p.

b Find the constant.

c Give an equation connecting z and p.

d Calculate z when $p = 5$.

e Rearrange your equation to give p in terms of z.

f Calculate p when $z = 86.4$.

10 Chunkie is a chocolate bar that comes in four different sizes of square prism. Each bar has the same mass of chocolate.
The length of a bar, l cm, is inversely proportional to the square of its width, w cm^2.
The 1.5 cm bar is 16 cm long.

a Give an equation connecting l and w.

b Calculate the length of a 2.5 cm Chunkie.

c Calculate the width of a Chunkie 25 cm long.

Working in 3D

1 Each of these solids is made from three cubes.

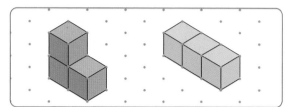

How many planes of symmetry has each solid?

2 **a** Draw a solid made from five cubes with 1 plane of symmetry.
b Draw a solid made from six cubes with 3 planes of symmetry.

3 How many planes of symmetry has:
a a cuboid with no square faces
b a cube?

4 Each prism P and Q has a capacity of one litre.

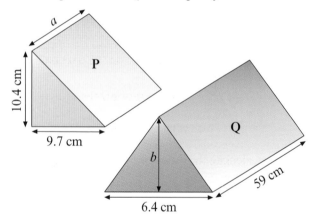

Find the values of a and b correct to 1 dp.

5 Calculate the area of the shaded ring.

6 This is a company logo. Calculate:
a its total area
b its perimeter.

7 A cylindrical cheese has a sector of angle 135° cut out vertically from one end.

7 cm radius

135°

16 cm

a Calculate the volume of the remaining piece of cheese.
b Calculate the surface area of the piece removed.

8 A bubblegum display cabinet is shaped like a frustum of a cone with a hemisphere on top.

Radius 34 cm

Radius 17 cm

60 cm

a Calculate the volume of the cabinet.
b Calculate its surface area.

9 The capacity of a hollow Russian doll is 1024 cm³.
A smaller similar doll from the set has a capacity of 640 cm³.
The height of the larger doll is 16 cm.
Calculate the height of the smaller doll.

10 In the following expressions, r, h and l each represent a length.
Decide if each expression represents:
a length, area, volume or none of these.

a $4h$ **b** h^2
c rh **d** rhl
e $2(h + l)$ **f** πr^2
g $hl + r$ **h** $\frac{1}{3}rh^2$
i $\sqrt{h^2 + l^2}$ **j** $\pi rh - 3l^2$
k $r^3 + h^2 + rl$ **l** $h^3 + rl^2$
m $5(rh + hl + rl)$ **n** $\pi rh(h + l)$
o $2h(r - l)$ **p** $\frac{4}{3}\pi(r + h)$

Probability

1. A 1 to 6 dice is rolled.
   What is the probability of getting:

   a   a multiple of 4
   b   a prime number which is a factor of 6
   c   a square number or a triangle number?

2. a   If you have six cards with the numbers 1 to 6 on them what is the probability of getting a Fibonacci number by picking a card
   b   If you have each of the first six Fibonacci numbers on six cards what is the probability of picking a card with 1 on it?

3. You roll two dice at the same time.
   What is the probability of getting:

   a   a total of 3
   b   a total score of 8
   c   a 3 on only one dice
   d   a 5 on both dice
   e   a total which is not 6?

4. In an experiment an object could land in three ways, on a face, on an edge or on a side. These are the results from a number of trials: face 68, edge 25, side 18. Calculate an estimate of the probability that the object will land:

   a   on a face
   b   not on a side
   c   on a side or a face.

5. Dom's top drawer has 2 red T-shirts, 3 blue ones and 1 yellow one. The draw below has 3 red socks 4 blue socks and 2 yellow ones. Dom is unconcerned with fashion and always picks his clothes from a drawer at random.

   a   He picks a T-shirt and one sock.
       What is the probability that:
       i   they are both blue
       ii one is yellow and one red
       iii they are the same colour?

   b   He picks two socks.
       What is the probability that:
       i   they are both red
       ii they are different colours
       iii neither of them is blue?

   c   He picks three socks.
       What is the probability that he has a pair the same colour amongst them?

   d   He picks a T-shirt and two socks.
       What is the probability that:
       i   they are all blue
       ii they are all the same colour?

6. Parveen is a disc jockey. She has 18 reggae and 14 jungle CDs to play. She chooses which CD to play at random and only plays any CD once.

   a   Draw a tree diagram to show the probabilities when she plays the first three CDs in her programme.

   b   What is the probability that the first three CDs Parveen plays:
       i   are all reggae CDs
       ii include exactly two jungle CDs
       iii include only one reggae CD
       iv have no two of the same type played consecutively.

   c   Parveen plays five CDs in the first twenty minutes of her programme. What is the probability that they are:
       i   all jungle
       ii all the same type?

7. The probability that snow will fall on the roof of the Weather Centre in London on a day in December is 0.07. If snow falls on one day, the probability that it will snow on the next day increases to 0.15.

   a   Draw a tree diagram to show the probabilities for two consecutive days in December.
       What is the probability that:
       i   there will be snow on both days
       ii there will be snow on only one day
       iii there will be no snow on either day?

   b   For three consecutive days in December calculate the probability that there will be snow:
       i   on only one day
       ii on all three days
       iii on exactly two days.

8. Amongst a group of 30 British students, 18 speak some French and 14 speak some German but 6 speak neither language.

   a   Draw a Venn diagram to show the information.
   b   What is the probability that a person chosen at random:
       i   speaks only German
       ii speaks both foreign languages
       iii speaks only one foreign language
       iv does not speak French?

Grouped data

⬭⬭⬭ 1996 Olympic Games – Men's Marathon
Top 100 finishers

Time (min)	132 –	137 –	139 –	142 –	146 –	150 – 157
Frequency	15	18	18	20	11	18

1 a Draw a histogram to show these times.
  b (Do **not** use the statistical function on your calculator to answer this question.)
  Calculate an estimate of the mean time.
  c Draw a cumulative frequency curve for the men's marathon.
  d Estimate:
    i the median time
    ii the interquartile range of the times.
  e Estimate how many times were:
    i less than 135 minutes
    ii greater than 155 minutes
    iii between 140 and 150 minutes.

⬭⬭⬭ 1996 Olympic Games
Women's Marathon
Top 60 finishers

Time	Frequency
146 –	5
151 –	9
154 –	8
156 –	12
158 –	9
162 –	10
167 – 176	7

2 a Draw a histogram to show these times.
  b Use your calculator to estimate the mean time.
  c Draw a cumulative frequency curve for the women's marathon.
  d Estimate:
    i the median time
    ii the interquartile range of the times.
  e Estimate how many times were:
    i less than 150 minutes
    ii greater than 165 minutes
    iii between 150 and 160 minutes.

3 Use your answers to Questions **1** and **2** to compare the marathon times for men and women.

⬭⬭⬭ 1996 Olympic Games
GB Athletics Team

Age	Frequency Track	Field
18 –	7	2
23 –	27	10
28 –	20	7
33 – 42	5	4
Totals	59	23

4 a Draw a histogram to show the age distribution of:
    i track athletes   **ii** field athletes.
  b Explain why drawing frequency polygons on the same diagram would not give a fair comparison of the ages of track athletes and field athletes.
  c Use your calculator to estimate the mean for:
    i track athletes   **ii** field athletes.
  d Compare the two distributions.

⬭⬭⬭ 1996 Olympic Games – Great Britain Team
Ages of Competitors at 20/7/96

```
22 21 29 18 26 16 23 23 28 31 26 29 27 20 27 20
20 24 19 23 21 24 25 18 21 20 21 23 26 20 21 19
21 31 30 24 27 31 27 23 30 35 27 25 23 22 27 36
27 24 20 23 27 27 26 30 35 23 30 24 29 24 24 31
31 26 23 19 29 29 27 24 32 32 25 23 24 21 38 39
28 25 32 31 27 31 24 21 30 32 24 29 38 29 34 22
29 23 24 29 32 24 40 30 24 21 23 27 31 22 23 29
35 31 24 24 22 32 23 29 27 30 27 26 21 27 29 26
23 21 22 25 27 32 26 26 28 29 22 25 37 25 18 22
29 35 34 32 30 25 29 28 27 35 25 28 34 29 29 28
23 27 22 27 34 35 30 30 41 37 40 31 27 26 35 31
33 38 42 35 36 40 36 29 20 16 22 16 26 23 21 29
29 27 27 23 28 25 34 30 27 28 30 23 33 20 33 26
26 29 30 29 29 25 28 27 25 24 28 31 32 27 25 26
26 31 23 23 21 30 20 32 28 35 31 28 24 29 24 27
24 30 27 28 27 26 28 29 34 22 27 32 26 24 27 20
27 22 29 28 31 26 24 25 28 30 34 27 24 30 21 30
21 29 21 27 27 28 48 19 34 47 31 36 25 29 28 29
21 27 22 28 31 26 23 25 19 29 31 30 25 32 24 29
28 28 25 29 30 26 29 34
```

5 a Group this age data using a class interval of 2.
  b Combine some of your classes at each end of the distribution.
  c Use your new groupings to draw a histogram.
  d The age data is listed at random. Choose a systematic sample of:
    i 20   **ii** 40   **iii** 80
  e For each of your random samples:
    i group the data   **ii** draw a histogram
  f Compare the shape of your distributions.

Solving equations graphically

1 Solve each pair of equations graphically.

   a $x + 4y = 6$
       $2x + 5y = 9$

   b $5x - 3y = 8$
       $3x + y = 2$

   c $5x + 7y = 29$
       $x + 3y = 9$

   d $3x + 2y = 15$
       $4x - 2y = 13$

   e $5x - 4y = 14$
       $3x + 2y = 4$

   f $3y + 2x = 2$
       $2y - 6x = {}^-17$

   g $4y + 2x = 23$
       $2y - 6x = 1$

   h $4x - 5y = 3$
       $2x + 3y = 18$

   i $2x + 3y = 16$
       $4x - y = 11$

   j $2x - 3y = {}^-2$
       $2x + 2y = 13$

2 Give the line of symmetry for each of these graphs.

   a $y = x^2 + 8$
   b $y = x^2 + 4x$
   c $y = x^2 - 8x$
   d $y = x^2 + 6x - 4$
   e $y = 12x - x^2$
   f $y = 5 - 8x - x^2$

3 For x: ${}^-4 \leqslant x \leqslant 4$ draw graphs of these curves on the same axes.

   a $y = x^2 - 2x - 5$
   b $y = 4x - x^2$

4 For x: ${}^-5 \leqslant x \leqslant 5$ draw graphs of these curves on the same axes.

   a $y = 2x^2 + 3x$
   b $y = 3x^2 - x$

5 For x: ${}^-8 \leqslant x \leqslant 6$ draw the graph of $y = x^2 + 3x - 5$.

   a Use the graph to solve these equations.
      i $x^2 + 3x - 5 = 4$
     ii $x^2 + 3x - 5 = {}^-3$
    iii $x^2 + 3x - 5 = 12.5$

   b What can you say about any values you read from the graph?

6 For values of x: ${}^-3 \leqslant x \leqslant 5$ draw the graph of $y = x^2 - 2.5$.

   a On the same axes draw the graph of $y = 1.5x$.
   b Use the graphs to solve the equation
        $x^2 - 2.5 = 1.5x$

7 Draw a suitable graph and solve the equation
        $(x - 4)^2 - 12 = 0$

8 For values of x from ${}^-2$ to 6 draw the graph of $y = 2x(x - 4) - 10$.

   Use the graph to solve $2x(x - 4) = 10$.

9 For x: ${}^-5 \leqslant x \leqslant 5$ draw the graph of $y = x^2 + 6x - 2$.

   a By drawing an additional graph use the graph to solve $x^2 + 4x + 1 = x + 4$.
   b Explain how you can use your graph to solve the equation $x^2 + x + 2 = 7 - 7x$.
   c Find an approximate value for x that will satisfy $x^2 + x + 2 = 7 - 7x$.

10 On a pair of axes draw a graph of $y = \dfrac{6}{x} - 4$.
   Use x: ${}^-5 \leqslant x \leqslant 5$.

11 For x: ${}^-6 \leqslant x \leqslant 6$ draw the graph of
   $y = \dfrac{12}{x} + 8$.

   Give the equation of any asymptotes to the graph.

12 For $x : 1 \leqslant x \leqslant 10$ draw the graph of
   $y = x + \dfrac{10}{x} - 12$.

   Use the graph to find approximate values for:
   a the minimum value of y
   b x when $y = {}^-3.4$.

13 For values of x from ${}^-4$ to 5 draw the graph of $y = x^3 + 4$.

14 On the same axes draw the graphs of:
   a $y = x^3 + 5$
   b $y = 5 - x^3$

15 Draw the graph of $y = x^3 - 2x^2$ for values of x from ${}^-4$ to 4.

   a Use the graph to solve $x^3 - 2x^2 = 0$.
   b From the graph find an approximate value for x when $y = 10.4$.

16 Sketch and label these graphs.
   a $y = 5x + 2$
   b $y = x^2 - 6$
   c $y = x^3 + 1$

17 Show how completing the square helps to sketch the graph of $y = x^2 + 6x - 1$.

18 For the graph of $y = x^2 + 4x - 6$ give:
   a the minimum value of y
   b the point at which the minimum value of y occurs
   c the intercept with the y-axis.
   d Sketch the graph of $y = x^2 + 4x - 6$.

Trigonometric graphs

1 The radial lines on the diagram below are drawn at intervals of 30°.

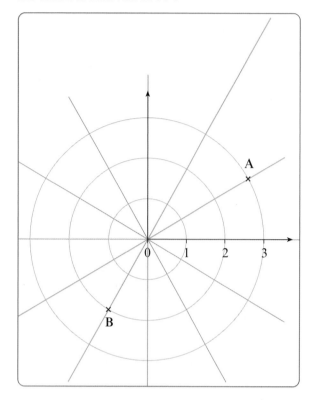

Calculate the Cartesian coordinates of points A and B.

2a Make a table of values for $y = 4 \cos 20t$ for $t = 0, 1, 2, ..., 20$.
  b Draw the graph of $y = 4 \cos 20t$ on axes with $0 \leqslant t \leqslant 20$ and $^-8 \leqslant y \leqslant 8$.
  c For what values of t is:
   i $y \leqslant 0$ **ii** $y \leqslant 2$?
  d What is the maximum value of y?
  e For what values of t is:
   i $y = 0$ **ii** $y = ^-2$?
  f **i** On the same axes sketch the graph of $y = 4 \cos 20t - 2$.
   ii Give the maximum and minimum value of $4 \cos 20t - 2$.

3 Solve each of these for $0° \leqslant x \leqslant 360°$.
Find two values of x such that:
  a $\cos x = 0.5$ **b** $\sin x = ^-0.5$
  c $\tan x = ^-1$ **d** $\sin x = \cos x$
  e $\cos x = \cos 205°$ **f** $\sin x = \sin 205°$
  g $\tan x = \tan 205°$ **h** $\sin x = \sin 105°$
  i $\cos x = \cos 105°$ **j** $\tan x = \tan 105°$

4 Solve each of these in the range $^-90 \leqslant p \leqslant 450$.
  a List all the values of p for which:
   i $\sin p = \sin 54°$ **ii** $\cos p = \cos 54°$
   iii $\tan p = \tan 54°$ **iv** $\sin p = \sin 154°$
   v $\cos p = \cos 154°$ **vi** $\tan p = \tan 154°$
  b Find all the solutions of these equations.
   i $\cos p = ^-\cos 62°$ **ii** $\sin p = ^-\sin 62°$
   iii $\sin p = 1$ **iv** $\cos p = 0$

5 Sketch each of these graphs for $0° \leqslant x \leqslant 360°$.
  a $y = \frac{1}{2} \cos x$ **b** $y = \frac{1}{2} \sin x$
  c $y = 5 \sin x$ **d** $y = \cos 3x$
  e $y = \sin x - 5$ **f** $y = 2 \cos x + 1$

6 Sketch each of these graphs for $^-90° \leqslant x \leqslant 540°$.
  a $y = \sin (x + 45°)$
  b $y = \cos (x - 90°)$

7 **a** On one pair of axes, with $0° \leqslant x \leqslant 360°$ draw the graphs of:
   i $y = \cos x$
   ii $y = \frac{1}{2} \sin x$.
  b Use your graphs to solve the equation:
   $\cos x = \frac{1}{2} \sin x$

8 Give the maximum and minimum value of y for each of these.
  a $y = 6 \cos x$ **b** $y = \sin x + 6$
  c $y = 8 \cos x$ **d** $y = \sin 2x$
  e $y = 3 \sin x + 6$ **f** $y = 2 \cos 3x - 4$

9 This is the graph of $y = a \sin bx + c$, where a, b and c are constants.

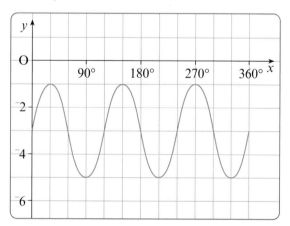

What are the values of a, b and c?

10 Solve each of these equations in the range $^-90° \leqslant p \leqslant 450°$.
  a $\sin p = \cos p$ **b** $\sin 2p = \sin 80°$
  c $\cos 3p = 0.5$ **d** $\tan 3p = 1$

Inequalities

1 Which of these numbers is not a possible value for t where $t \leqslant {}^{-}7$?
$^{-}8, 4, 71, {}^{-}3.2, {}^{-}7.003, {}^{-}28.6, {}^{-}7, {}^{-}0.33$

2 What are the integer values for k, where

a $9 > k \geqslant 4$ **b** $^{-}3 \leqslant k \leqslant {}^{-}1$
c $^{-}5 \leqslant k < 1$ **d** $^{-}4 \geqslant k > {}^{-}7$
e $^{-}57 < k < {}^{-}56$ **f** $24 \leqslant k \leqslant 24$
g $^{-}14.2 \geqslant k > {}^{-}16$ **h** $6 > k > 0$
i $k^2 \leqslant 16$ **j** $9 < k^2 + 8$
k $12 - k^2 \geqslant 3$ **l** $4(k^2 + 3) \geqslant 3(2k^2 - 2)$?

3 Write two other inequalities in h which describe the same integer values as $^{-}2 < h < 2$.

4 Explain why these two inequalities are different types of inequality from each other.

> This chair is suitable for people with weights given by $5 \leqslant w \leqslant 15$, where w is their weight in stones.

> The waiters in a restaurant are given by $5 \leqslant w \leqslant 15$ where w is the number of waiters.

5 Draw graphs and label the regions described by these inequalities:

a $7 \leqslant x \leqslant 10$ **b** $^{-}4 \leqslant x < 1$
c $^{-}5 < x < {}^{-}2$ **d** $0 < x \leqslant 4$
e $^{-}1 \leqslant y < 3$ and $x \geqslant 4$
f $0 \leqslant x \leqslant 6$ and $^{-}6 < y < {}^{-}2$
g $y \geqslant x$ and $9 \geqslant x \geqslant 6$
h $2x + y < 10$ and $y \geqslant \frac{1}{2}x + 1$

6 What two inequalities describe the shaded region on this graph?

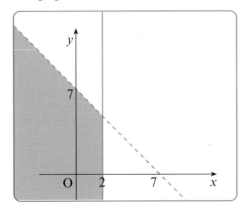

7 The conditions on x are given by the inequality $^{-}4 \leqslant x < 3$.
What is:

a the smallest possible value of x^2
b the largest possible value of x^2?

8 Solve the following inequalities.

a $3x \geqslant 27$ **b** $6t < {}^{-}42$
c $52 \geqslant 4p$ **d** $k^2 \leqslant 121$
e $1 + 3w < 7$ **f** $5q + 7 > 53.5$
g $19 \leqslant 3t - 5$ **h** $7 - 2h \geqslant 3$
i $4(3f - 2) < 28$ **j** $c^2 - 5 < 76$
k $36 \leqslant 3(2g + 3)$ **l** $3x + 5 > x - 1$
m $3j - 2 < 2j + 17$ **n** $5d + 20 \geqslant 6 - 2d$
o $24 - 8v > 6 - 4v$ **p** $2(x+3) \leqslant x - 7$
q $5 - 3s > 5 + 3s$ **r** $9u + 6 \leqslant 7u$
s $5(4 - 3j) < 7j - 4$ **t** $5 + 2r^2 > 23$
u $2(3x^2 + 2) > 3(4x^2 - 3) + 1$

9 If the limits for x and y are given by $4 < x < 7$ and $7 < y < 9$, what can you say about the limits for:

a xy **b** $x + y$ **c** $\dfrac{y}{x}$?

10 Sam is planting an orchard with a mixture of apple bushes and pear trees. An apple bush needs an area of 16 m^2 and a pear tree needs 24 m^2. An apple bush costs £8 and a pear tree £10. She has £200 to spend and her orchard can have a maximum area of 432 m^2.
Sam wants at least half of her plants to be apple bushes but at least 6 must be pear trees.
Let a represent the number of apple bushes and p the number of pear trees.
This graph shows only some of the boundaries.

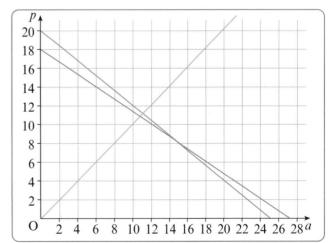

a Write inequalities for:
   i the land area   **ii** the cost of plants
   iii the number of pear trees.
b Explain why $p < a$.
c Draw the complete graph, label each line, and shade out all the regions not required.
d How many of each type gives the maximum total number of plants.
   What is the total cost of these plants?

Working with percentages

1 Calculate, giving answers correct to 2 dp:
   a 38 as a percentage of 60
   b £14 as a percentage of £55
   c 68 as a percentage of 24
   d 1550 as a percentage of 2500.

2 Nina bought a secondhand bicycle for £45.
  She later sold the bike for £58.
  Calculate her percentage profit to 2 sf.

3 a Increase 25 kg by 18%.
   b Increase 1400 km by 62%.
   c Increase 3560 miles by 4%.
   d Increase 1350 yards by 36%.

4 Last year one company sold 19.6 million CDs.
  Next year they plan to increase sales by 18.5%.
  How many CDs do they plan to sell next year?

5 a Decrease 485 ml by 12%.
   b Decrease £45.75 by 24%.
   c Decrease 65 mm by 65%.
   d Decrease 0.8 cm by 8%.

6 This year an arable farm used 12.4 tonnes of
  herbicides. They plan to decrease the herbicides
  used by 8.5% per year.
  Calculate, to 2 sf, the herbicide they plan to be
  using three years from now.

7 The price of each item is given ex.VAT.
  Calculate the price including VAT at $17\frac{1}{2}\%$,
  to the nearest penny.
   a crash helmet £185.85
   b cycle tyre £11.69
   c fishing rod £44.86
   d steam iron £21.75
   e microwave oven £268.55
   f VCR £159.99
   g personal CD player £135.38
   h CD £9.24
   i phone £49.99
   j multimedia PC £1499

8 A printer is advertised for £132 + VAT.
  Calculate the total price of the printer.

9 The VAT (at 17.5%) paid on a bill was £15.
  Calculate the total for the bill including VAT.

10 Jamal has a maximum of £10 000 to spend on
   building a garage. Calculate the maximum he can
   spend ex.VAT.

11 Callum sees the same model TV advertised by two
   shops in this way:

   | TV World | £199.99 inc. VAT |

   | Price busters | £169.99 ex.VAT |

   From which shop would you advise Callum to
   buy the TV?
   Give reasons for your answer.

12 Calculate the simple interest charged, or paid, on
   each of these:
   a £675 borrowed for 5 years at 12% pa
   b £12 400 borrowed for 2 years at 17% pa
   c £170 saved for 4 years at 3% pa

13 Rearrange the simple interest formula,
   $I = P \times R \times T$, to make R the subject.

14 £1400 was saved at 3.6% simple interest.
   The total interest paid was £378, for how long
   was the saving?

15 Calculate the compound interest charged, or paid
   on each of these:
   a £500 saved for 8 years at 6% pa
   b £1400 borrowed for 3 years at 19% pa
   c £250 saved for 12 years at 7.5% pa
   d £105 saved for 7 years at 3%
   e £12500 borrowed for 12 years at 16%
   f £32 saved for 13 years at 4%
   g £750 borrowed for 3 years at 21%
   h £3675 borrowed for 5 years at 17%
   i £125 saved for 9 years at 8%
   j £500 saved for 30 years at 4.5%.

16 These prices include VAT. Calculate each price
   ex.VAT.
   a freezer £299.99   b CD £12.99
   c camera £44.99   d phone £9.99
   e climbing boots £75   f tent £89.95
   g kettle £26.99   h PC £129.99
   i calculator £18.99   j TV £139.99

17 Jo bought a ski jacket in a '15% off sale' for £85.45.
   Calculate the pre-sale price of the jacket?

18 In 1995 Ferrykink made a profit of £3 600 000.
   This was 14% more than the profit for 1994.
   Calculate the profit made in 1994.

Circle properties

1 Draw any circle, and a chord AB.

  a Label:
    i the minor segment
    ii the major segment.

A chord CD is such that the circle is divided into two segments that are the same size.

  b What can you say about the chord CD?

2

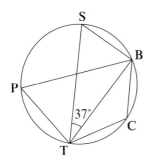

  a Name an angle in the minor segment.

  b Calculate the size of TB̂S when TP̂B = 75°. Explain your answer.

3 In the diagram PT is a chord and O the centre of the circle.

Calculate the size of TP̂O. Give reasons for your answer.

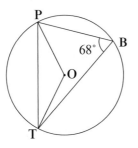

4 The circle has a centre O.

  a Calculate the size of PT̂B. Explain your answer.

  b What is the size of AĈB? Explain your answer.

  c Explain why AB̂P is 76°.

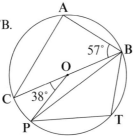

5 The circle has a centre O.

  a Explain why PÂT is 48°.

  b Calculate PĈT. Explain your answer.

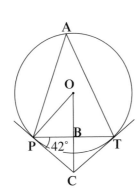

6 **a** Explain why TB̂P is 35°.

  b Calculate BP̂T. Give reasons for your answer.

  c Explain why AĈB is 73°.

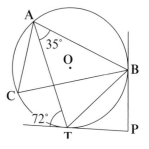

7 AC is a tangent to the circle with centre O. AC is 12.5 cm long and B is the midpoint.

  a If AE = 5 cm, calculate the length of EG to 1 dp.

  b If DF = 11.2 cm, calculate to 1 dp the length of CD.

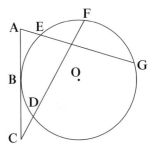

8 AC is a tangent to the circle with centre O. AC is 16.2 cm long and B is the midpoint.

  a If AD is 4 cm, and EF is 7.5 cm calculate the size of FD̂E to 2 sf.

  b Calculate the area of triangle FDE to 3 sf.

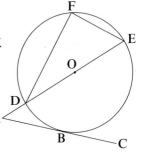

9 **a** Explain why EĈD = 31°.

  b Calculate the size of AB̂C. Explain your answer.

  c EÂB = 52° Give two different explanations to show this.

10 Show why an expression for DÂB is given as:

$$180 - a$$

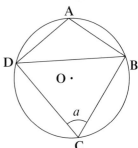

Working with angles

1 Calculate the area of each of these triangles:

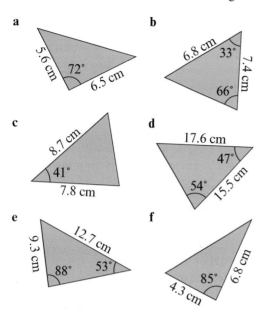

2 Triangle ABC has an area of 30.4 cm².

Calculate the length of AC.

3 Use the sine rule to calculate ? in each of these triangles.

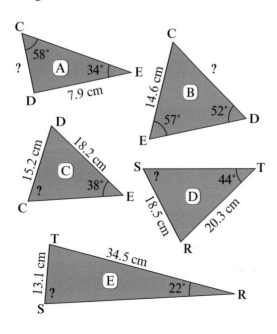

4 Calculate the length of CD in each of these triangles:

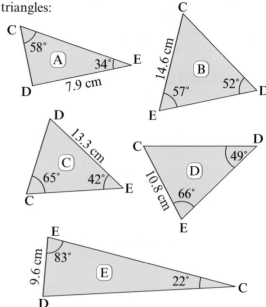

5 Calculate BÂC in each of these triangles:

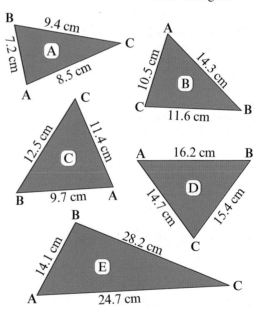

6 For triangle PQR, copy and complete the table.

Angle	p(cm)	q(cm)	r(cm)
P = 54°	a	7.3	8.5
Q = 63°	8.4	b	9.1
R = 49°	11.5	9.8	c
P = 74°	d	3.5	4.5
Q = 57°	37.5	e	31.8

Processing data

1

> ### Town Centre Survey
>
> **1** Do you come into the town centre often? ☐ Yes ☐ No
>
> **2** Do you agree that the town centre
> should be pedestrianised? ☐ Yes ☐ No
>
> **3** What do you think about buses? _____

    a Criticise each of these questions.
    b Write an improved question for each one.

2

> ### Body Matters
> Right-handed people are more likely to
> have a stronger left eye than right eye.

Design an experiment to test this hypothesis.

3   **a** Carry out your experiment.
      b Analyse the data you collect.

4   **a** Do you think the hypothesis is true or false?
      b Explain why.

5

> ### Body Matters
> Do right-handed people fold their arms
> differently to left-handed people?

Design an experiment to answer this question.

6   **a** Carry out your experiment.
      b Analyse the data you collect.
      c Interpret your results to answer the question.

7

Motorbikes – Size of Engine & Price

Engine size (cc)	250	900	600	125	650	900	500	750
Price (£)	4500	8100	6700	2400	5100	6700	3400	9200

    a Draw axes: horizontal 0 to 1300
                  vertical 0 to 12 000
    b Plot the motorbike data on your diagram.
    c Draw a line of best fit.
    d Describe any correlation between size of engine
       and price.

8 Estimate the price of a motorbike with engine size:
    a 800 cc   **b** 450 cc

9 Estimate the engine size of a motorbike costing:
    a £4000   **b** £6500

10 Extend the line of best fit on your scatter
diagram to estimate:

    a the price of a motorbike with a 1000 cc engine
    b the engine size of a motorbike costing £10 000.

11 The GB Team for the 1996 Olympic Games had
123 female competitors, and 189 male competitors.
Show how a stratified random sample of
60 competitors is chosen.

12 The ages of female and male competitors, listed
at random, are:

1996 Olympic Games – Great Britain Team
Ages of 123 Female Competitors at 20/7/96

```
21 26 16 23 31 27 20 20 24 24 18 23 26 21 31 24
27 20 23 27 23 24 29 24 24 31 26 23 29 32 23 24
38 28 32 31 31 24 21 30 38 29 22 24 32 40 30 31
23 32 29 27 21 27 23 27 25 25 22 35 29 28 25 28
34 35 30 37 31 26 35 35 36 16 16 33 20 33 26 26
29 30 29 29 25 28 27 25 24 28 31 32 26 31 23 30
20 28 31 28 24 29 30 27 27 29 22 29 28 30 27 28
47 25 29 27 28 31 26 31 29 28 34
```

1996 Olympic Games – Great Britain Team
Ages of 183 Male Competitors at 20/7/96

```
22 29 18 23 28 26 29 27 20 19 23 21 25 21 20 21
20 21 19 30 31 27 23 30 35 27 25 23 22 27 36 27
24 27 26 30 35 30 31 19 29 27 24 32 25 21 39 25
27 32 24 29 34 29 23 29 24 24 21 23 27 22 29 35
31 24 24 22 23 30 27 26 29 26 21 22 25 32 26 26
28 29 22 37 18 29 34 32 30 25 27 35 29 29 28 23
27 22 27 34 30 41 40 27 31 33 38 42 36 40 29 20
22 26 23 21 29 29 27 27 23 28 25 34 30 27 28 30
23 27 25 26 23 21 32 35 24 27 24 28 26 28 34 22
27 32 26 24 27 20 27 28 31 26 24 25 30 34 27 24
30 21 21 29 21 27 48 19 34 31 36 28 29 21 22 23
25 18 29 30 25 32 24 28 25 29 30 26 29
```

    a Use your answer to Question **11** and choose a
       systematic sample from each group.
    b For the 60 competitors in your sample:
       i group the data   **ii** draw a histogram.

13 For your grouped data, calculate an estimate of the
mean age.

14   **a** Choose another stratified random sample of
        60 competitors by allocating a number to each
        competitor in the group, and using a random
        number table.
     b **i** Group the data for your second sample using
           the same groups as in Question **12**
        ii Draw a histogram.

15 For your second sample, calculate an estimate of
the mean age.

16 Compare your two samples.

Distance, speed and time

1 Write these speeds in miles per hour.

   a 0.6 miles per minute
   b 1.2 miles per minute
   c 0.45 miles per minute
   d 0.1 miles per second

2 How far does a plane travel in 3 h 20 min at a constant speed of 960 kilometres per hour?

3 How far can a car travel at a constant speed of 51 mph in:

   a 1 h 30 min   **b** 45 min
   c 20 min   **d** 55 min
   e 2 h 25 min   **f** 3 h 45 min?

4 Calculate the time taken in hours and minutes, to the nearest minute, to travel 60 km at a speed of:

   a 120 km/h   **b** 30 km/h
   c 75 km/h   **d** 9 km/h
   e 55 km/h   **f** 49 km/h
   g 50 km/h   **h** 150 km/h.

5 Convert the following:

   a 4.38 hours to hours and minutes
   b 12.76 hours to hours and minutes
   c 5 hours 16 minutes to hours
   d 8 hours 51 minutes to hours
   e 24 m s^{-1} to km h^{-1}
   f 16 m s^{-1} to mph
   g 58 mph to m s^{-1}
   h 152 km h^{-1} to m s^{-1}.

6 A bike travels 96 miles in $8\frac{1}{2}$ hours.
   Calculate its average speed in mph.

7 How many miles does a car travelling at an average speed of 65 mph cover in 3 hours 45 minutes?

8 How long does it take Alison, walking at an average speed of $3\frac{1}{2}$ mph, to travel $8\frac{1}{2}$ miles?

9 Between traffic lights a car covered a distance of 132 metres in 9 seconds.
   What was its average speed in mph?

10 A balloon drifting at 6 m s^{-1} travelled a total distance of 16.8 miles.
   How long did this flight last?

11 How many metres would an arrow fly in 15 seconds at an average speed of 96 km h^{-1}?

12 This is a graph of the distance of a dog from its owner who sits still on a bench.

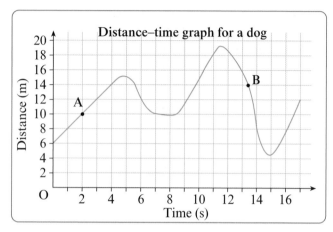

a Describe what the dog did over the 16 seconds.
b At what times was the dog 12 metres from its owner?
c How far from the owner did the dog start?
d When did the dog stop to sniff?
e At what time was the dog moving fastest?
f Estimate how fast the dog was running at:
   i point A   **ii** point B.

13 Calculate the average speed (in mph or km/h to 2 dp) of a car which travels:

   a 40 miles in 50 min
   b 50 km in 35 min
   c 70 miles in 1 h 20 min
   d 100 km in 1 h 12 min
   e 400 miles in 7 h 30 min
   f 500 metres in 1 min.

14 Mandy left Glasgow at 10:00 am and cycled 28 miles at a speed of 10 mph.
   Amin left Glasgow at 10:20 am and travelled along the same route at a speed of 12 mph.

   a Show both their journeys on one graph.
   b About what time did Amin pass Mandy?

15 Andy left Taunton at 3:00 pm and took 45 minutes to drive 50 miles to Bristol. He stayed there for 2 h 30 min. He then returned along the same route and arrived home at 7:05 pm.

   a Draw a graph to show Andy's complete journey.
   b At what time did he begin his return journey to Taunton?
   c Calculate his average speed for the journey to Bristol.
   d What was his average speed on the return journey?

Vectors

1

$$u = \begin{pmatrix} ^-2 \\ 5 \end{pmatrix} \qquad v = \begin{pmatrix} 1 \\ 4 \end{pmatrix} \qquad w = \begin{pmatrix} 5 \\ 6 \end{pmatrix}$$

Write each of these vectors as a column vector, and draw it on a coordinate grid.

a $2u$ **b** $3v$ **c** ^-2w **d** $v + w$
e $u + v$ **f** $2w - 3v$ **g** $2v - u$ **h** $3w - 5v + 2u$

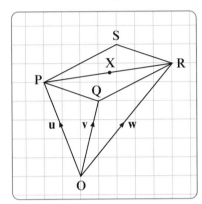

2 PQRS is a parallelogram.
Write each of these in terms of **u**, **v**, and **w**.

a $\overrightarrow{PQ}$ **b** $\overrightarrow{QR}$ **c** $\overrightarrow{SP}$ **d** $\overrightarrow{RS}$ **e** $\overrightarrow{OS}$

3

$$u = \begin{pmatrix} ^-2 \\ 5 \end{pmatrix} \qquad v = \begin{pmatrix} 1 \\ 4 \end{pmatrix} \qquad w = \begin{pmatrix} 5 \\ 6 \end{pmatrix}$$

a Write each of your answers to Question **2** as a column vector.
b Use the diagram to check your answers.

4 Give the resultant vector for:

a $\overrightarrow{PQ} + \overrightarrow{QR}$ **b** $\overrightarrow{PS} + \overrightarrow{SR}$ **c** $\overrightarrow{PQ} + \overrightarrow{QR} + \overrightarrow{RS}$

5 What is special about the vector $\overrightarrow{RS} + \overrightarrow{SP} + \overrightarrow{PR}$?

6 Use your answers to Question **2** to give the resultant vectors in Question **4** in terms of **u**, **v**, and **w**.

7 Show that $v - u$ is the negative vector of $u - v$:

a using a sketch
b using column vectors
c using algebra.

8 X is the midpoint of PR.
Prove that X is also the midpoint of QS.

9 These vectors include three pairs of parallel vectors.

$2v - 3u$	$6u + 4v$	$2u + 3v$	$6u - 9v$

$3v - 2u$	$4v - 6u$	$^-3u - 2v$

List each pair.

10

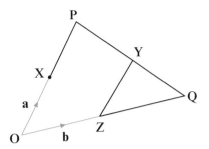

OPQ is a triangle.
X, Y, and Z are the midpoints of each of the sides.

a Give $\overrightarrow{PQ}$ in terms of **a** and **b**.

b Prove that ZY is parallel to OP and half its size.

11

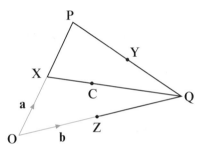

OPQ is a triangle.
X, Y, and Z are the midpoints of each of the sides.
The ratio XC:CQ is 1:2.

a Give these in terms of **a** and **b**.
   i $\overrightarrow{XQ}$ **ii** $\overrightarrow{XC}$
b Prove that P, C, and Z are collinear.
c Give the ratio PC:CZ
d Prove that O, C, and Y are collinear.
e What do your answers tell you about point C?

12

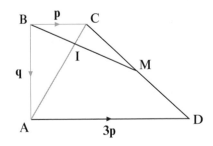

In this diagram, M is the midpoint of CD.
The ratio BI:IM is 2:3.

a Give these in terms of **p** and **q**.
   i $\overrightarrow{CD}$ **ii** $\overrightarrow{CM}$ **iii** $\overrightarrow{BI}$
b Prove that the ratio AI:IC is 4:1.

Transforming graphs

1 Functions f, g and h are defined so that:

$$f(x) = \frac{1}{x-5}$$

$$g(x) = (x+3)^2 - 5$$

$$h(x) = \frac{3}{x} + 4$$

a Calculate:

    i $f(6)$ **ii** $g(1)$ **iii** $h(2)$

    iv $f(^-3)$ **v** $g(^-3)$ **vi** $h(^-3)$

b Find values of x for which:

    i $f(x) = 0.1$ **ii** $g(x) = 4$ **iii** $h(x) = 7.75$

2 An experiment is carried out to investigate the bounciness of a ball. The ball is dropped from different heights and the maximum height of the rebound is measured.

The results are shown in the table below.

Drop height D (cm)	50	100	150	200
Rebound height R (cm)	46	92	139	180

a Draw a graph to show that R and D are linked by a formula of the form $R = aD + b$, where a and b are constants.

b Estimate the values of a and b.

c **(i)** What do you think the rebound height will be when the drop height is 350 cm?

    (ii) Why might your answer be unreliable?

3 A small weight is dropped from the top of a building. Its position is recorded at intervals of 0.5 seconds using an electronic camera.

The results are shown in the table below, giving distance from ground d (m) and time taken t (seconds).

t	0	0.5	1	1.5	2	2.5	3
d	50.0	48.8	45.1	40.0	30.4	19.4	5.9

a Draw the graph of d against t^2.

b **i** Does your graph support the claim that d and t are connected by an equation of the form $d = pt^2 + q$?

    ii If it does, estimate the values of p and q.

4

x	0	2	4	6	8	10	12
y	$^-2.4$	$^-0.8$	4.2	11.7	23.1	37.5	55.0

a Draw a graph to show that x and y are linked by a formula of the form $y = mx^2 + n$, where m and n are constants.

b Estimate the values of m and n.

c Find the value of y when $x = 5$.

5 This is a sketch of the graph of $y = f(x)$ where $f(x) = x^2 - 6x + 10$.

a Sketch graphs of:

    i $y = -f(x)$ **ii** $y = f(-x)$ **iii** $y = f(x) + 3$

    iv $y = f(x + 3)$ **v** $y = f(x - 2) + 1$

b Describe a transformation that maps $y = f(x)$ to each graph.

6 This is the graph of the function $y = g(x)$.

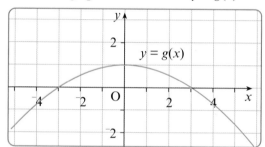

Sketch graphs of:

a $y = 2g(x)$ **b** $y = g(2x)$ **c** $y = g\left(\frac{1}{2}x\right)$

7 This is the graph of the function $y = k(x)$.

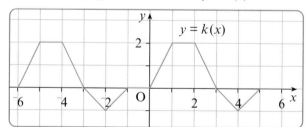

a For $^-3 \leqslant x \leqslant 3$, sketch graphs of:

    i $y = k(^-x)$ **ii** $y = k(2x)$ **iii** $y = k\left(\frac{1}{2}x\right)$

    iv $y = k\left(\frac{1}{3}x\right)$ **v** $y = \frac{1}{2}k(x)$ **vi** $y = 2k(x)$

    vii $y = k(x) + 3$ **viii** $y = k(x + 3)$

    ix $y = k(x - 2)$ **x** $y = k(x - 3) - 4$

b In terms of k, write the equation of the graph below.

For your GCSE Maths you will need to produce two pieces of coursework:

1. Investigative
2. Statistical

Each piece is worth 10% of your exam mark.
This unit gives you guidance on approaching your coursework and will tell you how to get good marks for each piece.

Investigative coursework

In your investigative coursework you will need to:

♦ Say how you are going to carry out the task and provide a plan of action

♦ Collect results for the task and consider an appropriate way to represent your result

♦ Write down observations you make from your diagrams or calculations

♦ Look at your results and write down any observations, rules or patterns – try to make a general statement

♦ Check out your general statements by testing further data – say if your test works or not

♦ Develop the task by posing your own questions and provide a conclusion to the questions posed

♦ Extend the task by using techniques and calculations from the content of the higher tier

♦ Make your conclusions clear and link them to the original task giving comments on your methods.

Assessing the task

Before you start, it is helpful for you to know how your work will be marked. This way you can make sure you are familiar with the sort of things which examiners are looking for.

Investigative work is marked under three headings:

1. **Making and monitoring decisions to solve problems**
2. **Communicating mathematically**
3. **Developing skills of mathematical reasoning**

Each strand assesses a different aspect of your coursework. The criteria are:

1. Making and monitoring decisions to solve problems

This strand is about deciding what needs to be done then doing it. The strand requires you to select an appropriate approach, obtain information and introduce your own questions which develop the task further.

For the higher marks you need to analyse alternative mathematical approaches and, possibly, develop the task using work from the higher tier GCSE syllabus content.

For this strand you need to:

♦ solve the task by collecting information
♦ break down the task by solving it in a systematic way
♦ extend the task by introducing your own *relevant* questions
♦ extend the task by following through alternative approaches

♦ develop the task by including a number of mathematical features
♦ explore the task extensively using higher level mathematics

2. Communicating mathematically

This strand is about communicating what you are doing using words, tables, diagrams and symbols. You should make sure your chosen presentation is accurate and relevant.

For the higher marks you will need to use mathematical symbols accurately, concisely and efficiently in presenting a reasoned argument.

For this strand you need to:

♦ illustrate your information using diagrams and calculations
♦ interpret and explain your diagrams and calculations
♦ begin to use mathematical symbols to explain your work
♦ use mathematical symbols consistently to explain your work
♦ use mathematical symbols accurately to argue your case
♦ use mathematical symbols concisely and efficiently to argue your case

3. Developing skills of mathematical reasoning

This strand is about testing, explaining and justifying what you have done. It requires you to search for patterns and provide generalisations. You should test, justify and explain any generalisations.

For the higher marks you will need to provide a sophisticated and rigorous justification, argument or proof which demonstrates a mathematical insight into the problem.

For this strand you need to:

♦ make a general statement from your results
♦ confirm your general statement by further testing
♦ make a justification for your general statement
♦ develop your justification further
♦ provide a sophisticated justification
♦ provide a rigorous justification, argument or proof

This unit uses a series of investigative tasks to demonstrate how each of these strands can be achieved.

Task 1

TRIANGLES

Patterns of triangles are made as shown in the following diagrams:

Pattern 1

Pattern 2

Pattern 3

What do you notice about the pattern number and the number of triangles?

Investigate further.

Note: You are reminded that any coursework submitted for your GCSE examination must be your own. If you copy from someone else then you may be disqualified from the examination.

Planning your work

A straightforward approach to this task is to continue the pattern further. You can record your results in a table and then see if you can make any generalisations.

Collecting information

A good starting point for any investigation is to collect information about the task.

You can see that:

- Pattern 1 shows 1 triangle
- Pattern 2 shows 4 triangles
- Pattern 3 shows 9 triangles

You can then extend this by considering further patterns.

> **Moderator comment**
>
> It is a good idea not to collect too much data as this is time consuming ... aim to collect 4 or 5 items of data to start with.

Pattern 4

16 triangles

Pattern 5

25 triangles

Drawing up tables

The information is not easy to follow so it is **always** a good idea to illustrate it in a table.

A table to show the relationship between the pattern number and the number of triangles

> It is important to give your table a title and to make it quite clear what the table is showing.

Pattern number	1	2	3	4	5
No. of triangles	1	4	9	16	25

> **Now you try ...**
>
> Using the table:
>
> - Can you see anything special about the number of triangles?
> - Ask yourself: are they odd numbers, even numbers, square numbers, triangle numbers, are they multiples, do they get bigger, do they get smaller ...
> - What other relationships might you look for?

You should now try and explain what your table tells you:

From my table I can . . .

Finding a relationship – making a generalisation

To make a generalisation, you need to find a relationship from your table of results. A useful method is to look at the differences between terms in the table.

Here is the table of results from task 1:

A table to show the relationship between the pattern number and the number of triangles

Pattern number	1	2	3	4	5
No of triangles	1	4	9	16	25
	+3	+5	+7	+9	+11
	+2	+2	+2	+2	

In this table the first "differences" are going up in two's.

The "second differences" are all the same ... this tells you that the relationship is quadratic, so you should compare the numbers with the square numbers

Here are some generalisations you could make:

From my table I notice that the number of triangles are all square numbers.

From my table I notice that the number of triangles are the pattern numbers squared.

Moderator comment

Remember that the idea is to identify some relationship from your table or, graph so that there is some point in you using it in your work ... a table or graph without any comment on the findings is of little use.

A graph may help see the relationship:

From my graph I notice that there is a quadratic relationship between the number of triangles and the pattern number.

Using algebra

You will gain marks if you can express your generalisation or rule using algebra.

The rule:

> I notice that the number of triangles are the pattern numbers squared.

can be written in algebra:

> $t = p^2$ where t is the number of triangles and p is the
> pattern number

> Remember that you must explain what t and p stand for.

Testing generalisations

You need to confirm your generalisation by further testing.

> From my table I notice that the number of triangles are the
> pattern numbers squared so that the sixth pattern will have $6^2 = 36$
> triangles.

You can confirm this with a diagram:

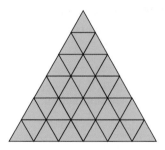

> My diagram confirms the generalisation for the sixth pattern.

> Always confirm your testing by providing some comment, even if your test has not worked!

Now try to use all of these ideas by following task 3.

> **Now you try ...**
>
> For task 3: 'Perfect tiles' given below:
>
> ◆ Collect the information for different arrangements
> ◆ Make sure you are systematic
> ◆ Draw up a table of your results.

Task 3

PERFECT TILES

Floor spacers are used to give a perfect finish when laying tiles on the kitchen floor.

Three different spacers are used including

> **L** spacer
> **T** spacer
> **+** spacer

Here is a 3 × 3 arrangement of tiles

Draw picture of a 3 × 3 arrangement

This uses   4 **L** spacers
             8 **T** spacers and
             4 **+** spacers

Investigate different arrangements of tiles.

Note: You are reminded that any coursework submitted for your GCSE examination must be your own. If you copy from someone else then you may be disqualified from the examination.

You should be able to produce this table:

Number of spacers for different arrangements of tiles

Size of square	1 × 1	2 × 2	3 × 3	4 × 4
Number of L spacers	4	4	4	4
Number of T spacers	0	4	8	12
Number of + spacers	0	1	4	9

Now you try ...

What patterns do you notice from the table?
What general statements can you make?
Now test your general statements.

Generalisations for the 'Perfect tiles' task might include:

$L = 4$ where L is the number of L spacers

$T = 4(n - 1)$ where T is the number of T spacers and
          n is the size of the arrangement ($n \times n$)

The formula $T = 4(n - 1)$ can also be written as $T = 4n - 4$.

Test:

For a 5 × 5 arrangement (ie $n = 5$)

$T = 4(n - 1)$
$T = 4(5 - 1)$
$T = 4 \times 4$
$T = 16$

The number of T spacers is 16 so the formula works for a 5 × 5 arrangement.

$+ = (n - 1)^2$ where $+$ is the number of $+$ spacers and
                  n is the size of the arrangement ($n \times n$)

Test:
For a 6 × 6 arrangement (ie $n = 6$)

$+ = (n - 1)^2$
$+ = (6 - 1)^2$
$+ = (5)^2$
$+ = 25$

The number of $+$ spacers is 25 so the formula works for a 6 × 6 arrangement.

Making justifications

Once you have found the general statement and tested it then you need to justify it. You justify the statement by explaining WHY it works.

For example, here are possible justifications for the rules in task 3:

WHY is the number of L spacers always 4?

The number of L spacers is always 4 because there are 4 corners to each arrangement.

WHY are all of the T spacers multiples of 4?

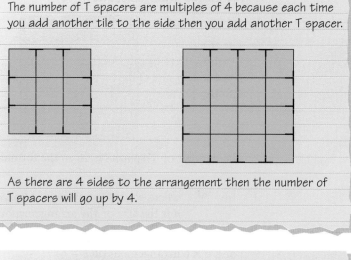

The number of T spacers are multiples of 4 because each time you add another tile to the side then you add another T spacer.

As there are 4 sides to the arrangement then the number of T spacers will go up by 4.

WHY are all of the + spacers square numbers?

Now you try ...

Explain why the number of + spacers are **always** square numbers.

Extending the problem – investigating further

Once you have understood and explained the basic task, you should extend your work to get better marks.

To extend a task you need to pose your own questions.
This means that you must think of different ways to extend the original task.

Extending task 1: The triangle problem

You could ask and investigate:

What about different patterns?

For example, triangles

What about patterns of different shapes?

For example, squares

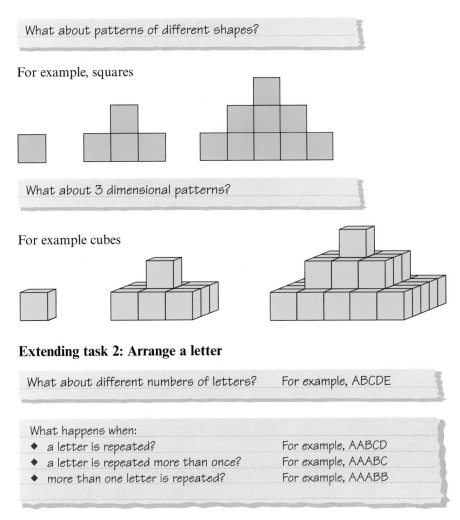

What about 3 dimensional patterns?

For example cubes

Extending task 2: Arrange a letter

What about different numbers of letters?   For example, ABCDE

What happens when:
* a letter is repeated?   For example, AABCD
* a letter is repeated more than once?   For example, AAABC
* more than one letter is repeated?   For example, AAABB

Of course, you will have to do more than just pose a question – you will have to carry out the investigation and come to a conclusion.

Now you try ...

Think of some different ways to extend task 3: Perfect Tiles.
What sort of questions might you ask?
What other areas might you explore?

Extending task 3: Perfect Tiles

You could ask:

What about rectangular arrangements of tiles?

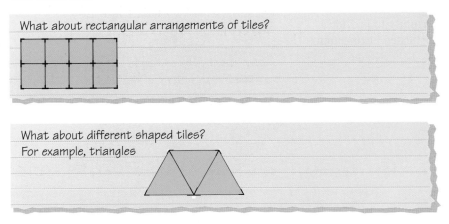

What about different shaped tiles?
For example, triangles

> Remember to work systematically.

Consider rectangular arrangements of tiles:

Number of spacers for different arrangements of tiles

Size of arrangement	2 × 1	2 × 2	2 × 3	2 × 4	2 × 5
Number of L spacers	4	4	4	4	4
Number of T spacers	2	4	6	8	10
Number of + spacers	0	1	2	3	4
Number of spacers	6	9	12	15	18

Number of spacers for different arrangements of tiles

Size of arrangement	3 × 1	3 × 2	3 × 3	3 × 4	3 × 5
Number of L spacers	4	4	4	4	4
Number of T spacers	4	6	8	10	12
Number of + spacers	0	2	4	6	8
Number of spacers	8	12	16	20	24

Rules for the 'Perfect tiles' task extension might include:

$L = 4$	where L is the number of L spacers
$T = 2(x - 1) + 2(y - 1)$	where T is the number of T spacers and x is the length of the arrangement and y is the width of the arrangement ($x \times y$)
$P = (x - 1)(y - 1)$	where P is the number of + spacers and x is the length of the arrangement and y is the width of the arrangement ($x \times y$)
$N = (x + 1)(y + 1)$	where N is the total number of spacers and x is the length of the arrangement and y is the width of the arrangement ($x \times y$)

> Note that the formula $T = 2(x - 1) + 2(y - 1)$ can also be written
> $T = 2x - 2 + 2y - 2$
> $T = 2x + 2y - 4$

> It is sensible to replace + by P so that P stands for the number of + spacers.

> **Moderator comment**
>
> The use of higher order algebra can result in high marks awarded on the middle strand as well as an opportunity to provide a sophisticated justification

The total number of spacers should equal the number of L spacers plus the number of T spacers plus the number of + spacers

Proof:
$$N = L + T + P$$
$$= 4 + [2(x - 1) + 2(y - 1)] + [(x - 1)(y - 1)]$$
$$= 4 + 2x - 2 + 2y - 2 + xy - y - x + 1$$
$$= xy + x + y + 1$$
$$= (x + 1)(y + 1)$$

Since $N = (x + 1)(y + 1)$ is true, then my theory is proved

Task 4

> **SQUARE SEA SHELLS**
>
> Square sea shells are formed from squares whose pattern of growth is shown as follows:
>
> Day 1
>
>
>
> Day 2
>
>
>
> The length of the new square is half that of the previous day
>
> Day 3
>
>
>
> The length of the new square is half that of the previous day
>
> Day 4
>
>
>
> The length of the new square is half that of the previous day
>
> This pattern of growth continues
>
> Investigate the area covered by square sea shells on different days.
>
> Investigate further.

For a square of side a

Day 1   Area $= a^2$

Day 2   Area $= a^2 + \dfrac{a^2}{4}$

Day 3   Area $= a^2 + \dfrac{a^2}{4} + \dfrac{a^2}{16}$

Day 4   Area $= a^2 + \dfrac{a^2}{4} + \dfrac{a^2}{16} + \dfrac{a^2}{64}$

Day . . .   Area $= a^2 + \dfrac{a^2}{4} + \dfrac{a^2}{16} + \dfrac{a^2}{64} + \ldots$

$$= a^2\left(1 + \frac{1}{4} + \frac{1}{16} + \frac{1}{64} + \ldots\right)$$

$$= \ldots$$

$$= \ldots$$

$$= \frac{4}{3}\,a^2$$

This work involves summing an infinite series which is beyond the mathematical content of the GCSE examination and so will get you higher marks.

Moderator comment

Remember that for the higher levels, you will need to explore the task extensively using higher level mathematics, use mathematical symbols concisely and efficiently to argue your case and provide a rigorous justification, argument or proof.

Extending task 4: square sea shells

For an equilateral triangle of side a

$$\text{Day 1} \qquad \text{Area} = \frac{1}{2}\, a^2 \sin 60°$$

$$= \frac{1}{2}\, a^2 \sqrt{\frac{3}{2}}$$

$$= \sqrt{\frac{3}{4}}\, a^2$$

or

For a regular n sided polygon of length a

$$\text{Day 1} \qquad \text{Area} = \frac{na^2}{4 \tan}\left(\frac{180}{n}\right)^{\!o}$$

In this unit we have tried to give you some hints on approaching investigative coursework to gain your best possible mark.

This mathematics is often useful in investigative tasks:

♦ Creating tables
♦ Drawing and interpreting graphs
♦ Recognising square numbers
♦ Recognising triangular numbers
♦ Finding the nth term of a linear sequence

Summary

These are the grade criteria your coursework will be marked by:

Testing general statements (grade D)

To achieve this level you must:
♦ break down the task by solving it in an orderly manner
♦ interpret and explain your diagrams and calculations
♦ confirm your general statement by further testing

Posing questions and justifying (grade C)

To achieve this level you must:
♦ extend the task by introducing your own relevant questions
♦ begin to use mathematical symbols to explain your work
♦ make a justification for your general statement
♦ provide a sophisticated justification

Making further progress (grade B)

To achieve this level you must:
♦ extend the task by following through alternative approaches
♦ use mathematical symbols consistently to explain your work
♦ develop you justification further

Justifying a number of mathematical features (grade A)

To achieve this level you must:
♦ develop the task by including a number of mathematical features
♦ use mathematical symbols accurately to argue your case
♦ provide a sophisticated justification

Exploring extensively (grade A*)

To achieve this level you must:
♦ explore the task extensively using higher level mathematics
♦ use mathematical symbols concisely and efficiently to argue your case and provide a rigorous justification, argument or proof

Statistical coursework

In your statistical coursework you will need to:

◆ Provide a well considered hypothesis and provide a plan of action to carry out the task
◆ Decide what data is needed and collect results for the task using an appropriate sample size and sampling method
◆ Consider the most appropriate way to represent your results and write down any observations you make
◆ Consider the most appropriate statistical calculations to use and interpret your findings in terms of the original hypothesis
◆ Develop the task by posing your own questions – you may need to collect further data to move the task on
◆ Extend the task by using techniques and calculations from the content of the higher tier
◆ Make your conclusions clear – always link them to the original hypothesis recognising limitations and suggesting improvements.

Assessing the task

It may be helpful for you to know how the work is marked. This way you can make sure you are familiar with the sort of thing that examiners are looking for.

Statistical work is marked under three headings:

1. Specifying the problem and planning
2. Collecting, processing and representing the data
3. Interpreting and discussing the results

Each strand assesses a different aspect of your coursework as follows:

1. Specifying the problem and planning

This strand is about choosing a problem and deciding what needs to be done, then doing it. The strand requires you to provide clear aims, consider the collection of data, identify practical problems and explain how you might overcome them.

For the higher marks you need to decide upon a suitable sampling method, explain what steps were taken to avoid possible bias and provide a well structured report.

2. Collecting, processing and representing the data

This strand is about collecting data and using appropriate statistical techniques and calculations to process and represent the data. Diagrams should be appropriate and calculations mostly correct.

For the higher marks you will need to accurately use higher level statistical techniques and calculations from the higher tier GCSE syllabus content.

3. Interpreting and discussing the results

This strand is about commenting, summarising and interpreting your data. Your discussion should link back to the original problem and provide an evaluation of the work undertaken.

For the higher marks you will need to provide sophisticated and rigorous interpretations of your data and provide an analysis of how significant your findings are.

This unit uses a series of statistical tasks to demonstrate how each of these strands can be achieved.

Planning your work

Statistical coursework requires careful planning if you are to gain good marks. Before undertaking any statistical investigation, it is important that you plan your work and decide exactly what you are going to investigate – do not be too ambitious!

Before you start you should:

♦ decide what your investigation is about and why you have chosen it
♦ decide how you are going to collect the information
♦ explain how you intend to ensure that your data is representative
♦ detail any presumptions which you are making

Getting started – setting up your hypothesis

Moderator comment

Your statistical task must always start with a 'hypothesis' where you state exactly what you are investigating and what you expect to find.

A good starting point for any statistical task is to consider the best way to collect the data and then to write a clear hypothesis you can test.

Task 1

> **WHAT THE PAPERS SAY**
>
> Choose a passage from two different newspapers and investigate the similarities and differences between them.
>
> Write down a hypothesis to test.
>
> Design and carry out a statistical experiment to test the hypothesis.
>
> Investigate further.

Note: You are reminded that any coursework submitted for your GCSE examination must be your own. If you copy from someone else then you may be disqualified from the examination.

First consider different ways to compare the newspapers:

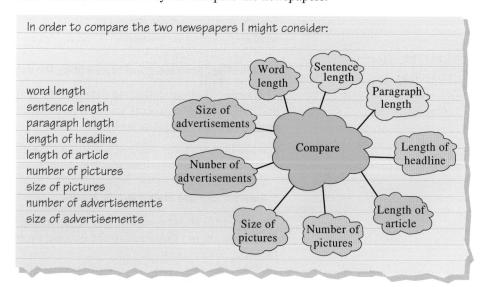

In order to compare the two newspapers I might consider:

word length
sentence length
paragraph length
length of headline
length of article
number of pictures
size of pictures
number of advertisements
size of advertisements

Now formulate your hypothesis.

Here are some possible hypotheses:

> For my statistics coursework, I am going to investigate the hypothesis that 'tabloid' papers use shorter words than 'broadsheet' newspapers.

> My hypothesis is that word lengths in the tabloid newspaper will be shorter than word lengths in the broadsheet newspaper.

> My hypothesis is that sentence lengths in the tabloid newspaper will be shorter than sentence lengths in the broadsheet newspaper.

> My hypothesis is that the number of advertisements in the tabloid newspaper will be greater than the number of advertisements in the broadsheet newspaper.

Remember:
it does not matter whether your hypotheses are true or false and you will still gain marks if your hypothesis turns out to be false.

Now you try ...

See if you can add some hypotheses of your own.

Explain how you would proceed with the task.

Choosing the right sample

Moderator comment

It is important to choose an appropriate sample, give reasons for your choice and explain what steps you will take to avoid bias.

Once you have decided your aims and set up a hypothesis then it is important to consider how you will test your hypothesis.

Sampling techniques include:

- **Random sampling** is where each member of the population has an equally likely chance of being selected. An easy way to do this would be to give each person a number and then choose the numbers randomly.
- **Systematic sampling** is the same as random sampling except that there is some system involved such as numbering each person and then choosing every 20th number to form the sample.
- **Stratified sampling** is where each person is placed into some particular group or category (stratum) and the sample size is proportional to the size of the group or category in the population as a whole.
- **Convenience sampling** or opportunity sampling is one which involves simply choosing the first person to come along ... although this method is not particularly random!

Moderator comment

You should always say why you choose your sampling method.

Here are some ways you could test the hypotheses for task 1:

Sampling method	Reason
To investigate my hypothesis I am going to choose a similar article from each type of newspaper and count the lengths of the first 100 words.	I decided to choose similar articles because the words will be describing similar information and so will be better to make comparisons.
To investigate my hypothesis I will choose every tenth page from each type of newspaper and calculate the percentage area covered by pictures.	I decided to choose every tenth page from each type of newspaper because the types of articles vary throughout the newspaper (for example headlines at the front and sports at the back of the paper).

327

Collecting primary data

Moderator comment

It is important to carefully consider the collection of reliable data. Appropriate methods of collecting primary data might include observation, interviewing, questionnaires or experiments.

If you are collecting primary data then remember:

- **Observation** involves collecting information by observation and might involve participant observation (where the observer takes part in the activity), or systematic observation (where the observation happens without anyone knowing).
- **Interviewing** involves a conversation between two or more people. Interviewing can be formal (where the questions follow a strict format) or informal (where they follow a general format but can be changed around to suit the questioning).
- **Questionnaires** are the most popular way of undertaking surveys. Good questionnaires are
  - simple, short, clear and precise,
  - attractively laid out and quick to complete

  and the questions are
  - not biased or offensive
  - written in a language which is easy to understand
  - relevant to the hypothesis being investigated
  - accompanied by clear instructions on how to answer the questions.

Moderator comment

It is always a good idea to undertake a small scale 'dry run' to check for problems. This 'dry run' is called a pilot survey and can be used to improve your questionnaire or survey before it is undertaken.

Avoiding bias

You must be very careful to avoid any possibility of bias in your work. For example, in making comparisons it is important to ensure that you are comparing like with like.

Jean undertook task 1: 'What the papers say'.
She collected this data from two newspapers by measuring (observation).

	Tabloid	Broadsheet
Number of advertisements	35	30
Number of pages	50	30
Area of each page	1000cm^2	2000cm^2

Her hypothesis is:

The tabloid newspaper has more advertisements than the broadsheet newspaper.

A quick glance at the table may make her claim look true: the broadsheet has 30 adverts but the tabloid has 35, which is more.

However, the sizes of the newspapers are different so Jean is not really comparing like with like.
To ensure Jean compares like with like she should take account of:

- the area of the pages
- the number of pages

and so on.

Percentage coverage per page:
Tabloid = $35 \div 50 \times 100\% = 70\%$
Broadsheet = $30 \div 30 \times 100\% = 100\%$

This shows that:

> The broadsheet newspaper has more advertisements per
> page than the tabloid newspaper.

The total area of the pages is:
Tabloid $= 50 \times 1000\text{cm}^2 = 50\ 000\text{cm}^2$
Broadsheet $= 30 \times 2000\text{cm}^2 = 60\ 000\text{cm}^2$

So the percentage coverage is:
Tabloid $= 35 \div 50\ 000 \times 100\% = 0.07\%$
Broadsheet $= 30 \div 60\ 000 \times 100\% = 0.05\%$

This shows:

> The tabloid newspaper has more advertisements per area
> of coverage than the broadsheet newspaper.

> Note: this still doesn't take account of the size of the adverts!

Methods and calculations

> You can represent the data using statistical calculations such as the mean, median, mode, range and standard deviation.

Once you have collected your data, you need to use appropriate statistical methods and calculations to process and represent your data.

Task 2

> **GUESSING GAME**
>
> Dinesh asked a sample of people to estimate the length of a line and the weight of a package.
>
> Write down a hypothesis about estimating lengths and weights and carry out your own experiment to test your hypothesis.
>
> Investigate further

Note: You are reminded that any coursework submitted for your GCSE examination must be your own. If you copy from someone else then you may be disqualified from the examination.

Maurice and Angela decide to explore the hypothesis that:

> Students are better at estimating the length of a line
> than the weight of a package.

To test the hypothesis they collect data from 50 children, detailing their estimations of the length of a line and the weight of a package.

Here are their findings:

A table to show the estimations for the length of a line and the weight of a package

	Length (cm)	Weight (g)
Mean	15.9	105.2
Median	15.5	100
Mode	14	100
Range	8.6	28
SD	1.2	2.1

Moderator comment

It is important to consider whether information on all of these statistical calculations is essential.

Note: the actual length of the line is 15cm and the weight of the package is 100g.

> **Now you try ...**
>
> Using the table:
>
> ♦ What do you notice about the average of the length and weight?
> ♦ What do you notice about the spread of the length and weight?
> ♦ Does the information support the hypothesis?

Graphical representation

Other statistical representations might include pie charts, bar charts, scatter graphs and histograms.

Moderator comment

You should only use appropriate diagrams and graphs.

Remember to consider the possibility of bias in your data:

The percentage error for the lengths is
$\frac{0.9}{15} \times 100\% = 6\%$
The percentage error for the weights is
$\frac{5.2}{100} \times 100\% = 5.2\%$

The data for task 2 was sorted into different categories and represented as a table.

It may be useful to show your results using graphs and diagrams as sometimes it is easier to see trends.

Graphical representations might include stem and leaf diagrams and cumulative frequency graphs and box-and-whisker diagrams.

Once you have drawn a graph you should say what you notice from the graph:

> From my representation, I can see that the estimations for the line are generally more accurate than the estimations for the weight because:
>
> ♦ the mean is closer to the actual value for the lengths and
> ♦ the standard deviation is smaller for the lengths
>
> However, on closer inspection:
>
> ♦ the percentage error on the mean is smaller for the weights
> ♦ so the median and mode value are better averages to use for the weights

Using secondary data

Moderator comment

If you use secondary data there must be enough 'to allow sampling to take place' – about 50 pieces of data.

You may use secondary data in your coursework.

Secondary data is data that is already collected for you.

Task 3

GENDER DIFFERENCES IN EXAMINATIONS

Jade is conducting a survey in the GCSE examination results for Year 11 students at her school.

She has collected data on last year's results, and wants to compare the performance of boys and girls at the school.

Jade explores the hypothesis that:

> Year 11 girls do better in their GCSE examinations than boys

To test the hypothesis she decided to concentrate on the core subjects and her findings are shown in the table:

A table to show the performance of Year 11 girls and boys in their GCSE examinations

		%A*-C	%A*-G	APS
English	Girls	62	93	4.9
	Boys	46	89	4.3
	All	54	91	4.6
Mathematics	Girls	47	91	4.2
	Boys	45	89	4.2
	All	46	90	4.2
Science	Girls	48	91	4.4
	Boys	45	88	4.3
	All	47	90	4.4

Now you try ...

Using the table:

- What do you notice about the percentages of A*-C grades?
- What do you notice about the percentages of A*-G grades?
- What do you notice about the average point scores?
- Does the information support the hypothesis?

The data has been sorted into different categories and represented as a table.

Jade could use comparative bar charts to represent the data as it will allow her to make comparisons more easily.

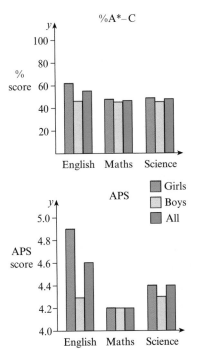

Summarising and interpreting data

Moderator comment

You should refer to your original hypothesis when you summarise your results

Hint:

You need to appreciate that the data is more secure if the sample size is 500 rather than 50.

Jade summarises her findings like this:

> From my graph, I can see that Year 11 girls do better in their GCSE examinations than boys in terms of A*-C grades, A*-G grades and average point scores.

> The performance of Year 11 girls is significantly better than boys in English although less so in mathematics.

Moderator comment

In your conclusion you should also suggest limitations to your investigation and explain how these might be overcome.

You may wish to discuss:

- sample size
- sampling methods
- biased data
- other difficulties

Extending the task

To gain better marks in your coursework you should extend the task in light of your findings.

In your extension you should:

- Give a clear hypothesis
- Collect further data if necessary
- Present your findings using charts and diagrams as appropriate
- Summarise your findings referring to your hypothesis

Extending task 3: Gender differences in examinations

Jade extends the task by looking at the performance of individual students in combinations of different subjects.

> I am now going to extend my task by looking at the performance of individual students in English and mathematics. My hypothesis is that there will be no correlation between the two subjects.

Note:

You should only draw a line of best fit on the diagram to show the correlation if you make some proper use of it (for example to calculate a students' likely English mark given their mathematics mark.)

She presents the data on a scattergraph.

She summarises her findings:

> From my scattergraph, I can see that there is some correlation between the
> performance of individual students in English and mathematics.

She extends the task further:

> I shall now look at the performance of individual students in mathematics and
> science. My hypothesis is that there will be a correlation between the two subjects.

She presents the data on a scattergraph.

Note:
The strength of the correlation could be measured using higher level statistical techniques such as Spearman's Rank Correlation.

> From my scattergraph, I can see that there is no correlation between the
> performance of individual students in mathematics and science.

Extending task 2: Guessing game

Maurice extends the 'Guessing game' like this:

> I am now going to extend my task by looking to see whether people who are good
> at estimating lengths are also good at estimating weights. My hypothesis is
> that there will be a strong correlation between peoples' ability at estimating
> lengths and estimating weights.

He draws a scattergraph:

He summarises his findings:

> From my scattergraph I can see that there is a strong correlation between
> peoples' ability at estimating lengths and estimating weights.

50 people were in the
survey so $n = 50$

The strength of the correlation can be measured using higher level statistical
techniques such as Spearman's Rank Correlation or Product Moment Correlation.

I am now going to extend my investigation by using Spearman's Rank Correlation
to calculate the rank correlation coefficient.

Person	Length	Weight	Rank Length	Rank Weight	Difference D	D^2
Jane	15 cm	102g	22	18	4	16
Suresh	16 cm	108g	11	12	-1	1
					Total	2250

$$r = 1 - \frac{6(\sum D^2)}{n(n^2 - 1)}$$

$$r = 1 - \frac{6(2250)}{50(50^2 - 1)}$$

$$r = 1 - \frac{13500}{50(2499)}$$

$$r = 1 - \frac{13500}{124950}$$

$$r = 1 - 0.108043.....$$

$$r = 0.891956.....$$

$$r = 0.89 \ (2dp)$$

The value for the rank correlation coefficient is quite close to 1 so that there is a
strong positive correlation between my results.

This tells me that there is a strong correlation between peoples' ability at
estimating lengths and estimating weights and confirms my original hypothesis.

Using a computer

It is quite acceptable that calculations and representations are generated by a
computer, as long as any such work is accompanied by some analysis and
interpretation.

Remember:
make sure that your computer generated scattergraph has labelled axes and a title to make it quite clear what it is showing

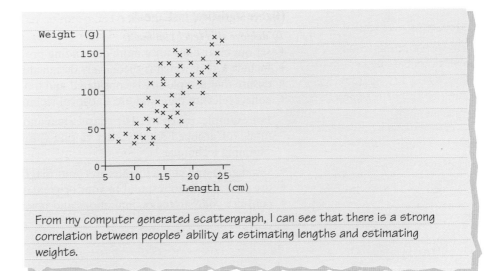

From my computer generated scattergraph, I can see that there is a strong correlation between peoples' ability at estimating lengths and estimating weights.

In this unit we have tried to give you some hints on approaching statistical coursework to gain your best possible mark.

This statistics is often useful in investigative tasks:

♦ Calculating averages (mean, median and mode)
♦ Finding the range
♦ Pie charts, bar charts, stem and leaf diagrams
♦ Constructing a cumulative frequency graph
♦ Finding the interquartile range
♦ Histograms
♦ Calculating the standard deviation
♦ Drawing a scatter graph and line of best fit
♦ Sampling techniques
♦ Discussing bias

Summary

These are the grade criteria your coursework will be marked by:

Foundation statistical task (grade E/F)

To achieve this level you must:
♦ set out reasonably clear aims and include a plan
♦ ensure that the sample size is of an appropriate size (about 25)
♦ collect data and make use of statistical techniques and calculations

For example: pie charts, bar charts, stem and leaf diagrams, mean, median, mode and scattergraphs

♦ summarise and interpret some of your diagrams and calculations

Intermediate statistical task (grade C)

To achieve this level you must:
♦ set out clear aims and include a plan designed to meet those aims
♦ ensure that the sample size is of an appropriate size (about 50)
♦ give reasons for your choice of sample
♦ collect data and make use of statistical techniques and calculations

For example: pie charts, bar charts, stem and leaf diagrams, mean, median, mode (of grouped data), scatter graphs and cumulative frequency

♦ summarise and correctly interpret your diagrams and calculations
♦ consider your strategies and how successful they were

335

Higher statistical task (grade A)

To achieve this level you must:

- set out clear aims for a more demanding problem
- include a plan which is specifically designed to meet those aims
- ensure that sample size is considered and limitations discussed
- collect relevant data and use statistical techniques and calculations

  For example: pie charts, bar charts, stem and leaf diagrams, mean, median, mode (of grouped data), scatter graphs, cumulative frequency, histograms and sampling techniques

- summarise and correctly interpret your diagrams and calculations
- use your results to respond to your original question
- consider your strategies, limitations and possible improvements

Past exam questions

Practice exam questions

Formula sheet

In the GCSE examination you will be given a formula sheet like this one.
You should use it as an aid to memory, and it will be useful to become familiar with the information on the sheet.
The formula sheet is the same for all Examining Groups.

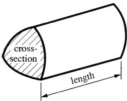

Volume of a prism = area of cross section $\times$ length

Volume of sphere = $\frac{4}{3}\pi r^3$

Surface area of sphere = $4\pi r^2$

Volume of cone = $\frac{1}{3}\pi r^2 h$

Curved surface area of cone = $\pi r l$

In any triangle ABC

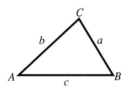

Sine Rule $\dfrac{a}{\sin A} = \dfrac{b}{\sin B} = \dfrac{c}{\sin C}$

Cosine Rule $a^2 = b^2 + c^2 - 2bc\,\cos A$

Area of triangle = $\frac{1}{2}ab\,\sin C$

The Quadratic Equation

The solutions of $ax^2 + bx + c = 0$ where $a \neq 0$, are given by

$$x = \frac{-b \pm \sqrt{(b^2 - 4ac)}}{2a}$$

Number

N1   Calculate the value of

$$\frac{21.7 \times 32.1}{16.20 - 2.19}$$

Give your answer correct to 3 significant figures.

[Edexcel]

N2   Sally estimates the value of $\dfrac{42.8 \times 63.7}{285}$ to be 8.

    a   Write down three numbers Sally could use to get her estimate.

    b   Without finding the exact value of $\dfrac{42.8 \times 63.7}{285}$, explain why it must be **more** than 8.

[Edexcel]

N3 $$p = 8 \times 10^3,$$
$$q = 2 \times 10^4$$

    a   Find the value of $p \times q$.
        Give your answer in standard form.

    b   Find the value of $p + q$.
        Give your answer as an ordinary number.

[Edexcel]

N4   **a**   Work out an estimate for

$$\frac{3.08 \times 693.89}{0.47}$$

    The length of a rod is 98 cm correct to the nearest centimetre.

    b   **i**   Write down the maximum value that 98 cm could be.
       ii   Write down the minimum value that 98 cm could be.

[Edexcel]

N5   The label on a jar of coffee says 'This 200 gram jar of coffee makes approximately 110 cups of coffee.'
200 grams is correct to 3 significant figures.
110 cups is correct to 2 significant figures.

    a   For the weight of the coffee in the jar write down
       i   the least upper bound
      ii   the greatest lower bound.

    b   For the number of cups of coffee write down
       i   the least upper bound
      ii   the greatest lower bound.

    c   Calculate the least upper bound for the mean weight of coffee in each cup.
       Write down all the figures on your calculator display.

[Edexcel]

N6 £500 is invested for 2 years at 6% per annum compound interest.

a Work out the total interest earned over the two years.

£250 is invested for 3 years at 7% per annum compound interest.

b By what single number must £250 be multiplied to obtain the total amount at the end of the 3 years?

[Edexcel]

N7 Fred imports cars from the USA. He sells them in the UK.
In May 1996, he bought a car in the USA for $24 000.
The exchange rate was £1 = $1.50.
It cost him £900 to import the car.
He sold the car in the UK. He made a profit of 20% on his total costs.

a Calculate the selling price of the car. Give your answer in pounds.

Fred's selling price in May 1996 for a car was 12.5% more than his selling price for the same model of car in May 1995.
In May 1996, the selling price of a car was £22 680.

b Calculate the selling price of the same model of car in May 1995.

[Edexcel]

N8 A shop is having a sale. Each day, prices are reduced by 20% of the price on the previous day.
Before the start of the sale, the price of a television is £450.
On the first day of the sale, the price is reduced by 20%.

a Work out the price of the television on
  i   the first day of the sale,
  ii the third day of the sale.

On the first day of the sale, the price of a cooker is £300.

b Work out the price of the cooker before the start of the sale.

[Edexcel]

N9 A clothes shop has a sale.
All the original prices are reduced by 24% to give the sale price.
The sale price of a jacket is £36.86.
Work out the original price of the jacket.

[Edexcel]

N10 Joe put £5000 in a building society savings account.
Compound interest at 4.8% was added at the end of each year.

a Calculate the total amount of money in Joe's savings account at the end of 3 years. Give your answer to the nearest penny.

Sarah also put a sum of money in a building society savings account.
Compound interest at 5% was added at the end of each year.

b Work out the single number by which Sarah has to multiply her sum of money to find the total amount she will have after 3 years.

[Edexcel]

N11   The price of a new television is £423.
This price includes Value Added Tax (VAT) at $17\frac{1}{2}\%$.

a   Work out the cost of the television **before** VAT was added.

By the end of each year, the value of a television has fallen by 12% of its value at the start of that year.
The value of a television was £423 at the start of the first year.

b   Work out the value of the television at the end of the **third** year.
Give your answer to the nearest penny.

[Edexcel]

N12   A shop has a sale of jackets and shirts.
In the sale there are a total of 120 jackets and shirts.
The jackets and shirts are in the ratio 5 : 3.

Work out the number of jackets.

[Edexcel]

N13   Jack shares £180 between his two children Ruth and Ben.
The ratio of Ruth's share to Ben's share is 5 : 4.

a   Work out how much each child is given.

Ben then gives 10% of his share to Ruth.

b   Work out the percentage of the £180 that Ruth now has.

[Edexcel]

N14   Here is a number pattern that describes the arrangement of counters.

a   Copy and complete the pattern for the 3rd, 4th, 10th and nth row.

1st row 1^2 = 0^2 +   1

2nd row 2^2 = 1^2 +   2   +   1

3rd row 3^2 = ...   +   3   +   2

4th row 4^2 = ...   + ...   +   3

10th row 10^2 = ...   + ...   + ...

nth row n^2 = ...   + ...   + ...

b   Show that the right hand side of the nth row simplifies to n^2.

[Edexcel]

N15 The table shows the number of hours of sunshine and the rainfall, in centimetres, in each of six places one day in December.

	Number of hours of sunshine	Rainfall in cm
Anglesey	5.7	0.06
Birmingham	4.4	0.35
Folkestone	3.6	0.42
Guernsey	7.2	0.08
Jersey	6.5	0.17
Torquay	6.9	0.04

The number of hours of sunshine is given correct to 1 decimal place. The rainfall is given correct to the nearest 0.01 cm.

a Write down
  i the lower bound of the number of hours of sunshine in Anglesey,
  ii the upper bound of the rainfall in Torquay.

b Calculate the lower bound of the sum of the number of hours of sunshine in Birmingham and in Folkestone.

c Calculate the greatest possible difference between the rainfall in Guernsey and the rainfall in Jersey.

[Edexcel]

N16 a Find the prime factors of 4891 by writing 4891 as $70^2 - 3^2$.

b By writing the nth term of the sequence 1, 3, 5, 7, ... as $(2n - 1)$, or otherwise, show that the difference between the squares of any two consecutive odd numbers is a multiple of 8.

[Edexcel]

N17 Use your calculator to work out the value of

$$\frac{\sqrt{12.3^2 + 7.9}}{1.8 \times 0.17}.$$

Give your answer correct to 1 decimal place.

[Edexcel]

N18 The distance from the Earth to the Moon is 250 000 miles.

a Express this number in standard form.

The distance from the Earth to the Sun is 9.3×10^7 miles.

b Calculate the value of the expression

$$\frac{\text{distance from the Earth to the Moon}}{\text{distance from the Earth to the Sun}}$$

giving your answer in standard form.

[Edexcel]

N19 Nesta invests £508 in a bank account paying compound interest at a rate of 10% per annum.

Calculate the total amount in Nesta's bank account after 2 years.

[Edexcel]

N20   There are 454 grams in 1 lb. There are 16 ounces in 1 lb.
Change $\frac{3}{4}$ ounce into grams.
Give your answer correct to 1 decimal place.

[Edexcel]

N21   The time taken for light to reach Earth from the edge of the known
universe is 14 000 000 000 years.

a   Write 14 000 000 000 in standard form.

Light travels at the speed of 9.46×10^{12} km/year.

b   Calculate the distance, in kilometres, from the edge of the known
universe to Earth.
Give your answer in standard form.

[Edexcel]

N22   The volume of Elspeth's house is 379.6 m³.

a   Write 379.6 in standard form.

The heat, H, needed to keep a house warm is given by the formula

$$H = \frac{5544 \times 1.4 \times 3 \times 22.5 \times \text{Volume of house}}{2000}$$

b   Calculate the value of H for Elspeth's house, giving your answer in
standard form.

[Edexcel]

N23   Use your calculator to evaluate

$$\frac{2.8(3.75 - 1.53)}{17.74 - 3.96}$$

[Edexcel]

N24   There are approximately 150 thousand ants in a tropical ant colony.

a   Write 150 thousand in standard form.

Each ant eats an average 2.4×10^{-3} kilograms of food per day.

b   Calculate the total average amount of food eaten by 150 thousand
ants in one day. Give your answer in kilograms.

[Edexcel]

N25   **a**   Calculate the value of

$$\frac{5.6(7.4 + 3.4)}{5 - 3.11}$$

b   Use your answer to part **a** to write down the values of

i $\dfrac{5 - 3.11}{5.6(7.4 + 3.4)}$

ii $\dfrac{50 - 31.1}{5.6(0.74 + 0.34)}$

[Edexcel]

N26   The speed of light is approximately 300 000 000 m/s.

a   Write 300 000 000 in standard index form.

b   Calculate the time, in seconds, light takes to travel 1 metre.
Give your answer in standard index form.

[Edexcel]

N27 Sarah uses the formula

$$t = \frac{2s}{u + v}$$

She has to calculate the value of t when $s = 623.25$, $u = 11.37$ and $v = 87.22$

She estimates the value of t without using her calculator.

a **i** Write down the numbers Sarah could use in the formula to estimate the value of t.

ii Work out the estimate for the value of t that these numbers would give.

A calculator is to be used to work out the actual value of t.

b To what degree of accuracy would you give your calculator answer? Give a reason for your answer.

[Edexcel]

N28 $$E = \tfrac{1}{2}m(v^2 - u^2)$$

Calculate the value of E when $m = 15$, $v = -3$ and $u = 4$.

[Edexcel]

N29 In 1990, a charity sold $2\tfrac{1}{4}$ million lottery tickets at 25p each. 80% of the money obtained was kept by the charity.

a Calculate the amount of money kept by the charity.

In 1991, the price of a lottery ticket fell by 20%.
Sales of lottery tickets increased by 20%.
80% of the money obtained was kept by the charity.

b Calculate the percentage change in the amount of money kept by the charity.

[Edexcel]

N30 Use the formula

$$A = \tfrac{1}{4}c\sqrt{(4a^2 - c^2)}$$

to calculate the value of A given that $c = 7.23$ and $a = 8.76$.

Give your answer correct to 1 decimal place.

[Edexcel]

N31 Work out $4 \times 10^8 - 4 \times 10^6$.

Give your answer in standard form.

[Edexcel]

N32 The mass of a neutron is 1.675×10^{-24} grams.

Calculate the total mass of 1500 neutrons.

Give your answer in standard form.

[Edexcel]

Algebra

A1 Using trial and improvement, or otherwise, solve the equation
$$t^3 + t = 17$$
Show ALL your working and give your answer correct to 2 decimal places.
[Edexcel]

A2 Expand and simplify
  i $(2x - 3)(x + 4)$
  ii $(x^2 + y^2)^2$
[Edexcel]

A3 **a** Solve
  i $7 - \dfrac{3x}{2} = 11$
  ii $\dfrac{4}{y} + 7 = 2$
  b **i** Factorise
      $x^2 + 4x - 12$
  Hence, or otherwise,
    ii Solve
      $x^2 + 4x - 12 = 0$
[Edexcel]

A4 **i** Solve the inequality $3n > -8$
  ii Write down the smallest integer which satisfies the inequality $3n > -8$
[Edexcel]

A5 **a** Expand and simplify
      $(2x + 1)(x - 3)$
  b Simplify
      $3a^3 \times 2ab^2$
  c Factorise completely
      $2t^2 + 4t$
  d Factorise completely
      $9x^2 - 4$
[Edexcel]

A6 A solution of the equation
$$x^3 - 9x = 5$$
is between 3 and 4.
Use the method of trial and improvement to find this solution.
Give your answer correct to 2 decimal places. You must show all your working.
[Edexcel]

A7   **a**   Simplify

       i $\dfrac{p^6}{p^2}$,   **ii** $q^3 \times q$,   **iii** $(4x^3)^2$.

   b   Simplify

       i $3a^2 \times 2a^2 b^3$,   **ii** $(2a^2)^{-3}$.

   c   Factorise completely

       $9x^2 y - 6xy^3$.

[Edexcel]

A8   **a**   Simplify

       $14a^6 \div 2a^2$

   b   Simplify

       $c^9 d^{-2} \times c^{-3} d$

   c   Simplify

       $(p^{-2})^{-4}$

   d   Simplify

       $(25m^6)^{\frac{1}{2}}$

   e   Solve the equation

       $x^2 - 6x - 27 = 0$

   f   Factorise

       $2y^2 - 11y + 12$

[Edexcel]

A9   **a**   Expand

       $x(x + 4)$.

   b   Solve the simultaneous equations

       $x + 8y = 5$

       $3x - 4y = 8$.

[Edexcel]

A10   **a**   Factorise

       $2x + 8y$.

   b   Factorise completely

       $3ac^2 - 6ac$.

   c   Factorise

       $x^2 - 9x + 18$.

[Edexcel]

A11 **a** Multiply out
$$t^2(t^3 - t^4)$$

b Multiply out and simplify
$$3(2a + 6) - 2(3a - 6)$$

c Simplify
$$\frac{12a^2b}{4ab}$$

The number x lies between 0 and 1.

d Write the following five expressions in order of size. Put the smallest one first.
$$x^2, \quad \sqrt{x}, \quad x^3, \quad \frac{1}{\sqrt{x}}, \quad x$$

The number x and the number y both lie between 0 and 1.

e Which of these expressions can have a value greater than 1?
$$xy, \quad xy^2, \quad (xy)^2, \quad \frac{x}{y}, \quad \sqrt{\left(\frac{x}{y}\right)}$$

[Edexcel]

A12 **a** Expand and simplify
$$5(3x + 1) - 2(4x - 3).$$

b Expand and simplify
$$(x + 5)(x - 3).$$

c Factorise completely
$$6a^2 - 9ab.$$

[Edexcel]

A13 The equation
$$x^3 - 5x = 38$$

has a solution between 3 and 4.
Use a trial and improvement method to find this solution.
Give your answer correct to 1 decimal place.
You must show ALL your working.

[Edexcel]

A14
$$C = 180R + 2000$$

The formula gives the capacity, C litres, of a tank needed to supply water to R hotel rooms.
Make R the subject of the formula $C = 180R + 2000$.

[Edexcel]

A15 **a** Calculate $\frac{1}{3} + \frac{1}{5}$
Give your answer as an exact fraction.

 b Express as a single fraction
$$\frac{1}{2n-1} + \frac{1}{2n+1}$$
$\frac{1}{3} + \frac{1}{5} = \frac{v}{s}$ where v and s are positive integers.

 c Show that there is a right-angled triangle with sides of length v cm, s cm and t cm, where t is also a positive integer.
$$\frac{1}{2n-1} + \frac{1}{2n+1} = \frac{x}{y}$$ where n, x and y are positive integers.

 d Show that there is a right-angled triangle with sides x cm, y cm and z cm, where z is also a positive integer.

[Edexcel]

A16 **a** Factorise $p^2 - q^2$
Here is a sequence of numbers
$$0, 3, 8, 15, 24, 35, 48, \ldots$$

 b Write down an expression for the nth term of this sequence.

 c Show algebraically that the product of **any** two consecutive terms of the sequence
$$0, 3, 8, 15, 24, 35, 48, \ldots$$
can be written as the product of four consecutive integers.

[Edexcel]

A17 **a** Copy this grid and draw the graph of $y = x^2 - x - 4$.
Use values of x between -2 and $+3$.

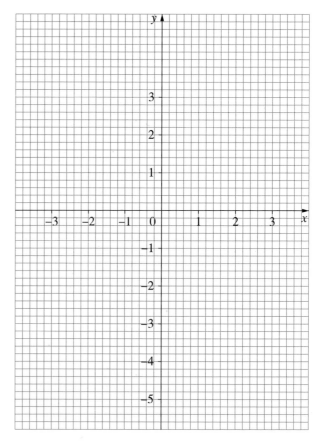

b Use your graph to write down an estimate for
  i the minimum value of y.
  ii the solutions of the equation $x^2 - x - 4 = 0$
  iii $(x + y)^2 - (x - y)^2$

A18

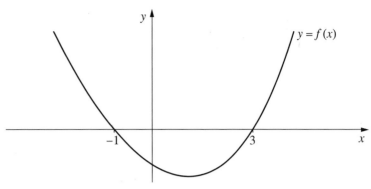

[Edexcel]

The diagram shows the curve with equation $y = f(x)$, where
$f(x) = x^2 - 2x - 3$.

a On the same diagram sketch the curve with equation $y = f(x - 2)$.
  Label the points where this curve cuts the x-axis.

The curve with equation $y = f(x)$ meets the curve with equation
$y = f(x - a)$ at the point P.

b Calculate the x coordinate of the point P. Give your answer in terms
  of a.

The curve with equation $y = x^2 - 2x - 3$ is reflected in the y-axis.

c Find the equation of this new curve.

[Edexcel]

A19

A

B

C

D

E

F

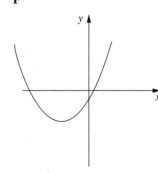

Each of the equations in the table represents one of the graphs A to F.
Copy the table below.
Write the letter of each graph in the correct place in the table.

Equation	Graph
$y = x^2 + 3x$	
$y = x - x^3$	
$y = x^3 - 2x$	
$y = x^2 + 2x - 4$	
$y = \dfrac{4}{x}$	
$y = x^2 + 3$	

[Edexcel]

A20 This is a sketch of the curve with equation $y = f(x)$.

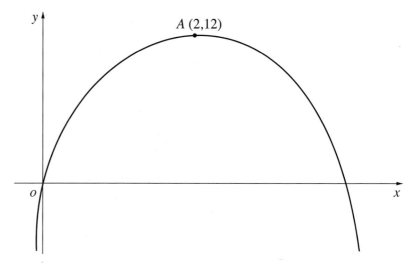

The vertex of the curve is $A(2, 12)$.
Write down the coordinates of the vertex for each of the curves having
the following equations.

a $y = f(x) + 6$

b $y = f(x + 3)$

c $y = f(-x)$

d $y = f(4x)$

[Edexcel]

A21

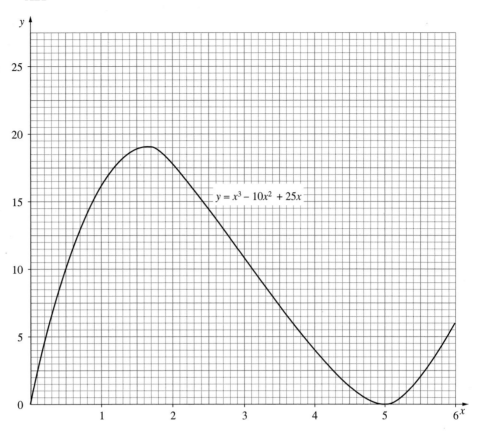

Part of the graph of $y = x^3 - 10x^2 + 25x$ has been drawn on the grid.

a Calculate an estimate for the gradient of the curve at the point (1, 16).

b Calculate an estimate for the value of the area enclosed by the curve, the line $x = 4$ and the x-axis.

[Edexcel]

A22

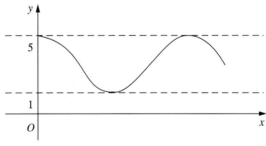

The diagram shows a sketch of part of the curve with equation

$$y = p + q \cos x°$$

where p and q are integers.

a Find the values of the integers p and q.

b Find the two values of x between 0 and 360 for which

$$p + q \cos x° = 2.$$

[Edexcel]

A23   The diagram shows the graph of
$$y = x^3 - 12x$$

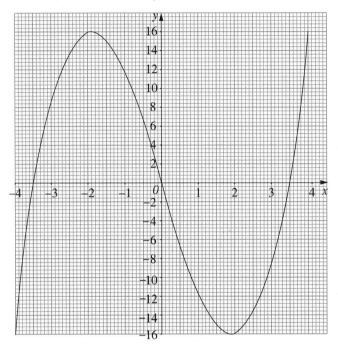

for values of x from -4 to 4. Make a copy of the graph.

a   Use the graph to find estimates of the 3 solutions of the equation
$$x^3 - 12x = 0.$$

b   By drawing a suitable straight line on the grid, find estimates of the solutions of the equation
$$x^3 - 12x - 5 = 0.$$

Label clearly the straight line that you have drawn.

c   By drawing a suitable straight line on the grid, find estimates of the solutions of the equation
$$x^3 - 14x + 5 = 0.$$

Label clearly the straight line that you have drawn.

[Edexcel]

A24 The graph of $y = x^3 - 2x^2 - 4x$ has been drawn on the grid below.

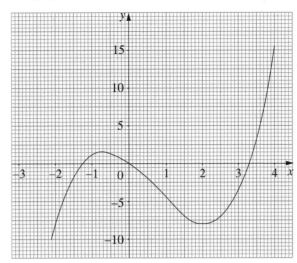

a Use the graph to find estimates of the solutions to the equation
i $x^3 - 2x^2 - 4x = 0$,
ii $x^3 - 2x^2 - 4x = 1$
Make a copy of the graph.

b By drawing a clearly labelled straight line on the grid, find estimates of the solutions to the equation
$x^3 - 2x^2 - 6x = 1$.

[Edexcel]

A25

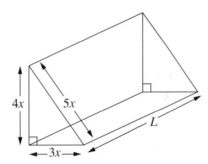

The diagram shows a prism.
The cross-section of the prism is a right-angled triangle.
The lengths of the sides of the triangle are $3x$ cm, $4x$ cm and $5x$ cm.
The total length of all the edges of the prism is E cm.

a Show that the length, L cm, of the prism is given by the formula
$L = \frac{1}{3}(E - 24x)$

[Edexcel]

A26

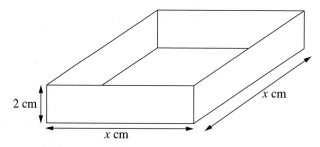

The diagram represents a tray.
The base of the tray is a square with sides x cm long.
The sides of the tray are 2 cm high.
The weight, W grams, of the tray is given by the formula
$W = ax^2 + bx$
where a and b are constants.
The values of W for some values of x are shown in the table.

x	5	10	15	20	25
W	34	122	260	450	690

a Work out the values of $\dfrac{W}{x}$ then copy and complete the table.

x	5	10	15	20	25
$\dfrac{W}{x}$				22.5	27.6

b Use the values from your table in **a** to plot a graph of $\dfrac{W}{x}$ against x.

c Use your graph to estimate the values of a and b.
The base of a tray is a square with sides 50 cm long.
d Calculate an estimate of the weight of this tray.

[Edexcel]

A27

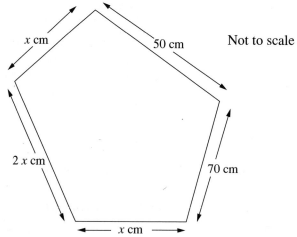

Not to scale

The perimeter of the pentagon is 200 cm.
Work out the value of x.

[Edexcel]

A28

3x + 2

2x

The diagram shows a rectangle with length $3x + 2$ and width $2x$.
All measurements are given in centimetres.
The perimeter of the rectangle is P centimetres.
The area of the rectangle is A square centimetres.

a Write down an expression in its simplest form, in terms of x, for
  i P,
  ii A.

$P = 44$.

b Work out the value of A.

[Edexcel]

A29 The diagram shows a rectangular pond and a path.
The outside edges of the path form the rectangle $ABCD$.

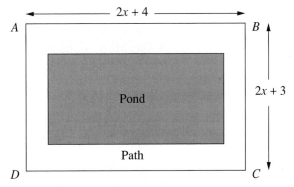

2x + 4

A   B   Diagram not
                              accurately drawn

Pond   2x + 3

Path

D   C

The length, in metres, of AB is $2x + 4$.
The length, in metres, of BC is $2x + 3$.

a Write down, in terms of x, an expression for the perimeter of the
rectangle $ABCD$.
Write your expression in its simplest form.

The area of the pond is 12 m^2.

b Show that the area, in m^2, of the path is $4x^2 + 14x$.

$x = 1.2$

[Edexcel]

A30 **a** Expand and simplify
$$5(3x + 1) - 2(4x - 3).$$

b Expand and simplify
$$(x + 5)(x - 3).$$

c Factorise completely
$$6a^2 - 9ab.$$

[Edexcel]

A31
$$t = \frac{8(p+q)}{pq}$$
$$p = 2.71$$
$$q = -3.97$$

a Calculate the value of t.
Give your answer to a suitable degree of accuracy.

b Make q the subject of the formula
$$t = \frac{8(p+q)}{pq}$$

[Edexcel]

A32 Make x the subject of the formula
$$y = \frac{x^2 + 4}{5}$$

[Edexcel]

A33 Using the method of trial and improvement, solve the equation
$$x^3 - 4x - 1 = 30$$
correct to one decimal place. You must show your working.

[Edexcel]

A34 The heat setting of a gas oven is called its Gas Mark.
A Gas Mark, G, may be converted to a temperature, F, in degrees Farenheit, using the formula
$$F = 25G + 250$$

a Factorise completely $25G + 250$.

A Gas Mark, G, may be converted to a temperature, C, in degrees Celsius using the formula
$$C = 14G + 121$$

b Make G the subject of the formula $C = 14G + 121$.

[Edexcel]

A35 Solve the simultaneous equations
$$2p - 3q = 7$$
$$p + q = 1$$

[Edexcel]

A36 **i** Solve the inequality
$$2n - 1 < n + 3$$

ii List the solutions that are positive integers.

[Edexcel]

A37 **a** Factorise $x^2 - y^2$

b Use your answer to **a** to work out the EXACT value of
$$123\ 456\ 789^2 - 123\ 456\ 788^2$$

The equation $x^2 - y^2 = 151$ has exactly one solution with x and y both positive integers.

c By replacing this equation by a suitable pair of simultaneous equations, find the values of x and y.

d Hence, or otherwise, find in terms of n, an integer value of x and an integer value of y for which
$$x^2 - y^2 = 2n + 1, \text{ where } n \text{ is an integer.}$$

[Edexcel]

A38 Use trial and improvement, or otherwise, to find the positive value of x for which

$$x^2 - x = 144$$

Use a copy of the table below to show your working.
Give your answer correct to 1 decimal place.

Trial number	Trial value	$x^2 - x$	Comment
1	5	20	too low
2			

[Edexcel]

A39 A formula is

$$v = \frac{x}{ut}$$

a Calculate the value of v when $x = 14.8$, $u = 2.8$ and $t = 5.2$. Give your answer correct to 1 decimal place.

b Write down a simple calculation which could be used to check that your answer in part **a** is sensible.

c Make t the subject of the formula.

[Edexcel]

A40 a Expand and simplify $(x + 5)(x - 3)$.

b Solve $x^2 - 5x - 14 = 0$

[Edexcel]

A41 Use the method of trial and improvement, or otherwise, to find the positive solution of

$$x^2 + x = 177.$$

Give your answer correct to 3 significant figures.

[Edexcel]

A42 The heat setting of a gas oven is called its Gas Mark.
A Gas Mark, G, may be converted to a temperature, F, in degrees Fahrenheit, using the formula

$$F = 25G + 250$$

a Factorise completely $25G + 250$.

A Gas Mark, G, may be converted to a temperature, C, in degrees Celsius, using the formula

$$C = 14G + 121$$

b Make G the subject of the formula $C = 14G + 121$.

c Use the formulas $F = 25G + 250$ and $C = 14G + 121$ **b** to express F in the form

$$F = kC + d.$$

Give the values of k and d correct to 2 significant figures.

[Edexcel]

A43 Mrs Rogers bought 3 blouses and 2 scarfs.
She paid £26.
Miss Summers bought 4 blouses and 1 scarf.
She paid £28.
The cost of a blouse was x pounds.
The cost of a scarf was y pounds.

a Use the information to write down two equations in x and y.

b Solve these equations to find the cost of one blouse.

[Edexcel]

A44 The cost, W pounds, of a chest of drawers may be calculated using the formula

$$W = k + md$$

k and m are constants and d is the number of drawers.
The cost of a chest of drawers with 4 drawers is £117.
The cost of a chest of drawers with 6 drawers is £149.
Use the information to find the value of m.

[Edexcel]

A45 Fred cycled from home to his friend's house and back again.
The distance from Fred's home to his friend's house is 20 km.
On his way from home to his friend's house, Fred cycled at x km per hour.
On the way back, Fred's speed had decreased by 2 km per hour.
It took Fred 4 hours altogether to cycle to his friend's house and back.

a Write down an equation for x.

b Show that the equation can be written as
$$x^2 - 12x + 10 = 0.$$

c Solve the equation in part **b**.
Give your answers correct to 1 decimal place.

Only one of the answers in part **c** can be Fred's speed.

d Explain why.

[Edexcel]

A46

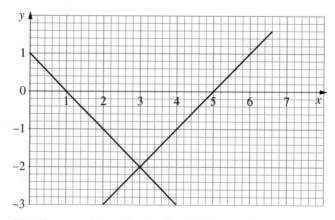

The diagram shows the graphs of the equations
$$x + y = 1 \qquad \text{and} \qquad y = x - 5$$
Use the diagram to solve the simultaneous equations
$$x + y = 1$$
$$y = x - 5$$

[Edexcel]

A47 $x^2 + 4x + 9$ can be written in the form $(x + p)^2 + q$, where p and q are integers.

    a   Find the value of
        i p
        ii q

    b   Hence, or otherwise,
        i   sketch the graph of $y = x^2 + 4x + 9$
        ii   write down the minimum value of $x^2 + 4x + 9$.

                                                          [Edexcel]

A48   The graph of $y = x^3 - 2x^2 - 4x$ has been drawn on the grid below.

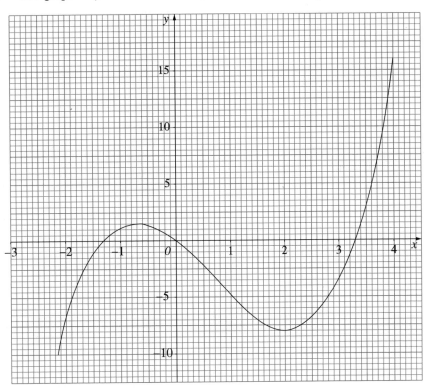

    a   Use the graph to find estimates of the solutions to the equation
        i $x^3 - 2x^2 - 4x = 0$,
        ii $x^3 - 2x^2 - 4x = 1$

    b   By drawing a clearly labelled straight line on a copy of the grid, find estimates of the solutions to the equation
$$x^3 - 2x^2 - 6x = 1.$$

                                                          [Edexcel]

A49 $y = x^3 - 4x - 1$

    a   Copy and complete the table of values

x	−2	−1	0	1	2	3
y		2	−1			14

    b   Draw the graph of $y = x^3 - 4x - 1$

    c   By drawing a suitable straight line on the graph, estimate a solution to the equation
$$x^3 - 4x - 3 = -4$$

                                                           [Edexcel]

Shape, space and measures

S1   The diagram shows a water tank.
The tank is a hollow cylinder joined to a hollow
hemisphere at the top.
The tank has a circular base.
The empty tank is slowly filled with water.

a   On a pair of axes, sketch a graph to show the
relation between

the volume, V cm^3, of water in the tank
and
the depth, d cm, of water in the tank.

Both the cylinder and the hemisphere have a
diameter of 46 cm.
The height of the tank is 90 cm.

b   Work out the volume of water which the
tank holds when it is full.
Give your answer correct to 3 significant
figures.

90 cm

46 cm

[Edexcel]

S2   Here are some expressions.

$\pi r^2 l$	$2\pi r^2$	$4\pi r^3$	$abrl$	$\dfrac{abl}{r}$	$3(a^2 + b^2)r$	πrl

The letters r, l, a and b represent lengths. π, 2, 3 and 4 are numbers that
have no dimensions.
List the three expressions that represent volumes.

[Edexcel]

S3

A skip is in the shape of a prism with cross-section *ABCD*.
AD = 2.3 m, *DC* = 1.3 m and *BC* = 1.7 m.
The width of the skip is 1.5 m

a   Calculate the area of the shape *ABCD*.

b   Calculate the volume of the skip.

The weight of an empty skip is 650 kg.
The skip is full to the top with sand.
1 m^3 of sand weighs 4300 kg.

c   Calculate the total weight of the skip and the sand.

[Edexcel]

S4

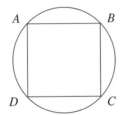

A, *B*, *C* and *D* are four points on the circumference of a circle.
ABCD is a square with sides 20 cm long.
Work out the diameter of the circle.
Give your answer correct to 3 significant figures.

[Edexcel]

S5   Diagram 1 and Diagram 2 show two circles with radii *R* and *r*, where
R > *r*.

Diagram **NOT**
accurately drawn

Diagram 1

The area of the shaded region is equal to the area of the smaller circle.

a   Express *R* in terms of *r*.

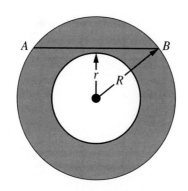

Diagram **NOT**
accurately drawn

Diagram 2

AB is a chord of the larger circle and a tangent to the smaller circle.

b Show that $AB = 2r$.

[Edexcel]

S6

Diagram **NOT**
accurately drawn

500 cm

A solid statue is contained within a hemisphere of diameter 500 cm.

a Calculate the total surface area of the hemisphere, including the base.
Give your answer in m², correct to 3 significant figures.

The solid statue has a height of 80 cm, and a mass of 1.5 kg.
A larger solid statue is geometrically similar and is made of the same material.
It has a height of 128 cm.

b Calculate the mass of the larger solid statue.
Give your answer in kg, correct to 3 significant figures.

[Edexcel]

S7

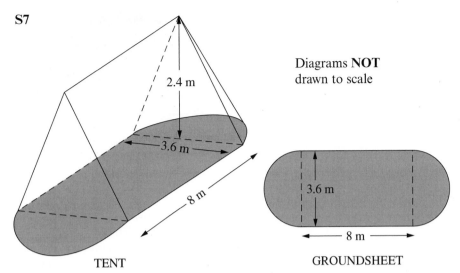

Diagrams **NOT**
drawn to scale

2.4 m

3.6 m

8 m

TENT

3.6 m

8 m

GROUNDSHEET

A tent has a groundsheet as its horizontal base.
The shape of the tent is a triangular prism of length 8 metres, with two
identical half right-circular cones, one at each end.
The vertical cross-section of the prism is an isosceles triangle of height
2.4 metres and base 3.6 metres.

a Calculate the area of the groundsheet.
Give your answer, in m², correct to one decimal place.

b Calculate the total volume of the tent.
Give your answer, in m³, correct to one decimal place.

[Edexcel]

S8

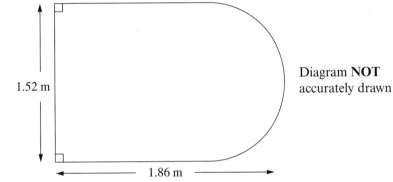

Diagram **NOT**
accurately drawn

1.52 m

1.86 m

A mat is made in the shape of a rectangle with a semicircle added at one
end.
The width of the mat is 1.52 metres.
The length of the mat is 1.86 metres.
Calculate the area of the mat.
Give your answer in square metres, correct to 2 decimal places.

[Edexcel]

S9 Here are 3 expressions

Expression	Length	Area	Volume	None of these
$3rl$				
$\dfrac{2(r+l)^2}{h}$				
$\dfrac{4\pi r^4}{3l}$				

Copy the table.

r, l and h are lengths.

π, 2, 3 and 4 are numbers and have no dimension.

Put a tick in the correct column to show whether the expression can be used for length, area, volume or none of these.

[Edexcel]

S10

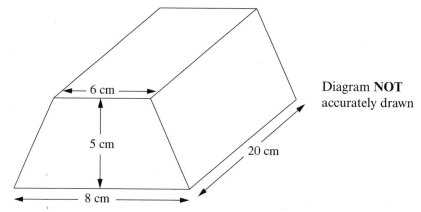

Diagram **NOT** accurately drawn

The diagram shows a prism.

The cross-section of the prism is a trapezium.

The lengths of the parallel sides of the trapezium are 8 cm and 6 cm.

The distance between the parallel sides of the trapezium is 5 cm.

The length of the prism is 20 cm.

a Work out the volume of the prism.

The prism is made out of gold.

Gold has a density of 19.3 grams per cm³.

b Work out the mass of the prism.
  Give your answer in kilograms.

[Edexcel]

S11

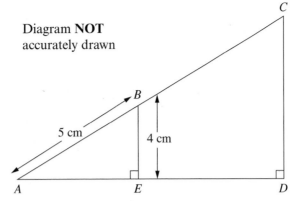

Diagram **NOT**
accurately drawn

5 cm

4 cm

$AB : AC = 1 : 3$

i   Work out the length of *CD*.
ii Work out the length of *BC*.

[Edexcel]

S12   Simone made a scale model of a 'hot rod' car on a scale of 1 to 12.5.
The height of the model car is 10 cm.

a   Work out the height of the real car.

The length of the real car is 5 m.

b   Work out the length of the model car. Give your answer in
centimetres.

The angle the windscreen made with the bonnet on the real car is 140°.

c   What is the angle the windscreen makes with the bonnet on the model
car?

The width of the windscreen in the real car is 119 cm correct to the
nearest centimetre.

d   Write down the smallest length this measurement could be.

[Edexcel]

S13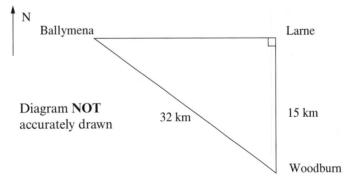

Diagram **NOT**
accurately drawn

32 km

15 km

Ballymena is due West of Larne.
Woodburn is 15 km due South of Larne.
Ballymena is 32 km from Woodburn.

a   Calculate the distance of Larne from Ballymena. Give your answer in
kilometres, correct to 1 decimal place.

b   Calculate the bearing of Ballymena from Woodburn.

[Edexcel]

S14

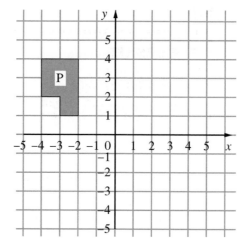

The shape **P** has been drawn on the grid. Make a copy of the grid.

a Reflect the shape **P** in the *y* axis.
Label the image **Q**.

b Rotate the shape **Q** through 180° about (0, 0).
Label this image **R**.

c Describe fully the single transformation which maps shape **P** to shape **R**.

[Edexcel]

S15

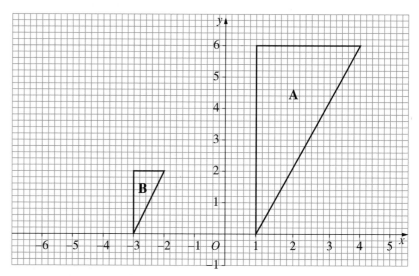

Describe fully the single transformation which maps triangle **A** to triangle **B**.

[Edexcel]

S16 $\mathbf{p} = \begin{pmatrix} 2 \\ 1 \end{pmatrix}$ and $\mathbf{q} = \begin{pmatrix} 1 \\ -2 \end{pmatrix}$.

a Write down as a column vector

   i $2\mathbf{p} + \mathbf{q}$,

   ii $\mathbf{p} - 2\mathbf{q}$.

A is the point (15, 15). *O* is the point (0, 0).
The vector $\overrightarrow{OA}$ can be written in the form $c\mathbf{p} + d\mathbf{q}$, where *c* and *d* are scalars.

b Using part **a**, or otherwise, find the values of *c* and *d*.

[Edexcel]

S17

THE SENATE

Petrol consumption:
9 litres per 100 km.

THE BRIGHTON

Petrol consumption:
30 miles per gallon.

1 km = $\frac{5}{8}$ mile. 1 gallon = 4.54 litre.

a Change 9 litres per 100 km into miles per gallon.

Correct to the nearest whole number, the petrol consumption of The Brighton is 30 miles per gallon.

b **i** Write down the maximum the petrol consumption could be.
    ii Write down the minimum the petrol consumption could be.

[Edexcel]

S18

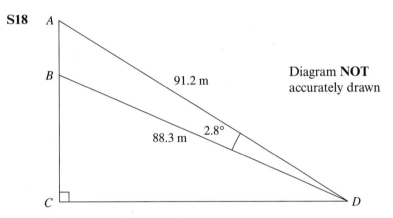

Diagram **NOT** accurately drawn

A statue stands on a column.
In the diagram AB represents the statue and BC represents the column.
Angle $ACD = 90°$.
Angle $BDA = 2.8°$.
$AD = 91.2$ m and $BD = 88.3$ m.
ABC is a vertical straight line.

a Calculate the height, AB, of the statue. Give your answer, in metres, correct to 3 significant figures.

b Calculate the height, BC, of the column. Give your answer, in metres, correct to 3 significant figures.

[Edexcel]

S19

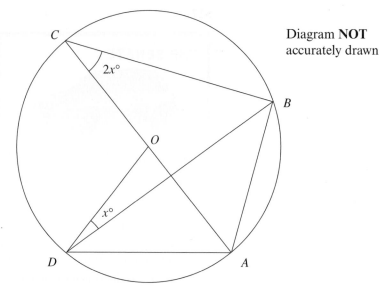

Diagram **NOT**
accurately drawn

A, B, C and D are points on the circumference of a circle centre O.
AC is a diameter of the circle.
Angle BDO = x°.
Angle BCA = 2x°.
Express, in terms of x, the size of

i   angle BDA,

ii   angle AOD,

iii   angle ABD.

[Edexcel]

S20

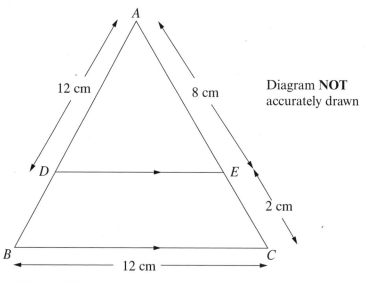

Diagram **NOT**
accurately drawn

DE is parallel to BC.
ADB and AEC are straight lines.

AD = 12 cm.	BC = 12 cm.
AE = 8 cm.	EC = 2 cm.

Calculate the length of

i   DE

ii   DB

[Edexcel]

S21

Diagram **NOT** accurately drawn

The diagram represents the frame for part of a building.
BC and *CD* are equal in length.
BD and *AE* are horizontal.

a Calculate the length *BC*.
   Give your answer correct to 3 significant figures.

b Calculate the size of the angle marked $x°$.
   Give your answer correct to 1 decimal place.

[Edexcel]

S22

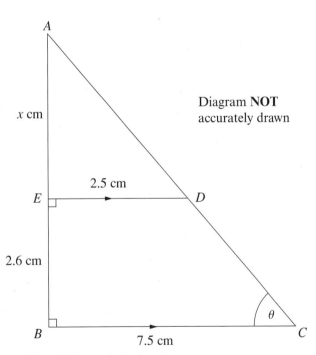

Diagram **NOT** accurately drawn

ABC is a right-angled triangle.
ED is parallel to *BC*.
$BC = 7.5$ cm, $ED = 2.5$ cm, $EB = 2.6$ cm.

a Calculate the area of trapezium *BCDE*.

$AE = x$ cm.

b Calculate the value of x.

The smallest angle of the trapezium is θ.
The lengths shown in the diagram are correct to the nearest millimetre.

c Calculate the least possible value for $\tan \theta$.

[Edexcel]

S23

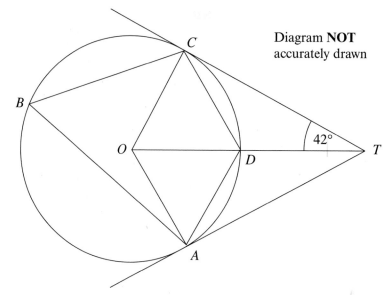

Diagram **NOT**
accurately drawn

A, *B*, *C* and *D* are points on the circumference of a circle.
TA and *TC* are tangents to the circle.
The centre of the circle is at *O*.
ODT is a straight line.
Angle *OTC* = 42°.

a Calculate the size of angle *COT*. Give reasons for your answer.

[Edexcel]

S24

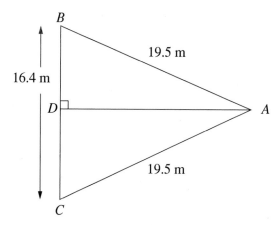

AB = 19.5 cm, *AC* = 19.5 cm and *BC* = 16.4 cm.
Angle *ADB* = 90°.
BDC is a straight line.
Calculate the length of *AD*.
Give your answer in centimetres, correct to 1 decimal place.

[Edexcel]

S25

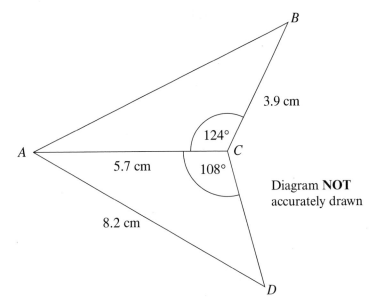

Diagram **NOT**
accurately drawn

$AC = 5.7$ cm.
$AD = 8.2$ cm.
$BC = 3.9$ cm.
Angle $ACD = 108°$.
Angle $ACB = 124°$.

a   Calculate the size of angle ADC.
    Give your answer correct to 1 decimal place.

b   Calculate the area of triangle ABC.
    Give your answer, in cm², correct to 3 significant figures.

c   Calculate the size of angle BAC.
    Give your answer correct to 1 decimal place.

[Edexcel]

S26

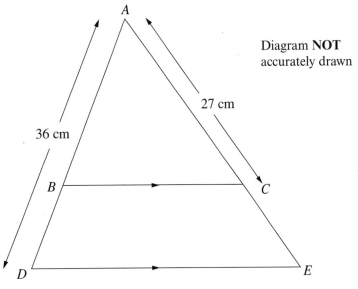

Diagram **NOT**
accurately drawn

BC is parallel to DE.
AB is twice as long as BD.
$AD = 36$ cm and $AC = 27$ cm

a   Work out the length of AB.

b   Work out the length of AE.

[Edexcel]

S27

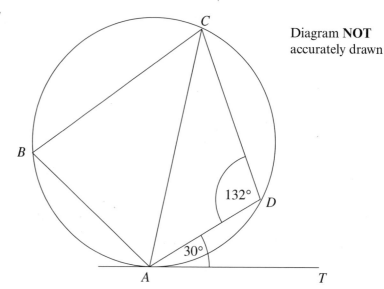

Diagram **NOT**
accurately drawn

A, *B*, *C* and *D* are four points on the circumference of a circle.
TA is the tangent to the circle at *A*.
Angle *DAT* = 30°.
Angle *ADC* = 132°.

a **i** Calculate the size of angle *ABC*.
    ii Explain your method.

b **i** Calculate the size of angle *CBD*.
    ii Explain your method.

[Edexcel]

S28

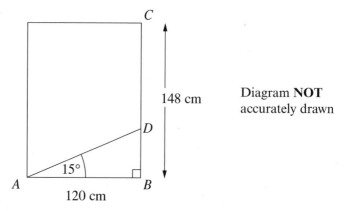

Diagram **NOT**
accurately drawn

AB and *BC* are two sides of a rectangle.
AB = 120 cm and *BC* = 148 cm.
D is a point on *BC*.
Angle *BAD* = 15°.

a Work out the length of *CD*.
   Give your answer correct to the nearest centimetre.

148 is correct to 3 significant figures.
120 is correct to 3 significant figures.
15 is correct to the nearest whole number.

b Write down the three values which should be used to work out the
   lower bound for the length of *CD*.

[Edexcel]

S29

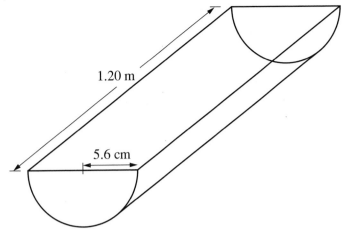

The diagram represents a metal girder in the shape of a half cylinder. The radius of each semi-circular end is 5.6 centimetres, correct to the nearest tenth of a centimetre.

a Write down the upper and lower bounds of the radius.

The length of the girder is 1.20 metres, correct to the nearest centimetre.

b Write down the upper and lower bounds of the length.

c Calculate the upper and lower bounds of the volume of the girder. Give your answer in cubic centimetres.

The girder is melted down and made into a sphere. No metal is wasted.

d Calculate the upper and lower bounds of the radius of the sphere. Give your answer in centimetres.

[Edexcel]

S30

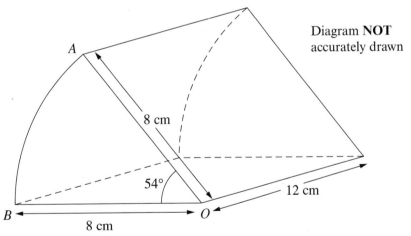

Diagram **NOT** accurately drawn

The diagram represents a prism. It has a cross-section in the shape of a sector *AOB* of a circle, centre *O*. The radius of the sector is 8 cm and the length of the prism is 12 cm. Angle *AOB* = 54°.

a Calculate
  i the area of sector *AOB*,
  ii the total surface area of the prism.

A geometrically similar prism is made of the same material as the original prism and has a mass 64 times the mass of the original prism.

b Calculate the length of the heavier prism.

[Edexcel]

S31

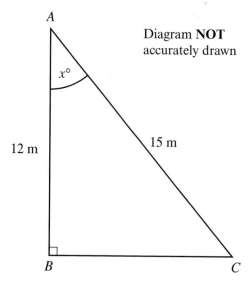

Diagram **NOT**
accurately drawn

$x°$

12 m

15 m

A

B

C

Calculate the size of the angle marked $x°$.
Give your answer correct to one decimal place.

[Edexcel]

S32   On a farm, wheat grain is stored in a
cylindrical tank.
The cylindrical tank has an internal diameter
of 6 metres and a height of 9 metres.

a Calculate the volume, in m^3, of the tank.
Give your answer correct to 2 decimal
places.

1 m^3 of wheat grain weighs 0.766 tonnes.

b Calculate the weight, in tonnes, of wheat
grain in the storage tank when it is full.

A scale model is to be made of the farm.
The scale of the model is 1 : 50.
A water tank on the real farm has a volume of 120 m^3.

c Calculate the volume, in cm^3, of the similar water tank in the scale
model.

[Edexcel]

9 m

6 m

S33 $\sin y° = 0.7$ and $y \geqslant 90$.
Write down two values of y.
Give your answers correct to 1 decimal place.

[Edexcel]

S34

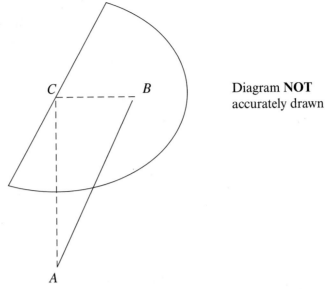

Diagram **NOT**
accurately drawn

The diagram represents a semi-circular shelf with a diameter of 60 cm.

a Calculate the area of the shelf.

The shelf is horizontal.
It is fixed to a vertical wall.
A support AB is fixed to the wall at A and to the shelf at B.
A is vertically below C, the centre of the semi-circle.
AB = 25 cm and BC = 14 cm

b Calculate the length of AC.

[Edexcel]

S35

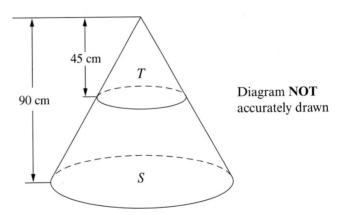

Diagram **NOT**
accurately drawn

The diagram represents a metal cone of height 90 cm made in two parts,
labelled T and S. The top part, T, has a height of 45 cm.
Given that the volume of S and T together is $10\,500\pi \text{cm}^3$

a Calculate the volume of S.

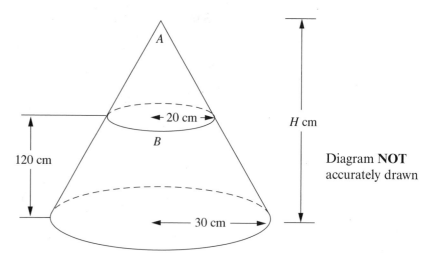

A second cone is also made up of two parts A and B. The radius of the top part is 20 cm and the radius of the base, B, is 30 cm. The height of bottom part B is 120 cm.

c   Calculate the height, H cm, of the cone.

[Edexcel]

S36   A cylinder is 13 cm high.
The diameter of its base is 1.76 m.

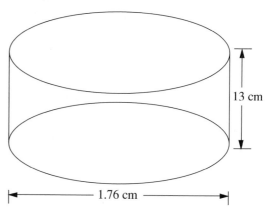

Calculate the volume, in cm^3, of the cylinder.
Give your answer correct to 3 significant figures.

[Edexcel]

S37   A cylindrical can has a radius of 6 centimetres.
The capacity of the can is 2000 cm^3.
Calculate the height of the can.
Give your answer correct to 1 decimal place.

[Edexcel]

S38

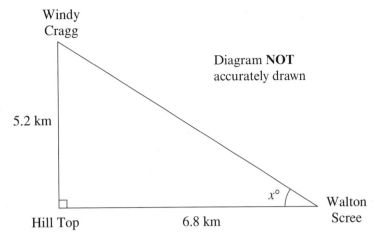

The diagram shows three places, which are on the same horizontal plane.
Windy Cragg is 5.2 km due North of Hill Top.
Walton Scree is 6.8 km due East of Hill Top.

a Calculate the distance from Walton Scree to Windy Cragg.
Give your answer correct to 1 decimal place.

b Calculate the size of the angle marked $x°$ in the diagram.
Give your answer correct to 1 decimal place.

The distance of 5.2 km has been rounded to 1 decimal place.

c Write down the minimum distance it could be.

[Edexcel]

S39

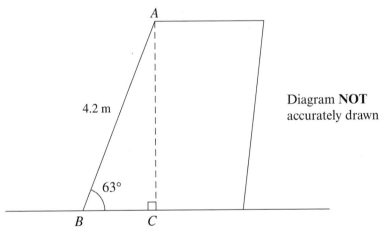

The diagram represents the tailfin of an aeroplane.
$AB = 4.2$ metres and angle $ABC = 63°$.

a Calculate the length AC.
Give your answer in metres correct to 2 decimal places.

Robin builds a scale model of the aeroplane using a scale of $1 : 72$.
The length of the real aeroplane is 16.8 metres.

b Calculate the length, in centimetres, of the scale model.
Give your answer correct to one decimal place.

[Edexcel]

S40

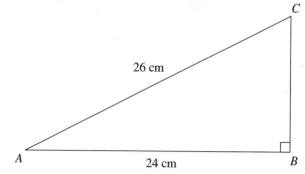

Diagram **NOT** accurately drawn

In the diagram, triangle *ABC* is right-angled at *B*.
AB = 24 cm and *AC* = 26 cm.

a Calculate the length of *BC*.

b Calculate the size of angle *A*.
Give your answer correct to 3 significant figures.

[Edexcel]

S41

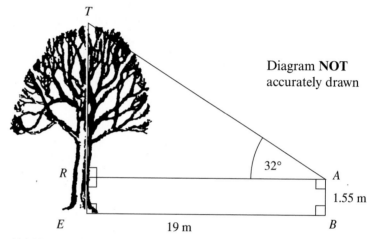

Diagram **NOT** accurately drawn

Abbi is standing on level ground, at *B*, a distance of 19 metres away from the foot *E* of a tree *TE*.
She measures the angle of elevation of the top of the tree at a height of 1.55 metres above the ground as 32°.
Calculate the height *TE* of the tree. Give your answer correct to 3 significant figures.

[Edexcel]

S42

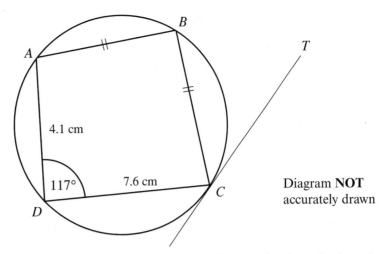

Diagram **NOT**
accurately drawn

In the diagram, *A*, *B*, *C* and *D* are points on the circumference of a
circle.
AB = *BC* and angle *ADC* = 117°.
A tangent is drawn from *T*, touching the circle at *C*.

a Calculate the size of angle *BCT*. Give reasons for the steps in your
working.

AD = 4.1 cm and *CD* = 7.6 cm

b Calculate the length of *AC*. Give your answer correct to 3 significant
figures.

[Edexcel]

S43

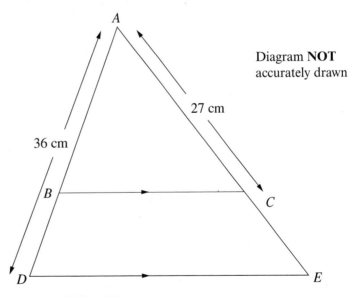

Diagram **NOT**
accurately drawn

BC is parallel to *DE*.
AB is twice as long as *BD*.
AD = 36 cm and *AC* = 27 cm

a Work out the length of *AB*.

b Work out the length of *AE*.

[Edexcel]

S44

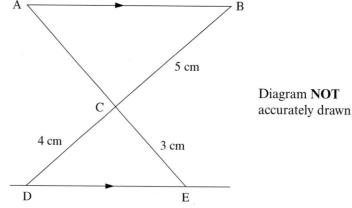

Diagram **NOT**
accurately drawn

In the diagram CD = 4 metres, CE = 3 metres and BC = 5 metres.
AB is parallel to DE.
ACE and BCD are straight lines.

a Explain why triangle ABC is similar to triangle EDC.

b Calculate the length of AC.

[Edexcel]

S45

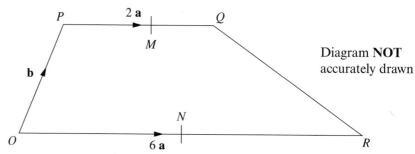

Diagram **NOT**
accurately drawn

OPQR is a trapezium. *PQ* is parallel to *OR*.
$$\overrightarrow{OP} = \mathbf{b}, \ \overrightarrow{PQ} = 2\mathbf{a}, \ \overrightarrow{OR} = 6\mathbf{a}.$$

M is the midpoint of *PQ*.
N is the midpoint of *OR*.

a Find, in terms of **a** and **b**, the vectors
  i $\overrightarrow{OM}$,
  ii $\overrightarrow{MN}$.

X is the midpoint of *MN*.

b Find, in terms of **a** and **b**, the vector $\overrightarrow{OX}$.

The lines *OX* and *PQ* are extended to meet at the point *Y*.

c Find, in terms of **a** and **b**, the vector $\overrightarrow{NY}$.

[Edexcel]

S46

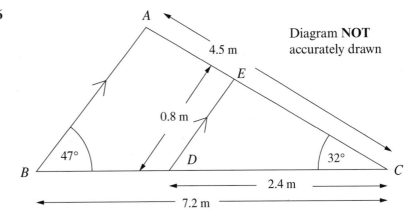

Diagram **NOT** accurately drawn

In the diagram *BA* is parallel to *DE*.
AEC and *BDC* are straight lines.
AC = 4.5 m, *DE* = 0.8, *CD* = 2.4 m, *BC* = 7.2 m
Angle *ABC* = 47°, Angle *BCA* = 32°

a Calculate the length of *EC*.

b Calculate the length of *AB*.

[Edexcel]

S47

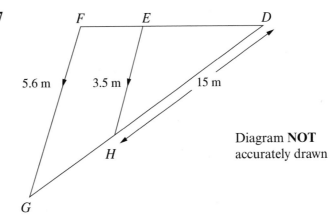

Diagram **NOT** accurately drawn

In the diagram *FG* = 5.6 metres, *EH* = 3.5 metres and *DH* = 15 metres.
EH is parallel to *FG*. *FED* and *DHG* are straight lines.
Calculate the length of *DG*.

[Edexcel]

S48

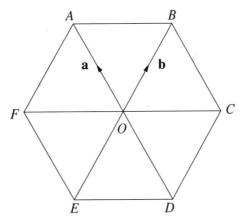

ABCDEF is a regular hexagon

$$\overrightarrow{OA} = \mathbf{a}, \overrightarrow{OB} = \mathbf{b}$$

a   Write down, in terms of **a** and **b**, the vectors
   i $\overrightarrow{AB}$
   ii $\overrightarrow{FC}$

b   Write down one geometrical fact about AB and FC which could be
   deduced from your answers to part **a**.

[Edexcel]

S49

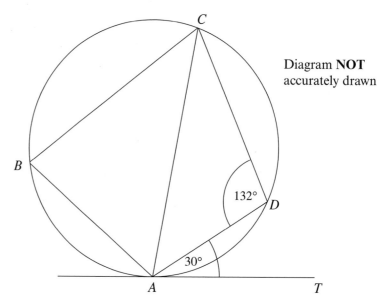

Diagram **NOT**
accurately drawn

A, B, C and D are four points on the circumference of a circle.
TA is the tangent to the circle at A.
Angle $DAT = 30°$.
Angle $ADC = 132°$.

a   i   Calculate the size of angle ABC.
   ii Explain your method.

b   i   Calculate the size of angle CBD.
   ii Explain your method.

c   Explain why AC cannot be a diameter of the circle.

[Edexcel]

S50

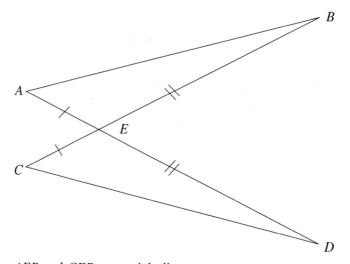

AED and CEB are straight lines.
$AE = CE$ and $BE = DE$.
Explain why triangles ABE and CDE are congruent.

[Edexcel]

S51

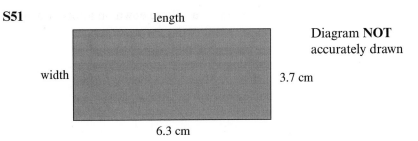

length

Diagram **NOT** accurately drawn

width   3.7 cm

6.3 cm

The dimensions of the rectangle are given correct to one decimal place.

a Calculate the greatest lower bound of the area of the rectangle.

1 metre

4 cm

Rectangles with the same dimensions as the one in part **a** are to be cut from a large piece of card of length of 1 metre, correct to the nearest centimetre, and width exactly 4 centimetres.

b Calculate the maximum number of rectangles that could be cut from the large piece of card.

[Edexcel]

S52

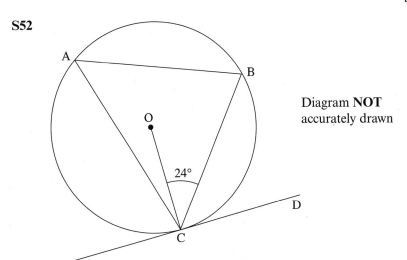

A

B

O

24°

D

C

Diagram **NOT** accurately drawn

The diagram shows a circle with its centre at O.
A, B and C are points on the circumference of the circle.
At C, a tangent to the circle has been drawn.
D is a point on this tangent.
Angle OCB = 24°.

a Find the size of angle BCD.
Give a reason for your answer.

b Find the size of angle CAB.
Give a reason for your answer.

[Edexcel]

S53

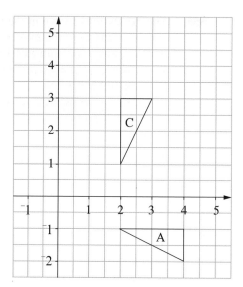

Describe fully the single transformation which maps the triangle A onto the triangle C.

[Edexcel]

S54

Volume of water (litres)

Time

The sketch graph above shows the volume of water in a water tank between 1000 and 1025.
During the morning, the water tank emptied itself completely.

a At what time was the water tank empty?

b Between which times was the volume of water in the water tank constant?

c Between which times was the volume of water in the water tank increasing at its greatest rate?

[Edexcel]

S55 $\sin x^{\circ} = 0.6$ and $90 < x < 360$.
Use the graph to help you work out $\cos x^{\circ}$.

[Edexcel]

S56 The expressions shown in the table below can be used to calculate lengths, areas or volumes of various shapes.

π, 2, 3, $\frac{2}{3}$ and $\frac{1}{6}$ are numbers which have no dimensions.

The letters h, l, r and R represent lengths.

Copy the table below.

Put a tick in the box underneath those expressions which can be used to calculate an area.

$2\pi r(h + r)$	$2\pi r$	$\frac{2}{3}\pi R^2 h$	$2\pi Rh$	$\frac{1}{6}\pi h(3r^2 + h^2)$	$\pi r l$

[Edexcel]

S57

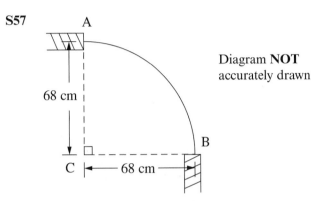

Diagram **NOT** accurately drawn

The diagram represents the plan of a window frame.

The arc AB is a quarter of a circle.

The centre of the circle is at C and the radius of the circle is 68 cm.

a Calculate the length of the arc AB.

(Use π = 3.14 or use the π button on your calculator.)

Give your answer correct to 3 significant figures.

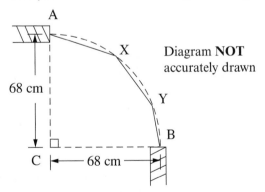

Diagram **NOT** accurately drawn

The window frame in **a** is replaced by double glazed panels.

These panels are made only in straight lengths.

The arc AB is replaced by three identical panels AX, XY and YB.

b Calculate the length of AX.

Give your answer correct to 2 significant figures.

[Edexcel]

Handling data

D1 The probability that a team will win a game is always 0.8.
The team plays *n* games.
The probability that the team will win every game is less than $\frac{1}{4}$.
Calculate the smallest possible value of *n*.

[Edexcel]

D2 The probability that a washing machine will break down in the first
5 years of use is 0.27.
The probability that a television will break down in the first 5 years of
use is 0.17.
Mr Khan buys a washing machine and a television on the same day.
By using a tree diagram or otherwise, calculate the probability that, in
the five years after that day

a both the washing machine and the television will break down,

b at least one of them will break down.

[Edexcel]

D3 Helen tries to win a coconut at the fair.
She throws a ball at a coconut.
If she knocks a coconut off its stand, she wins the coconut.
Helen has two throws.
The probability that she will win a coconut with her first throw is 0.2.
The probability that she will win a coconut with her second throw is 0.3.
Work out the probability that, with her two throws, Helen will win

i 2 coconuts,

ii exactly 1 coconut.

[Edexcel]

D4 The probability of a person having brown eyes is $\frac{1}{4}$.
The probability of a person having blue eyes is $\frac{1}{3}$.
Two people are chosen at random.
Work out the probability that

i both people will have brown eyes

ii one person will have blue eyes and the other person will have brown
eyes.

[Edexcel]

D5 Tony carries out a survey about the words in a book.
He chooses a page at random.
He then counts the number of letters in each of the first hundred words
on the page.
The table shows Tony's results.

Number of letters in a word	1	2	3	4	5	6	7	8
Frequency	6	9	31	24	16	9	4	1

A word is chosen at random from the hundred words.

a What is the probability that the word will have 5 letters?

The book has 25 000 words.

b Estimate the number of 5 letter words in the book.

The book has 125 pages with a total of 25 000 words.
The words on each of the first 75 pages are counted.
The mean is 192.

c Calculate the mean number of words per page for the remaining 50 pages.

[Edexcel]

D6 Sharon has 12 computer discs.
Five of the discs are red.
Seven of the discs are black.
She keeps all the discs in a box.
Sharon removes one disc at random. She records its colour and replaces it in the box.
Sharon removes a second disc at random, and again records its colour.

a Copy and complete this tree diagram.

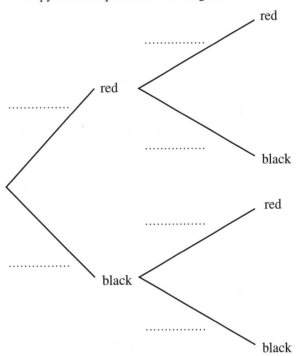

b Calculate the probability that the two discs removed
  i will both be red,
  ii will be different colours.

[Edexcel]

D7 On journeys between home and school Jaspal either walks or catches a bus.
The probability that Jaspal will walk to school is 0.6.
If Jaspal walks to school, the probability that she will walk back home is 0.85.
If she catches a bus to school, the probability that she will walk back home is 0.45.

a Calculate the probability that, on a particular day, Jaspal will walk to school and will also walk back home.

b Calculate the probability that, on a particular day, Jaspal will catch a bus back home from school.

[Edexcel]

D8 The diagram shows the board for a game played in a maths lesson.

FINISH	−3	−2	−1	0	+1	+2	+3	FINISH

Rules of the Game

Start with a counter on 0.
Throw a coin.
If the coin shows heads, then move the counter one space to the right.
If the coin shows tails, then move the counter one space to the left.
The game ends when the counter reaches 'Finish'.

Jim places a counter at **0**.
He throws a fair coin 3 times.

a Calculate the probability that the counter will be at
  i +3,
  ii 0.

Ann places a counter at **0**.
She has a biased coin. The probability that the coin shows heads is 0.7.
Ann throws the biased coin twice.

b Calculate the probability that her counter will be back at **0**.

Billy places a counter at **0**.
He has a biased coin. The probability that the biased coin shows heads on any throw is 0.7.
Billy throws the biased coin 3 times.

c Calculate the probability that after 3 throws
  i the counter will be at **+1**,
  ii the counter will have been at **+1** at least once.

[Edexcel]

D9 Jack has two fair dice.
One of the dice has 6 faces numbered from 1 to 6.
The other dice has 4 faces numbered from 1 to 4.
Jack is going to throw the two dice.
He will add the scores on the two dice to get the total.
Work out the probability that he will get

  i a total of 7,
  ii a total of less than 5.

[Edexcel]

D10 Tina has a biased dice.
When she rolls it, the probability that she will get a six is 0.09.
Tina is going to roll the biased dice twice.
Work out the probability that she will get

  i two sixes,
  ii exactly one six.

[Edexcel]

D11 A class took a test. The mean mark for the 20 boys in the class was 17.4. The mean mark for the 10 girls in the class was 13.8.

a Calculate the mean mark for the whole class.

5 pupils in another class took the test.
Their marks, written in order, were 1, 2, 3, 4 and x.
The mean of these 5 marks is equal to twice the median of these 5 marks.

b Calculate the value of x.

[Edexcel]

D12 Ben asked 50 people how much they paid for a new computer.
The results are shown in this frequency table. Copy the table.

Price (£P)	Number of computers		
$0 < P \leqslant 500$	7		
$500 < P \leqslant 1000$	20		
$1000 < P \leqslant 1500$	11		
$1500 < P \leqslant 2000$	9		
$2000 < P \leqslant 2500$	3		

a Calculate an estimate for the mean price paid for a new computer.

By the end of each year, the value of a computer falls by 15% of its value at the start of that year.
A new computer has a value of £1200.

b Calculate its value by the end of the third year.

[Edexcel]

D13 A travel company carried out a survey of the ages of its customers.
The results of the survey are shown in the table.

Age group (years)	Percentage of customers in this age group
11–20	8
21–30	28
31–40	19
41–50	21
51–60	13
61–70	11

a Draw a frequency polygon to show this information.

b In which age group is the median age?

[Edexcel]

D14 The unfinished histogram and table give information about the heights, in centimetres, of the Year 11 students at Mathstown High School. Make a copy of the histogram and the frequency table.

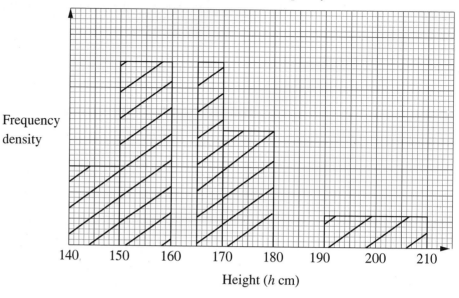

Frequency density

Height (h cm)

Height (h cm)	Frequency
$140 \leqslant h < 150$	15
$150 \leqslant h < 160$	
$160 \leqslant h < 165$	20
$165 \leqslant h < 170$	
$170 \leqslant h < 180$	
$180 \leqslant h < 190$	12
$190 \leqslant h < 210$	

a Use the histogram to complete the table.

b Use the table to complete the histogram.

[Edexcel]

D15 Fred conducted a survey into the times, in seconds, it took for passengers to get tickets from a ticket machine.

The results of the survey are summarised in the incomplete table below and shown on the incomplete histogram below. Make a copy of the table and the histogram.

Time (seconds)	Frequency
0 to less than 4	80
4 to less than 8	60
8 to less than 16	50
16 to less than 28	40
28 to less than 60	

a Use the information in the table to complete the histogram.

b Use the information in the histogram to complete the table.

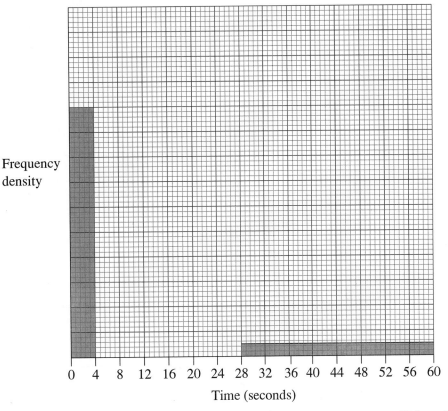

[Edexcel]

D16   A gardener records the heights of plants he has for a flower show.

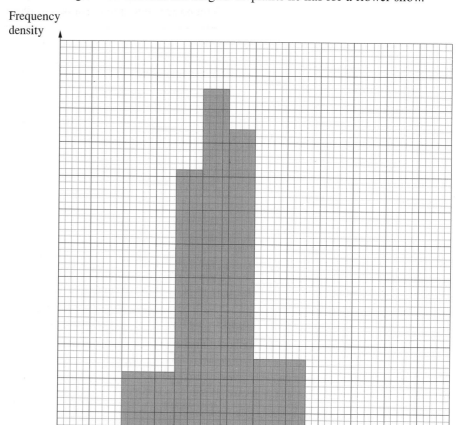

Height (*h*) cm

Make a copy of the histogram above.

a   Copy the frequency table below.
Use the information in the histogram to complete the frequency table.

Height (*h* cm)	Frequency
$20 \leqslant h < 25$	5
$25 \leqslant h < 29$	
$29 \leqslant h < 31$	
$31 \leqslant h < 33$	
$33 \leqslant h < 35$	
$35 \leqslant h < 39$	
$39 \leqslant h < 49$	10

b   Use the information in the frequency table to complete the histogram.

[Edexcel]

D17   Twenty five people took part in a competition.
The points scored are grouped in the frequency table below.

Points Scored	Number of people		
1 to 5	1		
6 to 10	2		
11 to 15	5		
16 to 20	7		
21 to 25	8		
26 to 30	2		

a   Work out an estimate for the mean number of points scored.

b   Copy and complete the table below to show the cumulative frequency for this data.

Points Scored	Cumulative frequency
1 to 5	
1 to 10	
1 to 15	
1 to 20	
1 to 25	
1 to 30	

c   Draw a cumulative frequency graph for this data.

d   Use your graph to find an estimate for the median of this data.

[Edexcel]

D18   The table gives information about the ages, in years, of 100 aeroplanes.

Age (t years)	Frequency
$0 < t \leqslant 5$	41
$5 < t \leqslant 10$	26
$10 < t \leqslant 15$	20
$15 < t \leqslant 20$	10
$20 < t \leqslant 25$	3

b Copy and complete the cumulative frequency table.

Age (*t* years)	Cumulative frequency
$0 < t \leqslant 5$	
$0 < t \leqslant 10$	
$0 < t \leqslant 15$	
$0 < t \leqslant 20$	
$0 < t \leqslant 25$	

c On a grid, draw a cumulative frequency graph for your table.

d Use your graph to find an estimate of the upper quartile of the ages. Show your method clearly.

[Edexcel]

D19 Fred carried out a survey of the time, in seconds, between one car and the next car on a road.
His results are shown in the cumulative frequency graph on the grid below.

a How many cars were there in the survey?

b Use the graph to estimate the median time.

c Use the graph to estimate the percentage of times that were greater than 25 seconds.

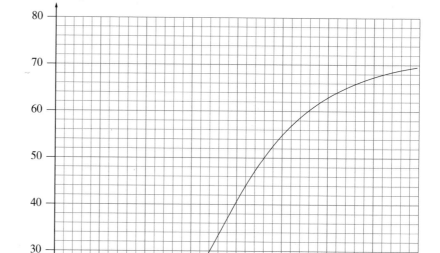

Cumulative
Frequency

Time in seconds

[Edexcel]

D20   The cumulative frequency table gives information about the heights, in centimetres, of some students at Bax School.

Heights (h) of students in cm	Cumulative frequency
$h < 135$	0
$135 \leqslant h < 140$	2
$135 \leqslant h < 145$	10
$135 \leqslant h < 150$	29
$135 \leqslant h < 155$	70
$135 \leqslant h < 160$	115
$135 \leqslant h < 165$	143
$135 \leqslant h < 170$	156
$135 \leqslant h < 175$	163

a   Draw a cumulative frequency graph for the data in the table.

b   Use your cumulative frequency graph to estimate
  i   the median height,
  ii   the number of students with height less than 151 cm.

[Edexcel]

D21   2400 people took an examination paper.
The maximum mark for this paper was 80.
The cumulative frequency graph on page 396 gives information about the marks.
The pass mark was 44 marks.

a   Use the cumulative frequency graph to estimate the number of people who did not pass this paper.

The same 2400 people took a second examination paper.
The table gives information about the marks for the second paper.
The maximum mark was 80.

Mark	Cumulative frequency
0–10	20
0–20	80
0–30	200
0–40	500
0–50	900
0–60	1800
0–70	2200
0–80	2400

b Draw a cumulative frequency graph to show this information.

The same number of people did not pass this paper.

c Use your cumulative frequency graph to estimate the pass mark for the second paper.

Marks in first examination paper

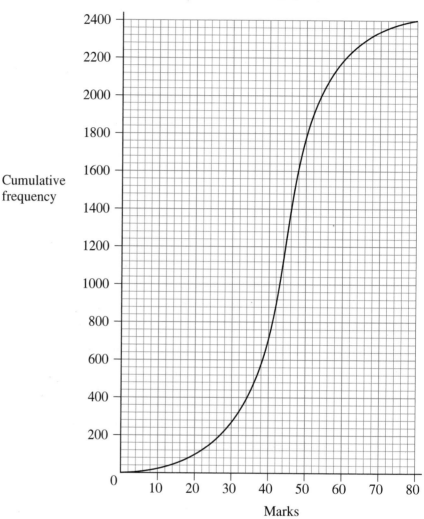

Cumulative frequency

Marks

[Edexcel]

D22 Nikki and Romana both try to to score a goal in netball.
The probability that Nikki will will score a goal on the first try is 0.65.
The probability that Romana will will score a goal on the first try is 0.8.

i Work out the probability that Nikki and Romana will both score a goal on their first tries.

ii Work out the probability the neither Nikki or Romana will score a goal on their first tries.

[Edexcel]

D23

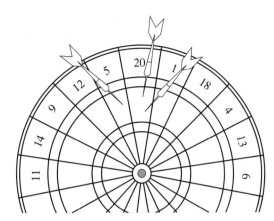

When there are no darts in the 20 sector of a darts board, a darts player estimates the probability of hitting the 20 sector as being 0.3. When she hits the 20 sector with one of her darts, her estimate of the probability of hitting the 20 sector changes to 0.15.
She throws three darts one after the other.
Calculate an estimate of the probability that she will miss the 20 sector with her first dart, hit the 20 sector with her second dart and hit the 20 sector with her third dart.

[Edexcel]

D24 A box contains 10 discs. 4 of the discs are green and 6 are red.
2 discs are removed at random from the box.
By drawing a tree diagram, or otherwise, calculate the probability that

i   both discs will be red

ii at least one disc will be red.

[Edexcel]

D25 All female chaffinches have the same patterns of laying eggs.
The probability that any female chaffinch will lay a certain number of eggs is given in the table below.

Number of eggs	0	1	2	3	4 or more
Probability	0.1	0.3	0.3	0.2	0.1

a Calculate the probability that a female chaffinch will lay less than 3 eggs.

b Calculate the probability that two female chaffinches will lay a total of 2 eggs.

[Edexcel]

D26 Darren estimates the probability of his passing a test at the first attempt as 0.6.
If he fails he can take the test again.
He estimates the probability of passing the test on the second attempt as 0.7.

a Using a tree diagram, or otherwise, calculate the probability that he will pass
i   at the second attempt,
ii at the first or second attempt.

Darren estimates the probability of his girlfriend passing the test at the first attempt as 0.8.

b Calculate the probability of them both passing the test, at the first attempt.

[Edexcel]

D27 Jean is going on an activities holiday. Each activity lasts a whole day. She can only do one activity a day.
The probability that she will go pony-trekking on any one day is 0.6.
The probability that Jean will go windsurfing on any one day is 0.25.

  a Work out the probability that Jean will either go windsurfing or pony-trekking on the first day.

  b Calculate the probability that Jean will go pony-trekking on the first day and will go windsurfing on the second day.

[Edexcel]

D28 A machine makes two parts which fit together to make a tool. The probability that the first part will be made correctly is 0.9. The probability that the second part will be made correctly is 0.95.

  a Copy and complete the tree diagram below giving the missing probabilities.

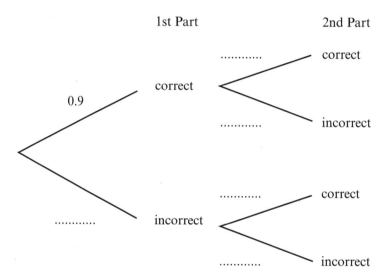

  b Use the tree diagram to work out the probability that both parts will be made correctly.

[Edexcel]

D29 Mr Chung is 70 years old.
The probability that he will reach the age of 71 is 0.94.
If he reaches the age of 71, the probability that he will reach the age of 72 is 0.93.

  a Calculate the probability that he will reach the age of 71 but will not reach the age of 72.

  b Calculate the probability that he will not reach the age of 72.

[Edexcel]

D30 There are 8 balls in a box. 7 of the balls are yellow and 1 ball is red.
Jean selects balls at random, without replacement, from the box until she
obtains the red ball.
When she obtains the red ball, then she stops selecting.
Copy and complete the tree diagram shown below, or otherwise, calculate
the probability that Jean selects the red ball on one of her first three
selections.

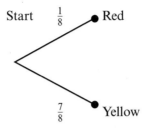

[Edexcel]

D31 A letter has a first-class stamp on it.
The probability that it will be delivered on the next working day is 0.86.
Sam posts 2 letters with first-class stamps.

a Copy and complete the tree diagram.
Give all the missing probabilities on the appropriate branches.

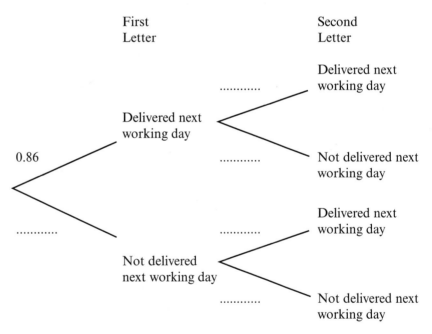

b Calculate the probability that both letters will be delivered on the next
working day.

[Edexcel]

D32

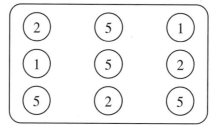

PLAY THIS GAME AND SEE HOW
MANY GIFTS YOU CAN WIN
1, 2 or 3?

2	5	1
1	5	2
5	2	5

How to play
if the numbers revealed add up to
2 .... WIN 1 GIFT
3 .... WIN 2 GIFTS
4 or more... WIN 3 GIFTS

The diagram shows a card used to play a game.
The nine circled numbers are covered and cannot be seen until the covering is removed.
The game is played by removing at random the covering from any two of the numbers and the score is the sum of the two numbers revealed.

a Calculate the probability that exactly 2 will be scored.

b Calculate the probability that exactly 3 will be scored.

c Calculate the probability that 4 or more will be scored.

[Edexcel]

D33 A travel company carried out a survey of the ages of its customers.
The results of the survey are shown in the table.

Age group (years)	Percentage of customers in this age group
11–20	8
21–30	28
31–40	19
41–50	21
51–60	13
61–70	11

a Draw a frequency polygon to show this information.

b In which age group is the median age?

[Edexcel]

D34   There are 1000 students in Nigel and Sonia's school.
Nigel is carrying out a survey of the types of food eaten at lunchtime.

a   Explain how Nigel could take a random sample of students to carry out this survey.

This table shows the gender and the number of students in each year group.

Year group	Number of boys	Number of girls	Total
7	100	100	200
8	90	80	170
9	120	110	230
10	80	120	200
11	100	100	200

Sonia is carrying out a survey about how much homework students are given.
She decides to take a stratified sample of 100 students from the whole school.

b   Calculate how many in the stratified sample should be
   i   students from Year 9,
   ii boys from Year 10.

[Edexcel]

D35   Sam was making a survey of pupils in his school.
He wanted to find out their opinions on noise pollution by motor bikes.
The size of each year group in the school is shown below.

Year Group	Boys	Girls	Total
8	85	65	150
9	72	75	147
10	74	78	152
11	77	72	149
6th Form	93	107	200
			798

Sam took a sample of 80 pupils.

a   Explain whether or not he should have sampled equal numbers of boys and girls in year 8.

b   Calculate the number of pupils he should have sampled in year 8.

[Edexcel]

D36 The grouped frequency table gives information about the weekly rainfall
(d) in millimetres at Heathrow airport in 1995.

Weekly rainfall (d) in mm	Number of weeks		
$0 \leqslant d < 10$	20		
$10 \leqslant d < 20$	18		
$20 \leqslant d < 30$	6		
$30 \leqslant d < 40$	4		
$40 \leqslant d < 50$	2		
$50 \leqslant d < 60$	2		

a Copy the table and complete it to calculate an estimate for the mean
weekly rainfall.

b Write down the probability that the rainfall in any week in 1995,
chosen at random, was greater than or equal to 20 mm and less
than 40 mm.

c Copy and complete this cumulative frequency table for the data.

Weekly rainfall (d) in mm	Cumulative frequency
$0 \leqslant d < 10$	
$0 \leqslant d < 20$	
$0 \leqslant d < 30$	
$0 \leqslant d < 40$	
$0 \leqslant d < 50$	
$0 \leqslant d < 60$	

d Draw a cumulative frequency graph to show the data.

e Use your cumulative frequency graph to estimate the median weekly
rainfall.

You must show your method clearly.

[Edexcel]

D37   In a survey on October 1st, pupils present at Bank school were asked how long they had taken to go from home to school that morning. Each pupil present ticked one and only one of the following responses.

0 minutes up to but not including 5 minutes	
5 minutes up to but not including 15 minutes	
15 minutes up to but not including 25 minutes	
25 minutes up to but not including 40 minutes	
40 minutes up to but not including 70 minutes	
70 minutes and over	

Exactly 96 pupils ticked the '5 minutes up to but not including 15 minutes' response.
No pupils ticked the '70 minutes and over' response.
Exactly 180 pupils ticked the '40 minutes up to but not including 70 minutes' response.

a Draw a histogram to show the results of the survey.

b Calculate the number of pupils who were absent on October 1st given that the total number of pupils at the school is 726.

[Edexcel]

D38   Sybil weighed some pieces of cheese.
The table gives information about her results.

Weight (w) grams	Frequency		
$90 < w \leqslant 94$	1		
$94 < w \leqslant 98$	2		
$98 < w \leqslant 102$	6		
$102 < w \leqslant 106$	1		

Work out an estimate of the mean weight.

[Edexcel]

D39   A group of people took a fitness test.
They exercised hard.
Then they were timed to see how long their pulses took to return to normal.
The time taken for a pulse to return to normal is called the recovery time.
The recovery times for the group are shown in the table below.

Recovery Time (seconds)	Frequency	Cumulative Frequency
0 up to but not including 20	0	0
20 up to but not including 40	7	7
40 up to but not including 60	9	16
60 up to but not including 80	18	34
80 up to but not including 90	13	47
90 up to but not including 100	12	59
100 up to but not including 120	9	68
120 up to but not including 140	6	74

a   Use the figures in the table to draw a cumulative frequency curve.

b   Use your cumulative frequency curve to estimate the value of
   i   the median,
   ii   the interquartile range.

A second group of people took the fitness test.
The recovery times of people in this group had a median of 61 seconds
and an interquartile range of 22 seconds.

c   Compare the fitness results of the two groups.

[Edexcel]

Do NOT use a calculator for this exam paper.

1   Ahmed, Baz and Colin share a bag of 30 Jelly Babies.
Ahmed has $\frac{2}{5}$ of the Jelly Babies.
Baz and Colin share the remaining Jelly Babies in the ratio $5:4$
What percentage of the bag of Jelly Babies does Baz have?   **(4 marks)**

2   **a**   Factorise $x^2 + 3x$ **(1 mark)**
     b   Hence, or otherwise, find the exact value of $997^2 + 3 \times 997$ **(2 marks)**

3   Multiply out and simplify the following
     a $3x^4 \times 2xy \times y^2$ **(2 marks)**
     b $(2x + 3)(2x - 3)$ **(2 marks)**

4   The formula

$$P = \frac{a^2 + b^2}{2a - 3b}$$

can be used to calculate the value of P.
$a = 9.67$ and $b = 4.82$

     a   Write down approximate values for a and b that can be
used to estimate the value of P.   **(2 marks)**
     b   Work out an estimate of P using these approximate
values.   **(2 marks)**

5   The dimensions of a cone are given.

     a   The following formulae represent certain
quantities connected with the cone.

$$\pi w \qquad \frac{\pi w^2 h}{12} \qquad 2\pi w l \qquad \frac{\pi w^2}{4}$$

        Which of these formulae represent volume?   **(1 mark)**

     b   Sand is poured into the cone at a constant rate.
Sketch the graph of the depth of sand against time.

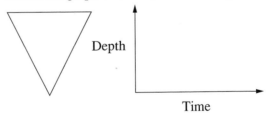

                    (1 mark)

6   **a**   Solve the equation $6x + 14 = 4(x + 3)$ **(2 marks)**
     b   Rearrange

$$y = mx + c$$

        to make m the subject.   **(2 marks)**

7 The map shows an island with three main towns, Alphaville, Betaville and Gammaville.
The map is drawn to a scale of 1 cm represents 15 kilometres.
A radio transmitter is to be installed.

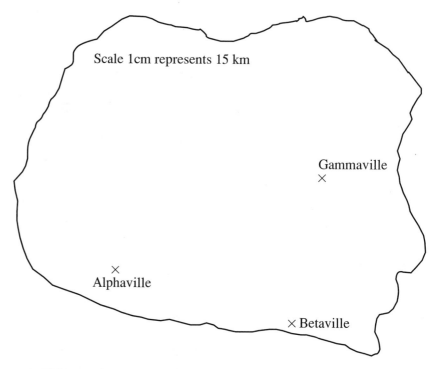

Scale 1cm represents 15 km

Using tracing paper, make a copy of the map.
The transmitter must be equidistant from Alphaville and Betaville.
The transmitter must be between 50 km and 80 km from Gammaville.
On your copy of the diagram show the possible sites that the transmitter may be drawn.

(5 marks)

8 Calculate the distance between the points A(−1, −1) and B(3, 2)

(3 marks)

9 **a** Match three of these equations with the graphs shown below.
In each case p is a positive integer.

Equation A: $y = p - x$ Equation B: $y = p - x^2$
Equation C: $y = px^2 + 2$ Equation D: $y = px$

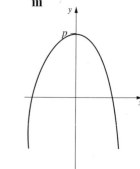

(3 marks)

b Sketch the graph of the equation you have not chosen.
Mark the values of the points where the graph crosses each axis.

(2 marks)

10 **a** Simplify each of the following expressions
   i $a^6 \times a^2$ **ii** $a^6 \div a^2$ **iii** $(a^6)^2$ **(3 marks)**

b Put a circle round the expression which has the smallest
value when $a = 0.2$
$$a^6 \times a^2 \qquad a^6 \div a^2 \qquad (a^6)^2$$

(1 mark)

11 Aimee travels to work by each day.
The probability that the bus is late on any day is 0.3.

a **i** Complete the tree diagram to show the possible outcomes
for Monday and Tuesday.

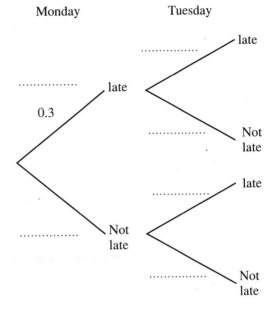

Monday   Tuesday

(2 marks)

ii What is the probability that the bus is not late on
both days?   **(2 marks)**

b What is the probability that the bus is late at least once in
a normal week of five days.   **(2 marks)**

12 The table shows the average speed of planets that orbit the sun.

Planet	Average speed of orbit (km/h)
Jupiter	4.7×10^4
Mercury	1.7×10^5
Neptune	4.2×10^4
Pluto	1.7×10^4
Saturn	3.5×10^4
Uranus	2.5×10^5

a Which planet is travelling the fastest?   **(1 mark)**
b What is the difference between the average speeds of
Neptune and Jupiter?
Give your answer in standard form.   **(3 marks)**

13 The energy values of 150 different foods are summarised in the table.

Energy, e (kcal per 100 g)	Frequency
$0 \leqslant e < 50$	25
$50 \leqslant e < 100$	50
$100 \leqslant e < 150$	45
$150 \leqslant e < 200$	30

Draw a histogram to represent the data. **(3 marks)**

14 Write down the value of

  a $27^{\frac{1}{3}}$ **(1 mark)**
  b 5^{-2} **(1 mark)**
  c $16^{\frac{3}{2}}$ **(2 marks)**

15 Mary wants to find out the height of the local church.
  She places a 2 metre stick vertically at 100 metres from the
  base of the church.
  She finds that she can line up the top of the stick and the top
  of the church at a further distance of 10 metres from the church,
  as shown in the diagram.
  Calculate the height of the church.

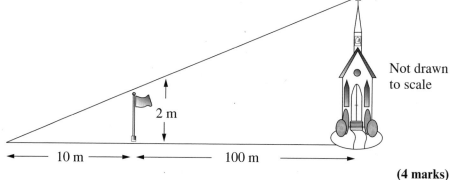

Not drawn
to scale

10 m   100 m

(4 marks)

16 A rectangle has sides of length $2x + 5$ and $2x + 1$ cm.
  The area of the rectangle is 54 cm^2

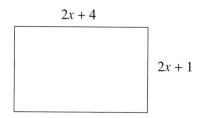

$2x + 4$

$2x + 1$

  a Show that x satisfies the equation
  $$2x^2 + 5x - 25 = 0$$

  (3 marks)
  b i Solve the equation $2x^2 + 5x - 25 = 0$ **(2 marks)**
      ii Find the perimeter of the rectangle. **(2 marks)**

17 a *AC* is a diameter of a circle centre O.
B and D are points on the circumference.
Angle *BAC* = 33°.

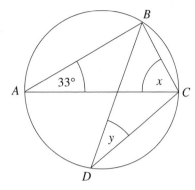

Not drawn
accurately

   i Find angle *BCA*, marked *x* in the diagram. **(1 mark)**
   ii Find angle *BDC*, marked *y* in the diagram **(1 mark)**

b *DE* and *DF* are tangents to a circle, meeting the circle at
A and *C* respectively.
B is a point on the circumference such that *CB* is parallel
to *DF*.
Angle *FAB* = 65°.
Find angle *BCE*, marked *x* on the diagram.

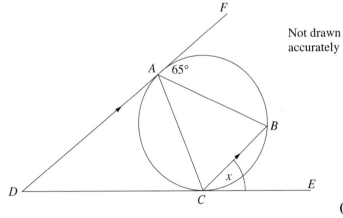

Not drawn
accurately

(4 marks)

18 The diagram shows the line joining the origin, O, to the
point A(6, 6).

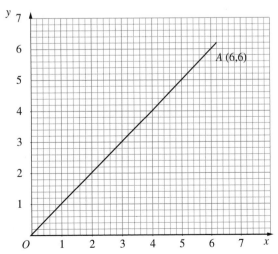

(3 marks)

Work out the equation of the line passing through the
mid-point of OA and perpendicular to OA.

409

19 The table shows the number of students in a school.

Boys	293
Girls	207

A stratified random sample of 150 students were asked some questions about school dinners.
How many boys were included in the sample? **(2 marks)**

20 A square has a side of $2 + \sqrt{3}$ cm.
What is its area?
Give your answer in the form $a + b\sqrt{3}$ **(2 marks)**

21 a, b and c are connected by the equation

$$\frac{a}{b-a} = \frac{c-a}{a}$$

Rearrange the equation to make a the subject. **(4 marks)**

22 Prove algebraically that the difference of the squares of any two consecutive integers is an odd number. **(3 marks)**

23 **a** Sketch the graph of $y = \sin x$ for $0° \leqslant x \leqslant 360°$. **(1 mark)**
   b One solution of the equation $\sin x = 0.6$ is $x = 37°$, to the nearest degree.
     Find the solutions of $\sin x = -0.6$ for $0° \leqslant x \leqslant 360°$ **(2 marks)**

24 In the triangle ABC, P and Q are the midpoints of AB and AC respectively.

$$AB = \mathbf{x}. \qquad AC = \mathbf{y}.$$

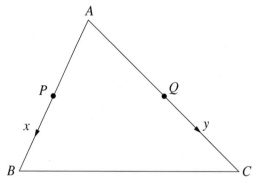

   a Find in terms of $\mathbf{x}$ and $\mathbf{y}$
     i BC **(1 mark)**
     ii AP **(1 mark)**
     iii PQ **(2 marks)**
   b What conclusions can you draw about the line segments AB and ST? **(2 marks)**

25   The graph of $y = \dfrac{10}{x} + 4$ is shown.

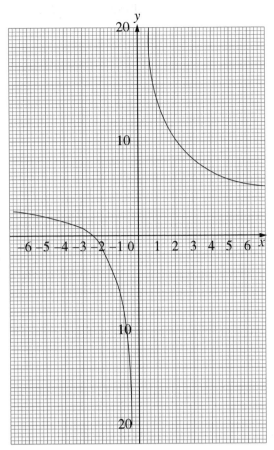

a   Use the graph to solve the equation

$$\frac{10}{x} + 3 = 0$$

(2 marks)

b   By drawing a suitable line on the graph solve the equation

$$x^2 - 4x - 10 = 0$$

Give your answers correct to 1 d.p.   **(3 marks)**

(Total 100 marks)

1 In a sale all the prices are reduced by 20%.
I bought a coat for £70 in the sale.
What was the price before the sale? **(3 marks)**

2 Given that $s = ut + \frac{1}{2}at^2$
Find the value of s when $u = 15$, $t = 4$ and $a = -7.5$ **(2 marks)**

3 The sketch graph shows the line $5x + 4y = 14$

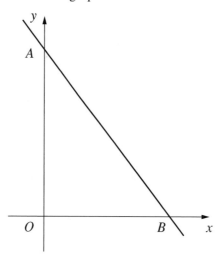

Write down the coordinates of the points A and B. **(2 marks)**

4 The diagram shows three quadrilaterals, P, Q and R.

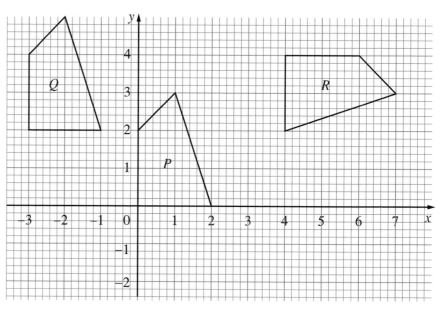

   a Describe fully the transformation which takes P to Q. **(2 marks)**
   b Describe fully the transformation which takes P to R. **(3 marks)**

5 List all the values of n, where n is an integer, such that
$$-2 < n - 1 \leqslant 3$$

(2 marks)

6   The diagram shows part of a roof structure.

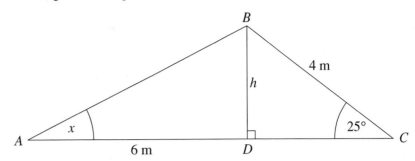

$AD = 6$ m, $BC = 4$ m and angle $BCD = 25°$

   a   Calculate the length of BD (marked h in the diagram).   **(3 marks)**

   b   Calculate angle BAD (marked x in the diagram).   **(3 marks)**

7   The rectangle below has a length of $2x + 5$ cm and a width of $3x - 2$ cm.

        2x + 5

        3x + 2   Not drawn
                to scale

   The perimeter of the rectangle is 20 cm.
   Find the value of x.   **(3 marks)**

8   Solve the following equation

$$\frac{x - 3}{2} - \frac{4x + 1}{3} = 0$$

                                                  (4 marks)

9   At the local Ice Rink the price of an adult ticket is £x and
the price of a child's ticket is £y.
It costs a family of two adults and three children £20 to go
ice-skating.
It costs one adult and four children £18 to go ice-skating.
Use this information to set up and solve a pair of
simultaneous equations.
Give the price of each ticket.   **(5 marks)**

10   The table shows the average age of 80 women who take part
in a marathon.

Age (a years)	Frequency
$20 \leqslant a < 30$	19
$30 \leqslant a < 40$	33
$40 \leqslant a < 50$	19
$50 \leqslant a < 60$	9

Calculate an estimate of the mean age of these women.   **(4 marks)**

11 The weights of a sample of 100 apples from an orchard at Holly Farm are shown in the table.

Weight, w (grams)	$50 \leqslant w < 100$	$50 \leqslant w < 100$	$50 \leqslant w < 100$	$50 \leqslant w < 100$	$50 \leqslant w < 100$
Frequency	11	21	32	27	9

a Copy and complete this cumulative frequency table. Use it to draw a cumulative frequency diagram for the sample of apples

Weight, w (grams)	< 100	< 150	< 200	< 250	< 300
Cumulative Frequency					

(3 marks)

b Estimate the median weight of the apples from Holly Farm. (1 mark)

c The box-plot below summarises the weights of a sample of 100 apples from Wood Farm.

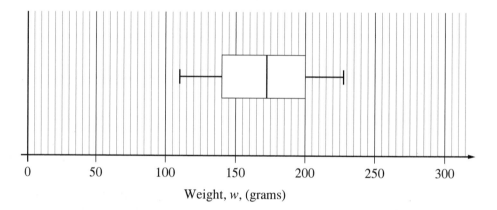

Weight, w, (grams)

Estimate the interquartile range of the apples from Wood Farm. (1 mark)

d Compare and comment on the differences in the samples of apples from the two farms. (2 marks)

12 A petri dish contains 2000 bacteria.
The bacteria increase by 12% each day.

a How many bacteria will there be after 1 day? (1 mark)

b How many bacteria will there be after 7 days?
Give your answer to a sensible degree of accuracy. (4 marks)

13   Mr Smith invests £1200 in a unit trust in 1994.
The table shows the value of the investment over the next 6 years.

Year	1994	1995	1996	1997	1998	1999	2000
Value £	1200	1179	1296	1278	1200	1410	1377

The following table shows the 3-year moving average of the value
of the investment

1995	1996	1997	1998	1999
1225	1251	1258	1296	

a   Calculate the value of the 3-year moving average for 1999.   **(1 mark)**
b   Mr Smith plots the values of the moving averages.

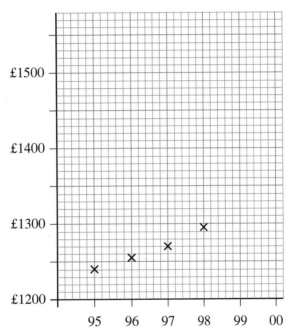

Use the graph to calculate the likely value of the
investment in **2001**.
You must show all your working.   **(3 marks)**

14   **a**   Write 0.085 as a fraction in its simplest form.   **(1 mark)**
     b   Write 0.08$\dot{5}$ as a fraction in its simplest form.   **(3 marks)**

15   **a**   Factorise $x^2 - 16$ **(1 mark)**
     b   Simplify fully the expression
$$\frac{x^2 - 16}{2x^2 - 7x - 4}$$ **(3 marks)**

16   The expression $x^2 - 10x + 14$ can be written in the form $(x - a)^2 - b$,
where a and b are integers.

a   Calculate the values of a and b.   **(3 marks)**
b   Solve the equation $x^2 - 10x + 14 = 0$, giving your answers
to 2 decimal places.   **(2 marks)**

17   A child's toy is in the shape of a cone on the top of a hemisphere, as shown below.
The radius of the hemisphere is 8.5 cm.
The height of the cone is h cm.

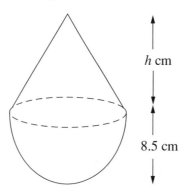

h cm

8.5 cm

The volume of the toy is 2050 cm³.
Calculate the height, h, of the cone.   **(5 marks)**

18   The lengths of the sides of a triangle are 9 cm, 14 cm and 11 cm.
Calculate the smallest angle of this triangle.   **(4 marks)**

19   Rearrange the equation

$$y = \frac{x}{x+3}$$

to make x the subject   **(3 marks)**

20   To measure the width of a river, Shameela paces two points A and B that are 100 metres apart.
She knows that this distance is accurate to the nearest 5 metres.
At each point she measures the angle between the river bank and a tree on the far bank. These measurements are accurate to the nearest 2°.
Her sketch is shown in the diagram.

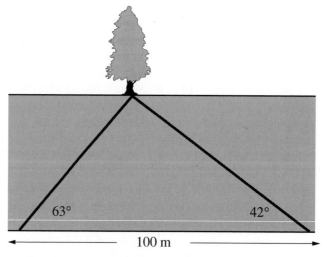

Not drawn to scale

63°   42°

100 m

Calculate the maximum possible width of the river.   **(6 marks)**

21   **a**   This is the graph of $y = x^2$.

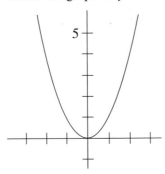

   i   Sketch the graph of $y = (x + 1)^2$ **(1 mark)**
   ii Sketch the graph of $y = -x^2$ **(1 mark)**
   iii The point $(1, 1)$ on the graph $y = x^2$ is transformed to
        the point $(1, 3)$ by a single transformation.
        Give the equation of the transformed graph.   **(1 mark)**

   b   This is the graph of $y = \sin x$

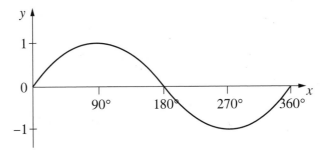

   Below are two transformations of $y = \sin x$
   Write down the equation of each transformed graph.
   i

                                                              (1 mark)

   ii

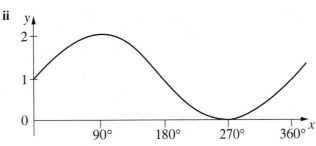

                                                              (1 mark)

22   Solve the equation

$$\frac{4}{x+1} + \frac{3}{x-1} = 1$$ **(5 marks)**

23   A 2-dimensional framework is made from wire.
It is three-quarters of a circle of radius 20 cm with two diameters as shown.

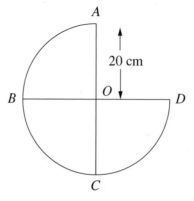

a   Calculate the total length of the wire in the frame.   **(3 marks)**

b   The frame is now formed into a cone by forming the arc *ABCD* into a circle and joining the radii *OA* and *OD*.

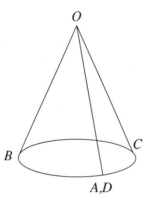

The cone is used as a framework for a lampshade.
Calculate the area of fabric needed to cover the lampshade.   **(4 marks)**

(Total 100 marks)

SECTION 1 Fractions

Starting points

A2   **a** 14   **b** 15   **c** 24   **d** 4

A3   **a** 1, 2, 3, 6   **b** 1, 5

A4   **a** 1   **b** 2   **c** 4   **d** 18

A5   It has only one factor

A6   31, 37

A7   Any other even numbers have at least 3 factors, i.e. 1, 2 and themselves.

B1   **a** $2^2 \times 5$ **b** $2^2 \times 3^2$ **c** $5 \times 7 \times 11$ **d** $2^3 \times 3^2 \times 7$

B2   **a** 2016   **b** 16335

C1 $\frac{4}{10}$

C3   **a** $\frac{3}{5}$ **b** $\frac{1}{6}$

D1   **a** $1\frac{1}{4}$ **b** $2\frac{2}{3}$ **c** $3\frac{1}{3}$ **d** 5

D2   **a** $\frac{18}{7}$ **b** $\frac{3}{2}$ **c** $\frac{37}{8}$ **d** $\frac{3}{1}$

E1   **a** $\frac{4}{5}$ **b** $\frac{1}{3}$ **c** $\frac{2}{5}$ **d** $\frac{3}{5}$ **e** $\frac{4}{7}$ **f** $1\frac{3}{5}$ **g** $\frac{5}{7}$ **h** $\frac{5}{13}$ **i** $\frac{5}{16}$ **j** undefined

E2   **a** $\frac{2}{7}$ **b** $\frac{11}{15}$ **c** $\frac{2}{7}$ **d** $\frac{1}{2}$ **e** $\frac{15}{16}$ **f** $\frac{1}{12}$ **g** $1\frac{1}{4}$ **h** $1\frac{4}{5}$

E3 $\frac{4}{7}$

Exercise 1.1

1   **a** **i** 24   **ii** 20   **b** **i** 180   **ii** 1800

3   **a**

Numbers	Product	HCF	LCM
12, 70	840	2	420
7, 24	168	1	168
4, 36	144	4	36
70, 110	7700	10	770

  b Product ÷ HCF = LCM   **c** 72

4   8, 160

5   31 July

6   960 cm³

7   **a** $2^2 \times 3 \times 7$

  b 1, 2, 3, 7, 2^2, 2×3, 2×7, 3×7, $2^2 \times 3$, $2^2 \times 7$, $2 \times 3 \times 7$, $2^2 \times 3 \times 7$

  c 12

  d 900 has 27 factors

Exercise 1.2

1   **a** $\frac{17}{20}$ **b** $3\frac{3}{4}$ **c** $1\frac{15}{16}$ **d** 4

2   **a** $1\frac{4}{15}$ **b** $\frac{-3}{8}$ **c** $\frac{3}{4}$ **d** $4\frac{1}{6}$

3   **a** $1\frac{7}{9}$ **b** $1\frac{1}{5}$ **c** $\frac{17}{18}$ **d** $5\frac{7}{20}$

4 $3\frac{1}{3}$

5   8

6   No unit fraction can be greater than $\frac{1}{2}$, so the sum of 2 unit fractions can never be greater than 1.

8   **a** **i** $\frac{15}{16}$ **ii** $\frac{511}{512}$

9 $\frac{1}{4}, \frac{1}{28}$

10 $\frac{1}{3}, \frac{1}{6}, \frac{1}{2}$

12 $\frac{9273}{18456}$

Exercise 1.3

1   L

2   P and S, Q and U, R and W, T and V

3   **a** $\frac{1}{(3n)}$ **b** $\frac{8}{x}$ **c** $\frac{(a-b)}{10}$ **d** $\frac{p}{2}$ **e** $\frac{3m}{4n}$ **f** $\frac{v}{8}$ **g** $\frac{z}{15}$ **h** 2

4   **a** $\frac{x}{5} - \frac{2}{5} = \frac{(x-2)}{5}$ **b** $\frac{2}{m} \times \frac{n}{6} = \frac{n}{(3m)}$ **c** $\frac{y}{x} + \frac{z}{x} = \frac{(y+z)}{x}$ **d** $\frac{6}{n} \div \frac{1}{n^2} = 6n$

  e $\frac{3t}{10} + \frac{2t}{10} = \frac{t}{2}$ **f** $\frac{2}{(b+3)} \div \frac{1}{(b-2)} = \frac{2(b-2)}{(b+3)}$

5   A and G, B and C, D and F, E and H

Exercise 1.4

1   **a** C   **b** $\frac{22}{(3c)}$

2   E and L, F and G, H and J, I and K

3   **a** $\frac{3m}{4}$ **b** $\frac{5p}{8}$ **c** $\frac{(5q+2r)}{10}$ **d** $\frac{(2s-st)}{2t}$ **e** $\frac{(4y-5x)}{xy}$ **f** $\frac{17}{2f}$ **g** $\frac{2(p+2)}{(p+3)(p-1)}$ **h** $\frac{(z+12)}{z(z+6)}$

4   **a** 8   **b** 3   **c** ⁻3   **d** 2

Exercise 1.5

1   **b** The numerators are always 3 and the larger denominator is 3 more than the smaller.

  c $\frac{3}{n} - \frac{3}{n+3} = \frac{9}{n(n+3)} = \frac{3}{n} \times \frac{3}{(n+3)}$

End points

A1   **a** 15, 180   **b** 25, 975   **c** 5, 6600   **d** 18, 432

  e 4, 1512   **f** 1, 28 350   **g** 5, 8000   **h** 1, 12 740

A2   *a* 21   **b** 630

A3   24, 27

BI   **a** $\frac{5}{9}$ **b** $\frac{5}{18}$ **c** $\frac{7}{10}$

B2   **a** $4\frac{7}{20}$ **b** $1\frac{3}{4}$ **c** $1\frac{7}{8}$ **d** $4\frac{1}{3}$

B3 $\frac{20}{81}$

C1   **a** $\frac{x}{2}$ **b** $\frac{3}{4}$ **c** $3z$ **d** $\frac{(3b-7a)}{ab}$ **e** $\frac{(c+5)}{c(c+1)}$ **f** $\frac{(2d+1)}{(d+6)(d-5)}$

SECTION 2 Properties of Shapes

Starting points

A1   **a** **i** reflex   **ii** acute   **iii** right angle

  b **i** equilateral   **ii** right-angled

  c triangles AED and BAD

B1   **a** 60°   **b** 300°   **c** 45°

B2   **a** 35°, 72.5°

  b The angles in a triangle add up to 180°, so if one angle is more than 90°, the other two must be less than 90°.

C1   116°, 116°, 64°, 64°

D1   1: trapezium 2: rectangle, square 3: square, rhombus

  4: rectangle, square, parallelogram, rhombus

E1   1080°

E2   142°

E3   129°

E4   **a** 1800°   **b** 150°

F1   **a** A quadrilateral can be split into two triangles by drawing in a diagonal. The angle sum of each triangle is 180°, so the angle sum of the quadrilateral is twice that, 360°.

  b 900°   **c** 12

F2   **a** 40°

  b AB̂C, + BÂC = x and BĈA = BĈA = 180° – x°

  so AB̂C + 180° – x° = x°

  ie AB̂C = $2x - 180$

Exercise 2.1

1   62°, 120°, 117°

2   **b** 74°, 53°, 53°, 74°, 53°, 53°

Exercise 2.2

1   **a** The corresponding angles are: any two out of *a*, *c* and *e*; any two out of *b*, *d* and *f*; any two out of *g*, *i* and *k*, any two out of *h*, *j* and *l*

  b The alternate angles are: *b* and *i* or *k*, *d* and *k*, *h* and *c* or *e*, *j* and *e*

2   72°, 135°, 45°

3   **a** **i** The corresponding angles are:

  any pair out of ADC, DHG, HLK and LPO;

  any pair out of angles EDH, IHL, MLP and QPS;

  any pair out of angles ADE, DHI, HLM and LPQ;

  any pair out of angles CDH, GHL, KLP and OPS

  ii The corresponding angles are:

  any pair out of angles BDC, DGF, GKJ and KON;

  any pair out of angles BDE, DGH, GKL and KOP

  any pair out of angles CDG, FGK, JKO and NOR;

  any pair out of angles EDG, HGK, LKO and POR

b BR and AS are not parallel

c The alternate angles are:
angles CDG and DGH, GKL or KOP;
angles FGK and GKL or KOP;
angles JKO and KOP;
angles EDH and DHG, HLK or LPO;
angles IHL and HLK or LPO;
angles MLP and LPO;
angles EDG and DGF, GKJ or KON; angles HGK and GKJ or KON;
angles LKO and KON;
angles CDH and DHI, HLM or LPQ;
angles GHL and HLM or LPQ;
angles KLP and LPQ

d i 65° **ii** 54° **iii** 61° **iv** 54° **v** 126° **vi** 61°

4 42°, 77°, 61°, 72°, 72°, 72°, 68.5°, 68.5°, 68.5°

Exercise 2.3

1 **b i** stays the same **ii** gets bigger **iii** gets smaller **c** gets smaller
d i obtuse **ii** right angle **iii** acute

2 **a** 3 **b** 1, 2, 3

Exercise 2.4

1 **a** 56°, 42°, 69°, 104°, 89°

2 **a** The 12 exterior angles are 12 equal turns which are equivalent to one full turn, 360°.
b 30° **c** 150°

3 40°, 140°, 70°, 40°

Exercise 2.5

1 **a** AMD is isosceles, so angle AMD = 180° − 2 × 22.5° = 135°
b i 67.5°, 157.5°

2 **a i** 67.5° at A, 67.5° at C, 45° at F
ii 112.5° at A, 112.5° at C, 135° at F
b 5 **c** 45°, 67.5°, 90°, 112.5°, 135°, 157.5°

End points

A1 42°, 67°, 109°

B1 **a i** C **ii** B and E

C1 **a** B 120°, 30°, 30°; C 60°, 60°, 60°; D 90°, 90°, 90°, 90°;
E 60°, 90°, 120°, 90°
b B 60°, 150°, 150°; C 120°, 120°, 120°; D 90°, 90°, 90°, 90°;
E 120°, 90°, 60°, 90°

C2 45°

SECTION 3 Algebraic Manipulation

Starting points

A1 C

A2 **a** $13a - 30$ **b** $4 - 5x$ **c** $12x - 29$ **d** $^-5x - 11$ **e** 4

B1 **a** $\frac{6p+8}{p(p+2)}$ **b** $\frac{4}{3}$ **c** $\frac{5}{p(p+5)}$ **d** $\frac{10}{3}$ **e** $\frac{(5p-1)}{(p^2-1)}$ **f** $\frac{7p-2}{(3p+2)(p-1)}$ **g** $\frac{9p+23}{20}$
h $\frac{5(p+3)}{4(p-2)}$ **i** $\frac{8p-12}{3p+15}$ **j** $\frac{4(4p+5)}{3(2p-1)}$

Exercise 3.1

1 **a** $a(a+5), b(b-2), c(c-6), d(12-d), 4(e+8), 7(8-f)$
b $a^2+5a, b^2-2b, c^2-6c, 12d-d^2, 4e+32, 56-7f$

2 **a** $5(2p+2), 4(3q-2), r(2r+2)$
b $10p+10, 12q-8, 2r^2+2r$

3 $2a, b, c, d+3, e+2$

4 **a** $4(x+3)$ **b** $2(3p-2)$ **c** $2(a+4)$ **d** $5(2-q)$ **e** $t(3t-4)$
f $s(6s+7)$

Exercise 3.2

1 **a** $8b-10$ **b** $24-6x$ **c** $3c-12$ **d** $11y-15$ **e** ^-2a **f** $5a-14+2b$

2 A and D

3 **a** $5a+5$ **b** $x+15$ **c** $7a-6$ **d** $^-4x+11$ **e** $3x-23$ **f** $7x+4$
g $x-9$ **h** $17x+4y$

Exercise 3.3

1 **a** $6ab$ **b** $3pq$ **c** $20xy$ **d** $30pq$ **e** $2x^2$ **f** a^2b
g $2xy^2$ **h** $6a^2b$ **i** $6p^2q$ **j** a^5 **k** $6b^3$ **l** $10bc^3$

2 A and E, B and F, C and H, G and I

3 **a** $ab+4a$ **b** $2mn+3mp$ **c** $6xy+4xz$ **d** $ac+c^2$ **e** p^2-pq
f $4a^2-4ab$ **g** $2ab-4ac$ **h** $6a^2+8ab$ **i** $8pq-12p^2$ **j** $6p^2q+4pq^2$
k $4x^2y-8xy^2$ **l** $3x^3y-3xy^3$

4 **a** $2x^2+x$ **b** $5ab+4a$ **c** x^2+x^3-2x **d** $11a+2b$
e $4p^2+6q$ **f** $6a$

5 C

6 **a** $9a+26b$ **b** $10x+5y$ **c** ^-7x **d** $10x^2+3xy$
e $2a^2b$ **f** $3a^2b+3ab-2ab^2+2b^2$

7 **a** $6a^2+6ab+12b^2$ **b** $16x^2y+20xy^2-6xy$
c pq^2-4p^2q **d** $12m^3-2m^2n-8mn^2$

8 **a** $\frac{(8x+5)}{(x+1)(2x+1)}$ **b** $\frac{(x-2)}{(x+2)(x+1)}$ **c** $\frac{(3x+26)}{(x-3)(x+4)}$ **d** $\frac{(3x^2+10x-4)}{(x+2)(x+4)}$

Exercise 3.4

1 **a** $2(x+7)$ **b** $2(4x-5y)$ **c** $x(5+y)$ **d** $p(q+7)$
e $2d(3+2e)$ **f** $3a(2b+3)$ **g** $2a(1-4b)$ **h** $3a(a+4)$
i $5y(3x+4z)$ **j** $ab(a+b)$ **k** $3cd(4c-5)$ **l** $5y(5x^2+3z)$

3 **a** b

7 **a** $5(x+2y+4)$ **b** $3(2a-3b+4c)$ **c** $x(2x+3+y)$
d $7(2x-4y+3z)$ **e** $2x(x+4y+3)$ **f** $ab(6b+2a+5)$

Thinking ahead to ...

A **a** $x^2, 3x, 2x, 6$ **b** x^2+5x+6

B **a** $(p+3)(2p+4), (2q+3)(3q+5)$ **b** $2p^2+10p+12, 6q^2+19q+15$

C **a** B, C, E, **b** n^2-2n-8

Exercise 3.5

1 C

2 D

3 **a** a^2+4a+3 **b** $d^2+14d+45$ **c** $3e^2+22e+7$ **d** $10a^2+13a+4$
e $6b^2+19b+15$ **f** $6c^2+25c+14$

4 **a** x^2+2x+1 **b** x^2+4x+4 **c** x^2+6x+9

5

×	x	$^-4$
x	x^2	^-4x
$^-2$	^-2x	8

$(x-4)(x-2) = x^2-6x+8$

6 **a i** $(x-3)(x-3)$ **ii** x^2-6x+9 **b i** $(x-4)(x-4), x^2-8x+16$
ii $(x-5)(x-5), x^2-10x+25$
iii $(x-y)(x-y), x^2-2xy+y^2$

7 $6x^2-13x-5$

8 **a** $2z^2+3tz+t^2$ **b** $6k^2+17km+5m^2$ **c** $2c^2+17cd+21d^2$
d $6p^2+13pq-5q^2$ **e** $5f^2-8fg+3g^2$ **f** $21w^2-4vw-v^2$

9 A and I, B and F, C and H, D and G

10 **a** z^2-t^2 **b** $4k^2-m^2$ **c** $4c^2-9d^2$
d $9p^2-q^2$ **e** $25f^2-9g^2$ **f** $49w^2-v^2$
The product of the sum and difference between two numbers is equal to the difference between their products.

11 M and N

12 **a i** x^2+2x+1 **ii** x^3+3x^2+3x+1 **iii** $x^4+4x^3+6x^2+4x+1$
b $x^6+6x^5+15x^4+20x^3+15x^2+6x+1$

13 **a** $a^3 + 3a^2 - 10a$ **b** $p^3 - 5p^2 - 2p + 24$
   c $4q^3 - 22q^2 - 42q$ **d** $2x^3 + 13x^2 + 13x - 10$

Thinking ahead to ...
   A **a** $6, 6, 6, (102 \times 103) - (100 \times 105) = 6$
      b They are all 6. **c** $(n + 2)(n + 3) - n(n + 5)$

Exercise 3.6
   1 **a** A $2, 2, 2, ...$ B $1, 1, 1, ...$ C $12, 12, 12, ...$
      b A $(n + 1)(n + 2) - n(n + 3)$ B $(n + 1)^2 - n(n + 2)$
         C $(n + 3)(n + 4) - n(n + 7)$
      c A 2 B 2 C 12

   2 **a** **i** $7, 3, 5$ **ii** $6, 6, 20$ **b** **i** $a + b = c$ **ii** ab

   3 **a** A $4, 2, 0, ...$ B $7, 6, 5$, C $^-3, ^-2, ^-1, ...$
      b A $(n + 2)(n + 3) - n(n + 7)$ B $(n + 2)(n + 4) - n(n + 7)$
         C $n(n + 5) - (n + 2)^2$
      c A Each term is 2 less than the previous term.
         B Each term is 1 less than the previous term.
         C Each term is 1 more than the previous term.

Exercise 3.7
   1 **a** $(x + 1)(x + 7)$ **b** $(p + 1)(p + 8)$ **c** $(t + 1)(t + 9)$
      d $(m + 2)(m + 6)$ **e** $(n + 3)^2$ **f** $(a + 4)(a + 9)$

   2 **a** 8 **b** 5 **c** 7 **d** 11 **e** $t + 3$ **f** $p - 8$

   3 $(x - 1)(x + 4)$

   4 $(x - 4)(x - 2)$

   5 **a** $(p - 1)(p + 3)$ **b** $(m + 5)(m - 2)$ **c** $(t + 1)(t - 5)$
      d $(r + 4)(r - 7)$ **e** $(x - 3)(x - 5)$ **f** $(n - 1)(n - 6)$
      g $(t + 3)(t - 4)$ **h** $(b + 2)(b - 6)$ **i** $(x + 6)(x - 2)$

   6 $(x - 4)(x + 4)$

   7 **a** $(t + 3)(t - 3)$ **b** $(r + 5)(r - 5)$ **c** $(4p + 1)(4p - 1)$
      d $(3x + 2)(3x - 2)$ **e** $(x + y)(x - y)$ **f** $(x + 3p)(x - 3p)$

   8 A and C

Exercise 3.8
   1 $(2x + 3)(x + 2)$

   2 **a** $(3x - 1)(x - 3)$ **b** $(4y - 3)(y + 1)$ **c** $(4p + 1)(p - 3)$
      d $(4x + 3)(x - 1)$ **e** $(3x - 1)(x + 3)$ **f** $(3a + 1)(a + 3)$
      g $(5n - 1)(n - 2)$ **h** $(3x - 4)(x + 1)$ **i** $(3x - 1)(x - 1)$

   3 Across
      2 $(2x + 1)(2x + 1)$ 4 $(x - 1)(x + 1)$ 5 $(x + 1)(3x - 5)$
      7 $(2x + 1)(2x + 3)$ 8 $(x - 1)(5x + 1)$ 10 $(x - 1)(x - 4)$
      13 $(x + 2)(x - 2)$ 14 $(x - 2)(4x + 7)$
      Down
      1 $(3x + 1)(3x - 1)$ 2 $(x - 1)^2$ 3 $(2x + 1)(2x - 1)$ 4 $(x - 1)(x - 3)$
      5 $(3x + 2)(x + 2)$ 6 $(x + 1)(x - 5)$ 9 $(5x - 4)(x + 1)$
      11 $(x + 2)(x - 7)$ 12 $(2x + 3)(2x - 3)$ 13 $(x + 7)(x - 7)$

   4 **a** $a = 36, b = 6$ **b** $a = 6, b = 3$ **c** $a = 2, b = 1$ **d** $a = 4, b = 2$

   5 **a** $3(x - 1)(x - 2)$ **b** $3(2x + 5)(x + 1)$ **c** $2(3x - 1)(x + 3)$
      d $7(2x + 1)(x - 2)$ **e** $3(x - 1)^2$ **f** $4(x + 1)(x - 1)$

   6 **a** $n(n + 1)(n - 1)$
      b $n - 1, n$ and $n + 1$ are consecutive numbers, so at least one of them
         must be even, making their product even.

   7 **a** $(x + y)^2$ **b** $4(x + y)^2$ **c** $(3x + 4y)(3x - 4y)$

Exercise 3.9
   1 **a** $p + 1, p + 2$
      b **i** $p + p + 1 + p + 2$ **ii** $3p + 3$ **iii** $3p + 3 = 3(p + 1)$

   2 **a** **i** $^-4$ **ii** 0 **iii** 6 **iv** 14 **b** $(n + 3)(n - 2)$
      c The two factors are 5 apart, so one of them must be even, giving an
         even product.

   3 $n^2 - 6n + 9 = (n - 3)^2$ and squares are always positive.

4 **a** **i** $y - 8, y - 1, y + 1, y + 8$
      ii $(y + 1)(y + 8) - (y - 8)(y - 1)$
      iii $(y + 1)(y + 8) - (y - 8)(y - 1) = 18y$
   b **i** $y - n, y - 1, y + 1, y + n$
      ii $(y + 1)(y + n) - (y - n)(y - 1)$
      iii 320

5 One of the numbers must be a multiple of 2, another a multiple of 3,
   so the product will be a multiple of 6.

Exercise 3.10
   1 **a** $(a + b)(a - b)$ **b** **i** 9600 **ii** 2200

   2 **a** $3, 5, 7, 9, 11, ...$
      b The answers are odd numbers.
      c $(n + 1)^2 - n^2 = 2n + 1$
      d **i** 2467 **ii** 246246246245

   3 **a** $(n + 5)^2 - n^2 = 10n + 25$
      b **i** 1255 **ii** 3045

Exercise 3.11
   1 **a** **i** $\frac{1}{2}$ **ii** $\frac{1}{3}$ **iii** $\frac{1}{4}$ **c** **i** $\frac{1}{(n + 1)}$
   2 **a** **i** $\frac{1}{(n - 1)}$ **ii** $\frac{(n + 2)}{n}$ **iii** $\frac{n}{2}$ **iv** $\frac{2n}{(n - 3)}$
      i $\frac{1}{49}$ **ii** $1\frac{1}{25}$ **iii** 25 **iv** $2\frac{6}{47}$
   3 **a** $\frac{(x + 1)(x + 2)}{2}$
      b $x + 1$ and $x + 2$ are consecutive integers, so one of them must be
         even, and so dividing by 2 gives an integer.

End points
   A1 **a** $22b + 16$ **b** $26b + 14$ **c** $10ab^2 + 4a^2b$ **d** $3x^2y - 37xy - 7xy^2$

   A2 C

   A3 **a** $a^2 + 9a + 8$ **b** $b^2 + 8b + 16$ **c** $5c^2 + 17c + 6$
      d $d^2 + d - 2$ **e** $6e^2 - 5e - 50$ **f** $3f^2 - 23f + 14$

   A4 **a** $(5 \times 10) - (4 \times 8), (6 \times 11) - (5 \times 9), (7 \times 12) - (6 \times 10)$
      b 66 **c** $(n + 1)(n + 6) - n(n + 4)$
      d $(n + 1)(n + 6) - n(n + 4) = 3n + 6 = 3(n + 2)$

   B1 **a** $4(2p + q)$ **b** $6(a - 2b)$ **c** $a(a + b)$
      d $m(7 + 3n)$ **e** $2y(4x + 5)$ **f** $2a(2b + 3a)$
      g $xy(3y - 5x)$ **h** $2pq(2 - 3p)$ **i** $h(2g^2 - 5h)$

   B2 **a** C and E **b** B and C **c** D and F

   B3 **a** $(x + 1)(x + 11)$ **b** $(x + 2)(x + 7)$ **c** $(x + 5)(x - 1)$
      d $(x + 3)(x - 2)$ **e** $(x + 4)(x - 5)$ **f** $(x - 2)(x - 3)$
      g $(x + 10)(x - 10)$ **h** $(2x - 5)(x - 3)$ **i** $(3x + 4)(3x - 4)$
      j $(5x - 1)(x + 1)$ **k** $(x + 2y)(x - 2y)$ **l** $(2x - y)^2$

   B4 B and D, C and E

   B5 **a** $\frac{(x - 4)}{3}$ **b** $x > 4$

SECTION 4 Comparing Data

Starting points
   A1 **a** Discrete **b** continuous **c** discrete **d** discrete

   B1 **a** 15 and 42, 25 **b** 39.5, 38 **c** 42.5, 48.8 **d** 69, 93

   C1 **a** £340 **b** £340 **c** £314.89
      d The mode and median are reasonable averages to use.
         The mean is too low because of one extreme value (£112).

D1

Colour of car	Frequency
Red	5
Blue	6
Green	2
White	3
Silver	2
Black	4
Brown	2

D2 Blue

Number of children in car	Frequency
0	11
1	7
2	4
3	1
4	1

D4 **a** 0 **b** 4

D5 **a** 1 **b** 0.9

E1 **a** Red 20.8%, Blue 25%, Green 8.3%, White 12.5%, Silver 8.3%, Black 16.7%, Brown 8.3%
  b Red 75°, Blue 90°, Green 30°, White 45°, Silver 30°, Black 60°, Brown 30°

F5 **a** 54.4% **b** 34.8% **c** 10.8%

F6 **a** 38.8% **b** 33.0% **c** 28.2%

Thinking ahead to ...
  A **a** 8 **b** His scores were mainly in the interval 4–7.

Exercise 4.1
1 **a i** William: 2, 4, 4, 4, 5, 5, 6, 6, 6, 6, 6, 7, 7, 7, 8, 8
      Bryony: 4, 4, 5, 5, 5, 5, 6, 6, 6, 7, 7, 7, 9, 9
      Daniel: 2, 3, 4, 4, 5, 5, 5, 6, 6, 6, 6, 7, 7, 7, 9, 9, 9, 10, 10
    ii William's interquartile range = 2.5, Bryony's = 2, Daniel's = 3
  b Bryony

Exercise 4.2

1 **a**
```
4 | 0 6
3 | 2 3 8
2 | 0 3 4 6
2 | 2 2 4 9
0 | 7
  ----------
  1 2 3 4 5 6
```

b
```
4 | 0
3 | 0 1 2
2 | 0 2 4 4 4 6 6
1 | 0 2 5
0 |
  --------------
  1 2 3 4 5 6 7
```

c
```
4 | 1 2 4
3 | 0 0 6
2 | 4 5 5
1 | 6 6 8
0 | 6 6 7 9
  ----------
  1 2 3 4 5 6
```

d
```
5 | 6
4 | 0 0 6
3 | 0 2 7 8
2 | 2 4 8 8 8
1 | 4 8
0 |
  ----------
  1 2 3 4 5 6
```

2 **a**
```
6 | 2
5 | 0 0 0 1 2 2 3 4 4 6 7 9
4 | 0 0 0 1 2 4 4 7
3 | 0 4 8 8
2 |
1 |
0 |
  --------------------------
  1 2 3 4 5 6 7 8 9 10 11 12
```

b 50

Exercise 4.3
1 **b** Supermarket A: 28, Supermarket B: 28
  c Supermarket A: 48, Supermarket B: 37

2 **a** Group A: 29, Group B: 33.5
  b Both have a range of 50.

3 **c** A: 42.6, B: 38

Exercise 4.4
1 17.2

2 **a** 53 **b** 13.6

Thinking ahead to ...
  A **b** 1.4, 1.6

Exercise 4.5
1 **a** 1.55 **b** Round 6

2 **b** Paula 2.7, Zoe 1.9, Matt 2.5

Exercise 4.6
1 **a** Zeta 61, Carlo 57.5 **b** Zeta 12.4, Carlo 13.3

2 Dean: 5.8, 1.26, Leah: 5.4, 1.19, Jack: 4.8, 1.52

3 **a ii** Eliza 4, Sam 4.5 **iii** Eliza 1, Sam 2.25

Thinking ahead to ...
1 **a ii** 7 **b ii** 8

Exercise 4.7
1 Lee 5, Faith 6, Aqib 7, Tegan 4.5

Exercise 4.10
3 **A** The area of the drops is misleading
  b The vertical scale does not start at zero

End points
A1 **a** 65.5 **b** 11.48

B1 60.5, 11.48

Cl 7.6, 1.49

Dl 7.6, 1.49

E1 8, 2.5

G1 X The vertical scale does not start at zero
  Y The areas are misleading

SECTION 5 Sequences

Starting points
A1 **a** 33, 39 **b** 30, 41

A2 31

A3 **a** 32, 38, 44 **b** 47, 65, 86 **c** 57, 83, 114

A4 **a** 6 **b** 79

B1 **b** 46
  c

Pattern number (n)	Number of matches (m)
1	6
2	11
3	16
4	21
5	26

  d $m = 5n + 1$

Exercise 5.1

1

Pattern number of		Number matches
1	→	3
2	→	4
3	→	5
4	→	6
20	→	22
n	→	$n + 2$

2 **a**

Pattern number of		Number matches
1	→	4
2	→	8
3	→	12
4	→	16
5	→	20
6	→	24

b $n \rightarrow 4n$ **c** 400 **d** Pattern 155 **e** Pattern 124

Thinking ahead to ...

A 301

Exercise 5.2

1 **a** $m = 2n + 1$ **b** 17

2 **a** $m = 4n + 1$ **b** 16 **c** 32nd

3 **a** $m = 6n - 2$ **b** 598

4 **b** $m = 4n + 2$

5 **a** $50 \rightarrow 249$, $n \rightarrow 5n - 1$
b $2 \rightarrow 22$
   $3 \rightarrow 18$
   $4 \rightarrow 14$
   $11 \rightarrow {}^{-}14$
c $28 \rightarrow {}^{-}75$
   $p \rightarrow 9 - 3p$

Thinking ahead to ...

A **a** 19, 21 **b** 29 **c** 105

Exercise 5.3

1 **a** A: $3n + 3$, B: $5n - 4$, C: $10n + 3$, D: $8n - 6$
b A: 153, B: 246, C: 503, D: 394

2 **a** He should have had $3n$ instead of $+3$.
b $3n + 2$

3 $n + 7$

4 $1, {}^{-}2, {}^{-}5, {}^{-}8, {}^{-}11$

5 **a** $22 - 2n$ **b** $32 - 10n$ **c** $1 - 2n$ **d** $15 - 5n$

Exercise 5.4

1 **a** 5th number, $40 = 5 \times 8$ **b** 130

2 **a** 5th triangle number, $15 = \frac{(5 \times 6)}{2}$
b 78 **c** $\frac{1}{2}n(n + 1)$

3 **a** 5th power, $32 = 2 \times 2 \times 2 \times 2 \times 2 = 2^5$
b 256 **c** 2^n

Exercise 5.5

1 **c** 204 **d** 80th

2 **a** $2n + 6$, $2(n + 3)$

Exercise 5.6

1 **a** 2^n **b** $2^n - 1$ **c** 2^{n-1} **d** 2^{n-3} **e** 3^{1-n} **f** 4^{-n}

2 **a** $\frac{n}{(100 - n)}$ **b** $\frac{n^2}{2^{n+1}}$ **c** $\frac{3}{n^2}$ **d** $\frac{(n^2 + 1)}{(2^n + 1)}$

3 **a** $200 - 4^n$ **b** 4^{5-n}

4 **a** 1st number ${}^{-}1 = (1 - 1)^2 - 1$
   2nd number $0 = (2 - 1)^2 - 1$
   3rd number $3 = (3 - 1)^2 - 1$
   4th number $8 = (4 - 1)^2 - 1$
   5th number $15 = (5 - 1)^2 - 1$
b $u_n = (n - 1)^2 - 1$

End points

A1 **a** $m = 2n + 3$ **b** 495 matches

B1 **A** $u_n = 4n + 1$, $u_{20} = 81$
   B $u_n = n + 5$, $u_{20} = 25$
   C $u_n = 3n + 6$, $u_{20} = 66$
   D $u_n = 5n^2$, $u_{20} = 2000$
   E $u_n = 2 - 5n$, $u_{20} = {}^{-}98$
   F $u_n = 8n - 57$, $u_{20} = 103$
   G $u_n = 12n - 13$, $u_{20} = 227$
   H $u_n = 9n - 5$, $u_{20} = 175$

B2 **a** 3^{n+2} **b** 2^{n+2} **c** $2^n + 2$ **d** $4^n - 3$

B3 **a** $\frac{2n}{(n^2 + 1)}$ **b** $\frac{(2n + 1)}{3n^2}$

SKILLS BREAK 1

1 **a** 90 **b** £24.10 **c** £20.51

2 **a** regular pentagon, 108° **b** 28p

3 **b** 1120 **c** 1176

4 **a** regular hexagon **b** 120° **c** 10 cm

5 **a** The dimensions of the tiles do not fit exactly into the dimensions of the room, so he should have worked out how many he needs along the length and width and then multiplied.
b 198 **c** £332.48

6 $2\frac{1}{2}$ litres, it is cheapest per litre.

7 £37.00

8 £7.45

9 **a** regular octagon **b** 135° **c** £14

10 Volume = $18 \text{ cm} \times \pi \times \text{radius}^2 = 2500 \text{ cm}^3$
So, radius = 6.65 cm and diameter = 13.3 cm = 133 mm

11 **a** No, if a tub is used to cover 4 m^2 that is 875 g/m^2.
b increase **c** 5%

12 2.2 g

13 **a** She has used the slant height instead of the height of each triangle.
b 442 cm^2

14 **b** Each rhombus is twice the size of each equilateral triangle.
c 16.7%

CONSTRUCTIONS AND LOCI

Starting points

A1 **c** 60°

A2 **a** no **b** yes **c** yes **d** no

B1 F

B3 No, the sides may be joined together in a different order, or the angles could be different.

Exercise 6.1

2 angle SRQ = 77°

3 Triangles LMN and PQR look identical.

Exercise 6.2

1 **a** $\triangle$EBD **b** $\triangle$DCB **c** $\triangle$CDA
   d $\triangle$AFD **e** $\triangle$FCB **f** $\triangle$AEC

2 **a** The angles at P and Q could be different to those at A and B.

3 **a** congruent by SSS **b** congruent by SAS
   c not necessarily congruent
   d congruent by RHS **e** not necessarily congruent
   f congruent by ASA

Thinking ahead to ...
A   A, C and H

Exercise 6.3
2   Each angle is 60°. When you bisect one of the angles you make an angle of 30°.

Exercise 6.4
1   **c** The distances from A and B are equal.
3   **c** At a single point.   **d** yes
4   **e** They intersect at the centre.

Exercise 6.5
1   **a** 2 cm   **b** 20 m
5   **b** 12 km

Exercise 6.6
1   **d** A circle with AB as diameter.
2   **e** 90°   **f** It is a right-angled triangle.
3   angles BCE, BAE, AGH, CGH, AGB, CGB
4   **a** 28.6 m   **b** 20.2 m

End points
B1   **e** The gradients are the same.
D1   **a** congruent by SAS   **b** not necessarily congruent
     c not necessarily congruent   **d** congruent by SAS
     e congruent by ASA   **f** congruent by RHS

SECTION 7 Powers and Surds

Starting points
A1   **a** $0.\dot{7}$ **b** $0.1\dot{2}\dot{3}$ **c** $4.5\dot{6}$
A2   **a** 5.65656 ...   **b** 56.5656 ...   **c** 565.656 ...
A3   **a** 0.25   **b** $0.\dot{3}$ **c** $0.5\dot{4}$ **d** $0.5\dot{6}$ **e** 0.375
B1   **a** 3^5 **b** 4^{-3}
B2   **a** 81   **b** $\frac{1}{9}$ **c** 1   **d** $\frac{1}{5}$ **e** 512   **f** 36   **g** $\frac{4}{9}$ **h** $\frac{1}{16}$
C1   **a** 13   **b** 10   **c** 2.6   **d** 2.1
C2   **a** 3.5   **b** 10.2   **c** 2.6
C3   **a** 7   **b** 1.5   **c** ⁻10
C4 $\frac{1}{5}$ **b** $\frac{7}{10}$ **d** $1\frac{1}{5}$
C5   Positive and negative numbers have different cubes.

Exercise 7.1
1   **a** 2   **b** 1.5   **c** ⁻1
2   a, d
3   a $\frac{3}{4}$ **b** $\frac{2}{3}$ **c** $\frac{1}{5}$
4   1.8
5   **a** 150.0625   **b** 3   **c** ⁻91.125
6   **a** 6^2 **b** 2^2 **c** 5^2
7   **a i** $x = 4$ **ii** $x = 6$

Exercise 7.2
1   **a** 6^5 **b** 5^4 **c** 7^8 **d** 3   **e** 2^{11} **f** 5^{-6}
2   **a** 5   **b** 0   **c** 6   **d** 10   **e** 5   **f** 5
3   **a** x^8 **b** x^6 **c** x^{10} **d** x^2 **e** x^4 **f** x^{-2}
4   **a** 3   **b** ⁻1   **c** ⁻4
5   **a** 5   **b** ⁻2   **c** ⁻1
6   **a** They multiplied the powers instead of adding them.
     b They divided the powers instead of subtracting.
     c They subtracted the powers the wrong way round.
     d They added the powers instead of multiplying them.
7   **a** $x = 8$ **b** $x = 6$ **c** $x = 1$
8   **a** $2p$ **b** $\frac{6q^4}{5}$ **c** $2r^4$

Thinking ahead to ...
A   **a** 5   **b** 9
B   2

Exercise 7.3
1   a and g, b and h, c and e, d and f
2   **a** 6   **b** 5   **c** 3   **d** $\frac{1}{7}$ **e** $\frac{1}{2}$ **f** 1
3   **a** $\frac{2}{3}$ **b** $\frac{1}{3}$
4   a and e, b and g, c and f, d and h
5   a and f, b and h, c and d, e and g
6   a
7   **a** 25   **b** 27   **c** 9   **d** 128   **e** $\frac{1}{8}$ **f** $\frac{1}{81}$
8   **a i** B, C, D   **ii** A, B, C, D, F   **iii** B, C, D, E
9   $p = 243$
10   **a** $\frac{1}{27}$ **b** 9

Exercise 7.4
1   **a** $x = 3$ **b** $y = {}^-1$ **c** $z = 2$ **d** $a = \frac{1}{5}$ **e** $b = \frac{-1}{3}$
     f $c = {}^-4$ **g** $p = 2\frac{1}{2}$ **h** $q = 1\frac{1}{3}$ **i** $r = \frac{-3}{4}$
2   Across
     2 61   3 1024   6 1331   8 27
     Down
     1 10   2 64   3 16   4 243   5 81   6 17   7 32

Thinking ahead to ...
A   B and E

Exercise 7.5
1   **a** B, D, E
2   **a** B, C, F, G and H give integer values.
3   A and H, B and D, C and F, E and J, G and I
4   **a** $2\sqrt{10}$ **b** $\sqrt{21}$ **c** 3   **d** 8   **e** $3\sqrt{5}$ **f** 45   **g** $11 + 4\sqrt{7}$ **h** $18 + 12\sqrt{2}$
     i $3 + \sqrt{5} - 3\sqrt{2} - \sqrt{10}$ **j** 2   **k** $33 + 6\sqrt{30}$ **i** 144
5   **a** $4\sqrt{5}$ m²   **b** 36 m²   **c** $\frac{(9\sqrt{35})}{2}$ m²   **d** $24\sqrt{3}$ m²
     e $(4\sqrt{15} - 2\sqrt{10} - 6\sqrt{2} + 2\sqrt{3})$ mm²
6   $\frac{\sqrt{54}}{\sqrt{216}} = \sqrt{(\frac{54}{216})} = \sqrt{\frac{1}{4}} = \frac{1}{2}$
7   $12\sqrt{2}$ cm
8   **a** 20 000 000   **b** 2   **c** 3

End points
A1   **a** 3   **b** 6   **c** 2
B1   **a** 8   **b** 6   **c** 3
B2   **a** $2x^7$ **b** x^4 **c** $81x^{12}$
C1   **a** 10   **b** 16   **c** $\frac{1}{8}$
C2   **a** $x = \frac{1}{3}$ **b** $x = {}^-2$ **c** $\frac{-1}{4}$
D1   **a** $\sqrt{10}$ **b** $4\sqrt{2}$ **c** 63   **d** $5 - 2\sqrt{6}$
E1 $180\sqrt{6}$
E2   **i** $\sqrt{2}$ **ii** $\sqrt{3}$

SECTION 8 Approximation and Errors

Starting points
A1   **a** 23.47   **b** 4.16   **c** 142.86   **d** 12.30
A2   **a** 56.5   **b** 0.3   **c** 6.0   **d** 600.0
B1   **a** 150   **b** 16   **c** 3400   **d** 6.3   **e** 0.36   **f** 1 100 000
B2   **a** 30   **b** 200   **c** 0.05   **d** 500 000   **e** 100   **f** 0.000 09
C1   **a** 8^{10} **b** 6^2 **c** 10^{-2} **d** 10^{-2} **e** 4^{-10} **f** 10^2 **g** 5^8 **h** 6^{-12}
D1   **a** 3.45×10^5 **b** 4.17×10^{-3} **c** 4.297×10
     d 4×10^6 **e** 2.3×10^{-6} **f** 6.413234×10^3
D2   **a** 6740   **b** 0.00015   **c** 652.41   **d** 0.000 000 2

Exercise 8.1

1   2.995 m

2   **a** 15.65 cm   **b** 15.55 cm

3   **a** 7 750 000 km^2 **b** 7 650 000 km^2 **c** 7 650 000 $\leqslant L <$ 7 750 000

4   0.16 $\leqslant t \leqslant$ 0.18

Exercise 8.2

1   **a** 755 g   **b** 745 g

2   **a** 46.2 cm   **b** 1.2 cm

3   **a** 132 < L < 135   **b** 42.89°

4   **a** 81.64 m^2, 81.84 m^2 **b** 38.98 m, 39.02 m

5   62.8875 cm^2, 64.5575 cm^2

Exercise 8.3

1   **a** 6000   **b** 24 000   **c** 4 000 000
    d 25 000   **e** 750   **f** 100   **g** 250   **h** 30 000

2   **a** £18 000   **b** Both numbers are rounded up

3   100 people per km^2

5   **a** too large   **b** about right   **c** about right   **d** too small
    e too small   **f** too large   **g** about right   **h** too small

6   The numbers are a different order of magnitude

Exercise 8.4

1   **a** 17784   **b** 17.784

Exercise 8.5

1   **a** 3.6×10^3 **b** 1×10^5 **c** 5.8×10^5
    d 5.6×10^{-2} **e** 7.6×10^{-4} **f** 6.3×10^{-6}

2   **a** 374 600   **b** 5808   **c** 34 200 000
    d 0.056 75   **e** 0.000 063 88   **f** 0.000 000 009 02

3   **a** 1.38×10^9 **b** 1.49×10^5

Exercise 8.6

1   875

2   8 minutes 20 seconds

3   **a** 1.50×10^8 km, 1.07×10^5 km/h   **b** 8808 hours, a year

4   **a** 5×10^2, 9.6×10^{-5} **b** 4.8 cm

5   **a** 7.32×10^{-23} g   **b** 1.37×10^{22}

6   2.6 seconds

7   6.7×10 m

8   **a** 5.3×10^{14} m^2 **b** 7.5×10^{-5} g

End points

A1   **a** 6.75 cm   **b** 9.75 cm   **c** 338.6 cm^3, 352.5 cm^3 **d** 208.9 cm^2

B1   **a** 300 000   **b** 3 000 000   **c** 0.000 05   **d** 150

C1   **a** 3.6×10^5 **b** 1×10^5 **c** 7.6×10^{-6}

C2 6.9×10^0

C3   12 960 tonnes

SECTION 9 Solving Equations Algebraically

Starting points

A1   **a** $y^2 + 8y + 15$ **b** $k^2 - k - 12$ **c** $n^2 - 6n - 27$
    d $w^2 - 9w + 20$ **e** $v^2 - 64$

A2   **a** $2n^2 - 5n - 12$ **b** $3w^2 - 22w - 16$ **c** $12y^2 - 25y + 12$
    d $4k^2 - 12k + 9$ **e** $3v^3 + v^2 - 9v - 3$

A3   **a** $2y^3 - 2y^2 - 12y$ **b** $3x^3 + 6x^2 + 3x$ **c** $x^3 + 3x^2 - 13x - 15$
    d $4n^3 - 4n^2 - 5n + 3$ **e** $x^3 + 6x^2 + 12x + 8$ **f** $6k^2 - 2k^3 + 8k - 24$

B1   **a** $(y+2)(y+7)$ **b** $(k+5)(k-8)$ **c** $(x+6)(x-2)$
    d $(w+9)(w-4)$ **e** $(x-3)(x-8)$ **f** $(y-1)(y-8)$
    g $(p+12)(p-5)$ **h** $(b+9)(b-8)$ **i** $(x-12)(x-4)$
    j $(n+5)(n-5)$ **k** $(y+10)(y-10)$ **l** $(a+b)(a-b)$
    m $(2y+6)(2y-6)$ **n** $(4x+6y)(4x-6y)$ **o** $(10a+b^2)(10a-b^2)$

C1   **a** $y = {}^-4.5$ **b** $y = 3.4$ **c** $x = 2$
    d $x = 3$ **e** $x = 4$

C2   **a** $x = {}^-2$ **b** $n = \frac{3}{8}$ **c** $w = 21$ **d** $k = 2$ **e** $v = 2.17$

C3   **a** $y = 8.67$ **b** $u = 8$ **c** $k = 10$ **d** $h = 12$ **e** $a = 2$

C4   **a** $w = {}^-7$ **b** $k = 3.5$ **c** $n = \frac{1}{8}$

D1   9 cm × 15 cm

D2   20

D3   53 fans, 44 fans, 50 fans

Thinking ahead to ...

A   **a** £2.30   **b** £6.90   **B a** £4   **b** 96p   **c** 28p   **d** 68p

Exercise 9.1

1   **a** $x = 6, y = 9$ **b** $x = 8, y = 1$ **c** $x = 6, y = 2$
    d $x = 2, y = {}^-1$ **e** $x = {}^-2, y = 3$ **f** $x = 3, y = {}^-4$

2   $m = {}^-1, n = 10$

3   **a** $v = 2, w = 12$ **b** $v = {}^-1, w = 3$ **c** $v = 3, w = {}^-2$ **d** $v = 3, w = 2$
    e $v = 3, w = {}^-1$ **f** $v = 3, w = {}^-2$ **g** $v = 2, w = {}^-1$ **h** $v = 1, w = 3$
    i $v = {}^-1, w = 3$

Exercise 9.2

1   **a** $a = 10, b = 2$ **b** $a = 2, b = 5$ **c** $a = 4, b = {}^-3$ **d** $a = {}^-2, b = 8$
    e $a = 3, b = 1$ **f** $a = 6, b = {}^-4$ **g** $a = 2, b = {}^-1$ **h** $a = 4, b = {}^-2$
    i $a = 3, b = {}^-2$ **j** $a = 2, b = 1$ **k** $a = 2, b = {}^-3$ **l** $a = {}^-1, b = 4$

2   $k = 5, n = 10$

3   $m = 6, n = 1$

4   **a** $x = 4, y = 2$ **b** $x = 3, y = 5$ **c** $x = 2, y = 1$ **d** $x = {}^-1, y = 2$
    e $x = 5, y = {}^-1$ **f** $x = 7, y = {}^-4$ **g** $x = {}^-3, y = {}^-2$ **h** $x = 3, y = {}^-4$
    i $x = 2, y = {}^-1$ **j** $x = 3, y = {}^-5$ **k** $x = {}^-1, y = 2$ **l** $x = {}^-2, y = 3$

Exercise 9.3

1   adult £6.50, children £4

2   16 g, 54 g

3   63, 26

4   13, 9

5   123, 157

6   5 and 7 or 4.5 and 6.5

7   4, $^-2$

8   16 200, 12 300

9   **a** 3, 8   **b** $y = 3x + 8$

10   **a** 1, 3, $^-5$ **b** $y = x^2 + 3x - 5$

11   **a** 2, $^-3$, 1   **b** $y = 2x^2 - 3x + 1$

12   **a** 3, $^-1$, $^-4$ **b** $y = 3x^2 - x - 4$

13   8.5 hours, 16.5 hours

14   18, 8

Exercise 9.4

1   **a** $^-4, ^-1$ **b** $^-6, ^-3$ **c** $^-8, 3$ **d** $^-7, 1$ **e** $^-9, 4$ **f** $^-9, 7$ **g** $^-4, 11$
    h $^-7, 15$ **i** $^-7, 16$ **j** 3, 5   **k** 5, 7   **l** 5, 6   **m** 2, 5   **n** $^-28, ^-3$
    o $^-2, 15$ **p** $^-12, 5$ **q** 5, 9   **r** $^-15, 3$ **s** $^-15, 14$ **t** $^-19, 21$
    u 3, 14   **v** $^-15, 12$ **w** 7, 8   **x** $^-8, 17$

Exercise 9.5

1   **a** $0, ^-8$ **b** 0, 5   **c** 0, 18   **d** $^-10, 10$ **e** $^-5, 5$ **f** $^-9, 9$

2   **a** 0, 12   **b** $^-79, 0$ **c** $^-\frac{1}{3}, 0$ **d** $0, \frac{1}{4}$ **e** $^-13, 13$
    f 0, 1   **g** $0, \frac{2}{5}$ **h** $^-\frac{5}{4}, 0$ **i** $^-\frac{2}{7}, 0$

Exercise 9.6

1   **a** $^-\frac{1}{4}, \frac{2}{3}$ **b** $^-\frac{1}{3}, \frac{5}{2}$ **c** $^-\frac{1}{2}, \frac{2}{3}$ **d** $^-\frac{1}{5}, \frac{1}{2}$ **e** $^-\frac{4}{3}, \frac{1}{3}$ **f** $\frac{1}{2}, \frac{2}{3}$ **g** $^-\frac{2}{3}, \frac{1}{3}$ **h** $^-\frac{1}{7}, 1$
    i $^-\frac{2}{3}, \frac{1}{2}$ **j** $\frac{1}{5}, 2$ **k** $^-3, \frac{1}{3}$ **l** $\frac{4}{3}, 4$ **m** $^-2, 3$ **n** $\frac{2}{3}, 2$ **o** $^-\frac{1}{6}, 2$

2   **a** $0, \frac{1}{2}$ **b** 0, 3   **c** $^-\frac{1}{4}, 0$ **d** $0, \frac{8}{5}$ **e** $0, \frac{1}{2}$ **f** $^-\frac{1}{5}, \frac{1}{5}$ **g** $^-\frac{1}{4}, \frac{1}{4}$ **h** 0, 9
    i 0, 5   **j** 0, 1   **k** $^-\frac{1}{3}, \frac{1}{3}$ **l** $0, \frac{4}{3}$ **m** 0, 31   **n** $0, \frac{3}{7}$ **o** $^-\frac{3}{4}, \frac{3}{4}$

Exercise 9.7

1 a $^-2.35, 0.85$ b $^-1.55, 0.80$ c $^-4.19, 1.19$ d $^-4.30, ^-0.70$
   e $^-3.35, ^-0.15$ f $^-1.46, ^-0.14$ g $0.23, 1.43$ h $0.29, 1.71$
   i $^-0.62, 1.62$ j $^-1.85, 1.35$ k $^-1.47, 1.81$ l $0.28, 0.72$

2 a $\frac{^-1 \pm \sqrt{7}}{2}$ b $\frac{^-1 \pm \sqrt{145}}{12}$ c $\frac{(1 \pm \sqrt{65})}{8}$ d $\frac{^-2 \pm \sqrt{6}}{4}$
   e $\frac{^-4 \pm \sqrt{11}}{5}$ f $\frac{^-9 \pm \sqrt{53}}{14}$ g $\frac{^-3 \pm \sqrt{41}}{4}$ h $\frac{(5 \pm \sqrt{37})}{2}$ i $\frac{3 \pm \sqrt{33}}{2}$

3 a $^-2.77, 1.27$ b $2.18, 0.15$ c $^-1.80, 0.55$

Exercise 9.8

1 b $^-10.48, 0.48$

2 $^-8.36, 0.36$

3 $(b^2 - 4ac)$ is negative

4 a $^-12.16, 0.16$ b $^-7.12, 1.12$ c $^-14.07, 0.07$ d no solution
   e no solution f $^-7.16, ^-0.84$

5 a $\pm\sqrt{(\frac{13}{2})} - \frac{5}{2}$ b $\frac{\pm\sqrt{57} - 7}{2}$ c $\frac{\pm\sqrt{5} - 3}{2}$

Exercise 9.9

1 a $^-4, 9$ b $^-5, 12$ c $^-7, 9$ d $^-9, 3$ e $^-4.79, ^-1.88$ f $^-6, 1$
   g $^-1.27, 6.27$ h $^-4.21, 0.71$ i $^-0.17, 0.17$ j $^-0.2, 0.2$ k $0, 1.67$
   l $^-2.91, 0.57$ m $^-1.90, 0.40$ n $^-1.38, 1.63$ o $^-0.1, 0.1$

Exercise 9.10

1 a $L(L - 12) = 448$, length = 28 cm, width = 16 cm b 32.25 cm

2 18, 24

3 a 36 cm (27 cm) b 972 cm²

4 37.61°

5 $^-14.72, 2.72$

6 a 27 cm, 36 cm b 108 cm

7 a 8.5 cm b 50.14 cm c 4.28°

8 50.5, 54.5

9 54 units²

11 b $6x^2 + 40x + 48$
    c $6x^2 + 40x + 48 = 398$, $x = 5$ cm d 495 cm³

End points

A1 a 3, $^-2$ b $^-3, ^-1$

B1 £4.80, £2.65

C1 a $^-8, 3$ b $^-5, 13$ c 3, 12 d $^-2, 3$

D1 a $^-6.32, 0.32$ b $0.35, 8.65$ c $^-4.14, ^-0.36$ d no solution

D2 a $^-4 \pm 2\sqrt{5}$ b $3 \pm \sqrt{17}$

E1 $^-5.54, 0.54$

E2 $\pm\sqrt{21} - 4$

F1 15 cm, 38 cm

SECTION 10 Transformations

Starting points

A1 a $x = 3$ 2b $y = ^-1$

B1 b i vertices at $(2, 0), (3, 0), (3, 2)$
       ii vertices at $(^-4, 3), (^-2, 3), (^-2, 2)$

C1 a 90° b $(0, 1)$

D1 U has vertices at $(2, 2), (2, 3), (4, 3)$;
    V has vertices at $(^-1, ^-1), (^-1, 0), (1, 0)$

E1 a vertices at $(1, 0), (1, 2), (5, 2)$
    b vertices at $(0, 3.5), (0, 4), (1, 4)$
    c vertices at $(2, 1.5), (6, 1.5), (6, 3.5)$

E2 a vertices at $(^-1.5, 0.5), (^-1.5, ^-2.5), (^-3, ^-1), (^-3, 0.5)$
    b vertices at $(4, 0), (4, ^-4), (2, ^-2), (2, 0)$
    c vertices at $(1, ^-1), (1, ^-7), (^-2, ^-4), (^-2, ^-1)$

F1 a V, Y, Z

Thinking ahead to ...

A b B has vertices at $(1, 2), (2, 2), (1, 4)$;
      C has vertices at $(^-2, 1), (0, 1), (0, 2)$;
      D has vertices at $(^-4, ^-1), (^-2, ^-1), (^-2, ^-2)$;
      E has vertices at $(2, ^-1), (2, ^-3), (3, ^-1)$;
      F has vertices at $(^-2, 3), (^-3, 4), (0, 3)$
   c rotation of 90° about $(1, 1)$
   d i rotation of 90° about $(0, 1)$
      ii reflection in $y = x - 1$
      iii rotation of $^-90°$ about $(^-2, ^-1)$

Exercise 10.1

1 a H has vertices at $(4, 1), (5, 1), (6, 2), (5, 3)$, G→H by $\binom{6}{2}$

2 a J has vertices at $(3, 1), (4, 0), (3, ^-1), (2, ^-1)$
      K has vertices at $(3, 1), (4, 0), (3, ^-1), (2, ^-1)$
   b They are the same.

3 1 and 4, 2 and 3

Exercise 10.2

1 a L has vertices at $(0, 2), (1, 4), (0, 4), (^-1, 3)$
      M has vertices at $(^-1, 1), (0, 2), (^-2, 3), (^-2, 2)$
      N has vertices at $(^-1, ^-4), (^-2, ^-4), (^-3, ^-3), (^-2, ^-2)$
   b i rotation +90° about $(1, 1)$
      ii rotation 180° about $(1, 2)$
      iii reflection in $y = ^-x$

Exercise 10.3

1 b i translation $\binom{-2}{-2}$ ii 180° rotation about $(2, 0)$
      iii 180° rotation about $(3, 1)$

2 a i reflection in $x = 5$
      ii reflection in $y = x$
      iii rotation 180° about $(4, 1)$

3 a P_5 has vertices at $(4, 0), (6, 0), (6, ^-2), (4, ^-4)$
      P_6 has vertices at $(^-2, 0), (^-2, 2), (0, 4), (0, 0)$
      P_7 has vertices at $(0, 2), (0, 4), (2, 6), (2, 2)$

Exercise 10.4

1 b B

   c
Object	Image	SF	Centre
S	Y	2	(4, 8)
Y	U	$\frac{1}{2}$	(8, 8)
E	A	2	(8, 8)
Q	W	$^-1$	(8, 6)

   d They are not in the same orientation.
   e i Rotate $^-90°$ about $(8, 8)$
      ii Enlarge SF $\frac{1}{2}$ with centre $(8, 12)$
      iii Rotate 180° about $(6, 8)$

Exercise 10.5

2 a B_1 has vertices at $(5, 2), (5, 4), (1, 4)$
      B_2 has vertices at $(5, 0), (7, 0), (7, 4)$
      B_3 has vertices at $(5, 6), (9, 6), (9, 4)$
      B_4 has vertices at $(3, 8), (5, 8), (3, 4)$
   b i rotation $^-90°$ about $(4, 1)$
      ii translation $\binom{4}{2}$
      iii rotation +90° about $(2, 5)$
   c i enlargement SF 2 with centre $(^-1, ^-2)$
      ii enlargement SF 2 with centre $(^-5, 4)$

3 a enlargement SF $\frac{1}{2}$ with centre $(^-1, 0)$
   b enlargement SF $\frac{1}{2}$ with centre $(^-3, ^-2)$

5 c i enlargement SF $^-2$ with centre $(0, 1)$
      ii enlargement SF 2.25 with centre $(0, 1)$
   d i enlargement SF $^-\frac{1}{2}$ with centre $(0, 1)$
      ii enlargement SF $\frac{4}{9}$ with centre $(0, 1)$

Thinking ahead to ...
   A   b The transformations have no effect.

Exercise 10.6

1   a translation $\begin{pmatrix} -1 \\ 2 \end{pmatrix}$

   b rotation +90° about (1, 1)
   c enlargement SF $\frac{1}{2}$ with centre ($^-$1, 2)

2   a reflection in $y = ^-x$
   b the reflection and its inverse are the same

3 reflection 180° about (x, y); enlargement SF $^-$1, centre (x, y)

End points

A1   b K has vertices at ($^-$4, $^-$3), ($^-$1, $^-$3), ($^-$1, $^-$5), ($^-$2, $^-$5), ($^-$2, $^-$4),

   ($^-$4, $^-$4)

   L has vertices at ($^-$3, 1), ($^-$1, 1), ($^-$1, 4), ($^-$2, 4), ($^-$2, 2), ($^-$3, 2)

   M has vertices at (1, $^-$1), (2, $^-$1), (2, $^-$2), (4, $^-$2), (4, $^-$3), (1, $^-$3)

   c   i rotation 180° about (0, −1)

   ii rotation 90° anticlockwise about (0, 0)

   iii translation $\begin{pmatrix} 0 \\ -4 \end{pmatrix}$

   d   i translation $\begin{pmatrix} 0 \\ 4 \end{pmatrix}$

   ii reflection in $y = ^-3$
   iii rotation 180° about (1, 0)
   e   i rotation 90° clockwise about (1, $^-$1)
   ii rotation 180° about (0, $^-$3); enlargement, SF $^-$1, centre (0, $^-$3)

B1   a enlargement SF 4 with centre (3, $^-$1)
   b rotation +270° about (0, 2)

   c translation $\begin{pmatrix} 0 \\ 3 \end{pmatrix}$

B2 reflection in $y = x + 1$

Skills break 2

1   a 12   **b** 12   **d** 132.7 m²   **e** 1805 cm²   **f** 7.37 m³

2   a 45°   **b** 135°   **c** 28.97 cm   **d** 695.26 cm²

3   a 1110 tons   **b** 46 m   **c** 9°   **d** 2.5°   **e** 370   **f** 0.005%

4 045°

5   a £7.43   **b** £5.94

6   a

Vowel	French	rel. freq.	English	rel. freq
a	38	0.21	40	0.24
e	72	0.39	49	0.29
i	26	0.14	35	0.21
o	21	0.11	36	0.21
u	27	0.15	10	0.06

   b French has longest words.

7   a $\frac{7}{12}$ **b** $\frac{1}{6}$ **c i** $\frac{1}{3}$ **ii** $\frac{1}{2}$ **d** loss

8   a £188   **b** £277

SECTION 11   Using formulas

Starting points

A1   a $d = 5.5$ **b** $y = ^-14$ **c** $x = 4$ **d** $p = 6$ **e** $x = 1.5454 \ldots$
   f $k = 0.66 \ldots$ **g** $n = 18$ **h** $g = ^-11$

A2   a $c = 7.5$ **b** $x = 0.8$ **c** $x = 12$ **d** $v = 1$
   e $w = ^-1$ **f** $a = 19$ **g** $x = 3.4$ **h** $y = ^-120$

B1   a $3(2bc - 5ax + by)$ **b** $6(3a^2 + 4b^2c)$ **c** $a(3ax - 5y^2 + 2b - c)$
   d $ax(y - ax + xy - b)$ **e** $3cd(2c - 5b)$ **f** $4ax(2y^2 + 2b - 5a + 4)$

C1   a $x = \sqrt{(4a + 3)}$ **b** $x = \sqrt{\left(\frac{5c + 1}{3}\right)}$ **c** $x = (3a - 7)^2$ **d** $x = \frac{49}{a}$ **e** $x = \frac{16a^2}{25}$

Thinking ahead to ...
   A   a 3 hours 20 minutes   **b** 3 lb

Exercise 11.1

1   a $y = \frac{(5x + 4)}{3}$ **b** $y = \frac{(8 - 9x)}{2}$ **c** $y = \frac{(5x - 9)}{4}$ **d** $y = \frac{(3x + 4)}{5}$
   e $y = \frac{(2a - 4)}{3x}$ **f** $y = \frac{(3a - 2x)}{2x}$ **g** $y = \frac{(4x - 3)}{6}$ **h** $y = \frac{(5x + 6)}{12}$
   i $y = \frac{(6 - 5x)}{8}$ **j** $y = \frac{(x + 4)}{2}$ **k** $y = \frac{(1 - 5a^2)}{2}$ **l** $y = \frac{(x^2 + 6)}{12}$
   m $y = \frac{(5a + 9x)}{10}$ **n** $y = \frac{(6 - x^2)}{8}$ **o** $y = \frac{(6x - 5)}{8x}$

2   a £10.25   **b i** $n = \frac{(c - 50)}{15}$ **ii** 129   **c** 63

3   a 900°   **b i** $n = \frac{S}{180} + 2$ **ii** 20
   d Putting 600° into the formula does not give a whole number of
      sides.

4   a i 55.924 m   **ii** No, closer to 1.5%.
   b i $t = \frac{(x - w)}{wk}$ **ii** 30.5 °C

5   a 3.428 m²   **b i** $h = \frac{(S - 2\pi r^2)}{2\pi r}$ **ii** 17 cm

Exercise 11.2

1   a 17.6 lb   **b** $k = \frac{5p}{11}$ **c** 1.4 kg

2   a $h = \frac{2A}{b}$ **b** 80 cm

3   a 20 °C   **b** $F = \frac{(9C + 160)}{5}$ **c** 75.2 °F

4   a $y = \frac{4z}{3}$ **b** $x = \frac{3m}{x}$ **c** $y = 2d - 4$ **d** $y = \frac{7k + 4h}{4}$

5   a 36.14 km/h   **b** $d = \frac{5st}{18}$ **c** $t = \frac{18d}{5s}$

6   a $^-24$ °C   **b** $h = 300(G - T)$ **c** 15 000 m

7 16.20

8   a $w = \frac{5}{6x}$ **b** $w = \frac{3}{(4 \sin 32°)}$ **c** $w = 3(5a + 4b)$ **d** $w = \frac{a}{t} + b$ **e** $w = \frac{a^2}{b}$
   f $w = \frac{(c^2 - b)}{4ab}$ **g** $w = \frac{(3x - 12)}{8}$ **h** $\frac{(3x + 2)}{2}$ **i** $w = \frac{(\tan 50° - 3)}{6}$ **j** $w = \frac{(2a + 15)}{5}$
   k $w = 10a - 4$ **l** $w = \frac{(41 + 2)}{3}$ **m** $w = \frac{6a - 5}{2}$ **n** $w = \frac{2a}{3}$ **o** $w = \frac{4ax}{15}$

Exercise 11.3

1   a $w = \frac{(S - 2ab)}{(2b + 2a)}$ **b** $a = \frac{(S - 2bw)}{(2b + 2w)}$ **c** 3.6

2   a $w = \frac{2P}{(4 + \pi)}$ **b** 50 m

3   a i $b = \frac{V}{(ac - 2ad)}$ **ii** 14.5 cm   **b** 12

4   a $h = \frac{3ac}{(4a - y)}$ **b** $h = \frac{4x}{(3 - 2a)}$ **c** $h = \frac{(2x - 5)}{(3x - a)}$ **d** $h = \frac{(4 - b^2)}{(a - c)}$ **e** $h = \frac{7}{(3 + x)}$
   f $h = \frac{9}{(a + b)}$ **g** $h = \frac{(2 - y)}{(3a + x)}$ **h** $h = \frac{5}{(1 - 3a)}$ **i** $h = \frac{3}{(5b + 3a)}$ **j** $h = \frac{(2 + by)}{(1 + 4a)}$
   k $h = \frac{2}{(x - y)}$ **l** $h = \frac{1}{(x - 6a)}$ **m** $h = \frac{7}{(2b - 3a)}$ **n** $h = \frac{20x}{a}$ **o** $h = \frac{3}{(a - 4)}$
   p $h = \frac{25}{18a}$ **q** $h = \frac{(a - 6b)}{6x}$

Exercise 11.4

1 9.5 seconds

2   b 8

3 $r = \sqrt{\left(\frac{3V}{\pi h}\right)}$

4   a $r = \sqrt[3]{\frac{3V}{4\pi}}$ **b** 2.9 cm

5 $b = s - \frac{A^2}{s(s - a)(s - b)}$

6   a $b = \sqrt{(y^2 - 3a + 4)}$ **b** $b = \sqrt{\left(\frac{(x - 3y)}{2a}\right)}$ **c** $b = \sqrt{\frac{(y - 1)}{x}}$ **d** $b = \sqrt{(4 + x)}$
   e $b = \sqrt{(2x + 5)}$ **f** $b = \sqrt[3]{\frac{(2 - 3x - 4a)}{2}}$ **g** $b = \sqrt[3]{(x - 1)}$ **h** $b = \sqrt{\frac{c}{(1 - 2a)}}$
   i $b = \sqrt{\frac{(1 + a^2)}{3}}$ **j** $b = 4a^2 + 2$ **k** $b = \sqrt{\left(\frac{(w^2 - 3)}{a}\right)}$ **l** $b = \sqrt{\left(\frac{1}{(c^2 - 1)}\right)}$
   m $b = \frac{1}{2}\sqrt{4a^2 - x^2 y^2}$ **n** $b = \frac{r^2}{\pi} - a$ **o** $b = \frac{k^2 y}{4\pi^2}$ **p** $b = \frac{(a + c + x)}{2}$
   q $b = \frac{(c - 3)^2 - 1}{2}$ **r** $b = \frac{(x - 2)^2}{4} + x$

Exercise 11.5

1 82.5 km

2   a 121.5 cm   **b** 64 cm³   **c** $x = 2$

3   a 42, 42, 47, 42, 42, 96   **b** $^-$8, 12, $^-$193, 12, $^-$28, $^-$64
   c 6, 12, $^-$4, 12, 0, $^-$15   **d** $^-$14, 0, $^-$16, 0, $^-$28, 5
   e 10.75, 15.75, $^-$3.63, 15.75, 5.75, $^-$9.63
   f $^-$14.25, 0.75, $^-$29.88, 10.75, $^-$29.25, 4.13

4   a i 31.1   **ii** 21.1   **b i** 120   **ii** 130   **iii** 17

5   a 1.098×10^{21} **b** $r = \sqrt[3]{\left(\frac{3V}{4\pi}\right)}$

End points

A1 **a** $x = \frac{(5 + a)}{3}$ **b** $x = \frac{(a - 3)}{6}$ **c** $x = \frac{(5 - 2y)}{6}$ **d** $x = \frac{(3a - b)}{5y}$ **e** $x = \frac{(2 - bc)}{4}$

B1 **a** $v = \frac{4(a - x)}{3}$ **b** $v = \frac{(3a - 14)}{10}$ **c** $v = \frac{(2a + 3)}{3a^2}$ **d** $v = \frac{(4ax + 8y - 5)}{2}$ **e** $v = \frac{-7a}{12}$

 f $v = \frac{(bc^2 - 3)}{2c^2}$ **g** $v = \frac{2w}{(3w - x)}$

C1 **a** $c = \frac{(3 - ax^2)}{x}$ **b** $c = \frac{8x}{(y - a)}$ **c** $c = \frac{(1 - 2a)}{5}$ **d** $c = \frac{(a^2b - 3 - 2a)}{a^2}$

 e $c = \frac{(3w - 2)}{3x^2}$ **f** $c = \frac{(ax - 1)}{(a^2 + x)}$

D1 **a** $y = \frac{25}{x}$ **b** $y = (a + x)^2 - 1$ **c** $y = \frac{4}{(2x-1)^2}$ **d** $y = \frac{ab^2}{9}$ **e** $y = 4\frac{a^2 - 25}{4}$

 f $y = \frac{8}{(b - a)}$ **g** $y = \sqrt{(3 - 4a - x)}$ **h** $y = \sqrt{\left\{\frac{(5x + 8)}{6}\right\}}$ **i** $y = \sqrt{(2ax - 3)}$

E1 **a** 652 cm² **b** 8.5 cm

E2 7.4

SECTION 12 Ratio and Proportion

Starting points

AZ **a** 3 : 1 **b** 1 : 3

B1 **a** 12 : 3 **b** 1 : 2½ : 2 **c** 3 : 4, 6 : 8

B2 2 : 5, 1 : 2½ and 10 : 25, 1 : 3 : 2 and 3 : 9 : 6, 10 : 20 and 2½ : 5

B3 **a** 3 : 2 **b** 2 : 3 **c** 2 : 4 : 1 **d** 10 : 1 **e** 4 : 3 : 6

C1 W and Y, X and Z

D1 **a** $\frac{5}{8}$, 0.625, 62.5% **b** $\frac{9}{5}$, 1.8, 180% **c** $\frac{7}{12}$, 0.583, 58.3%

 d $\frac{15}{11}$, 1.36, 136% **e** $\frac{11}{18}$, 0.611, 61.1% **f** $\frac{17}{24}$, 0.708, 70.8%

E1 £75, £45, £30

E2 **a** 1¼ hours **b** 1½ hours

F1 **a** It corresponds to angle K **b** angle L **c i** JL **ii** FG

G1 **a** $\frac{1}{2}$ **b** 4 **c** $\frac{1}{3}$ **d** $\frac{3}{4}$

Exercise 12.1

1 345 g caster sugar, 450 ml water, 75 g cocoa, 1800 ml chilled milk

2 **a** 60 g **b** 75 ml

 c 300 g white sugar, 100 ml milk, 100 ml water, 50 g butter, 20 g cocoa

3 **a** 7 drops **b** 175 g

Exercise 12.2

1 **a** 315 ml **b** 525 ml

2 **a** 250 kg **b i** 2 : 1 : 9 **ii** 2400 kg

3 **a** 6.3 cm **b** 1 : 5000

Exercise 12.3

1 **a** 2.5 **b** 12.75 cm **c i** 1.21 **ii** 1.21

Exercise 12.4

1 **a** MNOP

 b All corresponding angles are equal and all ratios of lengths of corresponding sides are equal.

Exercise 12.5

1 Should have divided by 1.25

2 **a** 4.56 cm **b** 4.2 cm

3 **a** 1.6 cm **b** angle LJK is equal to angle LMN

4 12.31 cm

Exercise 12.6

1 **a** They have the same angles **b i** AB **ii** CD
 c i 13.3 cm **ii** 10.7 cm

2 **a i** 1.5 **ii** 1.5

3 **b** 3.25 cm

4 It would be the other way up

Exercise 12.7

1 **d** $h = 0.25b$

2 **a** 4 **b** $b = 4h$

3 **b** no, the line isn't straight

4 **a**

	W	X	Y	Z
Height (h)	1	1.25	1.5	1.2
Area (A)	2	3.125	4.5	2.88

 c no

5 **a**

	W	X	Y	Z
h^2	1	1.5625	2.25	1.44
A	2	3.125	4.5	2.88

 c yes

7 **a ii** no **b iii** yes

Exercise 12.8

1 **a** approx √2
 b The measurements have been rounded **c** $h = \sqrt{2}w$

2 **a** 36 units² **b i** $h = \frac{36}{w}$ **ii** $wh = 36$ **iii** $w = \frac{36}{h}$

3 **a** 25, 49, 81, 100, 196 **b** $g = 0.4d^2$

Exercise 12.9

1 **a** $m \propto \frac{1}{v}$ **b** 54 **c** 12 **d** m is doubled

2 **a** $s \propto \sqrt{q}$ **b** $s = 7\sqrt{q}$ **c** 42

3 **a** $p = \frac{90}{t^2}$ **b** 10 **c** p is multiplied by 4 **d** $t = \sqrt{\left(\frac{90}{p}\right)}$ **e** 5

4 **a** $n \propto \frac{1}{d^2}$ **b** 20 000 **c** $n = \frac{20\,000}{d^2}$ **d i** 200 **ii** 102

5 **a** $A \propto d^2$ **b** 3.5 **c** $A = 3.5d^2$ **d** 1263.5 cm²

6 **a** $t = 1.6\sqrt{h}$ **b** 11.3 seconds

7 **a** $f \propto \frac{1}{a}$ **b** 42 **c** $f = \frac{42}{a}$ **d** 2.625 mm

8 **a** $r = \frac{4}{f^2}$ **b** 0.015625 **c** 2

9 **a** $m = 3.2w^3$ **b** 86.4 g **c** 1 : 8

End points

A1 **a i** 375 g **ii** 10 tablespoons **b** 3 eggs

B1 EFGH, NOPQ

C1 **a** 2.5 cm **b** 5.6 cm

D1 **b** 5.4 cm

E1 **a** $s = 2.25\sqrt{h}$ **b** 22.5 seconds

E2 **a** $w = \frac{6}{q}$ **b** 0.6 **c** w is halved **d** 0.8

SECTION 13 Mensuration

Starting points

A1 **a** A, C, F
 b cuboid, tetrahedron, cylinder, pentagonal prism, octagonal prism, hexagonal prism

B1 **a** 72 cm² **b** 84 cm² **c** 16 cm²

C1 4.5 m²

C2 8.3 cm

C3 area = $4\pi y^2$, circumference = $4\pi y$

D1 A 106 cm³, 182 cm² B 38.9 cm³, 96.12 cm² C 45.9 cm³, 82.2 cm²

E1 81.8 cm³, 113 cm²

E2 **a** 768π **b** 320π

Exercise 13.1

1 **a** 348 cm² **b** 243 cm² **c** 418.7 cm²

2 **a** 559 cm² **b** 1716.5 cm²

3 **a** 183.7 cm² **b** more **c** 85.4 cm

4 **a** 154 mm × 136 mm **b** 504 mm² **c** 1380 mm² **d** 16288 mm²
 e between $\frac{1}{5}$ and $\frac{1}{4}$

5 **a** 255 mm² **b** 763 mm² **c** 21%

6 **a** $\frac{\pi x^2}{4}$ **b** $\left(\frac{1 - \pi}{4}\right)x^2$ **c** $x^2\left(\frac{\pi}{2} - 1\right)$

Exercise 13.2

1 **a** 9.5 cm², 12.7 cm **b** 792.6 m², 143 m

2 **a** 192.7π cm², (22.7π + 34) cm **b** 36.0π m², (7.4π + 19.6) m

3 **a** 395.8 cm² **b** 80.0 cm

Exercise 13.3

1 **a** 240 cm³, 300 cm² **b** 343.6 cm³, 328.5 cm² **c** 1291 cm³, 746.7 cm²
    d 2204 cm³, 939.4 cm²

2 16.5 cm

3 **a** 27.2 m³ **b i** 390 bags **ii** £1996.80

4 **a** 46.25 m² **b** 555 m³ **c** 435 m³ **d** 0.435 litres

5 603 cm²

6 7 cm

7 **a** 960 cm³ **b** £840

8 43 800 cm³

9 **a** 30.2 cm² **b** 166 cm² **c** 578 cm² **d** 1630 cm²

10 **a** 13 300 m³ **b** 10 400 m²

11 **a** 1290 cm³ **b** 182 g

12 **a** $xyz - \pi r^2 x$ **b** $2(xy + xz + yz - \pi r^2 + \pi rx)$

13 $R = \frac{6V}{S}$

Exercise 13.4

1 **a** 300 cm³ **b** 75 ml **c** 170 g

2 **a** B **b** C **c** 575 cm³ **d** 4% **e** 44 cm³ **f** 38 g

3 **a** 21 700 000 cm³ **b** 21 700 litres

4 217 cm³, 1.07 g/cm³; 649 cm³, 0.952 g/cm³

Exercise 13.5

1 **a** B,C **b** 1 **c** A

3 **a i** C,D **ii** A, B **b** A 8, B 1, C 5, D 2

Exercise 13.6

1 **a** 168 cm³ **b** 135 cm² **c** 186 cm³

2 0.512 m³

3 **a** 41.6 cm² **b** 166 cm³

4 **a** B

Exercise 13.7

1 **a** π cm², 4π cm² **b** 4 times **c** $\frac{1}{6}\pi$ cm³, $\frac{4}{3}\pi$ cm³ **d** 8 times

2 **a** 34 cm **b** 191 mm

3 $(1.44 \times 10^{10})\pi$

4 24.8 cm

5 **a** 348 cm³ **b** 190 cm²

6 **a** 707 cm² **b** 707 cm²

Exercise 13.8

1 **a** 4.69 cm³ **b** 32.1 cm²

2 **a** 495.2 cm³ **b** 396.6 cm²

3 **a** 392.2 cm³, 27 cm² **b** 1696.5 cm³, 1017.9 cm²
    c 861 cm³, 850 cm² **d** 728.2 cm³, 690.8 cm²

4 **a** 18.6 cm³ **b** 12.5%

5 **a** 138 m³ **b** 1104 cm³

6 51.5 cm

7 **a** $h - 6$ **b** $h = 9.6$ cm, height of part cut off = 3.6 cm **c** 152.4 cm³

Thinking ahead to ...

A **a** 6 cm², 24 cm² **b** 1 cm³, 8 cm³ **c i** 1 : 4 **ii** 1 : 8

Exercise 13.9

1 **a** 13.1 cm³ **b** 124 cm²

2 **a** 1 : 1.27366 **b** 9.8 cm **c** 1 : 1.62222 **d** 1 : 2.06617

3 **a** 1 : 2.91003 **b** 760 cm³

4 1 : 15.625

5 1 : 1.65096

6 14 cm

7 **a** 128 000 cm² **b** 7 800 000 cm³

8 **a** 2.5 : 1 **b** 6.6 cm

9 **a** They have scaled by height, but as the shapes are 2D, they should
      have scaled by area.
    b Denopt System's £ sign should be 23 mm high.

10 **a** 64.0 cm² **b** 3560 cm³ **c** 1.78 cm² **d** 49.0 cm² **e** 39.1 cm³
    f 1060 cm³

11 4.76 m

12 **a** 2 **b** $\frac{1}{4}$ **c** 8 **d** $\frac{1}{8}$ **e** $\frac{1}{2}$ **f** 4

Exercise 13.10

1 **a** length **b** volume **c** area

2 **a** $\frac{1}{2}lz(x+y)$ **b** The other expressions are not for volumes.

3 **a** $\pi(a+b)$ **b** πab

4 **a** area **b** length **c** length **d** volume **e** volume **f** area

5 It is a mixture of volume and area terms.

End points

A1 73.9 cm²

B1 4

C1 **a** 3.85 m³ **b** 14.0 m² **c** 3850 litres

D1 **a** 26 cm **b** 720 cm³

E1 a, b, d

SECTION 14 Probability

Starting points

A1 **a** $\frac{1}{4}$ **b** $\frac{1}{12}$ **c** $\frac{1}{6}$

A2 **a** $\frac{5}{12}$ **b** $\frac{1}{3}$ **c** $\frac{2}{3}$ **d** $\frac{1}{6}$ **e** 1 **f** 0

A3 $p(A) = \frac{1}{4}$, $p(C) = \frac{1}{12}$, $p(D) = \frac{1}{6}$, $p(A \text{ or } B \text{ or } E \text{ or } F) = \frac{3}{4}$

A4 **a** $\frac{1}{3}$ **b** $\frac{1}{2}$ **c** $\frac{5}{6}$

B1 $\frac{1}{5}$

B2 $\frac{5}{8}$

C1 **a** $\frac{3}{16}$ **b** $\frac{1}{4}$ **c** $\frac{4}{7}$ **d** $\frac{1}{12}$

D1 0.23

D2 **a** 0.77 **b** 0.16 **c** 0.55 **d** 0.44

D3 all of them

E1 $\frac{1}{6}$

E2 $\frac{1}{3}$

E3 **b** $\frac{1}{4}$

Exercise 14.1

1 **a** Emmelle and Angeline, Emmelle and Bruno, Emmelle and Charles,
      Emmelle and Danielle, Angeline and Bruno, Angeline and Charles,
      Angeline and Danielle, Bruno and Charles, Bruno and Danielle,
      Charles and Danielle
    c 10

2 **a** Frederic and Emmelle, Frederic and Angeline, Frederic and Bruno,
      Frederic and Charles, Frederic and Danielle, Emmelle and
      Angeline, Emmelle and Bruno, Emmelle and Charles, Emmelle and
      Danielle, Angeline and Bruno, Angeline and Charles, Angeline and
      Danielle, Bruno and Charles, Bruno and Danielle, Charles and
      Danielle
    b 15

3 **a** 3, 6, 10, 15
    b The numbers of handshakes are the triangle numbers.
    c 21

4 **a** Sartre Vol I and Pascal, Sartre Vol I and Zola Vol I, Sartre Vol I
      and Sartre Vol II, Sartre Vol I and Zola Vol II, Pascal and Zola
      Vol I, Pascal and Sartre Vol II, Pascal and Zola Vol II, Zola Vol I
      and Sartre Vol II, Zola Vol I and Zola Vol II, Sartre Vol II and
      Zola Vol II
    b $\frac{1}{10}$ **c** $\frac{1}{5}$ **d** $\frac{9}{10}$ **e** $\frac{7}{10}$

5 $\frac{3}{14}$

Exercise 14.2

1 a $\frac{25}{81}$ b $\frac{5}{18}$ c $\frac{2}{27}$ d $\frac{1}{12}$

2 a $\frac{5}{12}$ b $\frac{4}{11}$ d $\frac{7}{22}$

3 b $\frac{1}{6}$ c $\frac{5}{9}$ d $\frac{5}{6}$

4 a $\frac{1}{10}$ b 0 c $\frac{3}{10}$ d $\frac{3}{5}$

5 a $1+4, 4+1, 3+1+1, 1+3+1, 1+1+3, 1+1+1+1$,
   d i $\frac{1}{252}$ ii $\frac{1}{4}$ iii $\frac{2}{9}$ e no, 48% f £161.71 profit

Exercise 14.3

1 b i 0.473 ii 0.4332

2 a 0.2809 b 0.4089 c 0.3102

3 0.0164

Exercise 14.4

1 a $\frac{4}{16}$ b $\frac{7}{16}$ c $\frac{11}{16}$

3 a $\frac{5}{16}$ b $\frac{4}{16}$

4 a $\frac{10}{16}$ b $\frac{8}{16}$ c Owen has a moustache and an earring

5 a $\frac{4}{16}$ b $\frac{4}{16}$ c $\frac{6}{16}$

Exercise 14.5

1 b No, some criminals have fair hair and a necklace.

2 a $\frac{11}{16}$ b $\frac{1}{4}$ c $\frac{5}{16}$ d $\frac{1}{8}$ e $\frac{1}{4}$

3 a $\frac{7}{16}$ b $\frac{3}{4}$ c $\frac{3}{4}$ d $\frac{9}{16}$

4 a No, some girls could play hockey and basketball.
   b Yes, boys and girls don't overlap.
   c Yes, you can't be a driver and a passenger.
   d No, tall women can drive buses.
   e No, some mechanics can dance.

Exercise 14.6

1 a 0.12 b 0.32 c 0.47 d 0.53 e 0.13

2 a 0.15 b 0.19 c 0.53

3 0.44

4 a a number can't be less than 5 and greater than 7 b 0.55 c 0.45

Exercise 14.7

1 b i $\frac{19}{44}$ ii $\frac{39}{44}$ iii $\frac{25}{44}$ iv $\frac{5}{44}$
   c Some people had English breakfast and cereal.

2 b i $\frac{7}{50}$ ii $\frac{2}{5}$ iii $\frac{7}{10}$ iv $\frac{27}{200}$

End points

A1 a $\frac{1}{4}$ c i $\frac{7}{26}$ ii $\frac{25}{39}$

B1 b 0.3544

C1 a mutually exclusive b mutually exclusive
    c not mutually exclusive d not mutually exclusive

D1 b i $\frac{9}{34}$ ii $\frac{14}{17}$ iii $\frac{3}{34}$

SECTION 15 Grouped Data

Starting points

A1 a 70, 3 b 70.5, 4

A2 70, 3

B1 a 69.85, 2.63

C1 The 2nd round scores are slightly lower on average.
    There is more variation in the 1st round scores.

C2 b The 3rd & 4th round scores are slightly higher on average.
    There is more variation in the 3rd & 4th round scores.

D1

Score	3rd round	4th round
64–66	3	2
67–69	11	11
70–72	17	19
73–75	9	8

D2 b The modal class is 70–72 for both rounds.

D3

Score	Frequency
64–65	1
66–67	2
68–69	11
70–71	14
72–73	6
74–75	6

E1 70.4

E2 70.4

Exercise 15.1

1 a Frequency densities: 0.08, 0.2, 0.26, 0.16, 0.16, 0.03
   b The width of the bar for 700–799 is twice the width of the bars for 900–949 and 950–999.

2 Frequency densities: 0.002, 0.01, 0.02, 0.06, 0.04, 0.009.

Exercise 15.2

1 a A continuous, B discrete, C continuous

2 Times would be improved if they were rounded down, and distances improved if they were rounded up.

3 a 24.5 b All the ages have been rounded down to the nearest year.
   c discrete

Exercise 15.3

1 Frequency densities: 3, 6, 6.3, 6, 1

2 a Frequency densities: 10, 22, 34, 16, 1
   b 19.75, 20.25, 20.75, 21.5
   c 20.1

3 a Frequency densities: 3.3, 26, 20, 18, 2.7 b 18.7

4 The men throw further on average. There is less variation in the men's throwing.

5 a Frequencies: 5, 3, 5, 12, 11, 3, 6, 2
   b i Frequency densities: 350, 1100, 1300, 1600, 1400, 1600, 450, 133
     ii Frequency densities: 250, 300, 500, 1200, 1100, 300, 300, 33

6 a Frequencies: 10, 6, 10, 24, 22, 6, 12, 4
   b Mid-class values: 0.13, 0.145, 0.155, 0.165, 0.175, 0.185, 0.2, 0.24
   c yes

7 a 0.173 s b 0.170 s

8 a true
   b The estimated mean for the finals is smaller than the estimated mean for the semi-finals.

Exercise 15.4

1 a Cumulative frequencies: 0, 8, 18, 31, 39, 47, 50

2 a Cumulative frequencies: 0, 6, 12, 20, 33, 46, 48

Exercise 15.5

1 a Cumulative frequencies: 0, 6, 12, 28, 35, 48, 52

2 a 77.9 m b 1.2 m

3 The distances were greater on average in the javelin final.
   There was more variation in the distance thrown in the javelin final.

4 b 840 points c 180 points

5 a 880 points b 120 points

6 Scores were higher on average on day 2.
   There was less variation in the scores on day 2.

7 a Cumulative frequencies: 7, 18, 28, 38, 45, 46
   c Use cumulative frequencies 11.5, 23 and 34.5.
   d 61 m, 4.5 m

Exercise 15.6

1 27

2 14

3 a Cumulative frequencies: 1, 8, 22, 28, 30, 31 b 15

Exercise 15.7

1 Frequency densities: 5, 18, 22.7, 29.5, 31.5, 17, 13.7, 9.4, 5.5, 1.9

3 a 36.8, 35.0, 33.8 **b** 13.0, 12.6, 10.8

4 The estimates improve as the sample size increases.

5 a no **b** There are more competitors.

End points

A1 a frequency densities: 1.75, 5, 6.5, 6.5, 1.5
b frequency densities: 1.25, 4, 8, 6.5, 0.75

B1 63

B2 63.02

C1 a i 7.95 **ii** 0.3

C2 6.8, 0.32

D1 The men jumped further but the women were more evenly matched.

D2 The distances were very similar.

E1 b i 15 **ii** 12

Skills break 3

1 a 1.2×10^{-4} m **b** 2.97×10^{-3} m^3

2 a 1.87×10^{-3} m^3 **b** 76

3 695 mm

4 a 15 **b** 24%

5 b 3457 cm^3 **d** $h = \frac{c}{\pi r^2} + \frac{r}{3}$

6 no, it is a 6 4% increase

7 a 4, 5.5, 6.6, 7, 6.6, 5.5, 4, 2.5, 1.4, 1, 1.4, 2.5, 4
c 6.2 and 11.8 seconds

8 Coffee 75p, tea 52p

9 $\frac{3n}{8}$

10 no, it would need 36.4 litres

12 a 131.42 cm^2 **b** 122.5 cm^2

Section 16 Solving Equations Graphically

Starting points

A1 a 4, 3 **b** $\frac{1}{5}$, $^-8$ **c** 0.8, 1.5 **d** $\frac{5}{4}$, $\frac{7}{4}$
e $^-0.25, 1$ **f** 6, 0 **g** 1, 0 **h** 0, 12

A2 $y = 2.5x + 3$

A3 $y = ^-x - 2$

B1 a $y = \frac{3}{5}x + 3$ **b** $y = \frac{-5}{2x-4}$ **c** $y = \frac{4}{3}x + 1$ **d** $y = \frac{-3}{2}x + 2$ **e** $y = \frac{7}{2}x - \frac{1}{2}$
f $y = \frac{1}{3}x - 1$ **g** $y = ^-2x + \frac{5}{4}$ **h** $y = \frac{-5}{4}x + \frac{3}{2}$ **i** $y = 4x - 2$ **j** $y = \frac{9}{2}x + \frac{3}{2}$
k $y = -\frac{1}{10}x + \frac{4}{5}$ **l** $y = \frac{3}{5}x - 5$ **m** $y = -\frac{9}{2}x + 6$ **n** $y = -\frac{1}{2}x + \frac{3}{10}$
o $y = \frac{-3}{10}x + 2$ **p** $y = 8x - 24$ **q** $y = 2x - 2$ **r** $y = 3x + \frac{1}{4}$
s $y = -\frac{1}{3}x + 3$ **t** $y = \frac{-3}{4}x + \frac{9}{4}$ **u** $y = \frac{1}{6}x + \frac{1}{2}$ **v** $y = ^-2x + 12$
w $y = \frac{6}{7}$ **x** $y = \frac{4}{3}x - 4$ **y** $y = -\frac{1}{2}x + \frac{3}{4}$ **z** $y = 2x + \frac{24}{5}$

Exercise 16.1

1 a $^-1, 2$ **b** 1, 4 **c** $^-2, 2$ **d** 2, 3 **e** 2, $^-3$ **f** 1, $^-1$

2 $^-1, 4$

3 c 2, 1

4 b 2.4, 1.8 **c** they do not cross

5 a $2y + 9 = x, y + x = 63$ **b ii** 18, 45

6 a $x + y = 500, 4x + 25 = y$ **b ii** 95, 405
c i $6x + 40 = y$ **ii** 65.7 litres, 434.3 litres

7 b 3, 5

8 $y = 0.5x + 3$

Exercise 16.2

1 a $x = ^-1$ **b** $x = ^-1$

2 b $x = 1.5$ **c** $y = x^2 - 3x - 8$

4 a $x = ^-2, ^-3$ **b** $x = 0.5, 2$ **c** $x = ^-2.5, 0$ **d** $x = 3, 1$
e $x = ^-3, ^-2$ **f** $x = ^-4, 3$ **g** $x = 0, ^-7$ **h** $x = 3, 8$ **i** $x = 3.5, 5$

Exercise 16.3

1 a $y = 10$ **b** intersections are solutions **c** $^-7.2, 2.2$

3 a Too little of the graph has been drawn **b** 3.4 **c** less than

4 a 2, 3 **c** 0.4, 4.6 **d** $^-0.7, 5.7$

5 a i $^-1, 5$ **ii** $^-2.2, 6.2$ **b** 2, 2

6 a ii 1, 3

7 a i $^-5.7, 0.7$ **ii** $^-4.6, ^-0.4$ **iii** $^-5.7, 0.7$
b i $^-3.3, 0.3$ **ii** $^-2.6, ^-0.4$ **iii** $^-3.4, 0.4$
c i $4.6, ^-0.6$ **ii** 3.7, 0.3 **iii** 4.2, $^-0.2$
d i $^-1.8, 0.3$ **ii** 0.9, $^-2.4$
e i 2.5, 0 **ii** 2.9, $^-0.4$

8 $^-4.2, 0.2$

9 0.2, 1.8

11 b 1, 5 **c** $^-1.8, 2.8$

12 b 0.2, $^-4.2$ **c** 2.6, $^-1.6$

13 a $y = x + 8$ **b** $y = 4 - 4x$

14 b 1, $^-7$ **c** 1.3, $^-2.3$ **d** $^-0.8, ^-37$

15 b $^-6.3, 1.3$ **c** $^-5.9, 0.9$ **d** $^-6.5, 1.5$ **e** $^-2, 2$ **f** $^-8.7, 0.7$

Exercise 16.4

1 a ii $x = 0, y = 0$

2 b $x = 0, y = 3$

3 $x = 0, y = ^-8$

4 b $y = 2$

5 b ii $x = 3$ **ii** $x = 5.3$ **iii** 3.5

7 b ^-x **c** $y = ^-x, x = 0$

Exercise 16.5

1 i $^-3.1$ **ii** 2.3, 5.2

2 a 6.3 **b** 0.4, $^-3.4$

3 a 15.3 **b** $^-0.6, ^-4.4$ **c** 0.8, $^-3.8$ **d** $^-1.3, ^-4.7$
e i 4.8 **ii** $^-3.6, 0.6$ **iii** $y = ^-2x + 7$

4 a i $^-3.6$ **ii** $^-0.8, 3.8$

5 a 2 **b** $x = 3$ is an asymptote to $y = \frac{2x}{3-x}$

Exercise 16.6

2 a 0, $^-2$ **b** 2.8 or $^-0.4$ **c ii** 0, 4 **iii** $^-1.1, 1.8$ **iv** 12.4 or $^-4.4$

3 a 3.5 **b** $^-1, 2$

4 a 10.4 **b** $^-2.6$ **c** 2.5 **d** $^-3.4, ^-0.3, 3.6$

5 a $^-2, 1, 2$ **b** 4.4 **c** $^-1.7, 0.4, 2.3$

6 b i 4.4 cm, 12.4 cm **ii** 1.8 cm, 9.8 cm **iii** 6.8 cm, 14.8 cm
c 45 cm^2 **d** 5.5 cm

7 a $A = w(2w - 4)$
c i 5.3 cm, 6.6 cm **ii** 6.7 cm, 9.4 cm **iii** 7.4 cm, 10.8 cm
d 40 cm^2 **e** 5.8 cm, 7.6 cm

Exercise 16.7

1 a $y = (x + 3)^2 - 11$ **b** $^-11$ **c** $(0, -2)$

5 b the graphs do not intersect

6 $y = x^2 + 6x + 5, a = 1, b = 6, c = 5$

End points

A1 a 2, $^-1$ **b** 3, 1

A2 £5, £3.50

B1 $x = 2$

B2 a $^-4, 2$ **b** $^-2, 5$ **c** $^-1.6, 2.6$ **d** $^-2, 3$

B3 b $^-1.2, 1.7$ **c** $^-1.7, 1.7$ **d** $^-2, 0.5$

C2 $y = 5, x = 0$

C3 $y = 4, x = 0$

D1 a $^-1.1$ **b** 2.4, 5

D2 a 14.25 **b** 0.7, $^-5.7$ **c** 1.2, $^-4.2$

D3 b i 5.2 cm, 11.2 cm **ii** 3.4 cm, 9.4 cm **c** 62 cm^2 **d** 3.6 cm

E5 $y = x^2 + 4x + 8, a = 1, b = 4, c = 8$

SECTION 17 Trigonometric graphs

Starting points

A1 **a i** (2.60, 2.34) **ii** 3.04 cm² **b** 75.4°

A2 110 cm²

A3 **a** $\frac{4}{5}$ **b** $\frac{3}{5}$

B1 **a** 0.77 **b** 0.64

B2 **a** 24° **b** 66°

B3 **a** 70° **b** 42° **c** 45°

Exercise 17.1

1 **a** 0.68 **b** 0.87 **c** 0.77 **d** 2.30 **e** 1.97 **f** 2.5

2 **a i** 3.86 **ii** 3.70 **iii** 3.19 **b i** 30° **ii** 20°

Exercise 17.2

1 **b** (⁻17.3, 10)

2 **b i** 22.98 km **ii** 19.28 km **c** (⁻22.98, 19.28)
  d i B(20, 70°), C(30, 250°), D(10, 320°) **ii** B(6.84, 18.79),
  C(⁻10.26, ⁻28.19), D(7.66, ⁻6.43)

3 **a** (13, 225°) and (⁻9.19, ⁻9.19), (40, 114°) and (⁻16.27, 36.54),
  (25, 291°) and (8.96, ⁻23.34)
  b (17, 169°), (31, 314°)

4 **a** $r = \sqrt{(x^2 + y^2)}$ **b** $(r\cos\theta, r\sin\theta)$ **c** $(\cos\theta, \sin\theta)$

Exercise 17.3

1 232°

2 **a** 0.616 **b** ⁻0.788

4 **a** ⁻0.809 **b** 0.809 **c** ⁻0.809

5 **a** sin 53° and sin 127°, sin 233° and sin 307°, cos 233° and cos 127°
  b 0.799, ⁻0.799, ⁻0.602

6 **a** 90° < θ < 270° **b** 180° < θ < 360°

7 **a i** 0, ⁻1 **ii** 0.616, ⁻7.88 **b i** ⁻306° **ii** ⁻260° **iii** ⁻160°

8 **a** cos 450° = cos(450 − 360)° = cos 90° = 0

Exercise 17.4

1 **a** 1, ⁻1 **b** 1, ⁻1

2 30°, 150°

3 **a i** 40°, 320° **ii** 145°, 215° **iii** 252°, 288°
  b i 64°, 116° **ii** 154°, 206°

4 **a** 420°, 660° **b** ⁻60°

5 **a** 450° **b** ⁻270°

Exercise 17.5

1 **a** ⁻4.5, ⁻9, ⁻4.5, 4.5, 9, 4.5, ⁻4.5, ⁻9, ⁻4–5 **c** 9 mm
  d i 360 milliseconds **ii** 180 milliseconds **e** 2

2 **b** yes **c** The maximum heights of the needle are different

Exercise 17.6

1 **a i** 3, 1 **ii** 2, ⁻2 **iii** 1, ⁻1

2 **b i** ⁻1, ⁻3 **ii** 3, ⁻3 **iii** 1, ⁻1

3 **a** 1, ⁻1 **b** 5, ⁻5 **c** ⁻3, ⁻5 **d** 2, 0 **e** 0, ⁻4 **f** 5, ⁻1

5 A: $y = \cos ax$, $a = 2$ B: $y = \sin x + a$, $a = 3$ C: $y = \cos x + a$, $a = ⁻1$
  D: $y = a\cos x$, $a = 2$ E: $y = a\sin x$, $a = 4$

9 A, C

Exercise 17.7

2 **a i** 45° **ii** 225° **b** 135°, 315°

4 **a** 50° **b** 230°, 410°

5 **a** 60°, 240°, 420° **b** ⁻25°, 155°, 335° **c** ⁻32°, 148°, 328°

6 **a i** 57.3 **ii** 114.6 **iii** 573.0 **iv** 5729.6
  b i ⁻57.3 **ii** ⁻114.6 **iii** ⁻573.0 **iv** ⁻5729.6 **d** 630°

End points

A1 **a** 70°, 290° **b** 110°, 250° **c** 140°, 320° **d** 208°, 332°

A2 cos 41° and cos 319°, cos 139° and 221°, cos 229° and cos 131°

B2 B and D

SECTION 18 Inequalities

Starting point

A1 **b** 2, ⁻2, 1.634, $4\frac{3}{4}$

A2 **a** 5, 6, 7, 8, 9 **b** ⁻2, ⁻1, 0, 1, 2, 3 **c** 68, 69, 70
  d ⁻11, ⁻10, ⁻9, ⁻8, ⁻7, ⁻6, ⁻5, ⁻4

A3 ⁻4 < h < 6

A4 ⁻3 ⩽ g ⩽ ⁻1, ⁻4 < g < 2

A5 ⁻3 ⩽ f < 7

B2 ⁻2 ⩽ x ⩽ 6, 3 < y ⩽ 7

C1 **a** x ⩾ 0, y ⩾ 0, y ⩾ x **b** x > y, y ⩾ 3

C4 y ⩽ 8 − x, y > $\frac{1}{2}x$

Thinking ahead to ...

A **a** true **b** true **c** true **d** true **e** true **f** false **g** false

Exercise 18.1

1 **a** y < 7 **b** s ⩽ 8 **c** p ⩾ 6 **d** b > 3.5 **e** a ⩽ ⁻8 **f** x > 8.4 **g** k ⩽ $\frac{14}{3}$
  h a ⩾ 7 **i** d ⩽ ⁻5 **j** a ⩽ ⁻13

2 **a** a ⩾ $3\frac{2}{3}$ **b** k < ⁻$\frac{14}{5}$ **c** x > ⁻9 **d** n ⩾ $\frac{7}{2}$ **e** q < ⁻$\frac{4}{5}$ **f** k > 2
  g h < ⁻$\frac{1}{3}$ **h** c < 2.5 **i** h < $\frac{12}{11}$ **j** p ⩾ $\frac{16}{7}$

3 **a** ⁻4 < x < 1 **b** ⁻2 < x < 5 **c** ⁻1 < x < 15 **d** ⁻3 < x < ⁻1

Exercise 18.2

1 **a** d ⩾ 6, d ⩽ ⁻6 **b** ⁻√17 < g < √17 **c** ⁻7 ⩽ a ⩽ 7 **d** h < ⁻4, h > 4
  e t < ⁻4, t > 4 **f** ⁻2 ⩽ c < 2 **g** c < ⁻1, c ⩾ 1 **h** f < ⁻2, f > 2

2 **a** ⁻6, ⁻5, ⁻4, ⁻3, ⁻2, ⁻1, 0, 1, 2, 3, 4, 5, 6 **b** ⁻4, ⁻3, ⁻2, ⁻1, 0, 1, 2, 3, 4
  c ⁻3, ⁻2, ⁻1, 0, 1, 2, 3 **d** ⁻2, ⁻1, 0, 1, 2 **e** ⁻2, ⁻1, 0, 1, 2 **f** ⁻1, 0, 1

3 squared numbers are never negative

4 c has no solutions

5 1, 2, 3

Exercise 18.3

1 **a** (19, 1) represents 20 birds and so is not a solution
  b (16.5, 2.5) doesn't represent whole birds
  d £65

2 **b** v ⩽ 7, n ⩽ 8
  d 10, 4 Vikings and 6 Neptune, or 5 Vikings and 5 Neptune

3 **a i** 8E + 10C ⩽ 120 **ii** 280E + 120C ⩾ 1680
  b A: 7E + 3C = 42, B: 4E + 5C = 60 **c** 2C ⩾ E **d** 13

End points

A1 **a** ⁻1 **b** ⁻5, 4, ⁻3, ⁻2, ⁻1, 0, 1, 2, 3 **c** 4, 5, 6, 7
  d ⁻59, ⁻58, ⁻57, ⁻56 **e** ⁻3, ⁻2, ⁻1, 0, 1, 2, 3
  g ⁻3, ⁻2, ⁻1, 0, 1, 2, 3

B1 **a** x ⩽ 6 **b** f > 3 **c** a ⩾ 12 **d** k > ⁻5 **e** s ⩽ 4 **f** d > 1.5
  g x > 10, x < ⁻10 **h** ⁻2 ⩽ x ⩽ 2

D1 **a** S > L **b i** S + L ⩽ 200 **ii** 4S + 5L ⩾ 720 **iii** 3L ⩾ S **d** £899

SECTION 19 Working with percentages

Starting points

A1 **a** 0.75, 75% **b** 0.625, 62.5% **c** 1.6, 160% **d** 1.25, 125%
  e 1.2, 120% **f** 0.65, 65% **g** 0.25, 25% **h** 3.17, 317%

B1 **a** 357.5 miles **b** £290 **c** 1587 **d** £116.20 **e** 16.2 m **f** £1.71
  g 12.5p **h** 0.24 miles

C1 **a** 65% **b** 46.2% **c** 12.5% **d** 125% **e** 3%

C2 14%

D1 **a** £13.60 **b** 5.6 mm **c** 1540 g **d** 20p **e i** 50.7 mm **ii** 5.07 cm

Thinking ahead to ...

A 45 ml, less

B $\frac{3}{20}$

C 345 ml

Exercise 19.1

1 **a** 87% **b** 506 g

2 **a** 413 kg **b** 518.52 km **c** 5.49 m **d** £37 800 **e** £36.30
   f 30 186 tonnes **g** 3 815 000 litres **h** 0.69 cm

3 £22 471

4 £1191

5 £3 281 000

6 425 litres per minute = 2.235×10^8 litres in 2005

7 no, the 20% will be calculated each year

Exercise 19.2

1 **a** £18.80 **b** £51.99 **c** £217.38 **d** £22.80 **e** 85p **f** £432.89
   g £307.85 **h** £28.85 **i** £10.99 **j** £221.72 **k** 40p **l** 13p

2 £34.50

3 £31.90

Exercise 19.3

1 **a** £115.32 **b** £29.78 **c** £63.82 **d** £56.00 **e** £158.94 **f** £12.33
   g £42.54 **h** £680.83 **i** £84.25

2 **a** £57 **b** £11.40

3 £24

4 500 g

5 £55.70

6 £137 515

7 **a** 70 875 **b** 25 515 **c** 16 : 9

8 **a** £20 384 **b** $p = \frac{3.15}{4.5}s$

9 147 428 to the nearest person

10 $c = \frac{p}{1.175}$

Exercise 19.4

1 **a** £324 **b** £67.20 **c** £1350 **d** £10 200

2 **a** £5950 **b** £9450

3 £66 440 000

4 4.6%

Exercise 19.5

1 **a** £103.27 **b** £175.71 **c** £1217.62 **d** £1529.58 **e** £1030.32
   f £7015.63 **g** £197.32 **h** £2.23 **i** £14 428.07 **j** £56.95

2 **a** £1947.46 **b** £6947.46

3 9

4 £22 841

5 **a** 2034 (less than 2 birds left) **b** 2005

6 $A(1 + \frac{r}{100})^5$

Exercise 19.6

1 £5108.77

2 £22 930.76

3 Celine

4 £47 098.84

5 **a** 4.7% **b** 5.9%

6 1494

Exercise 19.7

1 £19.64

2 **a** £1184.60 **b** £24.68

3 **a** £267.39 **b** £9171.84

4 **a** £38786.04 **b** £66.19

End points

A1 556.8 km

A2 426 ml

A3 £52.45

A4 39 203 breakdowns

B1 £998.74

B2 £569.91

C1 £2.27M

C2 380 766

D1 £74.03

D2 4.5%

E1 £12 836.47

F1 **a** £23.20 **b** £656.89

SECTION 20 Circle theorems

Starting points

A1 **b** The distances are the same. **c** yes **d** both 30°
   e both right angles **f** yes **h** both the same **i** yes **j** yes

A2 **b** angle AOB = 120°

A3 **b** OA = OB = OC = 3.6 cm

Exercise 20.1

1 **a** 116°, 122° **b** 94° **c** 90°, 70° **d** 107°

2 **a** angles ADC and AEC **b** angles CAD and CED
   c 58° **d** 41° **e** 41°

3 **a** 74° **b** 37° **c** 90° **d** 53° **e** 37°

4 **a** angle EFD **b** 284° **c** 38° **d** 52°

5 **a** 41° **b** 49°
   c If a tangent (FC) and a chord (EF) meet, the angle between them
   (EFC) is always equal to the angle in the opposite segment (FGE).
   d 61°

6 **a** 18.5 cm **b** 8.3 cm **c** 55.5 cm^2

7 **a i** $10a$ **ii** $90 - 5a$ **b i** $180 + 10a + 27 + 43 = 360$ **ii** $a = 11°$
   c $\sqrt{(64 + b^2)}$ **d** 125°

8 **a i** a **ii** b **iii** $2a$ **b** $180 - a - b$ **c** $180 - a$ **d** $90 - \frac{a}{2} - b$ **e** $\frac{a}{2}$

Exercise 20.2

1 Opposite angles are each 90° and so add up to 180°.

2 Not unless it is a rectangle. One pair of opposite angles will sum to
   more than 180°, the other pair to less than 180°

3 square

4 $v + x = 180° = 12 \times 15°$

6 102°

7 **a i** 60° **ii** 120° **b** 120°
   c No-opposite angles not supplementary. Also O not on
   circumference.

8 **a i** 67.5° **ii** 112.5° **iii** 127° **b** 106°

9 **a i** $\frac{1}{2}v$ **ii** $90 - \frac{1}{2}v$ **iii** $45 + \frac{1}{2}v$

10 **a** 28° **b** 69°

End points

A1 **a** 54° **b** 61°

A2 **a** angle EBD **b** angle CAB

B1 **a** 126° **b** 54°

C1 62°

D1 54°

D2 72°

D3 36°

E1 The four vertices of the quadrilateral lie on the circumference of the
   same circle.
   The angles at opposite vertices are supplementary.

E2 **a** $3k$ must be opposite $6k$, $4k$ must be opposite $5k$.
   b $9k = 180$, $k = 20°$

Skills break 4

3 £295 800

4 **a** 57 691 m^3 **b** 493 256 tonnes

5 **a** 14 knots **b** 3 hours 19 minutes **c** $1\frac{1}{2}$ hours

6 **a** $C = \frac{5(F-32)}{9}$ **b** $^-2.2°C$ **c** 55%

9 **a** 0.61 **b** 0.43 **c** 0.25

10 38%

11 70 000 tons

13 **a** 14° **b** 28.5 feet **c** 8.8 fet

14 **a** 2 000 000 **b** 2 180 000

15 11 people

SECTION 21 Trigonometry in 2-D and 3-D

Starting points

A1 **a** **i** 060° **ii** 300° **iii** 300° **b** 205° **c** 20 km

B1 **b** 36.1 km

C1 56°

C2 **a** 26 km **b** 15 km

D1 **a** 30°, 150° **b** 101.5° **c** 78.5° **d** 45°

E1 **b** 104°

E2 **b** 20°, 80°

F1 27°

F2 5.1 mm

Exercise 21.1

1 **a** 4.9 cm² **b** 5.2 cm² **c** 5.1 cm² **d** 1.85 cm²

2 **a** 6.0 cm² **b** **i** 30°, 150° **c** 90°

3 **a** 46°, 134° **b** 15 cm²

4 **a** 3.35 cm, 3.45 cm **b** 3.6 cm², 3.9 cm²

Exercise 21.2

1 **a** D

Exercise 21.3

1 **b** 5.3 cm

2 **a** 4.2 cm **b** 5.0 cm **c** 3.6 cm

3 **a** 8 cm, 7.5 cm

4 11.6 cm²

5 **a** 48.5° **b** 3.2 cm

Exercise 21.4

1 **a** 29.4° **b** 47.5° **c** 33.8°

2 **a** 119.5° **b** 139.2 cm²

3 **a** 0.57 **b** 34.8°, 145.2°

4 **b** **i** 74.6°, 105.4° **ii** 51.7°, 128.3°

Exercise 21.5

1 **a** **i** $d^2 = e^2 + f^2 - 2ef \cos D$ **ii** $f^2 = e^2 + d^2 - 2ed \cos F$
  b **ii** and **iii**

Exercise 21.6

2 94.8°, 6.8 cm, 4.7 cm

3 95.1°

4 26.7 cm²

5 **a** **i** 108° **ii** 36° **iii** 72°
  b 6.5 cm **c** 16.9 cm **d** 12.3 cm² **e** 8

6 **a** 11.3 cm **b** 39.9 cm, 62.9 cm² **c** 43.8 cm

7 **a** 73.5 cm² **b** 30.9 cm

8 192 cm²

9 **a** $\frac{1}{2}nr^2 \sin(\frac{360}{n})$ **b** **i** 3.09 **ii** 3.13 **iii** 3.14 **iii** 3.14
  The answers are tending to π.

10 9 cm

Exercise 21.7

1 **a** 036° **b** 127.6 km **c** 051°

2 **a** 323° **b** **i** 39.88 km **ii** 159°
  c **i** 14.4 km **ii** 19.2 km **d** 7.00 km

3 17.5 km

4 **a** 4573 m **b** 032°

5 8.016 km

6 15.81 nautical miles

Exercise 21.8

1 **a** 142° **b** **i** 43 m **ii** 30° **iii** 30°

2 **a** Jameston and Palter
  b 11.4 m

Exercise 21.9

1 **a** 68.6 m **b** 3.7°

2 **a** 13 m **b** 14.3 m **c** 25°

3 **a** 10.7 cm³ **b** 45° **c** 5.7 cm **d** 60°
  e 13.9 cm² **f** 2.3 cm **g** 35°

End points

A1 **a** 8.2 cm **b** 8.1 cm

A2 **a** 82° **b** 16 cm

B1 **a** 66.8° **b** 12.3 cm

C1 **a** 69.9° **b** 61.8°

C2 **a** 5.12 cm **b** 103.6°

D1 2.21 km

D2 72.9 nautical miles

E1 281.5 m

E2 75°

F1 110 cm

SECTION 22 Processing data

Starting points

D1 **a** Q **b** R **c** P

Exercise 22.1

1 **a** not clear, needs specific times

2 **a** The question seems to expect the answer 'yes'.

3 **a** It has more than one meaning

4 **a** 1: Leading
    2: Not clear
    3: Ambiguous
    4: There is no option for between £1.50 and £2.50.

Exercise 22.3

1

	Yr 7	Yr 8	Yr 9	Yr 10	Yr 11	Total
Boys	14	15	17	15	15	76
Girls	16	16	15	13	14	74
Total	30	31	32	28	29	150

2 75 competitors, 45 support staff

3 **a** Competitors: 45 male, 30 female. Support staff: 32 male, 13 female.

4 **a** 58.6 million **b** 417236, 14505, 43515, 24744

Exercise 22.4

1 **c** Negative

2 **c** Positive

Exercise 22.5

1 Moderate negative correlation

2 Strong negative correlation

3 Weak positive correlation

Exercise 22.6

1 **a** 50 miles **b** 80 miles

2 **a** £75 000 **b** £85 000

3 **a** 15 miles **b** £110 000

5 **b** Moderate positive correlation **c i** 272 days **ii** 3.8 kg

6 No, pregnancy doesn't usually last much longer than 9 months.

End points

A1 1: not clear, 2: ambiguous, 3: leading

C1 846, 825, 1220, 7109

D1 **d** Strong negative correlation

E1 **a** 33 mpg **b** 2 litres

E2 **a** 18 mpg **b** 4.8 litres

SECTION 23 Graphs involving compound measures

Starting points

A1 41 minutes

A2 47 mph

A3 2 minutes 26 seconds

A4 a 31.3 miles per hour **b** 17 m/s

B1 5200 cm^2

B2 375 square units

C1 A: Ravi, B: Sally, C: Charlie, D: Joe

C2 A and B

C3 B and C

C4 9 : 45 am

C5 **a** 80 miles **b** 135 miles **c** 100 miles **d** 120 miles

C6 1 hour 30 minutes

C7 C, 70 miles

C8 100 miles

C9 **a** 11 : 30 am, 3 : 05 pm **b** same direction, then opposite

C10 **a** 9.3 mph

C11 30 mph

C12 Faster in the morning (steeper gradient)

C13 **a** A **b** 12 noon

Exercise 23.1

1 Edinburgh

2 **a** 6.35 km/h **b** bicycle or similar

3 **a** 11 : 30 am **b** 35.6 km/h

4 Julie got faster, Simon slowed down

5 **a** 23 km/h **b** 23 km/h

6 Julie was travelling most quickly, then Ayesha, then Simon.

7 **a** 1 : 30 pm **b** 10 : 30 am

8 **a** 66 km **b** 92 km

9 11 : 45 am

10 64 km

Exercise 23.2

1 **a ii** 11.1 km/h **b ii** 3 : 16 pm **iii** 2 : 44 pm

2 **a ii** 9 mph **iii** 9.2 mph
b i 10 miles **iii** 12.8 mph
iv Alice was buying cakes as Emily passed
c ii 20 mph

Exercise 23.3

1 The gradient is steeper

2 **a** stationary **b** constant speed

End points

A1 **a** 2.5 miles **b** 26 minutes **c** twice **d** 10.3 mph
e i 20 : 40 and 21 : 08 **ii** steepest part
f 50 minutes **g** 60 mph **h i** 21 : 26 **ii** 15.5 miles

B1 **a** 2 s, 4.5 s, 8.5 s, 15.3 s **b** 0 s, 6.5 s **c** 0 s, 16 s **d** decelerating

SECTION 24 Vectors

Starting points

B1 **a** $\binom{5}{-1}$ **b** $\binom{-1}{2}$ **c** $\binom{1}{4}$

C1 **a** $2(2x - y)$ **b** $^-2(y - 2x)$ **c** $^-3(x - 3y)$ **d** $3(3y - x)$

C2 **a** $\frac{1}{2}(2x + y)$ **b** $\frac{1}{3}(x - 3y)$ **c** $\frac{1}{2}(3x + y)$ **d** $\frac{1}{3}(4x - y)$
e $\frac{2}{3}(x + y)$ **f** $\frac{2}{3}(2y - x)$

D1 **a** 3 : 1 **b** 1 : : 3

D2 **a** $\frac{1}{4}$ **b** $\frac{3}{4}$

Exercise 24.1

2 **a** $\binom{-1}{-3}$ **b** $\binom{8}{2}$ **c** $\binom{3}{6}$ **d** $\binom{-2}{-6}$ **e** $\binom{3}{-6}$

3 $\binom{5}{4}$

4 $\binom{5}{4}$

6 $\binom{5}{-1}$

Exercise 24.2

2 **a** $\mathbf{u} = \mathbf{p} + \mathbf{r}$ **b** $\mathbf{v} = \mathbf{p} + 2\mathbf{q}$ **c** $\mathbf{w} = 2\mathbf{q} - \mathbf{p}$

Exercise 24.3

1 **b** $^-(\mathbf{q} - \mathbf{p}) = ^-\mathbf{q} - ^-\mathbf{p} = \mathbf{p} - \mathbf{q}$

5 $2\mathbf{p} - \mathbf{q}, 2\mathbf{q} - \mathbf{p}, ^-3\mathbf{p} - \mathbf{q}$

6 $2\mathbf{q} - 6\mathbf{p} = -2(3\mathbf{p} - \mathbf{q})$

7 $^-2\mathbf{p} - \mathbf{q}$ and $2\mathbf{p} + \mathbf{q}$, $2\mathbf{p} - \mathbf{q}$ and $\mathbf{q} - 4\mathbf{p}$, $2\mathbf{p} + 4\mathbf{q}$ and $\mathbf{p} + 2\mathbf{q}$

8 **a** $2\mathbf{p}, 2\mathbf{q}, ^-2\mathbf{p}, ^-2\mathbf{q}$

Exercise 24.4

1 **a** $2\mathbf{c} - \mathbf{d}$

2 **a i** $\overrightarrow{ED}$ **ii** $\overrightarrow{EG}$ **iii** $\overrightarrow{HE}$ **iv** $\overrightarrow{EG}$

3 **b ii** $\frac{1}{3}(\mathbf{p} + 3\mathbf{q})$

Exercise 24.5

2 **a i** $\frac{2}{3}(\mathbf{p} + \mathbf{q})$ **ii** $2\mathbf{q} - \mathbf{p}$

3 **a i** $\mathbf{y} - \mathbf{x}$ **ii** $\frac{1}{3}(\mathbf{y} - \mathbf{x})$

End points

A1 **a** $\binom{2}{8}$ **b** $\binom{-6}{3}$ **c** $\binom{3}{3}$ **d** $\binom{3}{2}$ **e** $\binom{-6}{5}$ **f** $\binom{0}{10}$

B1 **a** $\overrightarrow{CB} + \overrightarrow{BA} + \overrightarrow{AD}$ **b** $2\mathbf{p} + \mathbf{q}$

B2 **b** $\frac{1}{2}(4\mathbf{p} - \mathbf{q})$

C1 $3\mathbf{r} + \mathbf{s}$ and $6\mathbf{r} + 2\mathbf{s}$, $3\mathbf{s} - \mathbf{r}$ and $2\mathbf{r} - 6\mathbf{s}$

D1 **a i** $2\mathbf{b} - 2\mathbf{a}$ **ii** $\mathbf{b} - \mathbf{c}$

D2 **a i** $\mathbf{d} - 2\mathbf{c}$ **ii** $\frac{2}{3}(\mathbf{d} - 2\mathbf{c})$ **iii** $2\mathbf{d} - 2\mathbf{c}$

SECTION 25 Transforming graphs

Starting points

B1 **a** $(^-2, 3), 7$ **b** $(1, 5), (0, 6)$ **c** $(^-3, 0), (0, 9)$ **d** $(^-5, ^-1), (0, 24)$
e $(8, -4), (0, 60)$

B2 $\binom{6}{5}$

C1 **a i** 43 **ii** $^-2$ **iii** 13.75 **iv** $^-5$ **b** 0.75

Exercise 25.1

1 **a** A: $y = 0.8y^2 - 2$, B: $y = 0.3 \times 2^x$, C: $y = 1.6x^2$, D: $y = 2.5\sqrt{x}$,
E: $y = 0.1x^3$, F: $y = \frac{1}{2}x$

2 6, 1.8

3 $\frac{1}{2}$, 4

Exercise 25.2

1 **c** approximately $d = 4.9t^2 + 0.06$ **d** 31 m **e** 4.5 s

2 **b** $C = 80r^2 + 65$ **c** £1685

3 c 20 **d** 155 s

4 A, $p = 640\,000$; C, $q = 0.4$

Exercise 25.3

1 a $y = 2x - 2$ **c** $y = -\frac{1}{2}x + 3$ **d** reflection in $y = 0$

2 b $y = -2x + 1$, $y = 3x - 4$, $y = -\frac{1}{2}x - 1$ **c** $y = -4x - 3$

3 $y + x = 8$

4 b $y = -x - 1$, $y = 2x - 3$, $y = -\frac{1}{4}x + 1$ **c** $y = 5x - 1$

5 b $p - q = 6$

6 $y = 3x + 1 - 3v + w$

7 $y = kx + l - ka + b$

Exercise 25.4

2 translation $\binom{2}{0}$

3 A

4 a i $\binom{-3}{2}$

5 It will map to $y = f(x + 4) + 5$

6 b i reflection in $y = 0$ **ii** yes

7 b reflection in $x = 0$ **c** yes

8 $(-x)^2 = x^2$

9 a C **b** A

12 a D **b** A **c** B **d** E **e** F **f** C

Exercise 25.5

2 b reflection in $y = 0$

3 b translation $\binom{-1}{-2}$ **c** -3

4 a i 3 **ii** 0.8 **iii** 0

5 A: $y = k(x + 1) - 2$, B: $y = k(2x)$

End points

A1 8, 1.5

B1 b 3.6, 6 **c** £14.10

C1 b $y = f(x - 1) - 2$

IN FOCUS 1

1 a i 1 **ii** 14 **b i** 5 **ii** 150 **c i** 7 **ii** 252 **d i** 10 **ii** 100 **e i** 18 **ii** 252 **f i** 60 **ii** 13 860

2 a $\frac{13}{36}$ **b** $1\frac{1}{6}$ **c** $\frac{7}{10}$ **d** $\frac{9}{10}$ **e** $\frac{5}{8}$ **f** $1\frac{17}{18}$ **g** $4\frac{7}{24}$ **h** $\frac{31}{44}$ **i** $1\frac{5}{8}$

3 a $\frac{5}{3}$ **1b** $\frac{5}{4}$ **c** $\frac{3}{2}$ **d** 3 **e** $\frac{76}{15}$ **f** $\frac{4}{3}$ **g** $\frac{125}{18}$ **h** $\frac{3}{50}$

4 a $3\frac{2}{3}$ **b** $1\frac{1}{9}$ **c** $\frac{3}{100}$ **d** $\frac{3}{10}$ **e** $5\frac{1}{2}$ **f** $4\frac{1}{2}$

5 a $\frac{1}{3}$ **b** $\frac{25}{144}$ **c** $\frac{1}{3}$ **d** $\frac{1}{8}$ **e** $4\frac{1}{2}$ **f** $\frac{4}{7}$

6 a $1\frac{1}{7}$ **b** $\frac{15}{19}$ **c** $1\frac{5}{16}$ **d** $\frac{10}{19}$

7 a $\frac{1}{2} + \frac{1}{6}$ **b** $\frac{1}{6} + \frac{1}{12}$ **c** $\frac{1}{12} + \frac{1}{36}$ (other answers possible)

8 a

$\frac{3}{2}$	$\frac{1}{3}$	$\frac{7}{6}$
$\frac{2}{3}$	1	$\frac{4}{3}$
$\frac{5}{6}$	$\frac{5}{3}$	$\frac{1}{2}$

b change $2\frac{1}{4}$ to $2\frac{7}{12}$

9 A and D, B and H, C and G, F and I

10 a $\frac{4x}{9}$ **b** $\frac{2}{5}$ **c** $\frac{3}{x}$ **d** 21 **e** $\frac{3x}{10}$ **f** $\frac{10}{3x}$ **g** $\frac{(7x + 2y)}{7}$ **h** $\frac{(2x + 12)}{x(x + 4)}$ **i** $\frac{(x - 2y)}{4}$ **j** $\frac{5}{(x - 1)}$ **k** $\frac{(x - 1)}{(x + 2)}$ **l** $\frac{(y + 2x)}{xy}$ **m** $\frac{(5x - 4)}{x(x - 1)}$ **n** $\frac{(y - x^2)}{xy}$ **o** $\frac{(x - 1)}{(x + 4)}$ **p** $\frac{(5x + 7)}{(x + 1)(x + 2)}$ **q** $\frac{5x - 1}{(x + 1)(x - 2)}$ **r** $\frac{6}{(x + 3)}$ **s** $\frac{(x + 4)}{x(x + 2)}$ **t** $\frac{(6x - 3)}{(x - 1)(x + 2)}$ **u** $\frac{(5y + x + 11)}{(x + 1)(y + 2)}$

11 a 6 **b** 9

IN FOCUS 2

1 a 47°, 133°, 47°, 133° **b** 51.5°, 128.5°, 51.5°, 128.5° **c** 11°, 11°, 169°, 11°

2 a 34°, 73°, 73° **b** isosceles **c i** 34°, 146°, 34°, 146° **ii** 73°, 107°, 73°, 107° **d** All sides are of equal length, opposite sides are parallel. **e** Only pairs of opposite sides are equal in length. **f i** 90° **ii** 73° **iii** 73° **iv** 17° **v** 17°

4 73°, 46°, 92°, 120°, 17°, 72°, 198°, 275°, 120°, 60°, 60°, 60°, 36°

IN FOCUS 3

1 a $m^2 n^2$ **b** $4p^2 q$ **c** $18a^2 b$ **d** $a^3 g^3$ **e** $20p^3$ **f** $28a^3 b$

2 a $24a - 18b$ **b** $pn - p^2$ **c** $s^2 + st$ **d** $6mn - 6m^2$ **e** $5x^2 + 5xy$ **f** $4u^2 + 3u$ **g** $5pq + 3pr$ **h** $12mn + 21n^2$ **i** $27ab + 9a^2$

3 a $2n + 7m$ **b** $21a^2 - a$ **c** $2b$ **d** $8x + 2xy - 2y$ **e** $4p + 3q$ **f** $8p^2 + 2pq + 5q^2$ **g** $4m^2 + 2mn - 6n$ **h** $2x - 2xy$

4 D

5 a $16x^2 + 4x$ **b** $30x^2 + 13xy$ **c** $6q - 6p$ **d** $9a + 6b$ **e** $p^2 - 4p + 6$

6 a $\frac{(8p + 2)}{(p^2 - 1)}$ **b** $\frac{2(p - 1)}{(p + 4)(p + 2)}$ **c** $\frac{(9p + 1)}{(2p + 1)(3p - 2)}$ **d** $\frac{(p + 11)}{6}$

7 A $2c + 3$ B $3 + 4b$

8 a $p(7 + 3q)$ **b** $m(1 + 3n)$ **c** $4q(2p + 1)$ **d** $3y(1 - 4x)$ **e** $2b(b + 5)$ **f** $6b(3a + 4c)$ **g** $xy(x - 2)$ **h** $3ab(3a + 2b)$ **i** $3mn(4m - 3)$

9 a $w^2 + 8w + 12$ **b** $y^2 + 14y + 45$ **c** $x^2 - 6x + 9$ **d** $v^2 - 5v + 6$ **e** $b^2 + 2b - 15$ **f** $b^2 - 8b + 15$ **g** $h^2 - 25$ **h** $t^2 - 9$

10 a $4w^2 - 9$ **b** $4p^2 + 4p + 1$ **c** $15x^2 + 8x - 12$ **d** $12g^2 - 43g + 35$

11 a $x + 3$ and $x + 4$ **b** $x + 2$ and $x + 6$ **c** $x + 1$ and $x + 6$ **d** $x + 2$ and $x + 3$ **e** $x + 1$ and $x + 12$ **f** $x + 2$ and $x + 4$

12 a $(x + 2)^2$ **b** $(x + 4)(x + 5)$ **c** $(x + 4)(x - 1)$ **d** $(x + 5)(x - 3)$ **e** $(x + 2)(x - 3)$ **f** $(x - 1)(x - 10)$ **g** $(x + 2)(x - 4)$ **h** $(x - 1)(x - 2)$ **i** $(x - 2)^2$

13 a $\frac{3}{(x + 3)}$ **b** $\frac{4}{(x + 6)}$

14 a $x - 2$ and $x + 3$ **b** $x - 3$ and $x + 1$ **c** $x - 3$ and $x - 2$ **d** $x - 2$ and $x + 2$ **e** $x + 2$ and $x + 3$ **f** $x - 3$ and $x + 3$

15 a $(3x + 4)(x + 3)$ **b** $3(x - 1)(x - 4)$ **c** $(2x - 1)(x - 4)$ **d** $(2x + 1)3(x - 1)$ **e** $3x(x - 2)$ **f** $(3x + 5y)(3x - 5y)$

16 a $p = 8$, $q = 4$ **b** $p = 9$, $q = 3$

17 a $\frac{(7p - 5)}{(p - 3)(p + 1)}$ **b** $\frac{(4 - 3a + 3b)}{2(a - b)^2}$ **c** $\frac{9a^2 p}{4}$ **d** $\frac{6}{(p^2 - 1)}$

18 a $(p + q)(p - q)$ **b i** 149 is prime. **ii** $p + q$ must be greater than 1 as p and q are both positive integers, so $p - q = 1$. **iii** $p = 75$, $q = 74$

19 264 826 482 647

20 $x + 2$

IN FOCUS 4

1 a 64, 63.5, 64.25 **b** 6.05, 6.16, 5.74

2 49.25, 5.74

3 80, 7.56

4 a Sally 6.17, 2.07; Gavin 6.5, 1.59 **b** Gavin's scores are higher on average. There is also less variation in his scores.

5 a Peggy 6, 2, Toby 5.5, 3; Sue 7, 3.5 **b** Sue's scores are highest on average. Peggy's scores are most consistent.

6 a 36, 38, 38.5 **b** 3, 3.5, 3

8 The scale does not start at 0 in the first diagram. Area (or even volume) should have been used to represent sales, not height.

IN FOCUS 5

1 **b** $a_n = 2n + 1$, $a_n = 4n$, $a_n = 12n - 8$
   c 201 matches, 400 matches, 1192 matches

2 **a** $20 \to 66$, $n \to 3n + 6$ **b** $40 \to {}^-153$, $t \to 7 - 4t$

3 **a** $n \to 4n^2$

4 **a** A $3n - 2$, B $6n + 1$, C $4n - 2$, D $5n + 2$, E $14 - 3n$, F $23 - 9n$
   b A 88, B 181, C 118, D 152, E $^-76$, F $^-247$

5 **a** $n^2 + 1$ **b** $12 - n^2$ **c** $n^2 - 2$ **d** n^2 **e** $2n^2 + 4$ **f** $n^2 - 899$

6 **a** A 2205, B 1, C 2.2, D 5.015
   b A diverges, B approaches 1, C approaches 2, D approaches 5

IN FOCUS 6

4 **a** not necessarily congruent **b** congruent by AAS
   c not necessarily congruent **d** congruent by SSS
   e not necessarily congruent **f** congruent by SAS

IN FOCUS 7

1 a, c, e

2 **a** 4 **b** 0.6 **c** $^-3$ **d** 1.1

3 **a** 2.5 **b** 1.6 **c** 2.2

4 **a** $\frac{1}{64}$ **b** $\frac{3}{5}$ **c** $\frac{1}{7}$

5 **a** 3.7 **b** 4 **e** 9 **d** $^-5.6 \times 10^{-35}$

6 **a** 4^8 **b** 3^{-1} **c** 2^0 **d** 2^{12} **e** 6^{-14} **f** 6^2 **g** 6^{-2} **h** 6^{14}

7 **a** 3 **b** $^-2$ **c** $^-1$

8 **a** y^5 **b** y^{30} **c** $81y^8$ **d** $12y^7$ **e** y **f** $2y^{-4}$ **g** $3y^6$ **h** $2y^{-2}$ **i** $\frac{11}{10}$

9 A, D and C, E.

10 **a** 7 **b** 9 **e** 3 **d** 7 **e** 1 **f** 5 **g** $\frac{1}{3}$ **h** $^-4$ **i** 2 **j** $\frac{1}{4}$ **k** $\frac{1}{6}$ **l** $\frac{1}{3}$
    m 49 **n** 64 **o** 4 **p** 32 **q** 64 **r** 125 **s** 8 **t** 81 **u** 243 **v** 81
    w $\frac{1}{16}$ **x** $\frac{1}{64}$ **y** $\frac{1}{27}$ **z** $\frac{1}{32768}$

11 **a** $x = 2$ **b** $x = {}^-3$ **e** $x = \frac{1}{3}$ **d** $x = 6$ **e** $x = 1$ **f** $x = \frac{-3}{2}$ **g** $x = \frac{2}{3}$
    h $x = \frac{3}{2}$ **i** $x = 8$ **j** $x = \frac{-1}{2}$ **k** $x = -\frac{2}{3}$ **l** $x = 1024$

12 **a** 6 **b** $\frac{1}{5}$ **c** $\sqrt{14}$ **d** 10 **e** $8 + 2\sqrt{15}$ **f** $9 - 2\sqrt{14}$ **g** $\sqrt{2}$
    h $21 + 4\sqrt{5}$ **i** $20 - 6\sqrt{11}$

13 **a** $\frac{1}{3}$ **b** $\frac{4}{11}$ **c** $\frac{1}{99}$ **d** $\frac{14}{111}$ **e** $\frac{5}{9}$ **f** $\frac{1}{11}$ **g** $\frac{6}{7}$ **h** $\frac{3}{11}$

14 b, c

IN FOCUS 8

1 **a** 5.67 **b** 12.7 **c** 10 **d** 2140 **e** 15.78 **f** 93748000 **g** 16 **h** 500

2 **a** 40 000 **b** 200 **c** 240 **d** 250 000 **e** 350 **f** 0.00075 **g** 120 000
   h 40 000 **i** 280 000 **j** 45 000

3 **a** 1200, 1.4% **b** 20 000, 9.8% **c** 20, 21.5% **d** 400 000, 26.9%
   e 16, 47.3%

4 **a** 5.55, 5.65 **b** 53.5, 54.5 **c** 685, 695 **d** 56.3715, 56.3725
   e 64.995, 65.005 **f** 95, 150 **g** 99.5, 105 **h** 159950, 160050
   i 12.85, 12.95 **j** 15 995 000, 16 005 000 **k** 999.995, 1000.005
   l 7.00005, 7.00015

5 **a** 31.6 m to 32 m **b** 59.3475 m² to 60.9375 m²
   c £623.15 to £700.78

6 20.2 m/s, 24.1 m/s

7 130.9 m³ 143.8 m³

8 **a** 4.35×10^5 **b** 1.2×10^7 **c** 3.21×10^{-4}
   d 5.426745×10^1 **e** 6.54×10^8 **f** 6.54×10^{-2}

9 **a** 5230 **b** 0.0000015 **c** 0.1094 **d** 0.03

10 **a** 1.58×10^5 **b** 2.25×10^8 **c** 1×10^{-7} **d** 7.29×10^{-4} **e** 6.48×10^{-4}

IN FOCUS 9

1 **a** $x = 4.5$ **b** $x = 4$ **c** $x = {}^-2.5$ **d** $x = 2$ **e** $x = 13$ **f** $x = 7.25$
   g $x = {}^-26$ **h** $x = 46$ **i** $x = 0.75$ **j** $x = 4$ **k** $x = {}^-2.17$

2 17 cm by 26 cm

3 **a** $x^2 - 2x - 15$ **b** $2x^2 - 7x + 3$ **c** $2x - 15x^2 + 8$ **d** $15x - 4x^2 - 9$
   e $x^2 - 16$ **f** $4x^2 - 9$ **g** $x^3 - 4x^2$ **h** $2x^3 + 6x^2 - 16x$
   i $3x^4 + 15x^3 + 12x^2 - 3x$ **j** $x^3 + 9x^2 + 11x - 21$
   k $10x^2 - x^3 - 22x - 15$ **l** $x^3 + 12x^2 + 17x - 60$ **m** $x^3 - 7x - 6$

4 **a** 3, 1 **b** 2, 1 **c** 1, $^-1$ **d** 3, $^-2$ **e** $^-1$, 2 **f** $^-1$, 2
   g $^-3$, 5 **h** $^-10$, $^-8$ **i** $^-2$, $^-3$ **j** 4, $^-2$

5 $^-4$ and 5

6 37 £5 notes and 18 £10 notes

7 £8.45, £12.95

8 1778, 472

9 165, 213

10 **a** $^-12$, 7 **b** 1, 7 **c** $^-9$, 6 **d** 3, 12 **e** $^-6$, $^-2$ **f** $^-16$, 20
    g $^-4$, 15 **h** 6, 8 **i** $^-15$, 9 **j** $^-5$, 13 **k** 4, 5 **l** 2, 14 **m** 0, 3
    n $^-8$, 8 **o** $^-14$, 14 **p** $^-100$, 100 **q** $^-0.5$, 3 **r** $^-5$, 2 **s** $^-1$, $\frac{2}{3}$
    t $\frac{-4}{3}$, 1 **u** $-\frac{1}{2}$, $\frac{2}{3}$ **v** $^-6$, 0.17 **w** $^-2$, 0.25 **x** $\frac{-2}{3}$, $\frac{1}{2}$

11 **a** 0.70, 4.30 **b** $^-6.32$, 0.32 **c** $^-7.87$, $^-0.13$ **d** $^-0.30$, 3.30
    e $^-2.79$, 1.79 **f** $^-3.83$, 1.83 **g** $^-0.56$, 3.56 **h** $^-7.12$, 1.12
    i $^-0.65$, 4.65 **j** $^-1.30$, 2.30 **k** $^-5.45$, $^-0.55$ **l** $^-1.62$, 0.62
    m $^-2.64$, 1.14 **n** $^-1.18$, 0.85 **o** $^-0.64$, 0.39 **p** $^-1.09$, 0.66

12 **a** $^-7.90$, 1.90 **b** 0.76, 5.24 **c** $^-3.83$, 7.83 **d** $^-5.12$, 3.12

IN FOCUS 10

2 **a** vertices: $(^-5, ^-1)$, $(^-11, ^-1)$, $(^-11, ^-3)$, $(^-7, ^-5)$, $(^-5, ^-3)$
   b vertices: $(4.5, 0)$, $(5, ^-0.5)$, $(5, ^-1)$, $(4.5, ^-0.5)$, $(4.5, ^-0.5)$

3 **b i** Rotation 90° anticlockwise about $(1, 1)$
   ii Reflection in $x = 5$ **c i** C **ii** F **iii** E
   c i Rotation $^-90°$ about $(6, 2)$
   ii Reflection in $y = -x$
   d i C **ii** F **iii** E
   e Rotion 180° about $(4, ^-1)$

4 **b** Rotation 180° about $(1, 0)$

   c i Rotation 180° about $(4, 0)$

   ii Rotation 90° clockwise about $(3, 0)$

   iii Translation $\begin{pmatrix} 2 \\ 2 \end{pmatrix}$

IN FOCUS 11

1 **a** $x = \frac{(4 - 5a)}{3}$ **b** $x = \frac{(5 - a)}{2}$ **e** $x = \frac{(3a - b)}{6}$ **d** $x = \frac{(1 + 2a)}{7}$ **e** $x = \frac{2}{3} - a$
   f $x = \frac{(5 + 3a)}{13}$ **g** $x = \frac{(n + 3)}{3a^2}$ **h** $x = \frac{(1 - 5y)}{ay}$ **i** $x = \frac{(2 - y^2 - ay)}{a}$ **j** $\frac{(1 - 3ac^2 + ac^3)}{bc^2}$
   k $x = \frac{(2bc + wy)}{w}$ **l** $x = \frac{(ab - 2an + cn)}{an}$ **m** $x = \frac{(ab - a^2)}{3b}$ **n** $x = a\frac{(\pi + 2)}{\pi y}$
   o $x = \frac{(5w - 1)}{3w}$ **p** $x = \frac{(2a^2 - 3a - 1)}{2a}$ **q** $x = \frac{-4}{a}$ **r** $x = \frac{(6 - a)}{7a}$ **s** $x = 2\frac{(h - ab)}{c}$
   t $x = \frac{w^2}{4}$

2 11 days

3 **a** £260.10 **b i** $t = \frac{(C - 3n)}{0.15}$ **ii** 850 miles

4 **a** $n = 3(a + 2)$ **b** $n = 10\frac{(1 - x)}{3}$ **c** $n = \frac{a}{2}$ **d** $n = \frac{(3x - 2)}{4a}$ **e** $n = \frac{(a^2 - b)}{6}$
   f $n = 2\frac{(5x + 9)}{3}$ **g** $n = 3 + (\frac{2}{ax})$ **h** $n = \frac{5a}{6}$ **i** $n = \frac{(3 - x^2)}{2x^2}$ **j** $n = 3 - (\frac{x^2}{w})$
   k $n = \frac{a}{(b \cos 30°)}$ **l** $n = \frac{3x^2}{2a}$ **m** $n = \frac{2(1 + 2a^2)}{3a^2}$ **n** $n = \frac{(a + 1)}{2}$ **o** $n = \frac{bc}{a}$
   p $n = \frac{10a}{15 - b}$ **q** $n = \frac{3}{(\cos 30°)}$ **r** $n = \frac{(x + ab)}{a}$ **s** $n = \frac{(5x^2 + 3)}{2}$ **t** $n = \frac{(a + 1)}{w}$

6 **a** $p = \frac{3}{(x - y)}$ **b** $p = \frac{1}{(t^2 - 3)}$ **c** $p = \frac{(c + 2)}{(3 - a)}$ **d** $p = \frac{(a + 6)}{(a + 4)}$ **e** $p = \frac{10}{(6 - a^2)}$
   f $p = \frac{(ab - 3)}{(2 - ab)}$ **g** $p = {}^-x$ **h** $p = \frac{(y - ax)}{(a - b^2)}$ **i** $p = \frac{2ay}{(6a - 1)}$ **j** $p = \frac{w}{(\sin x + \sin y)}$
   k $p = \frac{4}{(1 - 3w)}$ **l** $p = \frac{1}{b(b - a^2)}$ **m** $p = \frac{1}{(a - 2c)}$ **n** $p = \frac{b(3n + 2)}{(a - 3n)}$
   o $p = \frac{1}{(bc - 3a)}$ **p** $p = \frac{2}{(1 + 3a)}$ **q** $p = 2an - \frac{1}{2}$ **r** $p = \frac{(c^2n - 9b)}{3ab}$ **s** $p = \frac{5a}{(5y - 2)}$
   t $p = \frac{2}{(1 - 2a^2)}$

7 $\pi = \frac{S}{(2rh + 2r^2)}$

8 a $n = \frac{(C + 50y)}{(1.85 + y)}$

9 a $v = (1 + x)^2$ **b** $v = 1 - 9a^2$ **c** $v = \frac{2x}{\sqrt{3}}$ **d** $v = \frac{1}{2}(a - b)^2 + 1\frac{1}{2}$

e $v = \frac{(a^2 + 1)^2}{9}$ **f** $v = \frac{(2x - 1)^2}{5}$ **g** $v = 16 + 3a^2$ **h** $v = \frac{1}{(x + 3)^2}$

i $v = (y^2 - 1)$ **j** $v = \frac{\sqrt{(ax - 1)}}{\sqrt{2}}$ **k** $v = \frac{2}{\sqrt{(3 + a)}}$ **l** $v = \sqrt{\frac{3x}{y + 1}}$

m $v = \sqrt{\frac{ab}{b - a}}$ **n** $v = \sqrt{2}$ **o** $v = \frac{1}{\sqrt{(a^2 + 1)}}$ **p** $v = \frac{\sqrt{(1 + a^2 k)}}{\sqrt{(a^2 - k)}}$

q $v = \frac{1}{\sqrt{(3(2a - 1))}}$ **r** $v = \sqrt{(x + 2)}$

10 a $r = \sqrt{\frac{\pi R^2 - A}{\pi}}$ **b** 5 cm

11 $g = \frac{4\pi^2 a}{t^2}$

IN FOCUS 12

1 a 90 g icing sugar, 405 g margarine, 180 g plain chocolate, 405 g flour
b 20 g icing sugar, 90 g margarine, 40 g plain chocolate, 90 g flour

2 a 450 ml **b** 630 ml

3 a 2.9 cm **b** 1 : 3000

4 a 0.75 **b** 8.1 cm **c** both 0.704

5 IJKL and EFGH

6 i 3.9 cm **ii** 8.8 cm

7 b i BD **ii** BC **c** 9.8 cm

8 a both 1.75 **c** 0.5 cm

9 a $z \propto p^2$ **b** 0.6 **c** $z = 0.6p^2$ **d** 15 **e** $p = \sqrt{(\frac{z}{0.6})}$ **f** 12

10 a $l = \frac{36}{w^2}$ **b** 5.76 cm **c** 1.2 cm

IN FOCUS 13

1 2, 3

3 a 3 **b** 9

4 19.8 cm, 5.3 cm

5 82.5 cm²

6 a 73.5 cm² **b** 35.8 cm

7 a 1540 cm³ **b** 603 cm²

8 a 209 000 cm³ **b** 18 200 cm²

9 13.7 cm

10 a length **b** area **c** area **d** volume **e** length **f** area
g none **h** volume **i** none **j** area **k** none **l** volume
m area **n** volume **o** area **p** length

IN FOCUS 14

1 a $\frac{1}{6}$ **b** $\frac{1}{3}$ **c** $\frac{2}{3}$

2 a $\frac{2}{3}$ **b** $\frac{1}{3}$

3 a $\frac{1}{18}$ **b** $\frac{5}{36}$ **c** $\frac{5}{18}$ **d** $\frac{1}{36}$ **e** $\frac{31}{36}$

4 a 0.61 **b** 0.84 **c** 0.77

5 a i $\frac{2}{9}$ **ii** $\frac{7}{54}$ **iii** $\frac{10}{27}$ **b i** $\frac{1}{12}$ **ii** $\frac{13}{18}$ **iii** $\frac{5}{18}$ **c** $\frac{5}{7}$ **d i** $\frac{1}{12}$ **ii** $\frac{25}{216}$

6 b i 0.16 **ii** 0.33 **iii** 0.33 **iv** 0.25 **c i** 0.0099 **ii** 0.052

7 a i 0.011 **ii** 0.12 **iii** 0.86 **b i** 0.171 **ii** 0.0016 **iii** 0.023

8 b i $\frac{1}{5}$ **ii** $\frac{4}{15}$ **iii** $\frac{8}{15}$ **iv** $\frac{2}{3}$

IN FOCUS 15

1 a frequency densities: 3, 9, 6, 5, 2.8, 2.6 **b** 143 minutes
c cumulative frequencies: 15, 33, 51, 71, 82, 100
d i 142 minutes **ii** 9 minutes **e i** 9 **ii** 5 **iii** 42

2 a frequency densities: 1, 3, 4, 6, 2.25, 2, 0.8 **b** 159 minutes
c cumulative frequencies: 5, 14, 22, 34, 43, 53, 60
d i 157 minutes **ii** 9 minutes **e i** 4 **ii** 10 **iii** 35

3 The men's times were lower on average. The spread is the same for both sets of data.

4 a i frequency densities: 1.4, 5.4, 4, 0.6
ii frequency densities: 0.4, 2, 1.4, 0.44
b The total frequencies are different. **c i** 28 years **ii** 29 years
d The field athletes are slightly older on average.

IN FOCUS 16

1 a 2,1 **b** 1, ⁻1 **c** 3, 2 **d** 4, 1.5 **e** 2, ⁻1 **f** ⁻1,2.5 **g** 5, 1.5
h 4.5, 3 **i** 3.5, 3 **j** 3.5, 3

2 a $x = 0$ **b** $x = ⁻2$ **c** $x = 4$ **d** $x = ⁻3$ **e** $x = 6$ **f** $x = ⁻4$

5 a i ⁻4.9, 1.9 **ii** ⁻3.6, 0.6 **iii** ⁻5.9, 2.9

6 b ⁻1, 2.5

7 0.5, 7.5

8 ⁻1, 5

9 a ⁻3.8, 0.8 **c** 0.6

11 $y = 8, x = 0$

12 a ⁻5.7 **b** 1.4, 7.2

15 a 0, 2 **b** 3.1

18 a ⁻10 **b** (⁻2, ⁻10) **c** ⁻6

IN FOCUS 17

1 (2.6, 1.5), (⁻1, ⁻1.7)

2 c i $4.5 \leqslant t \leqslant 13.5$ **ii** $3 \leqslant t \leqslant 15$ **d** 4 **e i** 4.5 and 13.5 **ii** 6, 12
f ii 2, ⁻6

3 a 60°, 300° **b** 210°, 330° **c** 135°, 315° **d** 45°, 225°
e 155°, 205° **f** 205°, 335° **g** 25°, 205° **h** 75°, 105° **i** 105°, 255°
j 105°, 285°

4 a i 54°, 126°, 414° **ii** ⁻54°, 54°, 306°, 414° **iii** 54°, 234°, 414°
iv 26°, 154°, 386° **v** 154°, 206° **vi** ⁻26°, 154°, 334°

b i 118°, 242° **ii** ⁻62°, 242°, 298° **iii** 90°, 450°
iv ⁻90°, 90°, 270°, 450°

7 b 63°, 243°

8 a 6, ⁻6 **b** 7, 5 **c** 8, ⁻8 **d** 1, ⁻1 **e** 9, 3 **f** ⁻2, ⁻6

9 2, 3, ⁻3

10 a 45°, 225°, 405° **b** 40°, 50°, 220°, 230°, 400°, 410°
c ⁻20°, 20°, 100°, 140°, 220°, 260°, 340°, 380°
d ⁻45°, 15°, 75°, 135°, 195°, 255°, 315°, 375°, 435°

IN FOCUS 18

1 4, 71, ⁻3.2, ⁻0.33

2 a 4, 5, 6, 7, 8 **b** ⁻3, ⁻2, ⁻1 **c** ⁻5, ⁻4, ⁻3, ⁻2, ⁻1, 0 **d** ⁻6, ⁻5, ⁻4
e none **f** 24 **g** ⁻14, ⁻15 **h** 1, 2, 3, 4, 5
i ⁻4, ⁻3, ⁻2, ⁻1, 0, 1, 2, 3, 4 **j** all integers except ⁻1, 0, 1
k ⁻3, ⁻2, ⁻1, 0, 1, 2, 3 **l** ⁻3, ⁻2, ⁻1, 0, 1, 2, 3

4 The number of waiters has to be an integer, the weights do not.

6 $x \leqslant 2, x + y < 7$

7 a 0 **b** 16

8 a $x \geqslant 9$ **b** $t < ⁻7$ **c** $p \leqslant 13$ **d** $⁻11 \leqslant k \leqslant 11$ **e** $w < 2$ **f** $q > 9.3$
g $t \geqslant 8$ **h** $h \leqslant 2$ **i** $f < 3$ **j** $⁻9 < c < 9$ **k** $g \geqslant 4.5$ **l** $x > ⁻3$
m $j < 19$ **n** $d \geqslant ⁻2$ **o** $v < 4.5$ **p** $x \leqslant ⁻13$ **q** $s < 0$ **r** $u \leqslant ⁻3$
s $j > \frac{12}{11}$ **t** $r > 3, r < ⁻3$ **u** $⁻\sqrt{2} < x < \sqrt{2}$

9 a $28 < xy < 63$ **b** $11 < x + y < 16$ **c** $1 < \frac{y}{x} < 2.25$

10 a i $16a + 24p \leqslant 432$ **ii** $8a + 10p \leqslant 200$ **iii** $p \geqslant 6$
b At least half of the plants must be apple bushes.
d 17 apple, 6 pear, £196

In focus 19

1 **a** 63.33% **b** 25.45% **c** 283.33% **d** 62%

2 29%

3 **a** 29.5 kg **b** 2268 km **c** 3702.4 miles **d** 1836 yards

4 23.2 million

5 **a** 426.8 ml **b** £34.77 **c** 22.75 mm **d** 0.74 cm

6 9.5 tonnes

7 **a** £218.37 **b** £13.74 **c** £52.71 **d** £25.56 **e** £315.55 **f** £187.99
g £159.07 **h** £10.857 **i** £58.74 **j** £1761.33

8 £155.10

9 £100.71

10 £8510.63

11 **a** Price busters, they are cheaper by 25p

12 **a** £405 **b** £4216 **c** £20.40

13 $R = \frac{I}{PT}$

14 7.5 years

15 **a** £296.92 **b** £959.22 **c** £345.44 **d** £24.14 **e** £61700.34
f £21.28 **g** £578.67 **h** £4382.25 **i** £124.88 **j** £1372.66

16 **a** £255.31 **b** £11.06 **c** £38.29 **d** £8.50 **e** £63.83
f £76.55 **g** £22.97 **h** £110.63 **i** £16.16 **j** £119.14

17 £100.53

18 £3 157 895

In focus 20

1 **b** CD is a diameter

2 **b** 68°

3 136°

4 **a** 109° **b** 33°

5 **b** 96°

6 **b** 110°

7 **a** 2.8 cm **b** 2.8 cm

8 **a** 37° **b** 37.0 cm²

9 **b** 75°

In focus 21

1 **a** 17.3 cm² **b** 13.7 cm² **c** 22.3 cm² **d** 99.76 cm²
e 37 cm² **f** 14.6 cm²

2 6.6cm

3 **a** 5.2 cm **b** 15.5 cm **c** 48° **d** 50° **e** 81°

4 **a** 5.1 cm **b** 16.0 cm **c** 9.8 cm **d** 13.1 cm **e** 25.4 cm

5 **a** 73° **b** 53.1° **c** 72.1° **d** 59.6° **e** 88.9°

6 **a** 7.3 cm **b** 9.2 cm **c** 9.0 cm **d** 4.9 cm **e** 33.4cm

In focus 22

1 **a** 1 is too vague, 2 is a leading question, 3 is too vague

7 **d** moderate positive correlation

8 **a** £7200 **b** £4900

9 **a** 320 cc **b** 700 cc

10 **a** £8550 **b** 1220 cc

11 24 female, 36 male

In focus 23

1 **a** 36 mph **b** 72 mph **c** 27 mph **d** 360 mph

2 3200 km

3 **a** 76.5 miles **b** 38.25 miles **c** 17 miles **d** 46.75 miles
e 123.5 miles **f** 191.25

4 **a** 30 minutes **b** 2 hours **c** 48 minutes **d** 6 hours 40 minutes
e 1 hour 5 minutes **f** 1 hour 13 minutes **g** 1 hour 12 minutes
h 24 minutes

5 **a** 4 hours 23 minutes **b** 12 hours 46 minutes **c** 5.27 hours
d 8.85 hours **e** 86 km/h **f** 36 mph **g** 26 m/s **h** 42 m/s

6 11 mph

7 244 miles

8 2 hours 26 minutes

9 33 mph

10 1 hour 15 minutes

11 400 m

12 **b** 3, 6, 9, 13.6 sec **c** 6 m **d** 7 s **e** 14 s **f i** 2 m/s **ii** 4 m/s

13 **a** 48 mph **b** 85.71 km/h **c** 52.5 mph **d** 83.33 km/h
e 53.33 mph **f** 30 km/h

14 **a** 12 noon

15 **b** 6:15 pm **c** 67 mph **d** 60 mph

In focus 24

1 **a** $\binom{-4}{10}$ **b** $\binom{3}{12}$ **c** $\binom{-10}{-12}$ **d** $\binom{6}{10}$ **e** $\binom{1}{9}$ **f** $\binom{7}{0}$ **g** $\binom{4}{3}$ **h** $\binom{6}{8}$

2 **a** v − u **b** w − v **c** v − w **d** u − v **e** u + w − v

3 **a** $\binom{-3}{-1}$, $\binom{4}{2}$, $\binom{-4}{-2}$, $\binom{-3}{1}$, $\binom{2}{7}$

4 **a** $\overrightarrow{PR}$ **b** $\overrightarrow{PR}$ **c** $\overrightarrow{PS}$

5 It is the zero vector.

6 w − u, w − u, w − v

9 2v − 3u and 4v − 6u, 6u + 4v and ⁻3u − 2v, 6u − 9v and 3v − 2u

10 **a** 2b − 2a

11 **a i** 2b − a **ii** $(\frac{1}{3})(2b - a)$ **c** 2 : 1 **e** It is the centre of the triangle.

12 **a i** 2p + q **ii** p + $\frac{1}{2}$q **iii** $(\frac{1}{5})(4p + q)$

In focus 25

1 **a i** 1 **ii** 11 **iii** $5\frac{1}{2}$ **iv** $\frac{-1}{8}$ **v** ⁻5 **vi** 3 **b i** 15 **ii** 0 or ⁻6 **iii** 0.8

2 **b** 0.9, 2 **c i** 320 **ii** extrapolated far beyond range of data.

3 **b ii** ⁻5, 50

4 **b** 0.4, ⁻2.4 **c** 7.6

5 **b i** reflection in x-axis **ii** reflection in y-axis **iii** translation $\binom{0}{3}$
iv translation $\binom{-3}{0}$ **v** translation $\binom{2}{1}$

7 **b** $y = k(x + 2) + 1$

Practice Non-Calculator Paper

1 $33\frac{10}{3}$%

2 **a** $x(x + 3)$
b 99 700

3 **a** $6x^5y^3$
b $4x^2 - 9$

4 **a** $a = 10, b = 5$
b 25

5 **a** $\frac{\pi w^2 h}{12}$

6 **a** ⁻1
b $m = \frac{y - c}{x}$

8 5

9 **a i** to A **ii** to D **iii** to B

10 **a i** a^8 **ii** a^4 **iii** a^{12}
b $(a^6)^2$

11   **a**   **i**   0.7, 0.3, 0.7, 0.3, 0.7   **ii**   0.49
     b   0.83193

12   **a**   Uranus
     b 5×10^3

14   **a**   3
     b $\frac{1}{25}$
     c   64

15   22 m

16   **b**   **i** $x = 2.5, \ ^-5$ **ii**   30 cm

17   **a**   **i**   57°   **ii**   33°
     b   50°

18 $y + x = 6$

19   88, 89 or 90

20 $7 + 4\sqrt{3}$

21 $a = \frac{bc}{b+c}$

23   **b**   217°, 323°

24   **a**   **i** $y - x$ **ii** $\frac{1}{2}x$ **iii** $\frac{1}{2}y - \frac{1}{2}x$
     b   Parallel, and one is twice the length of the other.

25   **a** $^-3.3$
     b $^-1.7, 5.7$

Practice Calculator Paper

1   **a**   £87.50

2   0

3   A = (0, 3.5) B = (2.8, 0)

4   **a**   translation $\binom{-3}{2}$
     b   rotation, centre (4, 0), 90° clockwise

5   0, 1, 2, 3, 4

6   **a**   1.7 m
     b   15.7°

7   1.4 cm

8 $^-2.2$

9 $x = £5.20, \ y = £3.20$

10   37.25 years

11   **b**   178
     c   60

12   **a**   2240
     b   4400, 4000

13   **a**   £1329
     b   £1263

14   **a** $\frac{17}{200}$
     b $\frac{17}{198}$

15   **a** $(x - 4)(x + 4)$
     b $\frac{x+4}{2x+1}$

16   **a** $a = 5, b = 11$
     b   8.32, 1.68

17   10 cm

18   40°

19 $x = \frac{3y}{y-1}$

20   31.4 m

21   **a**   **iii** $y = x^2 + 2$
     b   **i** $y = 3 \sin x$ **ii** $y = \sin x + 1$

22   0 or 7

23   **a**   174.2 cm
     b   942.5 cm²

Exam Questions

N1   49.7

N2   **a**   40, 60, 300

N3   **a** 1.6×10^8 **b**   28 000

N4   **a**   4 200   **b**   **i**   98.5   **ii**   97.5 cm

N5   **a**   **i**   200.5 g   **ii**   199.5 g   **b**   115, 105   **c**   1.909... g

N6   **a**   £61.80   **b** 1.07^3

N7   **a**   £18 120   **b**   £20 160

N8   **a**   **i**   £360   **ii**   £230.40   **b**   £375

N9   £48.50

N10   **a**   £5755.11   **b** 1.05^3

N11   **a**   £360   **b**   £288.26

N12   75

N13   **a**   Ruth £100, Ben £80   **b**   60%

N15   **a**   **i**   5.65   **ii**   0.045 cm   **b**   7.9   **c**   0.10

N16   **a** 73×67

N17   41.2

N18   **a** 2.5×10^5 **b** 2.7×10^{-3}

N19   £614.68

N20   21.3 g

N21   **a** 1.4×10^{10} **b** 1.32×10^{23} km

N22   **a** 3.796×10^2 **b** 9.9×10^4

N23   0.451

N24   **a** 1.5×10^5 **b**   360 kg

N25   **a**   32   **b**   **i** $\frac{1}{32}$ **ii** $\frac{25}{8}$

N26   **a** 3×10^8 **b** 3.3×10^{-9} s

N27   **a**   **i**   600, 10, 90   **ii**   12   **b**   1 d.p.

N28 $^-52.5$

N29   **a**   £450 000   **b**   4%

N30   28.8

N31 3.96×10^8

N32 2.5125×10^{-21}

A1   2.44

A2   **i** $2x^2 + 5x - 12$ **ii** $x^4 + 2x^2y^2 + y^4$

A3   **a**   **i** $-\frac{8}{3}$ **ii** $-\frac{4}{5}$ **b**   **i** $(x+6)(x-2)$ **ii**   2, $^-6$

A4   **i** $n > -\frac{8}{3}$ **ii** $^-2$

A5   **a** $2x^2 - 5x - 3$ **b** $6a^4b^2$ **c** $2t(t + 6)$ **d** $(3x - 2)(3x + 2)$

A6   3.25

A7   **a**   **i** p^4 **ii** q^4 **iii** $16x^6$
     b   **i** $6a^4b^3$ **ii** $\frac{1}{8a^6}$ **c** $3xy(3x - 2y^2)$

A8   **a** $7a^4$ **b** c^6d^{-1} **c** p^8 **d** $5 m^3$ **e** $^-3, 9$ **f** $(2y - 3)(y - 4)$

A9   **a** $x^2 + 4x$ **b** $x = 3, y = \frac{1}{4}$

A10   **a** $2(x + 4y)$ **b** $3ac(c - 2)$ **c** $(x - 6)(x - 3)$

A11   **a** $t^5 - t^6$ **b**   30   **c** $3a$ **d** $x^3, x^2, x, \sqrt{x}, \frac{1}{\sqrt{x}}$ **e** $\sqrt{\frac{x}{y}}, \frac{x}{y}$

A12   **a** $7x + 11$ **b** $x^2 + 2x - 15$ **c** $3a(2a - 3b)$

A13   3.9

A14 $\frac{C - 2000}{180}$

A15   **a** $\frac{8}{15}$ **b** $\frac{4n}{(2n-1)(2n+1)}$

A16   **a** $(p + q)(p - q)$ **b** $n^2 - 1$

A17   **b**   **i** $^-4.2$ **ii** $^-1.5, 2.5$ **iii** $4xy$

A18   **c** $y = x^2 + 2x - 3$

A19   D, C, E, F, A, B

A20   **a**   (2, 18)   **b**   ($^-1$, 12)   **c**   ($^-2$, 12)   **d**   ($\frac{1}{2}$, 12)

A21   **a**   9   **b**   ~1 sq. unit

A22   **a** $p = 3, q = 2$ **b**   120°, 240°

A23   **a** $^-3.45, 0, 3.45$ **b** $^-0.4, 3.65$ **c**   0.35, 3.5

A24   **a**   **i** $^-1.3, 0, 3.3$ **ii** $^-1, ^-0.2, 3.4$ **b** $^-1.6, ^-0.2, 3.8$

A26   **a**   6.8, 12.2, 17.3   **c** $a = 1, b = 2$ **d**   2.6 kg

A27   20 cm

A28 **a i** $10x + 4$ **ii** $6x^2 + 4x$ **b** $112\,\text{cm}^2$

A29 **a** $8x + 14$

A30 **a** $7x + 11$ **b** $x^2 + 2x - 15$ **c** $3a(a - 3b)$

A31 **a** 0.94 **b** $\frac{8p}{tp - 8}$

A32 $\sqrt{5y - 4}$

A33 3.6

A34 **a** $25(G + 10)$ **b** $\frac{C - 121}{14}$

A35 $^-1, 2$

A36 **i** $n < 4$ **ii** 1, 2, 3

A37 **a** $(x + y)(x - y)$ **b** 246 910 000 **c** 76, 75 **d** $n + 1, n$

A38 **a** 12.5

A39 **a** 1.0 **c** $\frac{x}{vu}$

A40 **a** $x^2 + 2x - 15$ **b** $^-2, 7$

A41 12.8

A42 **c** $1.8C + 34$

A44 $m = 16$

A45 **c** 0.9, 11.1

A46 $x = 3, y = ^-2$

A47 **a i** 2 **ii** 5 **b ii** 5

A49 **a** $^-1, ^-4, ^-1$ **c** 1.9

S1 **b** $162\,000\,\text{cm}^3$

S2 $\pi r^2 l, 4\pi r^3, 3(a^2 + b^2)r$

S3 **a** $2.6\,\text{m}^2$ **b** $3.9\,\text{m}^3$ **c** $17\,420\,\text{kg}$

S4 28.3 cm

S5 $R = r\sqrt{2}$

S6 **a** $39.3\,\text{m}^2$ **b** 6.14 kg

S7 **a** $39.0\,\text{m}^2$ **b** $42.7\,\text{m}^3$

S8 $2.58\,\text{m}^2$

S10 **a** $700\,\text{cm}^3$ **b** 13.51 kg

S11 **a** 12 cm **b** 10 cm

S12 **a** 125 cm **b** 40 cm **c** 140° **d** 118.5 cm

S13 **a** 28.3 km **b** 298°

S14 **c** reflection in y-axis

S15 enlargement s.f. $\frac{1}{3}$, centre $(^-5, 0)$

S16 **a i** $\binom{5}{0}$ **ii** $\binom{0}{5}$ **b** $c = 9, d = ^-3$

S17 **a** 31.5 mpg **b i** 30.5 **ii** 29.5

S18 **a** 5.26 m **b** 46.9 m

S19 **i** $2x°$ **ii** $180 - 6x$ **iii** $90 - 3x$

S20 **i** 9.6 cm **ii** 3 cm

S21 **a** 16.6 m **b** 30.4°

S22 **a** $13\,\text{cm}^2$ **b** 1.3 cm **c** 0.5033

S23 48°

S24 17.7 cm

S25 **a** 41.4° **b** $9.21\,\text{cm}^2$ **c** 22.3°

S26 **a** 24 cm **b** 40.5 cm

S27 **a i** 48° **b i** 18°

S28 **a** 116 cm **b** 120.5, 15.5, 147.5

S29 **a** 5.55 cm, 5.65 cm **b** 1.195 m, 1.205 m **c** 6042, 5782 **d** 11.3, 11.1

S30 **a i** $0.2\,\text{cm}^2$ **ii** $343\,\text{cm}^2$ **b** 48 cm

S31 36.9°

S32 **a** $254.47\,\text{m}^3$ **b** 194.9 tonnes **c** $960\,\text{cm}^3$

S33 135.6°, 404.4°

S34 **a** $1414\,\text{cm}^2$ **b** 20.7 cm

S35 **a** $91\,875\,\pi\,\text{cm}^3$ **c** 360 cm

S36 $316\,000\,\text{cm}^3$

S37 17.7 cm

S38 **a** 8.6 km **b** 37.4° **c** 5.15 km

S39 **a** 3.74 m **b** 23.3 cm

S40 **a** 10 cm **b** 22.6°

S41 13.4 m

S42 **a** 58.5 **b** 10.1 cm

S44 **b** 3.75 m

S45 **a i** $a + b$ **ii** $2a - b$ **b** $2a + \frac{1}{2}b$ **c** $a + b$

S46 **a** 1.5 m **b** 2.4 m

S47 24 m

S48 **a i** $b - a$ **ii** $2b - 2a$

S51 **a** $22.8125\,\text{cm}^2$ **b** 17

S52 **a** 66°

S53 rotation 90° anticlockwise about (1, 0)

S54 **a** 1011 **b** 1004 to 1008 **c** 1001 to 1004

S55 $^-0.8$

S56 $2\pi r(h + r), 2\pi Rh, \pi rl$

S57 **a** 107 cm **b** 35 cm

D1 7

D2 **a** 0.0459 **b** 0.3941

D3 **i** 0.06 **ii** 0.38

D4 **i** $\frac{1}{16}$ **ii** $\frac{1}{6}$

D5 **a** 0.16 **b** 4000 **c** 212

D6 **b i** $\frac{25}{144}$ **ii** $\frac{70}{144}$

D7 **a** 0.51 **b** 0.31

D8 **a i** $\frac{1}{8}$ **ii** 0 **b** 0.42 **c i** 0.441 **ii** 0.406

D9 **i** $\frac{1}{6}$ **ii** $\frac{1}{4}$

D10 **i** 0.0081 **ii** 0.1638

D11 **a** 16.2 **b** 20

D12 **a** £1060 **b** £736.95

D13 31–40

D14 **a** 35, 35, 22, 6

D15 **b** 80

D17 **a** 18 **b** 1, 3, 8, 15, 23, 25 **d** 18.5

D18 **a** 41, 67, 87, 97, 100 **d** 13 yrs

D19 **a** 70 **b** 18.5 sec **c** 21%

D20 **b i** 156 cm **ii** 40

D21 **a** 1200 **c** 52

D22 **i** 0.52 **ii** 0.07

D23 0.0315

D24 **i** $\frac{1}{3}$ **ii** $\frac{13}{15}$

D25 **a** 0.7 **b** 0.15

D26 **a i** 0.28 **ii** 0.88 **b** 0.48

D27 **a** 0.85 **b** 0.15

D28 **b** 0.855

D29 **a** 0.0658 **b** 0.1258

D30 0.375

D31 **b** 0.7396

D32 **a** $\frac{1}{72}$ **b** $\frac{6}{72}$ **c** $\frac{65}{72}$

D34 **b i** 23 **ii** 8

D35 **a** No **b** 15

D36 **a** 16.5 **b** $\frac{5}{26}$ **e** 13 mm

D38 98.8 g

D39 **b i** 82 s **ii** 33 s